Differential Calculus: From Practice to Theory

Eugene Boman
The Pennsylvania State University,
Harrisburg campus

Robert Rogers
State University of New York
at Fredonia

January 22, 2024

ISBN: 978-1-942341-95-6

Cover art: "Problem of Delos Constructed from a Solution by Isaac Newton (Arithmetica Universalis)" by Crockett Johnson, courtesy of Ruth Krauss in memory of Crockett Johnson, Division of Medicine and Science, National Museum of American History, Smithsonian Institution

Published by Milne Open Textbooks, Milne Library
State University of New York at Geneseo,
Geneseo, NY 14454

A Note on the Cover

On the front cover you see the images of four central figures in the development of differential calculus. These are certainly not all of the players involved in this story but they represent a transition from the practical aspects (Isaac Newton and Gottfried Leibniz) to the foundational underpinnings (George Berkeley and Joseph Lagrange). On the following page and back cover you see a more complete (but certainly not exhaustive) timeline of some of the people involved and their contributions.

In 1707, in his book Arithmetica Universalis, Isaac Newton presented a solution of the ancient Problem of Delos (Doubling the Cube). In 1970 the artist Crockett Johnson used Newton's diagram as the inspiration for the painting Problem of Delos Constructed from a Solution by Isaac Newton which is reproduced (with the permission of the Smithsonian Institute) as the background image on the covers of this book. The original problem stipulates that the solution be constructed using only a compass and straightedge i.e., using the Geometry of Euclid. It is now known that the Problem of Delos cannot be solved using only Euclidean Geometry. Newton's solution is correct but it requires a very small extension of Euclid's Geometry.

Differential Calculus Chronology

Birth of Galileo	1564	
	1638	Discourses Concerning Two New Sciences — Galileo
Death of Galileo; Birth of Newton	1642	
Birth of Leibniz	1646	
Birth of L'Hôpital	1661	
	1665	Method of Fluxions — Newton
Birth of Bernoulli	1667	
	1684	A New Method for Maxima and Minima calculus — Leibniz
Birth of Taylor; Birth of Berkeley	1685	
	1687	Principia Mathematica — Newton
	1691	L'Hôpital's rule — Bernoulli
	1696	Analyse des Infiniment Petits – L'Hôpital
Death of L'Hôpital	1704	
Birth of Euler	1706	
	1715	Taylor series – Taylor
Death of Leibniz	1716	
Birth of Agnesi	1718	
Death of Newton	1727	
Death of Taylor	1731	
	1734	The Analyst — Berkeley
Birth of Lagrange	1736	
Death of Bernoulli	1748	Analytical Institutions — Agnesi
Death of Berkeley	1753	
	1772	Fonction Dérivée — Lagrange
Birth of Bolzano	1781	
Death of Euler	1783	
Birth of Cauchy	1789	
	1797	Mean-value theorem — Lagrange
Death of Agnesi	1799	
Death of Lagrange	1813	
Birth of Weierstrass	1815	
	1817	Continuity and the intermediate-value theorem — Bolzano
	1823	Limit definition of a derivative — Cauchy
Death of Bolzano	1848	
Death of Cauchy	1857	
	1861	Extreme-value theorem — Weierstrass
	1874	Formal definition of the limit of a function — Weierstrass
Death of Weierstrass	1897	
Birth of Robinson	1918	
	1960	Rigorization of infinitesimals — Robinson
Death of Robinson	1974	

Acknowledgments

The authors wish first and foremost to express our gratitude to the students who were subjected to various rough drafts of this textbook in a classroom setting. Our intention was always to write a student–centered textbook. To whatever extent we have succeeded in achieving that goal the insights and suggestions of these students were an invaluable help and we are very grateful to them for that.

Second, we wish to thank Dr. H. Joseph Straight, Distinguished Service Professor at SUNY, Fredonia for agreeing to use some of the earlier drafts in his classes. With grace and professionalism, he guided his students through, and sometimes around, the poor organization, murky examples, and innumerable typos of these early versions, simultaneously giving us precious insights and suggestions for improvement. His comments were always on point and we are deeply appreciative of all of his efforts.

We also wish to thank Allison Brown at Milne Open Textbooks for her patience with us. We are sure that she grew very tired of getting emails from us saying that we were almost done only to find that we still had a lot more polishing to do. Through it all her support was unwavering and we are deeply indebted to her for it.

Last, but certainly not least, we wish to thank our copy editor, Dr. Margo Boman, for all of her help in getting us to the current version of this book. When we employed her in this capacity, we thought that we were nearly done. It turned out that we were sadly mistaken. Margo's attention to detail and her pedagogical expertise were instrumental in transforming a collection of stories and problems into a much more coherent and polished narrative. It was more work than both she and we anticipated, but it was worth it and we are deeply beholden to her. Future teachers and students using this book will benefit enormously from her contribution.

Finally, any errors that might still appear in this text are the fault, and sole responsibility, of the authors.

Version 1.0

"Thus, a schism appeared between the theory and the practice of the calculus as the level of rigour in the calculus was raised: the foundationalists had one set of rules, the practitioners another. The situation has persisted to this day, with quite the unfortunate and unnecessary confusions for students. It is common experience for them to learn in calculus lectures that infinitesimally small differentials do not exist, but to use them constantly in the mathematical physics lectures. While Eulerian calculus is not rigorous, it should be taught for what it is: a powerful tool for the analysis of physical and geometric phenomena, which has left its considerable mark on the conceptions, terminology, and notations of later presentations of the subject. As things are, the treatment in textbooks is unsatisfactory. Some basically follow Cauchy's practice of notating the derivative by f' and defining the differential by some equivalent of this, while others notate the derivative by the single symbol $\frac{dy}{dx}$ and omit differentials altogether; and neither treatment warns the reader of the existence of the other. Further, both treatments give a prime place to limits without explaining why the standard of rigour and generality obtainable from this very difficult concept is desirable in the first place, or what kinds of less rigorous approaches are being superseded."

– Ivor Grattan-Guinness, *From Calculus to Set Theory 1630-1910*, p. 116

"This modern limit-theory cannot be recommended to beginners of the calculus. The physical notion of 'velocity' and the 'slope of a curve' must be retained as great aids to the young student."

– Florian Cajori (1859-1930)

"To think that there is one calculus for the pure mathematician and another for the physicist, the engineer, the geometer, or the cultured layman, is to fail to appreciate that that which is most central in the calculus is its *quantitative* character, through which it measures and estimates the things of the world of our senses. And instruction in the calculus that does not point out – not merely at the beginning or at the end, but all through the course – this close contact with nature, has not done its duty by the student."

– Wm. F. Osgood, (1864-1943)
The Calculus in our Colleges and Technical Schools

"To state a theorem and then to show examples of it is literally to teach backwards."

– Howard Eves (1887-1985),
Return to Mathematical Circles

Contents

To the Instructor: Read This First

"Teaching is to give a systematic opportunity to the learner to discover."

– George Polya (1887-1985)

For many years we (the authors) taught Differential Calculus in what has become in the last century or so, the traditional format. Limit definitions and theorems came first (presented formally when we were young; less so as we gained experience). From there we built up the necessary logical structure piece by piece until we had, after much effort, constructed the tools our students would need to solve the traditional problems of Calculus. It usually took a significant fraction of the semester to reach this point and we often found that for many of our students any bright eyed enthusiasm they might have brought to the course had been washed away in a cascade of unmotivated definitions (limit), apparently obvious statements made unnecessarily obscure (the limit of a constant is the constant), and rote computations utterly divorced from anything in the real world. We expect that you have encountered similar difficulties.

Even a cursory look at history shows us that new mathematics is almost never created by building it up logically from first principles in this fashion. New mathematics is created to solve a particular problem. It may or may not be a real-world problem, but always some specific problem is the focal point of our efforts. If new methods are needed then we invent, we try, we discard, invent again, try again, and discard again, *ad nauseum* until a viable approach is finally uncovered. Then, and only then, is a rigorous, logical foundation sought.

Think for a moment about how you do your research. First you identify a problem. Are the foundational issues at the front of your mind? Probably not. At first you're just curious. You kick ideas around, trying to find some workable approach. In short, you play with the problem. You have fun with it as a means to understanding it. When you solve your problem you probably *believe* your result long before you prove it. Foundational issues, proofs, come later when you need to show that your results are valid. This is usually less fun.

Creating new mathematics and learning new mathematics are very similar activities. Think about how you learn new mathematics. When reading a journal article do you plod from definition, to lemma, to proof, to theorem, to proof, entirely absorbing each before moving on to the next? Probably not. Most likely you read ahead to get an overall sense of the result. Then you backtrack, skip forward, play with the ideas, generate your own examples and counterexamples. When your example is inconsistent with a theorem in the article you examine it closely in order to resolve the discrepancy and better understand the ideas in the article. In short, you begin by playing with the ideas and having fun with them.

We rarely focus on rigor when we start to learn new mathematics ourselves because experience has taught us that rigor usually proceeds from a deep intuitive understanding. And as a result of training. It does not come easily, but with effort rigor emerges. If we force our students to plow through formal definitions, theorems, lemmas, and proofs before showing them the intuitive beauty and usefulness of our topic, before they can see the need for formal definitions, theorems, lemmas, and proofs, then we are demanding of them what we rarely ask of ourselves. The first job of the teacher is to foster enthusiasm in the student, to pique their curiosity and to show them, in Descartes' phrase, "the pleasure of discovery." For those who need it there is time later for the hard work of rigor.

In the first part ("From Practice . . .") of this text our audience is the usual mix of students in a typical first semester, college level, Calculus class. *All* of the students, not just the budding mathematicians, and certainly not the instructor[1]. We begin in part one as Leibniz did, with the highly intuitive – if questionable – notion of the differential. We do not hide the problems inherent in this approach. We simply don't dwell on them. We point out the logical problems that accompany the use of differentials whenever we can without breaking up the flow of the text. We do this because it is important for students, *all* students, to be aware of these issues. But we defer their resolution until part two (" . . . to Theory") when, hopefully, they will have gained an appreciation of the need for rigor.

In part two our purpose is to put a solid, rigorous foundation under the differentiation techniques derived in part one. Thus our style and approach changes. We become more formal, more "mathematical." We define and prove limit theorems and use these to derive the differentiation rules. But in contrast with the traditional approach we are not deriving the differentiation techniques in order to use them. In part two the point is to formally, rigorously justify rules with which the student should already be quite conversant.

In part one we address the question, "How can we use Calculus to explore, and explain, our world?" In part two the question is "Why does Calculus work?"

In this we follow our history. Calculus existed as an intuitive set of computational tools for approximately 200 years before the limit theory made it rigorous. Surely there is no harm in allowing our students to view it the same way for a few weeks.

Moreover proceeding in this way allows us to present the need for rigor itself as a problem to be solved, rather than an abstract theory untethered from reality. For example we do not pretend that the proof of the statement, "If $\lim\limits_{x \to a} f(x)$ and $\lim\limits_{x \to a} g(x)$ both exist then $\lim\limits_{x \to a} (f(x) + g(x))$ also exists and is equal to the obvious sum," is useful for anything other than establishing with full rigor what we already believe, intuitively, to be true. We make no such pretense because the history of our topic shows that this is in fact the truth. Limits were not invented to create Calculus, they were invented to justify it after the fact, to make it rigorous.

---

[1]Presumably we have nothing to teach the instructor, although we flatter ourselves that we might, occasionally, do so anyway.

0.1   What Do Students Need From Calculus?

A mechanical engineer who designs cars for a living must necessarily have a deep understanding of the inner workings of the propulsion, braking, cooling, and other systems built into every automobile.

A race car driver will understand some, but not necessarily all, of the mechanical principles underlying those systems. But the racer will have a much more comprehensive, and deeply intuitive, understanding of the physics of motion that keep the car on the road under the extreme conditions of a race.

A mathematician who merely drives to and from their workplace while daydreaming about mathematics needs to understand no more about the car than how to make it move, stop, and change direction[2].

But all of these people start at the same point: They learn how to drive the car.

Much the same can be said of any tool. Some need to understand it thoroughly at every level. Some need a deep intuitive grasp of its extreme capabilities. And some need only know enough to keep from hurting themselves with it. But all begin by learning how to use the tool properly.

Calculus is a tool. It was invented to solve real world problems in science and engineering. The racers in our metaphor are scientists, engineers, and businessfolk. They need, and many frequently have, a deep intuitive feel for the kinds of problems Calculus can be used to solve, and their intuitive understanding enables them to adapt Calculus techniques to novel problems. But their understanding is necessarily qualitatively different from that of a mathematician.

As mathematicians we have (indeed we must have) a deep understanding of what Calculus is, what it does, and what it can not do. We see and understand the purpose of every nuance in phrasing, the role of every lemma and theorem, every small change in notation. We understand the immense need to state our assumptions, to formulate careful, precise definitions and to rigorously prove our theorems.

Because most college level Calculus courses contain students with a wide variety of interests and goals a Calculus textbook must meet the needs of students with a wide variety of interests and goals. This seems like it must be nearly impossible until we think about it for a bit. Just as we can begin the education of engineers, racers, and ordinary drivers[3] at the same point – the location and use of the controls of a car – we can begin the education of engineers, scientists, and mathematicians at the same point – with the computational techniques from Calculus that are most useful and universal, with examples displaying how these techniques can be used to solve technical problems, and with problems and drills designed to develop skill with them. This is what we've tried to do in this textbook.

After learning to drive racers will go on to become more skillful at using the car, and there is no point in bludgeoning them with the details of say, the compressibility characteristics of steering fluid. Certainly they must be familiar with the need for steering fluid, and they should have a passing familiarity with the role of steering fluid in the overall steering system. In short, they need to know that the tools they are using have been carefully designed and that they work. But no more than that is necessary until and unless they need to help design a new steering system for their car.

---

[2]We may understand more than that, and many of us do, but this is all we need.

[3]The ordinary drivers in our metaphor are the, sadly rare, students in the liberal arts who take Calculus out of simple curiosity.

In the same way science, engineering and business students need to be aware of the need for rigor, even if it never impinges on their daily lives. They should be familiar with the need for limits as a means of providing rigor and they should have a passing familiarity with the role of epsilons and deltas. In short, they need to know that the tools they are using have been carefully designed and that they work. But no more than that is necessary until and unless there is some specific need.

On the other hand mathematics students do need a nuanced understanding of both the practice and theory of Calculus if they are to successfully continue their studies. In addition to the ability to use Calculus, they need to understand limits and they need to understand the role of epsilons and deltas

Calculus was invented as a problem solving tool, and in our opinion, this is how it is most easily and intuitively understood by the beginning student. So part one of this text is aimed at all of the students in a typical first year college class. As a result our approach is intuitive and problem oriented.

While the audience for part two is still all of the students in the class, it is aimed, primarily, at the budding mathematicians. You will see that in part two our language and presentation become more formal, more mathematical. This is deliberate. A young mathematician needs to be exposed to the formalisms of our discipline and this is an appropriate place to begin.

But this does not mean that part two should be reserved only for honors classes full of mathematics majors. The budding engineer, scientist, or financial analyst will most likely never need to use epsilons and deltas, or even limits, in their daily work. But, like the racer who should understand the need for steering fluid, but does not need a detailed understanding of its essential characteristics, these students should understand the need for rigor, even if they do not understand it in the same detail that a mathematician must. Many of these students will probably view this as an unnecessary burden, and will complain about it. But an education should provide students with what they need, not what they enjoy.

And sometimes, every now and then, some of them will find, much to their surprise, that the beauty and intricacy of a rigorous, well formed argument is as captivating to them as it is to us. We should provide our students with the opportunity to be captivated.

0.2   Some (Possibly Startling) Choices We've Made

You will very likely find some of the choices we've made quite startling. We describe some of them here and explain our rationale.

Leibniz' Differentials

We use Leibniz' differentials almost exclusively throughout part one of the text. We state the differentiation rules in their differential form (as apposed to their derivative form), and we think of the expression $\frac{dy}{dx}$ as the ratio of the differentials dy and dx, just as Leibniz did. We do this for several reasons.

1. Of all the various notations for the derivative we believe that the differential ratio $\frac{dy}{dx}$ to be the most intuitively expressive for the beginner. For Leibniz, the Bernoullis, Euler, and and their peers $\frac{dy}{dx}$ was a fraction. They thought of it as a fraction and they worked with it as a fraction. And this worked for them. They got correct results thinking this way,

and the results they obtained have come down to us with the name "Calculus." There is no reason not to teach our students to use this highly intuitive (albeit questionable) approach to computations.

Indeed, most teachers already do this. If you doubt the truth of the previous statement give a moment's thought to how you teach students to do integration by substitution, integration by parts, or line and path integrals.

2. We believe that the best pedagogy is one which meets the students where they are. In our experience students at this level have only the most tenuous grasp of the function concept[4], but they understand slopes, as fractions, very well. So they will naturally interpret the symbol $\frac{dy}{dx}$ as a slope, just as Leibniz did. Admittedly this is not a mathematically mature understanding, but mathematical maturity is a goal of the first course in Calculus, not its starting point.

3. The formula $y =$ (some expression in x) appears frequently and we will refer to it variously as a graph, an equation, or a function. We realize how annoying this lack of precision will be to you, a mature mathematician. But remember that this text is not written for you. Except in the section you are reading now we speak directly to the student, not to you. In our experience most students have only the most tenuous grasp of the distinctions between an equation, its graph, and the underlying function (or functions).

So we don't distinguish between them either, at first, for the simple reason that the distinction is lost on most students taking their first Calculus course.

You will, no doubt, argue that these distinctions need to be taught. And you are right of course. But taught by whom?

We do not believe that deep abstractions, the notion of a function for example, are best explained in a written textbook. Teaching an abstract concept requires many examples, drawings, verbal explanations and even, occasionally, vigorous hand waving.

In short, we believe this is the purview of the instructor who is physically in the classroom with the student – you. If it helps to give the students an impassioned, wild-eyed rant about these lazy, or incompetent authors who aren't using mathematical terminology correctly then by all means do that. We won't mind. We think of ourselves as your partners, or co-teachers. In that role we've tried to we create teachable moments for you to exploit. This is one such.

But, as a mature mathematician, you will surely find this very grating. Please know that our decision is not an oversight, and certainly not laziness. It is a deliberate pedagogical choice. When you find yourself being irritated by our choices we suggest you look for ways to use them effectively.

---

[4]As a result calling the derivative a "derived function" is not as helpful as it would be to a mature mathematician. In our experience students will generally see $f(x)$ and $f(a)$ as the same thing, even if they are explicitly told that x is a variable and a is a constant. Function notation is not the cause of this misinterpretation, but it doesn't prevent it either. If you ask a student at this level "If $g(x) = f(a)$, is $g'(x) = f'(x)$?" an alarming number will say yes.

Rigor, and the (Apparent) Lack Thereof

There are places where we will seem to be playing very fast and loose with definitions and concepts, and this choice will also grate on the sensibilities of a mature mathematician. This will be more pronounced in the beginning, but it will occur throughout. As we observed before, this is the nature of doing mathematics. Definitions and concepts emerge from our attempts to solve specific problems and there is nothing wrong with letting the student see this process in action.

But some students will surely find this apparent lack of precision upsetting. That can be be counterproductive if it is ignored. We've tried to anticipate this as much as possible by explicitly pointing out for example, that we are computing slopes of tangent lines before actually defining a tangent line and assuring them that a definition is coming (see Section 4.2). Essentially we ask the student to be patient. We will eventually circle back with the rigorous definitions necessary to clarify concept.

But we cannot anticipate all possible questions. When a student displays frustration with say, the lack of a definition, you may well have a fledgling mathematician on your hands. Point them to a place (either in this text or elsewhere) where their question is answered. Or answer it yourself.

Then invite them to major in mathematics. Tell them that in the mathematical community their detail-oriented predisposition for precision will make them welcome, not weird.

Fluxions, Fluents, and Newton's Dot Notation

When we have taught Calculus in the traditional format we have found that students come away believing that slope = derivative with distressing regularity. In order to stress that this is not always the right way to understand the symbol $\frac{dy}{dx}$ we sometimes use the dot notation when the derivative represents a velocity, a change of position with respect to time. We are also careful to point out that if $y = y(x)$ then $\frac{dy}{dx}$ is properly interpreted as "the rate of change of y with respect to x" and that it is only when x and y represent coordinates in the plane that this should be understood as a slope.

For Newton the only independent variable was time, and his dot notation reflects that assumption. If x represents a "flowing quantity" (Newton's phrase) then $\dot{x}$ indicates the velocity with which it flows. For Leibniz (and most of us) this is represented by $\frac{dx}{dt}$. Although the dot notation has fallen out of favor in mathematics, it is still widely used in the sciences and engineering. We believe it is a disservice to students in those majors to pretend that Newton's dot notation does not exist in the modern world. Worse, since many of our students take introductory physics (where they see dotted derivatives daily) and Calculus at the same time we only make ourselves look insular and dogmatic by pretending that the dot notation doesn't exist.

Not only do we use Newton's notation, but in Section 4.7 we sometimes also his language. When time is the variable we call $\dot{x} = \frac{dx}{dt}$ the "fluxion" of x, just as Newton did.

We did not originally intend to go this far because "fluxion" (and its counterpart "fluent") are very decidedly archaic words. No one uses them any more. But having decided to use the dot notation we soon realized that we could also use Newton's language to emphasize that the derivative should not always be interpreted as a slope. And no one is harmed by learning more words.

Polar Coordinates and Parametric Equations

Traditionally parametric equations and polar coordinates have been taught in the second Calculus course. But we've brought them, lightly, into the this first course.

We have done this for a couple of reasons. First, we believe it is pedagogically advantageous to introduce new concepts, and the associated notation, in the simplest possible context first. Thus, in this text we go no further than to observe that if t represents time then the parametric function

$$P(t) = \begin{Bmatrix} x(t) \\ y(t) \end{Bmatrix} = \begin{Bmatrix} t^2 \\ t^3 - t \end{Bmatrix}$$

can be thought of as representing the motion of a point in the plane.

A second impetus was our desire to address the derivative = slope problem we mentioned above. When working with the formula $r(\theta) = \sin(3\theta)$ in polar coordinates it is not at all helpful to think of the function $\frac{dr}{d\theta} = -3\cos(3\theta)$ as the slope of anything. A broader understanding of the symbolism is necessary.

Similarly if x and y coordinates are given by the parametric function $P(t)$ above then $\frac{dy}{dx}$ is still the slope but $\frac{dx}{dt} = \dot{x}$ and $\frac{dy}{dt} = \dot{y}$ are velocities (or "fluxions" in Newton's phrase).

Problems in Context

You will notice that the problems do not appear all-in-a-lump at the ends of sections. They are embedded in the text at the point where we discuss the methods needed to solve them. This seems to us a much better practice than lumping them all together in "Problem Sections" and forcing students to search backward through each section for the appropriate discussion.

We find that it also encourages the students to actually read the text, since they know that the exposition near to their problem will be relevant to the problem. We suggest that you explicitly point out this aspect of our text to your students, since by the time they get to college many students have concluded that the only relevant parts of the textbook are the problems and the examples and they habitually skip everything else.

There is No Solution Manual

We have not written a solution manual for this text. Nor do we intend to. There are several reasons for this.

First, in an age when every college student can open a web browser and type in, for example, Differentiate y=x^2*cos(x) and instantly get back not only the correct derivative, but also a step-by-step guide for how to do the computation, the point of spending any part of our lives providing the solution to such drill problems is completely lost on us. We have better things to do.

Second, many Calculus problems can be checked by an appropriately drawn graph. For example, if the problem is to find an equation of the line tangent to the graph of $y = 3\sqrt{x} - x^2$ at $x = 5$ the student need only graph the function and their solution to see if they have found the correct line. Until now it would have been unreasonable to ask students to check their work by graphing but modern students have access to a dizzying array of graphing tools at the click of a mouse. And this will most likely always be true. In our opinion they should be encouraged to use the resources available to them.

Third, as much as possible we have written the problems in such a way that the results of any computations needed are part of the problem statement. For example, one problem asks the student to show that if $x^2 + y^2 = 1$ then $\frac{d^2y}{dx^2} = -\frac{1}{y^3}$. Notice that the value of the second derivative is given in the problem. As much as possible we want to keep the students focused on understanding the problem, rather than rote computations.

0.3 Some Practical Advice

Precalculus vs. Pre-Calculus

Chapter 2 is about both precalculus (meaning that it uses only the tools students learn before taking Calculus) and pre-Calculus (meaning that it is about the mathematical tools that were the historical precursors of Calculus).

It is about precalculus because in this chapter we attempt to solve a number of Calculus-like problems using precalculus techniques (and clever tricks). As such, this chapter fulfills the customary purpose of the introductory chapter of a Calculus text. It reinforces the idea that the students already have many very powerful tools in hand that are supplemented, not replaced, by Calculus. And it gives them a quick reminder of how to use some of these.

Chapter 2 is about pre-Calculus because we use it to set the stage for the "new method" (Leibniz' phrase) of Differential Calculus. It is, after all, difficult to understand the point of a new method if the methods being replaced are unknown. In Chapter 2 we examine a few of the very clever tools invented by Fermat, Descartes, and Roberval which anticipated the Calculus of Newton and Leibniz. These ideas were very influential and helped shape the form that modern Calculus has taken, and they can be understood, with effort, by anyone reasonably skillful with the tools of precalculus.

When we've taught in the traditional format we've tended to skip the introductory, or "review" chapter that appears in every Calculus text. Or, at least, we've given it very short shrift. We've done this because for the student it is frequently little more than a short recitation of previously studied algebraic, geometric, and trigonometric formulas. As faculty we of course see and understand the need for facility with these formulas in the upcoming material. But the student does not. From the point of view of the student this is simply a dull rehashing of known material[5]. We serve neither our students nor ourselves if we start the semester out by boring them.

However we advise you very strongly to *not* give Chapter 2 short shrift. We have not simply rehashed a set of algebraic and trigonometric facts. Instead we use some basic Algebra and Geometry to study and discuss a few of the optimization and slope finding techniques that were precursors of Calculus. These techniques[6] are very Calculus-like so they foreshadow the ideas to come. And the student has most likely never seen them before. Thus they are inherently interesting[7]. It is useful to examine them, to see where they fall short, before diving into Calculus itself. Also later in the text, we return to some of the problems and examples from this chapter in order to compare and contrast the Calculus and pre-Calculus methods.

---

[5]Yes, we understand that many students have not sufficiently mastered this material. That is irrelevant. They have *seen* it, sometimes over and over, and they believe they understand it.

[6]Particularly Fermat's *Method of Adequality*.

[7]Or at least not mind-numbingly dull.

But be warned: The techniques developed by the pre-Calculus pioneers are very clever. They are so genuinely appealing that it is easy to get caught up in them and spend too much time on them. We speak from experience. Be careful.

Inquiry Based Learning (IBL)

We did not specifically design this to be an IBL text. However we are strong proponents of the idea that interesting and illuminative problems should drive any math course. We therefore believe that this text will work well in an IBL, as well as a more traditional, environment.

Even if you do not teach in a 100% IBL style, there is nothing wrong with coming in to class and telling your students, "Let's look at some of your homework in class and see if we can figure out how to do it." Of course, you will want to build a lesson around it and judge carefully how much of the solution to reveal.

There is also nothing wrong with using some of the problems as possible test questions and putting a subset of them on tests, verbatim. You can also let students know that you might do this. Our experience says that if this doesn't make them pay attention, then nothing will.

Finally, there is also nothing wrong with saying, "I didn't assign Problem #(whatever), but it looks kind of interesting. Let's take a look at it anyway."

That is how this book is written. The problems really are the course. We tried very hard to let the problems drive the presentation, and we recommend that you do the same. If you don't like our problems use your own. We won't mind. In fact, if you have better problems please share them with us (see "A Plea For Help" below).

0.4   The TRIUMPHS Project

The TRIUMPHS project[8] consists of a collection of over 80 Primary Source Projects (PSPs) on a wide range of topics from courses across the undergraduate mathematics curriculum and all are freely available for download at the TRIUMPHS website:

https://blogs.ursinus.edu/triumphs/.

We quote from the project website:

> The TRIUMPHS project creates materials for use in the undergraduate mathematics classroom which teaches content based around original mathematical sources such as the writings of Poincaré, Euclid, Lobachevsky, Hausdorff, and many others. These materials are freely available and downloadable for use in the clasroom. The goal of the project is to write, develop, disseminate, and test these curricular materials.

The TRIUMPHS project was ongoing at the same time we were writing this textbook. Since both projects proceed from the premise that history is a useful organizing strategy for teaching mathematics, and both are published under a Creative Commons license it seemed to us that our text could be enhanced by including (in Appendix A) those TRIUMPHS PSPs which were relevant to Calculus.

---

[8]**TR**ansfoming **I**nstruction in **U**ndergraduate **M**athematics **I**nstruction via **P**rimary **H**istorical **S**ources

At those points in the text which correspond to particular PSP a reference (and link) is provided. For example, at the beginning of Section 5.9 the following link appears:

 See also the TRIUMPHS Primary Source Project in Appendix A.5.

We are grateful for the work of the specific TRIUMPHS authors we have included in this text, but we are also grateful for the TRIUMPHS project in general. There are TRIUMPHS PSPs for many, many more topics than we are able to include here and we highly recommend that you take a look at them and consider incorporating any appropriate PSPs into every course you teach. The TRIUMPHS project is described more fully in Appendix A.

0.5 Rantings From the Cranky Old Guys in the Back of the Room

We (the authors of this text) have watched the following scene play out over and over again at professional meetings. The actors change but the script is surprisingly stable.

A speaker is introduced, rises, and talks briefly about a problem they have encountered while teaching Calculus . . . or Basic Algebra . . . or Trigonometry . . . or whatever. At some point the talk is shanghaied by a **Cranky Old Guy** (it is usually a guy) in the back of the room. He has identified the solution to **The Problem** with teaching Calculus . . . or Basic Algebra . . . or Trigonometry . . . or whatever, and in order to fix **The Problem** all we have to do is follow his recipe. The audience is then treated to a sincere, vehement, wild-eyed, and often spittle-spewn description of his recipe that clearly emanates from the fervor of divine inspiration.

We do not criticize the **Cranky Old Guy**. We recognize that when you believe you have found a lighted path in a darkening forest it is hard to contain your excitement. Also we fear we may have more in common with him than we are entirely comfortable with.

This text grew from our conviction that an historical approach to Calculus, particularly the use of the highly intuitive notion of the differential, which was used to excellent effect by the likes of Leibniz, the Bernoullis, L'Hopital, and the master, Euler, to name just a few, provides a viable, interesting, and useful framework for teaching Calculus.

As we complete our text we are more convinced than ever that this is true.

But if we're being honest we must admit the possibility that we're wrong. We don't believe we've found the only way to teach Calculus, or even the best[9], or that everyone should teach this way. What we do have is a way to teach Calculus that is very *different* from what has been done for the past century or so. You will have to decide for yourself whether or not it works for you.

It is also possible that in our conviction we may be edging into **Cranky Old Guy** territory. But we will leave that judgment to you. We don't really want to know.

---

[9]Well, OK, sure. We actually do believe this is the best way. Without that conviction we'd never have finished. But we haven't completely lost touch with reality. As far-fetched as it seems to us, we recognize the possibility that we might be wrong.

0.6 A Plea For Help

This text is not finished. No textbook ever is. Eventually the authors simply stop writing.

But always there a very illuminating problem, a nice turn of phrase, a revealing metaphor, or a tangential subject which wasn't known at the time of writing that should have been included. And typos. Always, there are typos.

A nice feature of publishing an online Open Educational Resource (OER) text like this one is that it can be revised more-or-less continuously as needed[10].

Even better, we are not limited to only using the work of the original authors. If you have a favorite problem that you use in your classroom and that you'd be willing to share please share it with us. If yours works better than a problem we already have, we'll happily swap it in. If yours simply fills a need that we've left unaddressed we'll be happy to include your problem. Naturally, we will give you credit for your work if you want.

If you think we have a good approach but don't think we've really pulled it off you are free to obtain the source[11] and re-write any part of it, or all of it, to suit your needs.

We are publishing this book under the Creative Commons CC BY-NC-AS 4.0 License which means, among other things, that you are free use and modify this text as long as you:

1. Give us proper attribution as the original authors.

2. Do not use it for any commercial purpose (don't try to make money from it).

3. License any product you create from our text using the same "CC BY-NC-AS 4.0" license we've used.

If you find this textbook useful please help us make it better by letting us know when you find an error or a lack of clarity. Any suggested change, from correcting our spelling to a complete re-write of a passage will be welcome.

Eugene Boman
Penn State, Harrisburg
ecb5@psu.edu

Robert Rogers
SUNY, Fredonia
robert.rogers@fredonia.edu

---

[10]Obviously some care must be taken. We would not, for example, want to insert a new problem – thereby changing the numbers of all subsequent problems – during a semester while the text is being used. But spelling errors and typos can be addressed at any time.

[11]As of this writing the only way to do that is to ask us for it. Eventually (meaning, as soon as Boman figures out how to do it), the source files will be available in at least one online repository.

Preface: Calculus is a Rock

Commercial transactions were hard to do using Roman numerals. So in Europe during the Middle Ages such computations were usually done using pebbles on a small table called a counting board. The board was marked off so that placing a pebble here we meant "one," there meant "ten," over there meant "a hundred," and so on. Think of an abacus. Obviously the only computational skills a merchant needed were a thorough knowledge of rules for moving the pebbles and how to read the board afterward.

A medieval European counting board.

The Latin word for "rock" or "pebble" is "calculus." Thus the English word "calculus" has come to refer to any computational scheme where it was not really necessary to understand the computations in order to apply them, at least for basic applications.

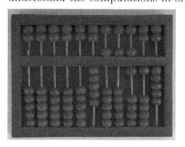

A traditional Chinese *suanpan* (abacus).

There are many calculuses (calculi?) in mathematics but the one we will be studying is of such profound and fundamental importance that it has come to be called **The Calculus** or just **Calculus**.

Nevertheless it is a calculus in the original sense. That is, it is possible to simply memorize the rules for manipulating symbols ("move the pebbles") and thereby solve a great many otherwise very difficult problems without any very deep understanding. There is nothing wrong with using Calculus this way. Indeed, this is precisely what it was invented to do. The difficulty is that those who learn only to manipulate symbols are in a position similar to the merchants of the Middle Ages. They can do the calculations but they only understand how to move the pebbles (use the notation). If a problem comes up that is outside the reach of their pebbles they are completely helpless.

This was not a problem for say, Marco Polo. He rarely had to do much mathematics besides add, subtract, multiply and divide. A deep understanding of these operations is not needed for the simple financial transactions of the Middle Ages. However, in the modern era such routine, rudimentary computations are done by machines. The role of humans is to figure out how to apply the fundamental concepts in novel arenas and in novel ways. Simply learning to compute, without a deeper understanding of the principles involved, is not a foundation upon which a modern education can be built. Modern practioners must be flexible, and flexibility

18

comes from a deep understanding of principles.

As you will soon see many otherwise very difficult problems become straightforward, even simple if we know how to manipulate Calculus notation correctly. So simple in fact, that it is easy to confuse the manipulation of notation with understanding. Don't make that mistake.

Notation is not mathematics. Notation is simply the best way we've found for representing mathematical ideas and communicating them to other people. Notice that we did not say that it is *the* best way. Only that it is the best we've found so far. Sometimes our notation falls short of our needs; sometimes far short. When it does only a deep understanding of fundamental concepts will clarify the problem for you.

Even though the rules for manipulating the notation of Calculus were designed to be used blindly, this does not make them unimportant. If anything it is more important in the modern era than it has ever been that students learn to read the notation with understanding and to use the computational rules skillfully because it is through mastering these fundamentals that the underlying concepts emerge and become clear.

So we will begin with the Calculus notation, and the rules for its manipulation. But we (your teacher, and the authors of this book) cannot master this for you. We are only your guides. You must stay focused on understanding not mere computation. The process is slow. It takes time and practice and it can be very frustrating. Prepare yourself. Arrange your study schedule to give yourself as much time for practice as you can possibly manage. Do not accept simply "getting the right answer" as "good enough." If you can correctly perform some computation but don't take the time to understand why that particular manipulation of the symbols led you to the "right answer" then you are wasting your time. Your goal is to understand, not to compute.

It may surprise you to learn that when it was first invented the validity of the Calculus was very suspect. The underlying ideas were very *ad hoc* and did not stand up to close scrutiny at all. Indeed, the foundations of the topic were so murky that the only reason Calculus remained viable was the simple fact that it worked. Or at least, it seemed to. This was taken as evidence that the underlying principles were valid but no one was very comfortable with the fact that those principles could not be unambiguously stated. It took about 200 years to finally work out a supporting logical foundation that explained why the symbol manipulations of Calculus worked and, perhaps more importantly, when they wouldn't work.

This text follows the history of our topic. In the first part (**"From Practice . . . "**) we begin with the rules for performing Calculus computations – we'll learn to move the pebbles. When these have been mastered we'll learn to use these computational methods to solve some (hopefully) interesting and (definitely) substantial problems.

We will not address the logical underpinnings of the Calculus until the second part (" . . . **To Theory"**) where we will examine the logical support structure that took some the greatest minds our species has known almost 200 years to develop. Naturally this will require a shift in our focus. In the first part of this text you will learn how to *use* Calculus. In the second part you will learn why it works the way that it does.

This will be hard. At times it will be very hard. But it is worth the effort. At the other end, when it all comes together, there is a transcendent beauty to the Calculus which is impossible to convey to the uninitiated. A poet once wrote, "Euclid alone has looked on beauty bare," but this is not true. Everyone who has studied and understood mathematics beyond the level of moving the pebbles has seen the same beauty that Euclid saw. If you have never seen it this is your chance.

Part I

From Practice . . .

Chapter 1

Introduction: Some Advice on Problem Solving

> *"The most difficult thing is the decision to act, the rest is merely tenacity."*
>
> – Amelia Earhart $(1897 - 1937)$

> *"You just keep pushing. You just keep pushing. I made every mistake that could be made. But I just kept pushing."*
>
> – Renè Descartes $(1596 - 1650)$

Our purpose here is to give you our very best advice on how to succeed in this course and a realistic impression of the level of difficulty of the course material. Please read this carefully and take our advice. We know what we are talking about. Believe us.

Because the topic we will be studying is called **Calculus** there is a strong tendency to assume that only the concepts and techniques of Calculus are needed to solve the problems you will encounter in this course. That is not true. You will need all of the mathematics you know. And probably more. Really.

1.1 Using Letters Instead of Numbers

Before we begin, a few comments on notation are apropos.

Suppose your teacher starts a lecture with the statement, "Suppose a and b are two positive numbers. Then $a < a + b$ and $b < a + b$." A common complaint is that we're making the problem harder. This is often accompanied with a request to replace a and b with numbers, just to make it easier to understand. For example, if a and b are numbers why not just say that a is 23 and b is 17? In that case it is clear that $23 < 40 \ (= 23 + 17)$ and $17 < 40$. Why do we have to make it more complicated?

This seems like a reasonable point until you think about it a bit more. Suppose we use the numbers $a = \frac{\sqrt{11}-\pi}{4}$ and $b = 2.93 \times 10^{1000}$ instead? Is it obvious to you that

$$\frac{\sqrt{11}-\pi}{4} < \left(\frac{\sqrt{11}-\pi}{4}\right) + \left(2.93 \times 10^{1000}\right)$$

or

$$2.93 \times 10^{1000} < \left(\frac{\sqrt{11}-\pi}{4}\right) + \left(2.93 \times 10^{1000}\right)?$$

Our point here is that the symbol a is no different than the symbol 23. Or the symbol $\frac{\sqrt{11}-\pi}{4}$. These are all valid symbols representing numbers. So we treat them all the same. For example, all of the following are valid statements:

$$a + b = b + a$$
$$23 + 17 = 17 + 23, \text{ and}$$
$$\left(\frac{\sqrt{11}-\pi}{4}\right) + \left(2.93 \times 10^{1000}\right) = \left(2.93 \times 10^{1000}\right) + \left(\frac{\sqrt{11}-\pi}{4}\right).$$

The difference is this: If $a = 23$ and $b = 17$ the first statement includes the second as a specific case. Similarly if $a = \frac{(\sqrt{11}-\pi)}{4}$ and $b = 2.93 \times 10^{1000}$ the first statement includes the third. The first statement is more general. It is true no matter what a and b are.

Problem #1:

(a) Use the fact that $\sqrt{7} < \sqrt{9}$ to show that $\frac{\sqrt{7}-\pi}{5} < 0$. Do not use a calculator.

(b) Check the validity of the following statements. Are they true?
$$\frac{\sqrt{7}-\pi}{5} < \left(\frac{\sqrt{7}-\pi}{5}\right) + 2.93 \times 10^{1000}$$
$$2.93 \times 10^{1000} < \left(\frac{\sqrt{7}-\pi}{5}\right) + 2.93 \times 10^{1000}$$
(**Hint:** Using a calculator on 2.93×10^{1000} would be rather pointless. Try it and see.)

(c) Show that it is not always true that if a and b are numbers then

$$a \le a + b. \tag{1.1}$$

(d) Find a restriction on the possible values of a and b that will guarantee that inequality (1.1) is true.

Keeping things simple is laudable as a goal and we don't want to suggest that you shouldn't do it. It can be very useful to look at a special case of a general statement just to get a sense of the problem. For example, a good way to "trick yourself into abstraction" is to think 23 and 17, but write down a and b. As long as you don't try to do anything that relies on the particular properties of 23 and 17, you should be fine. But you wouldn't want to say something like $a+b$ is an even integer (even though $23+17$ is). The sum $23+17$ is an even integer because both 23 and 17 are odd integers, but this is special to these numbers and won't be true for a and b in general.

Drill #2:

(a) Suppose a and b are both integers. Find restrictions on the possible values of a and b that will guarantee that $a + b$ is an even, positive integer.

(b) Now suppose a and b are both numbers. Find restrictions on the possible values of a and b that will guarantee that $a + b$ is an even, positive integer.
(**Comment:** This is not the same problem as part (a). Read it carefully.)

When looking at 23×17 most people are inclined to compute this to get 391. If the problem is: Find the value of 23×17, then sure, doing the arithmetic is the correct thing to do. But the last time you were asked to do multiplication for its own sake you were probably 11 years old. Elementary computations like this will only come up in the context of a more advanced problem. Before doing this calculation, you should ask yourself if it will help you solve the more advanced problem.

Now suppose the problem is: Determine if the number 23×17 is divisible by 17. Do you see that computing $23 \times 17 = 391$ will only make the problem harder?

Your college professors will never ask you to do an arithmetic calculation for its own sake. Instead arithmetic problems will come up in the context of a more advanced problem and you will need to use your arithmetic skill to uncover patterns. But doing the arithmetic, boiling everything down to a single number usually hides the patterns!

For example, is it easier to see the pattern in the following list of numbers when they are presented like this:
$$1, 2, 10, 110, 220, 1100, 12100, 24200, 121000, 1331000, \ldots$$
or like this:
$$(2^0 5^0 11^0), (2^1 5^0 11^0), (2^1 5^1 11^0), (2^1 5^1 11^1), (2^2 5^1 11^1), (2^2 5^2 11^1), (2^2 5^2 11^2), \ldots \qquad .$$

Problem #3:
Actually, there is something rather liberating about using letters to represent a broad class of numbers. Consider the following questions:

(a) Is the number $2^{24} 5^{49} 11^{1002}$ a perfect square? If so, what is its square root?

(b) What about $2^{24} 5^{50} 11^{1002}$? Was your calculator of any use on this? Notice that these numbers were completely factored into their prime factorizations. Did that help? How?

(c) Now suppose that n is a positive integer. Is $2^{2n} 5^{3n} 11^{4n}$ always a perfect square? If not, for which values of n will it be a perfect square?

(d) What can you say, in general, about whether or not an integer greater than one is a perfect square in terms of its prime factorization?

1.2 Substitution, or Making Things "Easy on the Eyes"

> *"Mathematicians do not study objects, but relations between objects. Thus, they are free to replace some objects by others so long as the relations remain unchanged."*
>
> – Henri Poincaré (1854 − 1912)

A common misconception is that mathematicians are people who love complicated formulas. In fact, the opposite is true. We really very much prefer to keep things as simple as possible. We only accept complexity when we are forced to. Moreover, with experience we have learned that complexity is usually borne of an inadequate understanding of the problem. Better understanding usually results in a simpler formulation.

This works in reverse too. If we can find a simple way to express what appears to be a complex problem we can usually gain a deeper understanding of the problem and its solution. A judicious substitution is one way to re-express a complex problem.

Example #1:

For example, suppose you were asked to solve the following equation for x:

$$\frac{\frac{\pi x}{\sqrt{(28 - \sqrt[3]{26})^{\frac{1}{3}}}}}{\pi^2 - \sqrt{3}} - \sqrt[21]{2^{\frac{11}{2}}} = (\pi^3 - \sqrt{2})x.$$

At first glance this looks horribly complicated. But look at it again. On the right the coefficient of x is $\pi^3 - \sqrt{2}$. That's just a number. It is approximately 29.6 but who cares? For purposes of algebraically isolating x all we need to know is that it is a number. Rather than calling it $\pi^3 - \sqrt{2}$, let's just call it something simple, like A. Think of it as giving the expression $\pi^3 - \sqrt{2}$ a nickname; something shorter, and easier to remember.

If we make that substitution our equation is now

$$\frac{\frac{\pi x}{\sqrt{(28 - \sqrt[3]{26})^{\frac{1}{3}}}}}{\pi^2 - \sqrt{3}} - \sqrt[21]{2^{\frac{11}{2}}} = Ax.$$

which is a bit "easier on the eyes."

But wait. The expression $\sqrt[21]{2^{\frac{11}{2}}}$ is also just a number. Let's make it "easier on the eyes," too. If we let $B = \sqrt[21]{2^{\frac{11}{2}}}$ we have

$$\frac{\frac{\pi x}{\sqrt{(28 - \sqrt[3]{26})^{\frac{1}{3}}}}}{\pi^2 - \sqrt{3}} - B = Ax.$$

which is even easier to look at. By now you see where this is going. If we let $C = \frac{\frac{\pi}{\sqrt{(28 - \sqrt[3]{26})^{\frac{1}{3}}}}}{\pi^2 - \sqrt{3}}$ then our equation is

$$Cx - B = Ax$$

which is much "easier on the eyes" than the original equation was. In fact, we can now see that this is really a very simple equation and the solution is $x = \frac{B}{C-A}$. Of course we inserted A,

B, and C into the problem so now we need to unwind our substitutions. When we do that we get

$$x = \frac{\sqrt[21]{2^{\frac{11}{2}}}}{\frac{\sqrt{(28-\sqrt[3]{26})^{\frac{1}{3}}}}{\pi^2-\sqrt{3}} - \left(\pi^3 - \sqrt{2}\right)}.$$

If a decimal number is required we could enter this formula into whatever computational tool we're using. Good luck with that.

End Of Example #1

The previous example was clearly contrived. Obviously we went out of our way to make a simple problem look complicated just so we could simplify it. As a result it would be easy to dismiss this as a silly example. But it is not. There is a serious lesson to be learned here. One that we will use over and over again in the near future. By its very nature mathematical notation is not easy to read. It is so dense, with so much information packed into a few symbols, that it is easy to misinterpret. Making a formula easier to read can be very helpful. A well chosen substitution can make a complex looking formula much easier to work with.

Example #2:

When you were learning Algebra you almost certainly encountered problems like this: Given

$$x^{\frac{2}{3}} - 4x^{\frac{1}{3}} + 3 = 0 \tag{1.2}$$

solve for x.

At first glance, this looks like a formidable problem. However, if we look closer we see that it actually has a very familiar form. Because $x^{\frac{2}{3}} = \left(x^{\frac{1}{3}}\right)^2$ we can rewrite Equation (1.2) as

$$\left(x^{\frac{1}{3}}\right)^2 - 4x^{\frac{1}{3}} + 3 = 0 \tag{1.3}$$

and if you look closely you'll see that Equation (1.3) is "quadratic in form." That is, it is really a quadratic equation – which we know how to solve – in disguise. However it is still rather difficult to see the quadratic nature of Equation 1.3. To make this very clear we let

$$z = x^{\frac{1}{3}}.$$

That is, just as in Example 1 we give the expression $x^{\frac{1}{3}}$ the nickname, z, which is shorter, easier to remember, and "easier on the eyes." Then Equation (1.3) becomes the quadratic equation:

$$z^2 - 4z + 3 = 0.$$

Our problem is not solved. Indeed, we haven't even tried to solve it yet. But it is much more simply expressed. And because it is more simply expressed we can now see how to solve it. Factoring, we have

$$0 = z^2 - 4z + 3 = (z - 1)(z - 3)$$

so we have $z = 1$ and $z = 3$. But, of course, these are not solutions of our problem. We have found z (which we inserted into the problem) not x (which is what we need to find). To complete the solution we need to unwind the substitution we made and solve the two equations

$$x^{\frac{1}{3}} = 1 \text{ and } x^{\frac{1}{3}} = 3,$$

yielding the solutions $x = 1$ and $x = 27$, respectively.

End Of Example #2

In making a substitution our goal is always to make the formulas we are dealing with simpler to understand and easier to read. In Examples 1 and 2 it was straightforward[1] to see how to do that. There were expressions that were hard to read so we simply replaced a complicated part of the problem with something simple. It isn't always that easy. Sometimes just finding a good substitution presents challenges of its own.

For example, the Quadratic Formula can be derived by making a very simple substitution that allows us to solve the general quadratic equation

$$ax^2 + bx + c = 0. \tag{1.4}$$

Once the substitution is found it is very easy to work through the algebra, but finding the right substitution in the first place is not straightforward at all.

Problem #4:

Before reading any further see if you can come up with the right substitution for Equation (1.4). (**Hint:** The goal is to eliminate the linear term, bx. You can see how this would help. If bx were not present in Equation 1.4 we could easily solve $ax^2 + c = 0$.)

Were you able to solve Problem 4? It's actually very hard to do without some guidance. Here's another hint. Try the substitution $x = y - \frac{b}{ka}$ where k is a parameter to be determined. That is, make this substitution and find the value of k that eliminates the linear term.

After making this substitution the problem will be given in terms of y, not x. That's OK. Solve the problem in this form, and then unwind your substitution back to the original x variable.

Problem #5:

Notice that after making our substitution we get:

$$a\left(y - \frac{b}{ka}\right)^2 + b\left(y - \frac{b}{ka}\right) + c = 0.$$

which is more complicated, not less. Of course it is. Sometimes you have to complicate before you can simplify. Don't give up. Multiply everything out to see what you've got.

Once you've found k make the substitution and eliminate the linear term – that was the objective, remember? At that point you should see the Quadratic Formula starting to emerge. Don't forget to unwind the substitution and solve for x

---

[1] "Straightforward" is not the same as "easy."

1.3   An "Easy" Problem From Geometry

"Ideas are like rabbits. You get a couple and learn how to handle them, and pretty soon you have a dozen."

– John Steinbeck (1902-1968)

We've chosen the following example because it is neither particularly easy nor particularly difficult. It is typical of the kinds of medium level problems that appear in most Calculus textbooks.

Example #3:

The lengths of two sides of a triangle are a and b. If the third side is chosen in such a way that the area of the triangle is as large as possible what is the length of the third side?

End Of Example #3

You may be able to intuit the correct answer to this problem. That's OK, but you should try to solve it, too. By "solve" we mean that you should be able to explain to someone with the same mathematical skills you have at the moment why your answer is correct.

Before reading further do your best to solve this problem in Example 3. We'll wait.

No, really. Give this problem a serious shot before you go on. It is not important that you succeed. Only that you try.

Partial Solution:

At first it is difficult to see where to begin[2]. Don't let this stop you! In our experience the most common mistake is giving up too soon.

Don't. Do. That. Keep thinking.

Since we know the lengths of the sides a and b of our triangle let's draw it. The sketch at the right would be typical. The question is, what length for side c makes the total area enclosed by the triangle as large as it can possibly be?

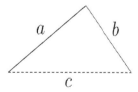

Now what?

Well, this looks like a right triangle doesn't it? If it is a right triangle, then we can find the length of c via the Pythagorean Theorem:

$$c = \sqrt{a^2 + b^2},$$

right?

Before you go on take a moment and really think about this problem. Can it really be that simple? Can you find any flaws in our reasoning.

Once you think about it you see that we have no reason to believe that the triangle we seek must be a right triangle. It was completely accidental that we drew our diagram that way. If this seems like a simple-minded mistake, the sort of mistake that you would never make, be careful. It is a mistake to rely too heavily on the diagrams we draw. But it is an easy mistake

---

[2]That's why it's called a problem.

to make, especially when the problems are more complicated, because as problems get complex we will need to rely on visualization more and more. This was not a dumb mistake. It was just a bit careless, and it is easy to be careless, especially when we first start thinking about a problem.

Digression #1: Making Mistakes

"Being wrong isn't a bad thing like they teach you in school. It is an opportunity to learn something."

– Richard Feynman (1918-1988)

"Experience is the name everyone gives to their mistakes."

– Oscar Wilde (1854-1900)

By definition, mistakes are wrong. A mistake is always obvious after you recognize it as a mistake. Everyone makes mistakes in the course of solving a problem. The process of making mistakes, recognizing them as mistakes, and figuring out why they are mistakes is called learning. The very smartest people, for example Isaac Newton, Gottfried Leibniz, Galileo, Pierre Fermat, Marie Curie, Emmy Nöther, Albert Einstein, or Richard Feynman, made lots of mistakes. Making mistakes is how they got to be smart.

Isaac Newton was once asked how he had been able to solve problems that no one before him had solved. His reply: "By thinking, and thinking, and thinking about them." Of course, when he described his solutions he left out all of the errors like anyone would do, because, who cares about those? Making mistakes doesn't typically get the attention it deserves.

An expert is someone who has made every possible mistake. This is why your teacher, an expert, will seldom err[a]. Each mistake you make reflects the level of your current understanding of the problem. Each mistake you make takes you a little closer to expertise. Embrace your mistakes and make lots of them! They are proof that you are making progress. But make no mistake (Gasp!) about it, making and embracing a mistake is just the first step. You also have to figure out what went wrong.

Sadly, mistakes are too often seen as a source of embarrassment. Too many students will berate themselves as stupid every time they make a mistake. Don't do that. It is pointless and counter-productive. All it will do is destroy your self confidence. Don't do it[b]. Learning Calculus can be hard, but you would not have made it this far if you couldn't do it. So keep making mistakes. Ask for help when you need it. And don't give up. You have not failed until you stop trying.

---

[a]And will be embarrassed when they do.

[b]Did we mention that you shouldn't berate yourself when you make a mistake? You really shouldn't.

=== End Of Digression #1 ===

Let's look at this problem again. The triangle we seek might look like the first one we drew, or it might look like either of the ones drawn in the diagram below, or myriad others. We simply don't have enough information to decide at this point.

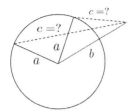

But from the diagrams we've drawn so far we can see that one end of side a must be pinned to one end of side b and for each angle between a and b we have a different possible triangle. We don't have to think of both of them as in motion. We can think of one of them, say b, as fixed while the other swings around their common endpoint. The circle in our diagram indicates all of the possible positions a.

Do you see how that worked? Our first attempt was simple-minded, but by drawing our first, simple-minded sketch, making a stab at a solution, and figuring out why our simple-minded approach won't work, we were led to this insight: We can think of b as static, and we can think of a as swinging freely while pinned to the end of b.

Clearly we need to find the angle between a and b — call it ϕ as in the sketch at the right — that maximizes the area of the triangle. But which angle does that?

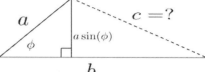

Whenever triangles are involved it is a good idea to recall your Trigonometry. After all, that's what Trigonometry is about, isn't it? Since we are thinking of b as fixed, we may as well use it as the base. This makes the height equal to $a\sin(\phi)$. Also, since we're trying to maximize the area we should probably write down the area formula: $A = \frac{1}{2}(b)\text{ase} \times (h)\text{eight}$. Thus the area of the triangle is $A = \frac{1}{2}ab\sin(\phi)$.

Is it clear that our initial guess was correct? The angle, ϕ, that maximizes the area will be the one whose sine is as large as possible. That would be $\phi = 90°$ so $c = \sqrt{a^2 + b^2}$ provides the maximum area.

You might be a little uncomfortable with our argument that $a\sin(\phi)$ is maximized when $\phi = 90°$. If so, then for you, this problem is not finished. Possibly we've made a mistake. Let's follow our own advice and see why it is a mistake, if it is.

Problem #6:
Replace $a\sin(\phi)$ with h in the diagram above. Use the Pythagorean Theorem to reason that if $\phi < 90°$ then $h < a$. How does this apply to the problem of maximizing the area of the triangle?

Until we can demonstrate that $c = \sqrt{a^2 + b^2}$ with a convincing and rigorous argument, this problem is not solved. Instead it is only a conjecture; an educated guess. Our evidence so far is very convincing so it is a very well educated guess, but it is still only a guess.

1.4   Our advice, a synopsis:

"There are times when I feel like I'm in a big forest and don't know where I'm going. But then somehow I come to the top of a hill and can see everything more clearly. When that happens it's really exciting."

— Maryam Mirzakhani (1977-2017)

"If you see a whole thing – it seems that it's always beautiful. Planets, lives . . . But up close a world's all dirt and rocks. And day to day, life's a hard job, you get tired, you lose the pattern."

— Ursula K. Le Guin (1929-2018)

In order to solve a problem, any problem, you must:

Have an idea.

Solving a mathematical problem is a bit like getting dropped in the woods without a map or any GPS technology and being told to find your way out[3]. First you have to find a path. Once a path is found, you have to follow it. Nothing else really has a chance of working. Following your path will eventually lead you to another path. Now you have to decide which path to follow, so you look around and make your best guess. If you guess right, great! If not you will have to backtrack and take the other path. And so it goes. Guess. Backtrack. Guess again. As you learn the terrain and get familiar with the network of paths your guesses get better. Sometimes none of the paths you've found seem to be getting you closer to your destination. So you have to try something different, like getting off of the path completely.

Eventually you'll get where you're going but the one thing you can't do is give up. You will never get anywhere if you don't keep trying.

Having an idea is like following a path in the woods. It's a start, but that's all it is. You still have to follow it. After you've taken it as far as you can you need to look for another idea; a new path to follow.

Finding your way out of the woods takes patience, diligence, and a lot of hard work. So does solving a mathematics problem.

If an idea occurs to you, follow it. Most likely you will not hit on a good, or even a workable approach the first time. Or the first three times. That's OK. Keep thinking about the problem anyway. It is frustrating and it doesn't feel like progress, but it is. As long as you are having and discarding ideas you are making progress.

---

[3]Except, of course, that you won't die of exposure, and you always have the option of declaring the math problem "Stupid" and doing something else. If you are dropped in the woods you don't have that option. You must solve the problem or you will die. It is astonishing how quickly that knowledge will focus the mind.

Really, have an idea. If you don't have a good idea, then use a bad one.

OK, we hear you say, but what if I don't have any good ideas? What do I do then?

Easy. Use a not-so-good idea.

This is what you've been doing all of your life anyway isn't it? You just didn't tell anyone because you were sure you were doing something wrong, right? You weren't.

The most important thing you can do is get started. That's what having an idea is for, getting started. All we did to start the problem in Example 3 was draw the lines a and b. Look back up at our partial solution and see. The first thing we did was make the drawing below:

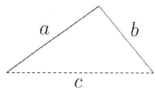

Can you think of anything more simple-minded? And yet it worked. It didn't work right away, but it got us moving in the right direction.

Have another idea.

Because this is a textbook we couldn't really waste time and pages by running down blind alleys, so we started off with an idea that we knew would take us in the right direction. In real life this usually won't happen. Most often your first (two or three or four) ideas aren't going to take you in the right direction. That's OK. Figure out what is wrong with them. You had some intuition about the problem that led you to your idea. Figuring out why it didn't work will clarify things for you just a bit. That will help.

So, have another idea that is based on what you learned from your first idea. And another. And another after that. Keep having ideas until you find one that works. Another way to say this is: Don't give up.

Ask for help when you get stuck, not before.

Sometimes ideas just won't come to you. That's OK. Sometimes you will need help. Ask for it. Ask your teacher, another student, a tutor, your Mom, your Dad, a former teacher.

Ask. For. Help.

But ask constructively. If you are asking another student, a peer, it is fine to ask, "How do I do this problem?" But if you are asking your teacher, or a tutor, this sounds a lot like, "This problem looks hard, my friends are meeting up in half an hour and, besides, I don't really want to spend any more time on it. Please, do this problem and let me watch so I can turn it in and go have fun with my friends[4]." This is not usually effective.

---

[4]To be clear, your teacher knows that a serious student does not mean this, that you really just want to learn how to do the problem. The difficulty is that there are always some students who have no qualms about asking their instructor to do problem after problem with no intention of learning anything. They just want to copy the answers down and quit. Teachers quickly learn to identify these students from the way they ask questions. If you approach your instructor in the same fashion that a non-serious student does the response you get won't be as helpful as you would like.

Teachers *want* to help serious students, but non-serious students are a waste of time. Be a serious student. Just as importantly, *act* like a serious student.

Moreover some teachers will get a little testy about it. Instead ask something like, "I've tried this, and this, and this, but I keep getting stuck here. Can you give me some direction?" That shows that you have already put real effort into solving the problem and are willing to continue working on it.

Or, if you find the problem so mystifying that you can't even think of a first idea ask, "I really don't know where to begin on this problem. Can you point me in the right direction to get me started?"

Keep thinking about the problem after you solve it.

After you've solved a problem, pause for a moment, take a sip of coffee, or tea, or whatever and think about the problem you just solved. This is like the difference between looking at a mountain from its base, when all you can see is the tangle of brush in your way, and looking at it from the peak. From the peak all of the obstacles you overcame getting there look small and unimportant. You can see the broad outlines of the mountain and the path you took climbing it. Frequently you will also see a better path than the one you took.

This kind of reflection is the most neglected aspect of problem solving. After you've been struggling with a problem you probably don't ever want to see it again. This is a natural response. However, before you put the problem away reflect on your solution and make this part of your knowledge base. Think about which ideas you had that worked, and which ideas you had that didn't work. Think about why they did, or didn't work. Do this immediately, while the problem is still in your mind. Later, if something reminds you of this problem, think about it some more to see why you were reminded of it.

The difference between the teacher and the student is not intelligence, but experience. The more problems you solve, the more experience you gain. But you need to be able to use that experience for subsequent problems. Reflecting on a problem after you solve it is how you make the knowledge you gained from the problem available for later use.

For example, see if you can use what you learned from the triangle problem to solve this one.

Problem #7: Out of all parallelograms with sides a and b, which would have the largest area?

Use your intuition, but don't trust it

Finally, because many problems in Calculus are about motion and you are very familiar with how things move, you will often have a good deal of intuition into their solution. Paradoxically you need to learn to use, but not to trust, your intuition.

When approaching a problem intuitively, there is a tendency to add assumptions to familiar looking problems. Notice how easy it was to believe that our triangle must be a right triangle just because our first drawing looked like a right triangle.

As we said, you will have some intuition into many problems, and intuition can be very helpful, but it can also lead you astray. You need to learn to support your intuition with reasoning.

Drill #8:

You will probably have a strong insight, or intuition, about each of the following claims. Do your best to explain why each is true, or why it is false. Read each problem carefully and take care not to add assumptions that are not in the problem. Back up your claim with reasoning, not intuition,

(a) Given a regular polygon inscribed in a fixed circle, if you double the number of sides, then the area inside the polygon becomes larger.

(b) Given a polygon inscribed in a fixed circle, the more sides there are, the bigger the area inside the polygon is.

(c) Given a polygon inscribed in a fixed circle, the more sides there are, the bigger the perimeter is.

(d) Given the following parabola with axis $\overline{AM}$, M is the midpoint of $\overline{BC}$.

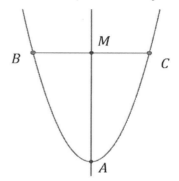

(e) In part (d), what if we insist that $\overline{BC}$ is perpendicular to $\overline{AM}$?

Chapter 2

Science Before Calculus

"In any particular theory there is only as much real science as there is mathematics."

— Immanuel Kant (1724-1804)

"The mathematician may be compared to a designer of garments, who is utterly oblivious of the creatures whom his garments may fit. To be sure, his art originated in the necessity for clothing such creatures, but this was long ago; to this day a shape will occasionally appear which will fit into the garment as if the garment had been made for it. Then there is no end of surprise and delight."

— George Dantzig (1914-2005)

2.1 Apologia

Like the authors, your instructor is probably a highly trained, professional mathematician. As mathematicians we solve problems and we build logical structures. This is what we were trained to do.

The structures we build are what makes mathematics useful but that is not why we build them. Most of the time we create simply for the love of the creative act itself. Usefulness, as such, is often a secondary consideration. In this, mathematicians are more like poets or artists than scientists or engineers. By and large, we consider the act of creation to be its own reward[1]. It is a remarkable fact that sometimes the logical structures we build turn out to be applicable to problems in the real world.

When we explain our mathematical works to each other we mathematicians only display the finished product in much the same way that an artist or an architect will display their

---

[1]This is why mathematicians sometimes seem to be out of touch with the real world. Much like poets and artists, when we are doing mathematics we actually are out of touch, at least a little.

work without all of the behind-the-scenes sketches and pencil lines (and mistakes), that they made along the way. We start with simple ideas and bit by bit, piece by piece, we assemble our mathematics like we would a puzzle. When we explain it to others we ignore all of the mistakes we made along the way for the same reason that artists do. They are not part the finished product. That is how we understand, and think about our mathematics, and that is how we talk to each other about it. Displayed in this manner a mathematical structure is truly as beautiful as any artistic creation.

But in this text we are not talking to other mathematicians. We are talking to you, a mathematics student. And you are (presumably) encountering Calculus for the first time. This is not the time to build Calculus up from its logical foundations and expect you to appreciate its beauty. This is the time to show you where Calculus came from, how it was built, what problems it was invented to solve, and, perhaps most importantly, how well Calculus addresses those problems. Once that is done you will appreciate it, or not, as your own sense of aesthetics allows.

As you proceed through this text know that it took several centuries for some of the most brilliant persons who have ever lived to polish the ideas of Calculus to their current luster. But just as a painting is unappealing before it is finished, Calculus is not lustrous until you can look back on it as a whole. Until then it takes a lot of calculation and thought to see how the ideas work together. In the end, we hope you will come to see that it is worth all of the work and frustration.

In this chapter we will be exploring the *ad hoc* techniques used by the mathematical pioneers who were trying to solve some very real and very specific problems using only the tools that you possess now: Geometry, Algebra, and Trigonometry. The pre-Calculus techniques they came up with substantially influenced the form that Calculus eventually took. If the pioneers had been different people, or if they had begun with different tools Calculus would likely have taken a different form. Or it might not have been invented at all. The pre-Calculus methods we will see in this chapter represent the first ideas that eventually led to Calculus. The supporting logical structure came later, much later.

Thus we will begin with the intuitive notions that preceded Calculus. But we will not hide the problems inherent in this approach. Quite the reverse. It is our intention to highlight them as much as possible. The underlying difficulties are real and they need to be understood. We want you to be aware of them so that in Chapter 12 when we begin to address them, the necessity of the rather severe formalism we are forced to adopt will be clear to you.

For example, we will soon start talking about "the line tangent to a curve." You have a very clear image of what is meant by "tangent line" and that will suffice to begin. But, it is actually very hard to define precisely what we mean by "the line tangent to a curve[2]."

Later we will encounter a similar difficulty with the idea of a continuous curve. The phrase "continuous curve" surely conjures up a very clear image in your mind. Nothing could be clearer really. Continuous curves are unbroken curves, right? This is so intuitively obvious that mathematicians did not bother to define it formally for millennia. Most likely you don't see the need for a formal definition either. Yet. But "continuity" is very hard to define in a mathematically rigorous manner. The first person to give a rigorous definition in the modern sense was Bernhard Bolzano in 1817.

---

[2]You almost certainly don't believe this because nothing could be clearer than the image of tangency you have in your head. Nevertheless we will eventually see that it is true.

Bernhard Bolzano
1781-1848

One of our goals is to set up the conditions under which it will become very clear to you why your intuitive image of a "tangent line," or a "continuous curve" is not sufficient; why these are hard concepts to define. We want you to bump into the difficulties that come with the intuitive understanding you have right now so that you will see – and appreciate – why the definitions we will eventually be offering are better. Or at least more useful.

But have some sympathy for the poor instructor! Everything we do in the first part of this text, especially in this section, goes directly against all of the instructor's training as a mathematician[3]. Instructors would be much happier with us if we would define the terms "the line tangent to a curve" and "continuous curve" before we use them because that is the way they see and appreciate the beauty of our topic.

The problem is that this is not (in our opinion) a good way to learn Calculus. So we will be following in the footsteps of our forebears. We will proceed using intuitive ideas until they become too unwieldy to use. Only after we have found the properties we need from a concept (like "tangent") will we offer formal definitions. Hopefully it will then be clear to you why the definitions are needed, and why they are stated as they are.

So to the instructor, or anyone else of a mathematical bent who might be reading this, we offer our apologies for proceeding in what we know looks like the wrong way around. As mathematicians ourselves we certainly feel the same discomfort you do. But in this text we are not writing as mathematicians for other mathematicians, we are writing as teachers for students. Please bear with us. "Though this be madness, yet there is method in't[4]."

2.2   Some Preliminaries

In 1537 Niccolo Fontana (1500-1557), also known as "Targtaglia" (The Stutterer), wrote a book titled *Nova Scientia (New Science)* wherein he analyzed the motion of objects

Niccolo Fontana, The Stutterer
1500-1557

moving under the influence of gravity near the surface of the earth as it was understood at the time.

There is much allegory in the title page of his book (next page). Inside the large ring is a group of Muses surrounding Tartaglia and observing the trajectory of a cannonball. This represents the fact that this was one of the first works which studied the science of projectile

---

[3]Indeed, it may well go against your own sensibilities as well. If you find yourself getting irritated with the imprecision of our presentation you may well be a mathematician yourself, at least by temperament. In that case, all you lack is training and you can get that by changing your major to mathematics. Think about it.
If you are not a mathematician at heart then this first part of the text is the part you will probably find most useful and interesting. This is where we will try to elucidate the most powerful problem solving tools that came from Calculus and show you how to use them. But the problems are only representative. Pay attention to the techniques, not to the problems themselves.

[4]Hamlet, Act 2, Scene 2

motion using mathematical principles rather than empirical data and guesswork. At the door of the larger ring is Euclid, representing the notion that one can only enter through an understanding of Euclid's Elements (Geometry). Clearly the man trying to scale the wall does not understand Geometry. His ladder is far too short.

The smaller, slightly raised ring is occupied by Philosophia (wisdom) seated on a throne. Of course, the only entrance to the ring of philosophy, and therefore understanding, is through the larger ring of mathematics. At that gate are Aristotle (384–322 BCE) (on the mathematics side) and Plato (427–347 BCE) (on the philosophy side). On the banner is the motto of Plato's Academy, "Let no one ignorant of geometry enter." Of course, such allegory is open to interpretation, but it seems pretty clear that Geometry (mathematics[5]) would play an important role in the *New Science*.

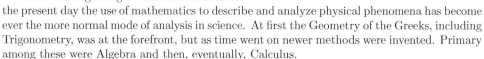

The caption below the illustration means, "The Mathematical sciences speak: Who wishes to know the various causes of things, learn about us. The way is open to all."

From the beginning of the Renaissance to the present day the use of mathematics to describe and analyze physical phenomena has become ever the more normal mode of analysis in science. At first the Geometry of the Greeks, including Trigonometry, was at the forefront, but as time went on newer methods were invented. Primary among these were Algebra and then, eventually, Calculus.

Algebra came first but it merged with Geometry to form what we now call Analytic Geometry. When Calculus was invented it supplemented, enhanced, and expanded its predecessors.

But none of the other fields of mathematics disappeared. Geometry, Trigonometry, Algebra, and Analytic Geometry remain very useful tools in science. But they have, in a sense, become subordinate to Calculus.

There are physical problems that are very difficult to solve using either Algebra or Geometry but which become relatively easy once Calculus has been mastered. Attempts to address those difficult-to-solve problems are what led to the invention of Calculus and several of the very ingenious techniques developed were very Calculus-like. In this chapter we will look briefly at some of these pre-Calculus techniques.

Warning: You may be tempted to disregard this chapter and get on to "the Calculus part." This is an error. The story of Calculus, what sorts of problems it was invented to address, and why the tools of Calculus developed in the way that they did, will help you understand what Calculus is, and what it is not.

---

[5]In those days there wasn't a clear distinction between Geometry and mathematics.

2.3 The Laziness of Nature

In order to apply mathematical principles to the study of physical phenomena we need to agree on some foundational assumptions which seem to govern the behavior of nature. A fundamental tenet that scientists use is this: *Nature is lazy!* That is, nature optimizes. It tries to do things in the most efficient (optimal) manner possible. The most common form such **Optimization Problems** take is to find the value of the independent variable (often denoted x) which makes the dependent variable (often denoted y) as large or as small as possible.

To illustrate the usefulness of this principle consider a beam of light bouncing off of a flat mirror. Empirical evidence[6] suggests that the angle of incidence is equal to the angle of reflection. However, no matter how many experiments we run there is always the chance that there is some configuration of lights and mirrors we've missed. A configuration where the angles are not equal.

Let's try a thought experiment[7].

We want to discover what path a beam of light would travel between the points A and B in the figure below assuming that it first reflects off of the line m (m for mirror, not slope).

From our assumption that *Nature is Lazy*, it is clear that our task is to find the shortest path[8] from A to m to B. That is, we have an **Optimization Problem.**

Begin by reflecting B across m in our imagination and denote this reflection by B_R.

Clearly if the mirror were not present then the solid line from A to B_R in the figure above will be shorter than any other path from A to B_R. For example it is shorter than the dotted path from A to B_R.

Next we reflect B_R back across m so that it falls onto B, and we reflect those portions of the solid and dotted paths that are below line m, in the same way.

Since the two dotted paths have equal lengths, and the two solid paths have equal length it is

---

[6]That is, evidence gained from measuring the angles.

[7]This means that we'll think about it.

[8]Actually we want to minimize the amount of time it takes to pass between two points, but for this problem minimizing the time and minimizing the distance are equivalent. The modern name for this idea is the "Principle of Least Action."

clear that the solid path from A to m to B is shorter than the dotted path from A to m to B, and is thus the shortest possible path from A to m to B.

Problem #9:
Suppose we label the angles in the previous diagram as follows:

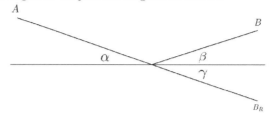

(a) Explain why $\angle\gamma = \angle\beta$.

(b) Explain why $\angle\gamma = \angle\alpha$.

(c) And finally, conclude that
$\angle\alpha = \angle\beta$.

Thus the angle of incidence (α) will equal the angle of reflection (β) provided light adheres to the *Nature is Lazy* principle and really does travel by the shortest possible path.

Problem #10:
If a spotlight is mounted at point A, how far from point C must point D be so that the light will be reflected to point B? Justify your answer.

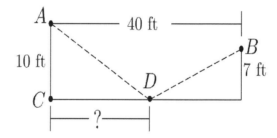

Problem #11:
As long as it is not spinning sideways a billiard ball will bounce just like a beam of light. In the sketch below what must x be to sink the ball into the side pocket at S? Make sure that you explain how you obtained your answer.

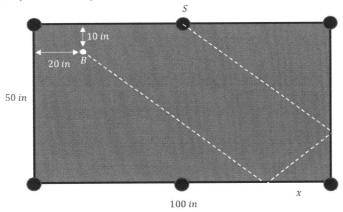

Another optimization problem that we can solve without Calculus (this time we'll use Algebra) is the following.

Example #4: **Maximizing Area**

Out of all rectangles with a given fixed perimeter, which one encompasses the greatest area?

A reasonable guess is that the correct shape is a square. But a guess, no matter how much it feels right, is just a guess. We need a convincing demonstration.

To see that this actually is the correct shape, consider a square whose side is s. If s is the length of one side then the perimeter of our square is (the fixed value) $4s$ and the area is s^2 (also fixed). Suppose we now increase of two opposite sides the length by x. To maintain the same perimeter, we must now decrease the width by the same x. The area of this new rectangle is $(s - x) \times (s + x)$ is $(s - x)(s + x) = s^2 - x^2 < s^2$ but its perimeter is still $4s$.

Thus the square has a larger area than this rectangle with the same perimeter. Moreover, since we didn't specify a value for x our conclusion holds for all possible values of x. That is, every rectangle with perimeter $4s$ has a smaller area than the square with perimeter $4s$.

End Of Example #4

Digression #2: Variables, Constants, and Functions

It is easy to have the impression that using a letter, like s, to represent quantity automatically means that the quantity can vary – that it is "variable." This is not true. There are three situations in which which a letter is used to represent a given quantity.

Variables: For example, the area of a square is given by $A = x^2$, where x is the length of one side. If we think of x as a **variable** — if it can take on any positive value — then this expression gives us the area of all possible squares.

Constants: Sometimes letters are used to designate unchanging quantities — **constants** (also called **parameters**) — when the actual value of the constant is irrelevant. For example, the area of all rectangles where one side is some fixed value, say c, but the other varies is given by $A = c \cdot x$, where x is variable as before. Since we don't care what the size of the fixed side is we don't choose a specific length for it. We just let c represent that fixed size, whatever it is. The crucial fact here is that we have a rectangle, not what size the rectangle is.

The difference between **variables** and **constants** is mostly in the way we think about them. Constants are fixed, but unknown. Variables are not fixed.

Functions: Sometimes a varying quantity depends on the values of one or more other varying quantities. In that case the dependent variable is said to be a **function** of the independent variable. We saw this above when we said the area of a rectangle with a fixed side length, c, was

$$A = c \cdot x.$$

Most often we would write this as

$$A(x) = c \cdot x.$$

The "(x)" part of "$A(x)$" just tells us that what the dependent variable A depends on is the independent variable[a] x.

These are simple distinctions now, but it will be useful for you to get in the habit of making sure it is clear in your mind what is variable, what is constant, and which variables are functions of other variables. As the problems get more complex and we need several variables, parameters, and functions, just untangling all of this can become problematic. Keep in mind that the distinction is purely in how we choose to "think about" a given symbol, not in how we manipulate it algebraically.

---

[a]If you are inclined to be persnickety, you can make a reasonable argument that if $A(x) = cx$ then A depends on both c and x. And you'd be right. But the tradition is to only put variables inside the parentheses, not parameters.

━━━━━ End Of Digression #2 ━━━━━

The following problem is a variation on Example #4 and can be solved similarly.

Problem #12: Out of all rectangles with a fixed perimeter, which one has the shortest diagonal? Justify your answer.

As we mentioned above, Problem 12 can be done in a manner similar to Example 4. But what about the following?

Example #5:

Consider all square based boxes with a fixed surface area S. Does the cube enclose the largest volume?

To do this problem in the same manner as Example 4, observe that a cube with side s would have a volume of s^3 and a surface area of $6s^2$. Suppose we change the lengths on the base from s to $s + x$. Notice that if $x > 0$ then we will be increasing the lengths on the base and if $x < 0$ then we will be decreasing the lengths. The only restriction is that $0 < s + x$ so as to be a length. This says that $-s < x < \infty$. (In theory, we can make the lengths of the base as long as we wish.) To maintain a surface area of $6s^2$, we will need to adjust our height appropriately. Let's call this new height h.

Problem #13:

Proceed as in Example 5 to show that in order to maintain a surface area of $6s^2$, h must be $h = \frac{s^2 - sx - \frac{x^2}{2}}{s+x}$. Use this to show that the volume of this new box is

$$V = s^3 - x^2 \left(s + \frac{s + x}{2} \right).$$

How does this address the original question about the cube having the largest volume?
(**Hint:** Why did we write V in this rather peculiar way.)

End Of Example #5

Problem 13 shows that proceeding in this *ad hoc* manner is becoming more difficult. Difficulties of this kind are what prompted mathematicians in the seventeenth century to search for more systematic methods for handling such optimization. These techniques ultimately led to the invention of Calculus. We'll come back to the this problem later in this chapter.

2.4   Fermat's Method of Adequality

 See also the TRIUMPHS Primary Source Project in Appendix A.1.

Pierre de Fermat
1601-1665

In its simplest form an **Optimization Problem** can be described as follows: Given that y depends on x, find the value of x that makes y as large (or as small) as it can possibly be.

For example, if $y = x^2 - \frac{29}{21}x + \frac{10}{21}$ then y will be as small as it can possibly be when $x = \frac{29}{42}$. The question is, how did we find $x = \frac{29}{42}$?

One of the mathematicians who developed techniques for solving optimization problems was Pierre de Fermat $(1601 - 1665)$ who created what has been called the *Method of Adequalty*. Fermat's[9] method was based on the simple observation that if the maximum value of y occurs when x is equal to say, 6, then when x is very near 6, y will almost be equal to its maximum value.

You can see this in the graph at the right[10]. Notice that the maximum number of daylight hours (about 14.5) occurs just after 169 days (in fact, at day 172) and that for several days before or after we have about the same number of hours of daylight. This is also true near the minimum which occurs at day 356. Regardless of what the variables represent if the graph of a function, $f(x)$, is continuous the near a maximum or minimum: $f(x + h) \approx f(x)$ as long as h is not too big.

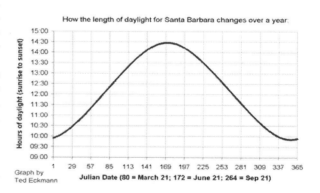

How the length of daylight for Santa Barbara changes over a year:

Graph by Ted Eckmann

Julian Date (80 = March 21; 172 = June 21; 264 = Sep 21)

Fermat's simple idea was to purposely make the mistake of setting $f(x+h)$ actually equal[11] to $f(x)$. He then rearranged the formulas algebraically and at the crucial point he would set $h = 0$ to "make it correct." An example will make this clearer.

---

[9]His name is pronounced "fair mah", not "fur mat".

[10]Since there is only one number associated with each day of the year this should be a discrete graph. Since we'll be more interested in continuous functions we connect the dots to create a continuous approximation.

[11]The Latin root *adaequāre* means to equalize. When something is adequate, then it is equal to the need.

Example #6:

In Example 4, we showed that out of all rectangles with a fixed perimeter, the one with the largest area is a square. Next we will use Fermat's Method of Adequality to examine the related question: Out of all rectangles with a fixed area, does a square have the smallest perimeter?

Consider a rectangle whose length is given by x and width is given by y. The area of the rectangle is given by $A = xy$ and the perimeter is given by $P = 2x + 2y$.

The problem is to minimize P while holding A constant. More precisely, our objective is to minimize the function $P = 2x + 2y$, subject to the constraint that the area, $A = xy$, is fixed. First, we will use our constraint $A = xy$ to eliminate one of the variables and substitute into P. Solving for y, we get $y = A/x$. Then,

$$P = P(x) = 2x + \frac{2A}{x}.$$

We have used function notation for $P(x)$ to emphasize that P is a function of x alone. (Remember that A is constant or "fixed.")

Fermat's method says to first set

$$P(x + h) = P(x).$$

This gives:

$$2(x + h) + \frac{2A}{x + h} = 2x + \frac{2A}{x}. \tag{2.1}$$

Rearranging a bit, we get

$$2x + 2h + \frac{2A}{x + h} = 2x + \frac{2A}{x}$$

so that

$$h = \frac{A}{x} - \frac{A}{x + h}.$$

Adding the fractions gives

$$h = \frac{A(x + h) - Ax}{x(x + h)} = \frac{Ah}{x(x + h)}. \tag{2.2}$$

Finally, and crucially, dividing both sides by h, gives

$$1 = \frac{A}{x(x + h)}. \tag{2.3}$$

Earlier we had made the "mistake" of setting $P(x + h) = P(x)$ (knowing that this is not true). Now we "make it correct" by setting $h = 0$. This gives: $1 = \frac{A}{x^2}$, or $x^2 = A$. Substituting this into $y = \frac{A}{x}$, we get $y = \frac{A}{x} = \frac{x^2}{x} = x$.

Thus P is minimum when $y = x$, which is to say, when the rectangle is actually a square. A moment's thought should make it clear that there is no maximum value for P.

Fermat's method is very slick. However it contains an inherent logical flaw. We begin by setting $P(x + h)$ equal to $P(x)$, even though we know we are making an error. This seems like it might be a flaw but it really isn't. When we set $P(x + h) = P(x)$ we are asking, "What happens if they are equal?" The computations leading up to equation (2.3) are the answer to that question.

But notice that we got from equation (2.2) to equation (2.3) by dividing by h. From arithmetic you know that you can only divide by h if h is not zero. Fortunately it is clear that $h \neq 0$ since the whole point of introducing h is for $x + h$ and x to be two different values. However, in the final step, after Equation (2.3), we took $h = 0$ to "make it correct" but if h is zero then we couldn't have divided by h. We seem to be chasing our tails. We need for h to be equal to zero and not be equal to zero at the same time!

This is the logical flaw.

Since we began with the assumption that $h \neq 0$ we can't just change our minds later. We can't have both $h = 0$ and $h \neq 0$.

End Of Example #6

Despite this logical flaw, Fermat's technique does seem to produce the correct answer. So let's explore it and see what happens.

Drill #14:

Apply Fermat's Method of Adequality to find all maxima or minima of the following functions. In each case examine a graph the function to see if Fermat's Method provides the correct answer.

(a) $f(x) = x(100 - x)$ **(b)** $q(x) = x^2 - 2x + 4$ **(c)** $g(x) = x^4 - 4x^3 + 6x^2 - 4x$

Drill #14 shows that Fermat's method does not indicate whether the computed value of x is at a maximum or a minimum. Often the context of the problem provides the additional information needed to make that determination. Example #6 and Problem #15 both provide such a context.

Problem #15:

Consider a rectangular box with a square base, as seen at the right.

(a) Find a formula for the volume, V, and the surface area, S, of the box.

(b) Suppose we want to determine which box has the least surface area, given a fixed volume. What is our objective and what is our constraint? Use Fermat's Method of Adequality to find the dimensions of the box that solves this problem. Is the minimal box a cube?

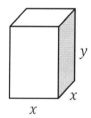

A few minutes of thought should convince you that what makes Fermat's method work is the fact that near a maximum or minimum, the curve is practically horizontal. That is, its slope is nearly zero.

Fermat recognized that finding a maximum or minimum by his method was a special case of finding the slope of (the line tangent to) the curve and he modified his method to determine the slope of a curve even when it is not horizontal.

Before we pursue Fermat's modification, it might be a good time to brush up on some basics regarding the slopes of lines. No doubt you are already familiar with all of the following formulas for the equation of a line:

Slope-Intercept formula: $y = mx + b$

Point-Slope formula: $y - y_0 = m(x - x_0)$

Two-Point, or Point-Point formula: $y - y_0 = \dfrac{y_1 - y_0}{x_1 - x_0}(x - x_0)$

These formulas are all really just rearrangements of one another. We use three different rearrangements because in different contexts one of them is usually simpler to use than the others. Through most of Calculus you will probably find the Point-Slope version to be the most convenient to use.

Drill #16:

(a) Use the appropriate formula for the equation of a line to find an equation of each of the following lines:

    (i) with slope 2 and y-intercept $(0, 7)$

    (ii) with slope -8 and y-intercept $(0, 5)$

    (iii) with slope -2 and x-intercept $(7, 0)$

    (iv) with slope 5 and passing through the point $(2, -8)$

    (v) with slope -4 and passing through the point $(6, -1)$

    (vi) passing through the points $(2, 8)$ and $(4, -2)$

    (vii) passing through the points $(4, 3)$ and $(2, 3)$

(b) Show that the Point-Slope formula follows from the fact that the slope of a line can be determined using any two points on the line.

(c) Show that the Slope-Intercept formula is really a rearrangement of the Point-Slope formula.

(d) Show that the Point-Slope formula follows from the Two-Point formula.

(e) (i) What does the two-point formula reduce to if $y_0 = y_1$?

    (ii) What does the two-point formula reduce to if $x_0 = x_1$?
    (**Hint:** Notice that in the two-point formula, as given we need to assume that $x_0 \neq x_1$. Can you rearrange the formula so that this is not a problem?)

(f) Show that the equation of the line with x-intercept $(a, 0)$ and y-intercept $(0, b)$ can be written in the form: $\frac{x}{a} + \frac{y}{b} = 1$. Notice that this equation is only valid if $a \neq 0$ and $b \neq 0$.

(i) Determine the equation of the line if $a = 0$.

(ii) Determine the equation of the line if $b = 0$.

Problem #17:

(a) In the diagram below L_1 is obtained from L_2 by translating (but not rotating) L_2, as indicated by the arrows. Use the diagram to show that parallel lines have the same slope.

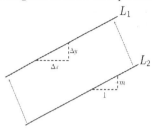

(b) In the diagram below we have taken L_1 from the previous figure, and rotated by 90°. Use this diagram to show that perpendicular lines have slopes that are negative reciprocals of each other.

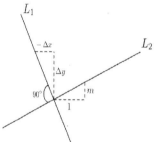

Drill #18:

Find the equation of the line:

(a) parallel to $y = 3x - 2$
and passing through $(3, -3)$

(b) perpendicular to $y = 3x - 2$
and passing through $(3, -3)$

(c) parallel to $2x + 3y = 7$
with y-intercept $(0, 5)$

(d) perpendicular to $2x + 3y = 7$
and passing through the point $(-1, 5)$

Problem #19:

Find the equations of the two lines such that each one is a perpendicular distance of 5 units away from the line $y = \frac{4}{3}x + 2$ and parallel to it.

Now that you've had a chance to brush up on slopes, let's see how Fermat modified his method to determine the slope of a curve[12]. We will start by determining the slope of the graph of $y = x^2$ at the point $(1, 1)$.

We need two points to determine the slope of a line, so with Fermat's method in mind, we choose another point on the curve $y = x^2$ very close to $(1, 1)$. Since we don't really care which point we take as long as it is close to $(1, 1)$ we introduce the parameter, h, which we think of as very small. The points $(1, 1)$ and $(1 + h, (1 + h)^2)$ are thus very close together. This is represented in the sketch at the right.

The slope of secant line joining $(1, 1)$ and $(1 + h, (1 + h)^2)$ is given by

$$\frac{(1 + h)^2 - 1}{(1 + h) - 1} = \frac{1 + 2h + h^2 - 1}{h}$$
$$= 2 + h.$$

As before we set $h = 0$. Thus the slope of the line tangent to the graph of $y = x^2$ at $(1, 1)$ is 2.

Problem #20:

(a) **(i)** Use Fermat's method for tangents to compute the slope of the line tangent to $y = x^2$ at the generic point (a, a^2).

(ii) First plot the graph $y = x^2$. Then, on the same set of axes, plot the line the line through the point (a, a^2), and tangent to the graph of $y = x^2$, for each of $a = -2, -1, 0, 1, 2$.

(iii) What is the relationship between the slopes at (a, a^2) and $(-a, a^2)$? Is this consistent with what you see when you plot the graph of $y = x^2$?

(b) **(i)** Use Fermat's method for tangents to compute the slope of the line tangent to $y = x^3$ at the point (a, a^3).

(ii) First plot the graph $y = x^3$. Then, on the same set of axes, plot the line the line through the point (a, a^2), and tangent to the graph of $y = x^3$, for each of $a = -2, -1, 0, 1, 2$. You should notice something interesting about the tangent lines at ± 1 and ± 2.

(iii) What can you say about the tangent lines at (a, a^3) and $(-a, -a^3)$?

---

[12]That is to say, the slope of the line tangent to the curve.

Problem #21:

(a) Use Fermat's Method to find a formula for the slope of the tangent line to $y(x) = x^3 + 2x^2$ at the point $(a, y(a))$. How does this answer compare with the results of the previous two problems?

(b) What would happen if we used Fermat's Method to find the slope of the tangent line to $y(x) = x^3 + 2x^2 + b$ at the point $(a, y(a))$ where b is any constant? Does this make sense graphically? Explain.

2.5   Descartes's Method of Normals

René Descartes
1596-1650

As we noted earlier, while Fermat's Method of Adequality seems to work it has a fundamental logical flaw. Fermat's contemporary, René Descartes (1596 − 1650), provided an alternative method in his book *Discourse on Method* which is free of logical issues. Unfortunately Descartes' technique is also very difficult to use and as we will see is of limited applicability.

Descartes's method is often called the Method of Normals[13] because what he actually finds is the line normal to (perpendicular to) a curve. Once the line normal to the curve at a point is obtained, the line perpendicular to the normal line will be tangent to the curve. Descartes' Method relies solely on the fact (from Greek Geometry) that at each point of a circle the radius and tangent line through the point are perpendicular. We'll illustrate Descartes' idea with the following example.

Example #7:

To find the slope of the normal (and, eventually the tangent) line to the graph of the curve $y = \sqrt{2x}$ at the point $(2, 2)$ Descartes' approach was to look at the family of circles with centers on the x-axis and passing through the point $(2, 2)$. The sketch at the right displays several members of of that family of circles. Notice that each circle crosses the parabola at the point $(2, 2)$. We are searching for the center of the solid black circle which touches (is tangent to) the parabola at $(2, 2)$. If we can find the center of the black circle then the radial line through the point $(2, 2)$ will

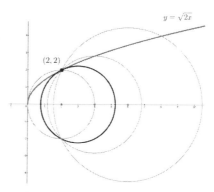

[13]The English word, "normal" comes from the Latin word *norma* which literally means a carpenter's square. In construction, it is important that vertical posts be perpendicular to the horizontal ground, so a vertical post is normal.

be normal to the parabola at $(2,2)$ and the slope of the tangent line will be the negative reciprocal of the slope of the normal.

We now want to turn the geometric problem of finding the intersection of our circle and parabola into an algebraic problem. Let $(a,0)$ denote the coordinates of the center of a circle in that family, then the equation of the circle with center $(a,0)$ is $(x-a)^2 + y^2 = r^2$ where r is the length of the radius of the circle and a is a parameter. Since we require our circle to pass through the point $(2,2)$ the length of this radius will be the distance from $(2,2)$ to $(a,0)$, $r = \sqrt{(2-a)^2 + 2^2}$. Thus we have

$$(x-a)^2 + y^2 = (2-a)^2 + 2^2. \tag{2.4}$$

Since we are looking for the point where $y = \sqrt{2x}$ and the circle intersect, we substitute $y = \sqrt{2x}$ into Equation (2.4) to get

$$(x-a)^2 + 2x = (2-a)^2 + 4$$
$$x^2 - 2ax + a^2 + 2x = 4 - 4a + a^2 + 4$$
$$x^2 + (2-2a)x + (4a - 8) = 0. \tag{2.5}$$

At this point it is tempting to use the Quadratic Formula to solve for x and get (typically) two distinct solutions for x in terms of a. But the fact is we really don't care about the variable x. We want to find the value of a which ensures that the circle and the curve intersect exactly once.

Think about this for a moment. We get a single solution when we use the Quadratic Formula to solve this equation precisely when the discriminant (the part under the square root) is zero.

Drill #22:
Use the Quadratic Formula to show that the discriminant of Equation (2.5) is $(2-2a)^2 - 4(4a-8)$.

Setting the discriminant in Drill 22 equal to zero and solving, we get

$$4 - 8a + 4a^2 - 16a + 32 = 0$$
$$4(a^2 - 6a + 9) = 0$$
$$4(a - 3)^2 = 0.$$
$$a = 3,$$

So the center of the circle touching the curve only once is at $(3,0)$ and the line segment from $(3,0)$ to $(2,2)$ is normal (perpendicular) to the graph of $y = \sqrt{2x}$.

Descartes and Fermat are generally credited with the invention of Analytic Geometry which is a technique that allows us to move problems from Algebra to Geometry or, as in this problem, from Geometry to Algebra.

Problem #23:

Descartes would not have approached this problem using the idea of a discriminant as we just did. He knew that the only way the circle and the parabola could be tangent at $x = 2$ is if 2 is a double root of Equation (2.5). Since a quadratic polynomial only has two roots, this means that Equation (2.5) must be

$$(x - 2)^2 = 0 = x^2 - 4x + 4. \tag{2.6}$$

By comparing the coefficients of Equation (2.5) and the right side of Equation (2.6) show that $a = 3$.

Like any powerful tool, Analytic Geometry must be used carefully. Sometimes, as in this problem, the transition from Geometry to Algebra can generate algebraic solutions that have no corresponding geometric solution. An extraneous root is the most common example of this.

Problem #24: Extraneous Roots

Show that the roots of $x^2 + (2 - 2a)x + (4a - 8) = 0$ are $x = 2$ and $x = 2a - 4$. Notice that when $a \geq 2$ and $a \neq 3$ we the parabola and circle will have two intersection points (as seen in the graph in Example 7). When $a < 2$ we get one positive and one negative root, but the parabola and the circle cross only at $(2, 2)$. How do we make peace with this apparent contradiction? (**Hint:** Look closely at the equation for the parabola. Can x be negative?)

Example 7 illustrates that there is a significant difference between curves touching (curves that are tangent) and curves crossing (curves that intersect). Finding the line tangent to a curve is actually much more subtle than you would expect at first. But this is not the appropriate place to start that conversation so we will hold off until we reach Section 4.

Drill #25:

Now that we've found the center of the circle tangent to the curve $y = \sqrt{2x}$ at $(2, 2)$, use this to find the equation of the lines normal and tangent to the curve at that point. Plot the curve and these two lines on the same set of axes to see if they really are normal and tangent to the curve.

End Of Example #7

Problem #26:

Use Descartes' Method of Normals to find the slope of the line tangent to the curve $y = \sqrt{x}$ at the point $(4, 2)$.

Problem #27:

Use Descartes' Method of Normals to find the slope of the line tangent to the curve $y = x^2$ at the point $(3, 9)$ and compare with Problem 20.

(**Hint:** You may want to use circles that are centered on the y-axis instead of the x-axis.)

Problem #28:

Apply Descartes' Method of Normals to the line $y - 3x = 2$ at the point $(1, 5)$. What equation did you find for the tangent line? Does this make sense to you?

Descartes' Method, unlike Fermat's, is free of the logical pitfalls. But it is algebraically cumbersome because it requires that we find the "double root" of a polynomial. Double roots of quadratic functions like the one in Example #7 are relatively easy to find. But for higher degree polynomials this can be a substantial problem. For transcendental functions like $y = 1 - \cos(x)$ this problem is almost insurmountable without Calculus.

2.6   Roberval, Conic Sections, and the Dynamic Approach

Speed, Velocity, and Rates of Change

Descartes and Fermat were co-creators of Analytic Geometry – the use of Algebra to solve geometric problems – so their methods are simultaneously algebraic and geometric in nature. That is, their methods are static. There is no motion involved. But at it's heart, Calculus gives us a way of dealing with the properties of objects as they change. It is the mathematics of motion. So we will need to think more dynamically.

If quantity A changes by ΔA each time quantity B changes by ΔB we say that the rate of change of A **with respect to** B is $\frac{\Delta A}{\Delta B}$.

For example, in a video game if your character gains one hundred hit points whenever you cast a certain spell we would say that the rate of change of your hit points is one hundred points per spell, denoted $100\frac{\text{points}}{\text{spell}}$. If you gain fifty hit points every second time you quaff a potion we write $\frac{50 \text{ points}}{2 \text{ quaffs}}$ or, equivalently, $25\frac{\text{points}}{\text{quaff}}$ and we say that the rate of change of hit points with respect to quaffs is twenty-five. Notice how naturally the properties of fractions come into play: $\frac{50 \text{ points}}{2 \text{ quaffs}} = 25\frac{\text{points}}{\text{quaff}}$.

On the other hand if you lose 15 hit points each time an enemy strikes you three times with a sword then your hit points are decreasing at a rate of $\frac{15 \text{ points}}{3 \text{ strikes}} = 5\frac{\text{points}}{\text{strike}}$. It is inconvenient to specify whether A is increasing or decreasing verbally so we adopt the convention that a negative rate of change is decreasing and a positive rate of change is increasing.

Speed is the rate of change we are most familiar with in daily life. If you are driving on a flat, straight, road your speed is the **rate of change** of your position, Δx, **with respect to** the passage (change) of time, Δt. If your speedometer reads 60 we say your speed is sixty miles per hour:[14] $60\frac{\text{miles}}{\text{hour}}$, meaning of course that in one hour you will travel sixty miles. This

---

[14] At least that's what we say in the United States. In most of the rest of the world it means your speed is

is often abbreviated to 60 mph. We will model a flat, straight, road as the x-axis with the positive direction to the right, as is customary. Of course, on this flat, straight, road we could be going $60\frac{\text{miles}}{\text{hour}}$ to the right or to the left. Since there are only two directions possible, we can again use negative numbers to indicate the direction of travel as depicted in the sketch below.

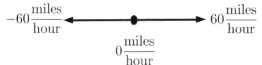

However if we are on a broad flat plain, as depicted in the sketch below:

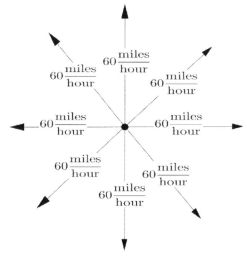

we can travel in any direction whatsoever. Notice that our sketch indicates that there are eight cars, all traveling at $60\frac{\text{miles}}{\text{hour}}$, but in different directions. That is, the **speed** of each car is $60\frac{\text{miles}}{\text{hour}}$. But it should be clear that a single number is not adequate to fully describe the motion of these cars. We also need to specify the direction of travel and simply using plus or minus is no longer sufficient.

When we specify the speed and direction of motion of some object we are stating its **velocity**. This can be difficult at first because in casual conversation we use the words speed and velocity interchangeably, so we tend to think of them as synonyms. But in a technical setting speed and velocity, while related, have different meanings. **Speed** is how fast we're going. In the sketch at the left the speed of all of the cars is $60\frac{\text{miles}}{\text{hour}}$. But their **velocities** are all different. The velocity of one car is $60\frac{\text{miles}}{\text{hour}}$ to the north, the velocity of another is $60\frac{\text{miles}}{\text{hour}}$ to the west, the velocity of a third is $60\frac{\text{miles}}{\text{hour}}$ to the southeast, and so on.

Gilles Personne de Roberval $(1602-1675)$, a contemporary of Fermat and Descartes, used arrows to indicate the velocity of moving objects just as we have. The length of the arrow represents the speed of the object and the direction of travel is the direction that the arrow points. This works well in the kind of geometric arguments he used as it enabled him to develop

---

sixty kilometers per hour: $60\frac{\text{kilometers}}{\text{hour}}$, or 60 kph.

a method for constructing tangents which is dynamic in nature.

Suppose you are on a moving sidewalk like those in an airport and the sidewalk is moving at $3\frac{\text{feet}}{\text{second}}$. If you stand still on the sidewalk then you are still moving at $3\frac{\text{feet}}{\text{second}}$.

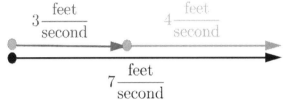

If you are walking along the sidewalk at $4\frac{\text{feet}}{\text{second}}$ and in the same direction the sidewalk is moving then it is pretty clear that you are moving at a rate of $7\frac{\text{feet}}{\text{second}}$.

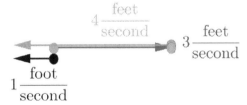

Of course, if you turn around and walk against the sidewalk, then your speed would be $1\frac{\text{foot}}{\text{second}}$.

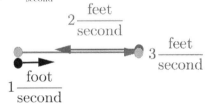

If you are walking against the sidewalk but slower than the sidewalk is moving, say at $2\frac{\text{feet}}{\text{second}}$, then you are again moving at $1\frac{\text{foot}}{\text{second}}$ but in the other direction.

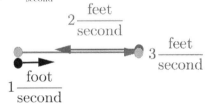

Since there are only two possible directions all this could have been done without arrows by just adding signed numbers where the sign indicates the direction: $3 + 4 = 7$, $3 + (-4) = -1$, $3 + (-2) = 1$, but what if there are more directions available?

Using arrows allows us to bring this discussion into a more general setting. In the examples above notice that the resulting velocity (the black arrow) was always obtained by attaching the tail of the green or red arrow to the head of the blue arrow.

This works equally well if more directions are available, like when we are moving in a plane instead of a straight line.

For example, suppose we are swimming across a river at a speed of $2\frac{\text{feet}}{\text{second}}$ and the river is flowing at $3\frac{\text{feet}}{\text{second}}$. Assuming that we are swimming perpendicular to the current, we have the situation depicted below.

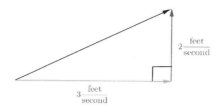

Drill #29:

(a) In the diagram above what does the length of the black arrow represent physically?

(b) What is the length of the black arrow?

In general you can think of the velocity of an object moving in a plane as being compounded of a horizontal velocity (the blue arrow in Drill 29) and a vertical velocity (the red arrow in Drill 29). This is easiest to think about when the component velocities are perpendicular but this isn't strictly necessary. For example, you don't need to be swimming perpendicular to the current. As seen in the diagram at the right to find the result of two non-perpendicular velocities (the solid red and blue arrows) we need only form the parallelogram as shown. The resulting velocity is then represented by the black diagonal arrow.

Roberval assumed that a curve in the plane is generated by a point whose motion is an aggregate of two known motions, which can be represented as arrows. The arrows are then "added" by finding the diagonal of the parallelogram generated by the two arrows. This diagonal will point in the direction of motion at that point on the curve and will point tangent to the curve.

Example #8:

Suppose a point is moving in the plane so that its horizontal speed is 1 unit per second and its vertical velocity is 2 units per second as in the diagram at the right. Clearly our point is moving along the line $y = 2x$.

If t represents time in seconds and if the point starts at the origin, then its coordinates are given by $x(t) = t$ and[15] $y(t) = 2t$. Since both x and y are needed to locate the point we will join them together notationally like this:

$$P(t) = \left\{ \begin{matrix} x(t) \\ y(t) \end{matrix} \right\} = \left\{ \begin{matrix} t \\ 2t \end{matrix} \right\}.$$

---

[15]Observe that $x(t) = t$ is the algebraic representation of a horizontal arrow with length t, and $y(t) = 2t$ is the algebraic representation of a vertical arrow with length $2t$. Translating statements and concepts between Algebra and Geometry is the essence of Analytic Geometry.

You might quite reasonably ask why we've gone to all this bother just to have two different ways to represent a particular line: $y = 2x$, and $P(t) = \begin{Bmatrix} t \\ 2t \end{Bmatrix}$. The difference is in how we "think about" the graph. When we write $y = 2x$ we are thinking of the entire graph. When we write $P(t) = \begin{Bmatrix} x(t) \\ y(t) \end{Bmatrix}$ there is an implicit understanding that (t)ime is passing and we are thinking about the motion of the point. Thus when $t = 1$ the point is at $(1, 2)$ when $t = 2$ it's at $(2, 4)$.

Think of the line as a road. The formula $y = 2x$ describes the entire road, whereas the expression $P(t) = \begin{Bmatrix} t \\ 2t \end{Bmatrix}$ tells us the point's location on the road at any given time, t.

The idea of representing velocities with arrows is quite a powerful and common technique for representing non-linear motion. Roberval used this technique to find the tangent lines of the conic sections (as we will soon see) as well as more general curves. Since Roberval's time this idea has been developed considerably beyond what Roberval did. In fact we are skirting the edge of some very deep ideas here. In modern terms these arrows would be called **vectors**. **Vector Addition** is then done by the **Parallelogram Rule**, which is essentially what we did with our arrows above: Form the parallelogram and find its diagonal. The full force of vector analysis was not available to Roberval, and we won't need it, so we will not take you any further down this path but we encourage you visualize velocities, and any other directed quantity, as composed of horizontal and vertical components whenever you can. You will see this representation in more detail later in your education and it will help if you have already begun thinking in these terms.

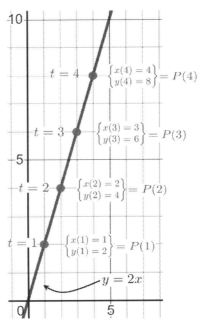

End Of Example #8

Problem #30:

Suppose the position of a point in the plane is given by $P(t) = \begin{Bmatrix} 3t \\ 6t \end{Bmatrix}$.

(a) What is the horizontal speed of the point?

(b) What is the vertical speed of the point?

(c) What is the speed of the point in the direction of motion?

(d) Compare the motion of the point in this problem to the motion of the point in Example 8.

Problem #31:

Suppose a point is moving along the line $y = mx + b$ with a horizontal speed of 1 unit per second.

(a) Find a representation of the point's position in the form $P(t) = \begin{Bmatrix} x(t) \\ y(t) \end{Bmatrix}$

   (**Comment:** There are a variety of correct solutions here. You must find a representation and then show that it is correct.)

(b) What is the speed of the point in the vertical direction?

(c) What is the speed of the point in the direction of motion?

Problem #32:

Suppose a point is moving along the line $y = mx + b$ with a horizontal speed of 5 units per second.

(a) What is the speed of the point in the vertical direction?

(b) What is the speed of the point in the direction of motion?

Problem #33:

Suppose the position of a point in the plane is given by $P(t) = \begin{Bmatrix} 2t \\ 5t \end{Bmatrix}$.

(a) What is the horizontal velocity of the point?

(b) What is the vertical velocity of the point?

(c) What is the velocity of P in the direction of motion?

Problem #34:

We drop an object from a helicopter which is traveling horizontally with a constant velocity of 1 meter per second. After it leave the helicopter the vertical velocity of the object at time t will be $-9.8t$ meters per second[16] as in the following diagram:

---

[16]This is because the acceleration due to gravity at the surface of the earth has been determined (by Galileo) to be $9.8 \frac{m}{\sec^2}$. We'll discuss this in more depth in Section 4.4.

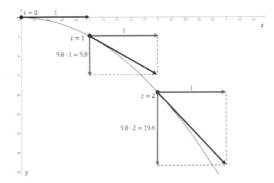

If Roberval's method works then the speed of the point at any time, t, will be the length of the diagonal of parallelogram of velocity arrows at time t. Find a formula for the speed of the point and any time t.

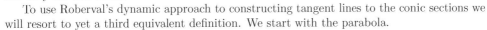

The Tangent Lines of the Conic Sections

Parabolas, ellipses, and hyperbolas are called conic sections, or just conics, because they were originally defined as the intersection of a cone with planes situated at various angles, as shown in the sketches at the right.

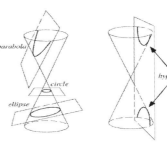

While interesting, the original geometric definitions won't do for our purposes[17] because they are entirely static. There is no motion involved.

The more modern algebraic forms are a bit better:

Parabolas: $y = ax^2 + bx + c$,

Ellipses: $\frac{x^2}{a^2} + \frac{y^2}{b^2} = 1$,

Hyperbolas: $\frac{x^2}{a^2} - \frac{y^2}{b^2} = \pm 1$.

but they are also static.

To use Roberval's dynamic approach to constructing tangent lines to the conic sections we will resort to yet a third equivalent definition. We start with the parabola.

The Tangent to a Parabola

A parabola can also be thought of as the set of points, P, in a plane which are equidistant from a fixed point, F, called the **focus** of the parabola, and a specific line, d, called the **directrix**

---

[17]This is primarily because we depend very heavily on our modern algebraic notation, not because of any inherent flaw in the definition. Without any notation at all ancient Greek scholars understood the nature of parabolas at least as well as we do today. Possibly better.

of the parabola. Adopting Roberval's dynamic viewpoint, we can think of P as tracing out the parabola by moving so that these distances stay equal to each other.

Problem #35:

(a) Explain why it must be that the speed at which P moves away from F must equal the speed at which P moves away from d.
(**Hint:** Suppose these speeds were not equal. What would this say about the distances from P to F and from P to d?)

(b) Consider the following diagram.

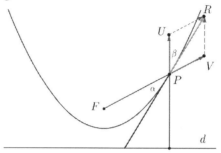

If PV represents the velocity of the motion of P away from F, and PU represents the velocity of the motion of P away from d, then according to Roberval, the diagonal, PR of the parallelogram $PVRU$ is tangent to the parabola. Use the result of part (a) to explain why this parallelogram is a rhombus[18].

(c) In our sketch the angle β is between the arrows PU and PR. We have also extended the arrow PR downward to form the angle α with FP. Given that the parallelogram $PVRU$ in the previous figure is a rhombus, show that the two angles, α, β are congruent.

That α and β in the previous problem are congruent has an interesting consequence in optics. Imagine that the inside of our parabola is a mirror, and that a light source has been placed at the point F. As we have seen when light reflects off of a flat mirror the angle of incidence is equal to the angle of reflection. Since this mirror isn't flat the angles of incidence and reflection are measured from the line tangent to the parabola at the point where the light strikes the mirror. Thus the angle of incidence of a beam emerging from F and striking the parabola at P will be α in our diagram 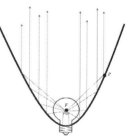 and the angle of reflection will be $\beta(=\alpha)$. It follows that a light beam emerging from F and reflecting from the parabola at any point will follow a path parallel to the axis of symmetry of the parabola after reflecting from the interior of the parabola.

---

[18]A **rhombus** is a parallelogram where the four sides have equal length.

You can see this in action with your car headlights or a flashlight. The reflector is cast in the shape of a parabola and the light emitting filament is place at the focus, so all of the light which strikes the reflector gets reflected in that direction.

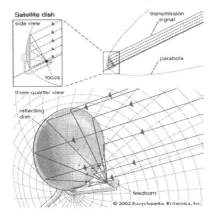

Now turn this around. Any light beam coming parallel to axis of symmetry and striking the parabolic mirror will pass through the focal point F. The light is thus focused and the image appears larger. This fact was used by Isaac Newton in the seventeenth century to design a new, and better, telescope than the one used by Galileo a generation earlier. Galileo's telescope was based on the refraction of light as it passes through shaped lenses. Through his study of optics Newton learned that the magnification effect could also be achieved via reflection. It was his invention of the reflecting telescope that first brought Newton into scientific prominence.

The fundamental optical principle he used, a light beam traveling parallel to the axis of symmetry, after reflecting from the interior of a parabolic mirror, will pass through the focus of the parabola, is the underlying design principle of all reflective telescopes, large and small, today.

In fact, you use this every day. Since radio waves are a form of electromagnetic radiation, just like visible light, this is also a fundamental design point for both radar antennas, satellite cable TV dishes, and the antennas at the tops of cell phone towers.

The Tangent to an Ellipse

Geometrically, an ellipse is the set of points in a plane, the sum of where the sum of the distances from two fixed points (foci) is a constant. Following Roberval we can generate an ellipse by combining two motions: one away from one focus (F_1P) and one toward the other focus (PF_2) as in the sketch at the right. If we set d_1 equal to the length of F_1P and d_2 equal to the length of PF_2, then $d_1 + d_2$ is constant.

Because $d_1 + d_2$ is constant it should be clear that the rate at which d_1 lengthens is related to the rate at which d_2 shortens. These rates of change are represented by the red arrows in our sketch.

Problem #36:

Explain why the parallelogram in the sketch above must be a rhombus and use this to show that angle α is congruent to angle β.

(**Hint:** An argument very similar to the one used in Problem #35 will work.)

From Problem #36 we see that any light ray, sound wave, etc., emanating from one focus of an ellipse will reflect off of the interior of the ellipse to the other focus.

A playful example of the reflective properties of an ellipse are the so-called "whisper galleries." If you and a friend stand at the foci of a room in the shape of an ellipse you will be able to converse in whispers even if you are very far apart. This is because the sound waves from your friend's voice will spread out to the walls and then reflect back to the other focus, where you are standing. Naturally, the volume of sound from any single location in the interior of the ellipse will have dropped considerably in transit. However, since all of them travel the same distance to get to you they arrive at the same time and the volume you hear is the sum of all of the individual reflected volumes.

The whisper gallery shown at the left is the one in Grand Central Station in New York City. The young woman on the left and the young man on the right are standing at the foci and speaking to each other quietly.

There is another whisper gallery in Statuary Hall in the Capitol building in Washington DC. This room was originally the meeting hall for the House of Representatives. It is said that when John Quincy Adams was a representative he would eavesdrop on his political enemies by placing himself at one focus of the room whenever he saw them talking quietly at the other. A more serious application of this reflective property is used in modern medicine to treat kidney stones. The treatment is called Extra-corporeal Shock Wave Lithotripsy[19].

The Tangent to an Hyperbola

If an ellipse is the locus of points the sum of whose distances from two given points is constant it is natural to ask, "What do we get when the difference of their distances is constant?" That is the shape called the hyperbola seen in the diagram below.

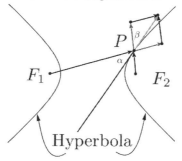

As before, we set d_1 and d_2 equal to the lengths of F_1P and F_2P, respectively. An hyperbola has the property that $d_1 - d_2$ is constant.

---

[19]Lithotripsy literally means "rock grinding."

Problem #37:
Explain why the parallelogram in the sketch above must be a rhombus and use this to show that angle α is congruent to angle β. As before in our diagram the red arrows represent the velocity of P in the direction from F_1 to P and from F_2 to P.

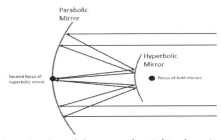

The hyperbola also has interesting reflective properties. If a beam of light is aimed at one focus it will reflect off of the hyperbola toward the other focus. This property can be used to further refine the design of reflecting telescopes and antennae. The figure at the right shows the design of Cassegrain antenna. The large, primary mirror on the left is parabolic and shares a focus with the smaller, secondary, hyperbolic mirror on the right. Light reflecting off of the primary mirror is directed at the shared focus on the right where it is reflected to the other focus at the primary mirror. A detection device is then placed at the secondary focus to collect the amplified signal.

Roberval's use of arrows to represent velocities provides an intuitive way to understand the reflective properties of the conic sections. Moreover, thinking of curves as being traced out in time it gives us a dynamical way of looking at curves. This was a viewpoint that Newton adopted in his version of the Calculus.

2.7 Snell's Law and the Limitations of Adequality:

When light passes from one medium to another, say from air to water, it bends. This property is called refraction. The physical law governing refraction is known as Snell's Law, named after the Dutch Astronomer Willebrord Snell ($1580 - 1626$) though it was accurately described before that time. In modern terms, Snell's Law can be stated as follows.

Snell's Law of Refraction: Suppose that light travels with a velocity of v_1 in the first medium and velocity v_2 in second medium, and that θ_1 and θ_2 are as seen in the diagram below.

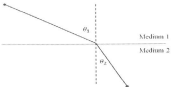

Then the path that light follows satisfies

$$\frac{\sin(\theta_1)}{v_1} = \frac{\sin(\theta_2)}{v_2}.$$

Notice that if $v_1 = v_2$ this says that $\sin(\theta_1) = \sin(\theta_2)$ and the path of the line would be a straight line.

A number of mathematicians, including both Snell and Fermat, gave derivations of Snell's Law, but we will focus on Fermat's method. To attack this problem, Fermat refined the *Nature is Lazy* assumption a bit. Instead of assuming that that light would follow the shortest path, he assumed that light would follow the path that takes the least time.

Notice that this is consistent with our observations concerning reflections from a mirror. In that case, the speed of light was constant so the shortest path was, in fact, the fastest path. But refraction occurs because the velocity of light changes when the surrounding medium changes.

Let's see what happens when we try to use Fermat's Method of Adequality to find this fastest path.

Problem #38:

Assuming that the velocity[20] of light is v_1 in the first medium and v_2 in the second, use the following diagram:

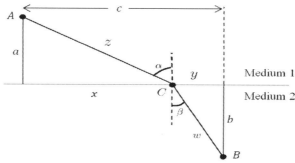

to show the time, t, for light to travel along the path from A to C B is $\frac{\sqrt{a^2+x^2}}{v_1} + \frac{\sqrt{b^2+(c-x)^2}}{v_2}$.

Of course the next step would be to use Fermat's Method of Adequality to minimize t, but the square roots involved make the Algebra daunting to say the least. Despite these difficulties Fermat was able to show that t is minimized precisely when Snell's Law holds.

Although it is possible to derive Snell's Law with the tools we now have it is very difficult so we won't attempt it here. Instead we will return to this problem in Chapter 8 where we will complete the derivation of Snell's Law using the rules of Calculus. That will be much simpler.

It seems that our efforts to solve optimization problems using pre-Calculus techniques has hit an impasse. To be sure those techniques, and others of a similar nature, were very clever and it must be admitted that they yielded interesting and correct results. However for the most part they were *ad hoc* methods and quite limited in their applicability. We need a way to overcome these limitations.

---

[20]Is it clear to you that we've used velocity here when we really mean speed? If not, think about it for a moment. We're really only interested how fast light travels in either medium, not in the direction it is going. This was the language used in the seventeenth century so it is accurate historically, but not mathematically. Unfortunately, it is still common to use these words interchangeably, even among folks who know better. This can be quite confusing for the beginner but there isn't much that can be done except be aware of the problem. Whenever you encounter either word pause of a moment and ask yourself if the speaker or author means speed, or velocity. It should always be clear from the context.

This is exactly what the invention of Calculus in the mid-seventeenth century did. The title of Leibniz' first published work on Calculus makes this very clear:

> *A New Method for Maxima and Minima, as Well as Tangents, Which is Impeded Neither by Fractional nor Irrational Quantities, and a Remarkable Type of Calculus for This.*

It is time for us to learn about this *Remarkable Type of Calculus.*

Chapter 3

Differentials, Differentiation, and the Derivative

"By relieving the brain of all unnecessary work, a good notation sets it free to concentrate on more advanced problems, and, in effect, increases the mental power of the race."

– Alfred North Whitehead (1861-1947)

3.1   Historical Introduction

Since the Covid-19 pandemic of 2020 the following story has become very popular. In 1665 an outbreak of Bubonic Plague[1] closed Cambridge University. One of the students, a young man named Isaac Newton, decided to continue his studies on his own at his country home in Woolsthorpe, Lincolnshire, UK. It was during this time that Newton worked out the basic principles of Optics, his Law of Universal Gravitation, and his version of the Calculus. He was under 25 years old at the time.

Woolsthorpe Manor today

The basic facts of this story are essentially correct. The Plague did close Cambridge University in 1665, Newton was under 25, he did retire to Woolsthorpe, and he did investigate Optics and Gravitation during this time. The mathematics that he needed did not exist at the time so he invented it. Today we call it Calculus.

But telling Newton's story this way is misleading. It leaves the impression that he did all

---

[1] Also called the Black Death.

66

of these things during his two years at Woolsthorpe; sewed them up in a neat little package; bequeathed them to the rest of humanity and then ascended directly into heaven as a scientific demi-god.

Isaac Newton
1642-1727

This is not true[2]. In fact, he continued to work on optics after returning to Cambridge, but did not publish his first results until 1672. He worked on his gravitational theory until at least 1687 when he published the first edition of his book *Philosophiae Naturalis Principia Mathematica* (Mathematical Principles of Natural Philosopy[3]).

When you're a genius you can do that.

Newton's story is often treated as inspirational but the fact that he did so much, so young seems to us (the authors of this book) more intimidating than inspiring. We are considerably older than 25 and taken together we haven't done anything as impressive as Newton did in his youth.

But comparing ourselves to Newton is pointless. Newton was a true genius. We are merely ordinary people just like you. We didn't invent Calculus, and you don't have to either. Newton did that for us. Everyone since has merely had to learn it; a much less imposing task.

Well, almost everyone.

About ten years after Newton entered Cambridge University, and quite independently, Gottfried Wilhelm Leibniz developed his rules for Calculus while employed as a diplomat in Paris from 1672 to 1674. He was 26 years old at the time.

Though their approaches are fundamentally different, the computational techniques they worked out were essentially equivalent. Newton's approach was dynamic. He was thinking about objects in motion: the moon, the planets, and falling apples. Leibniz was thinking about geometric relationships, more like Fermat or Descartes.

As a matter of pure logic it doesn't really matter which viewpoint is adopted. However, there are some situations where thinking dynamically (like Newton) is more helpful, and others where thinking geometrically (like Leibniz) is more helpful. Throughout this text we will switch back and forth, adopting whichever approach seems to us more advantageous for a given situation. You should too.

Newton was a private, almost secretive man. At first he didn't tell anyone about his invention and so Leibniz was the one to publish the first paper on Calculus in 1684. We referred to his paper at the end of Chapter 2:

Gottfried Wilhelm Leibniz
1646-1716

---

[2]To be sure Newton did a *lot* during his retreat to Woolsthorpe, and he was a scientific demi-god. But if he ascended into heaven he did it in the usual way in 1727 at the age of 84.

[3]It is usually just called *The Principia*.

A New Method for Maxima and Minima, as Well as Tangents, Which is Impeded Neither by Fractional nor Irrational Quantities, and a Remarkable Type of Calculus for This.

From this rather imposing title we can infer that Leibniz was aware the Calculus would empower mathematicians to more easily solve both old problems (like Snell's Law) and new problems alike.

In his paper Leibniz displayed all of the General Differentiation Rules you will see at the beginning of the next section. He called his computational rules "*Calculus Differentialis*" which translates loosely as "rules for differences." In English this is called **Differential Calculus**.

Newton and Leibniz each created and used a notation that reflected his own viewpoint. Newton's notation has (mostly) fallen away over the years. Leibniz' notation is much more intuitive and has become standard in mathematics.

Both assumed that a varying quantity could be increased or decreased by an infinitely small amount. Leibniz called this an infinitesimal difference, or a **differential** and denoted it with the letter "d" – presumably for "differential". So if x is some quantity, then its differential, dx, represents an infinitely small increase or decrease in x.

To talk of infinitely small increments may sound strange to you. It does to most people, because it is in fact a truly weird idea. Johann Bernoulli[4] described differentials this way: "a quantity which is increased or decreased by an infinitely small quantity is neither increased nor decreased[5]." You may judge for yourself how helpful this is.

The idea of an infinitesimal was not new. Before the invention of Calculus mathematicians had been using the notion both successfully, and informally, for many years. Galileo and his students used them. So did Archimedes. The idea was "in the air."

But the vagueness of the notion was very troubling. In fact, late in his life Newton attempted to repudiate the idea of differentials by founding his version of Calculus on what he called *prime and ultimate ratios*. Leibniz simply continued the tradition of using differentials and invented the notational formalism that we still use today.

Although neither of them could precisely answer the question, "What is a differential?" neither Leibniz nor Newton allowed this to hold them back. They developed their computational schemes, verified that they worked – at least on the problems they were interested in – and proceeded to use them to attack other problems. That was enough for them. Both men followed the example of their forebears and treated the notion of an infinitely small increment as a convenient fiction. Something that doesn't exist in reality but is useful as way to think about certain problems. We will adopt a similar attitude – at least for now.

But this is mathematics. Eventually we will reach a time of reckoning when we must define our concepts clearly and precisely. All of them, not just the convenient ones.

The question "What is a differential?" cannot simply be swept under the rug and ignored indefinitely. Since everything we do will depend in a fundamental way on differentials, we must resolve this question or all of our work will rest on a foundation of shifting sands and we will never really know whether it is valid or not. If we do not proceed carefully, logically, from clearly stated first principles we can never truly know if what we are doing is valid.

Indeed, Newton, Leibniz, and generations of mathematicians since understood this very well and worked hard to either give rigorous meaning to the idea of a differential or to abandon

---

[4]Johann and his brother Jacob both learned Calculus from Leibniz, and both went on to mathematical greatness in their own right

[5]From "Great Moments in Mathematics After 1650", Lecture 32

it altogether in favor of some other concept. Newton's idea of prime and ultimate ratios was probably the first such attempt.

Abraham Robinson,
1918-1974

But it took some of the greatest minds in history nearly two hundred years to resolve the question of differentials.

Well, *resolve* might be too strong a word. The theory of limits, adopted in the late 19th century, doesn't resolve the matter as much as it simply avoids it altogether. You'll see what we mean when we come to Chapter 16

In the mid-twentieth century Abraham Robinson (1918−1974) was finally able to put a develop the notion of a differential in a solid, rigorous manner. Unfortunately, to do this Robinson required some high level techniques from the field of Mathematical Logic which are quite beyond the scope of this text.

Besides, Calculus already had a rigorous foundation. The theory of limits had been established nearly a hundred years before Robinson's work and it provides an entirely adequate foundation for Calculus. Unfortunately, the theory of limits does very little to help anyone actually *use* Calculus. It simply provides rigor for the logical foundations.

On the other hand the differentials of Leibniz and Robinson do provide aid in using Calculus. Newton, Leibniz, and their contemporaries did truly amazing things by treating differentials as *convenient fictions*. There is no reason we can't do the same.

For now we will follow the example of our forbears and develop the Rules For Differences (**Differential Calculus**) using Leibniz' differentials. In particular, we will not concern ourselves with the question, "What is a differential?"

There is precedent for this. The ancient Greek mathematician Euclid, (325BC - 265BC) defined geometric points with the phrase "A point is that which has no parts." But that is simply a clever way of admitting that he didn't know what points are, despite the fact that they are enormously useful. What is a point, really, but a convenient fiction? And yet the notion of a point is foundational for all of Geometry. After all, what is a line but the relationship between two points? Moreover, mathematical points are highly intuitive and can be visualized in the mind's eye as long as we don't look too closely.

Differentials will play a similar role in Calculus.

3.2 The General Differentiation Rules

". . . mathematical analysis is to the technical man merely a tool or instrument for doing his work, of which he must have not only the knowledge and understanding but also the expertness which he has with other tools."

– Arthur S. Hathaway(1855-1934)

"You've got to learn your instrument. Then, you practice, practice, practice. And then, when you finally get up there on the bandstand, forget all that and just wail."

– Charlie "Bird" Parker (1937-1955)

Warning: Be sure you understand the purpose of this chapter.

Imagine a surgeon using a scalpel, an auto mechanic using a torque wrench, or a professional golfer swinging a club. These people endure countless hours of practice learning to use the fundamental tools of their trade. It is not fun, nor do they expect it to be. They do it in order to become so skillful that they can use their tools seamlessly; so they can focus on what they are doing, not how they are doing it. They don't think of the tool, they think of the task. The tool simply becomes an extension of their hands. In precisely the same way, the differentiation rules we'll be discussing in this chapter are the basic tools of your trade and you need to become so skillful with them that you can use them without thinking about them.

The computational rules in the table at the right are the basic tools of Differential Calculus. They need to become an extension of your mind. You need to be able to perform these calculations while holding a larger problem in your mind. Sometimes a much larger problem.

The Constant Rule	If a is a constant then $da = 0$.
The Sum Rule	$d(x + y) = dx + dy$.
The Constant Multiple Rule	If a is a constant then $d(ax) = a\,dx$.
The Product Rule	$d(xy) = x\,dy + y\,dx$.
The Power Rule	If n is a rational number then $d(x^n) = nx^{n-1}\,dx$
The Quotient Rule	$d\left(\dfrac{x}{y}\right) = \dfrac{y\,dx - x\,dy}{y^2}$

The General Differentiation Rules

You need to become so familiar with them that they become the simple part of bigger problems.

The purpose of this chapter is to give you practice with these computations; to give you a chance to internalize them before you have to use them in a larger context. For that reason we will be providing a lot of drill problems for you to practice on. *Do them.*

These drill problems are not important in themselves, but once we move past this chapter it will be assumed that you can compute a differential – even if the computation is long and complex – easily. If you have not given yourself enough practice here, you will struggle through the rest of this course. And the ones that come after. You may even fail.

So, right here, right now, resolve to do all of the problems in this chapter. Do them even if your instructor has not assigned them all. The more practice you get with this now, the less you will struggle later. Find other problems from other books and do them too. Make up your own problems. Practice until you can compute a differential with a quick glance.

This is important. We, the authors of this text, know what we are talking about. Listen to us. Your goal in this chapter is to completely internalize these differentiation rules. They need to become second nature to you. This work will pay off in the long run.

Differentials

> *"It is better to do the right problem the wrong way than the wrong problem the right way."*
>
> – Richard W. Hamming (1915-1998)

The General Differentiation Rules are surprisingly easy to learn and remember. Moreover, despite the fact that we have six entries in our table there are really only three rules. The Constant Rule, The Sum Rule, and the Product Rule are fundamental. The other three, The Constant Multiple Rule, The Power Rule, and the Quotient Rule are straightforward consequences of the first three. We only state them separately for convenience.

We call these rules "general" because each one of them can be applied to a wide variety of expressions. In addition to the general rules there is a large set of specific rules that only apply to specific functions. We will come back to these beginning in Chapter 5

To begin, suppose a point is moving along the x-axis. As in Chapters 1 and 2 when we think of a point in motion we write $x(t)$ to express the idea that the position x, depends on the time, t. At a specific time, t, the position $x(t_1)$, is expressed as more compactly as x_1 and at time t_2 the position is x_2..

The (small, finite) change in x is the difference between x_2 and x_1: $x_2 - x_1$, and the (small, finite) change in t is the difference between t_2 and t_1 : $t_2 - t_1$.

It is customary to denote these small, finite changes with the notation:

$$\Delta x = x_2 - x_1, \text{ and } \Delta t = t_2 - t_1.$$

We will denote infinitely small changes in x and t as $\mathrm{d}x$ and $\mathrm{d}t$. The symbol $\mathrm{d}x$ is called the **differential** of x.

Notationally, the distinction between Δx and $\mathrm{d}x$ is small, but conceptually it is profound. When we write Δx there is some measurable distance between x_2 and x_1. When we write $\mathrm{d}x$ the distance between x_2 and x_1 is immeasurably (infinitesimally) small.

If x is changing in time, $\mathrm{d}x$ represents how much x changes in an infinitesimally small increment of time $\mathrm{d}t$. If the concept of an infinitely small increment troubles you (it should) it is safe, for now, to think of $\mathrm{d}x$ as a very, very, very, small change in x.

In general, if two variables, say x and y, are related we will be interested in asking (and answering) the question: If x is incremented by $\mathrm{d}x$ how will y be affected?

The General Differentiation Rules

Now that we understand our notation the first differentiation rule is quite obvious. In fact, it is the same whether we are thinking of a small finite change or of a differential. If x is unchanging, if it is *not* moving, then "the (infinitesimal) change in x" between two different times is zero. It doesn't really matter whether we are talking about a finite Δx or an infinitesimal dx. Both are zero because x doesn't change. Thus we have the following rule:

The Constant Rule: If x is a constant, then $dx = 0$.

Drill #39:
Compute the differential, dy, of each of the following:

(a) $y = 1$ **(c)** $y = \frac{\sqrt{2}}{\pi}$ **(e)** $y = 2,000,000,000$

(b) $y = \pi$ **(d)** $y = \sqrt{2}\pi$ **(f)** $y = \sin^2(\theta) + \cos^2(\theta)$

Problem #40:
In the table of General Differentiation Rules at the beginning of this chapter we stated the Constant Rule using a as the constant, in the statement above we used x, and in Drill #39 we used y. Does it matter what symbol we use? Explain.

This first rule was particularly simple since only one quantity was involved and it was unchanging. The second is only slightly more complex. Suppose we have two variable quantities, x and y. Then:

The Sum Rule: $d(x + y) = dx + dy$.

If x_1 and x_2 are infinitely close together, then $dx = x_2 - x_1$. Similarly if y_1 and y_2 are infinitely close together then $dy = y_2 - y_1$. Then:

$$d(x + y) = (x_2 + y_2) - (x_1 + y_1)$$
$$= (x_2 - x_1) + (y_2 - y_1)$$
$$= dx + dy,$$

which verifies the Sum Rule. Notice that like the Constant Rule, the Sum Rule is true regardless of whether we are talking about finite differences or differentials.

The Sum Rule is stated as if it only applies to the sum of *two* quantities. This is typical of mathematical writing. We tend to be minimalists so we don't state more than we absolutely have to. However, if the Sum Rule applies to the sum of two quantities it is straightforward to show that it also applies in the obvious fashion to a sum of three, four, or more quantities.

Problem #41:

(a) Show that $d(x + (y + z)) = dx + dy + dz$
(**Hint:** Notice how we placed the parentheses.)

(b) Show that $d(x + y + z + w) = dx + dy + dz + dw$

(c) Explain how you would show that

$$d(x_1 + x_2 + x_3 + \cdots + x_n) = dx_1 + dx_2 + dx_3 + \cdots + dx_n$$

where n is an arbitrary positive, integer.

The Constant Multiple Rule: If a is a constant, then $d(ax) = a\,dx$.

Suppose a is a constant and x is a variable. Since $d(ax) = ax_2 - ax_1$ is the differential between infinitely close values of ax we see that the differential of ax is given by:

$$d(ax) = ax_2 - ax_1 = a(x_2 - x_1) = a\,dx.$$

which verifies the Constant Multiple Rule.

Example #9:

To get a sense of how we will be using differentials consider the line which is the graph of the equation $3x + 2y = 5$. Let's differentiate both sides of this formula using the tools we have so far.

Obviously if two quantities are equal then their differentials are also equal. So,
$$d(3x + 2y) = d(5).$$
From the Sum Rule and the Constant Rule we have,
$$d(3x) + d(2y) = 0$$
and from the Constant Multiple Rule we see that,

$$3\,dx + 2\,dy = 0. \tag{3.1}$$

Notice that Equation (3.1) can be rearranged as follows: $\frac{dy}{dx} = -\frac{3}{2}$.

So it appears that the **differential ratio** $\frac{dy}{dx}$ is the slope of our line. This makes sense since $\frac{dy}{dx}$ is the (infinitesimal) change in y divided by the (infinitesimal) change in x. From your study of lines in Algebra you know that the change in y divided by the change in x is the definition of slope. It continues to be the slope even if the changes in x and y are infinitesimal.

End Of Example #9

Drill #42:

Compute $\mathrm{d}y$ for each of the following:

(a) $y - x = 0$ **(e)** $y = 0.0002x$ **(i)** $y = \sqrt{2}x$ **(l)** $y = \dfrac{(\pi + \sqrt{2})x}{x}$

(b) $y - x = 5$ **(f)** $\frac{y}{x} = \pi$ **(j)** $y = (\pi + \sqrt{2})x$

(c) $y - 2x = 7$ **(g)** $y = 3 + 2x$

(d) $20x - y = -1$ **(h)** $\frac{7 - \pi y}{x} = 17$ **(k)** $y = \pi x + \sqrt{2}x$ **(m)** $y = \dfrac{(1 - x)x^4}{x^3 - x^4}$

In his 1684 paper on Calculus, Leibniz presented all of the General Differentiation Rules with no justification whatsoever, stating simply that *"The demonstration of all this will be easy to one who is experienced in these matters ..."* Our first three rules seem to bear this out. They are really the same as the analogous rules for finite differences. His claim is a bit more suspect for the next differentiation rule.

The Product Rule: $\mathrm{d}(xy) = x\,\mathrm{d}y + y\,\mathrm{d}x$.

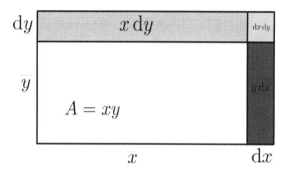

Think of the product xy as the (A)rea of the rectangle with sides of length x and y so that $A = xy$, as shown in the sketch at the left. If we increase the sides by $\mathrm{d}x$ and $\mathrm{d}y$, respectively, then the area will change by an infinitesimal amount $\mathrm{d}A$ which is the sum of areas of the blue, yellow, and red regions shown in the sketch. The area of the blue region is $x\,\mathrm{d}y$, the area of the red region is $y\,\mathrm{d}x$ and the area of the yellow region is $\mathrm{d}x\,\mathrm{d}y$. Since $\mathrm{d}A$ is the sum of these three regions we have

$$\mathrm{d}A = x\,\mathrm{d}y + y\,\mathrm{d}x + \mathrm{d}x\,\mathrm{d}y. \tag{3.2}$$

But remember that $\mathrm{d}x$ and $\mathrm{d}y$ represent infinitely small changes. Thus, their product $\mathrm{d}x\,\mathrm{d}y$ is even more infinitely small[6] than they are. In fact, the product $\mathrm{d}x$ times $\mathrm{d}y$ is so small compared to any of the that other terms in Equation 3.2 that it simply doesn't matter. So we will ignore it.

This leaves us with $\mathrm{d}A = \mathrm{d}(xy) = x\,\mathrm{d}y + y\,\mathrm{d}x$ verifying the Product Rule.

You should feel at least a little uncomfortable with this logical sleight of hand. Some questions present themselves immediately: How can we choose not to ignore infinitesimals like $\mathrm{d}x$ and $\mathrm{d}y$, but then choose to ignore their product $\mathrm{d}x\,\mathrm{d}y$? What happens if x or y is negative? What happens if $\mathrm{d}x$ or $\mathrm{d}y$ is negative?

Perhaps this is why Leibniz left out the demonstrations (proofs) of his rules – he knew this would be controversial. However, he was not lying when he said that those familiar with

---

[6] Quadratically infinitely small?

infinitesimals would understand. Newton also ignored products of infinitesimals in his version of Calculus. As we discussed in Section 3.1, it took mathematicians some 200 years to sort this out. We will begin to address this problem in Chapter 12. For now, we will simply accept that the Product Rule works as we've stated it knowing full well that we are on shaky ground that will eventually need to be firmed up.

Problem #43: Use the Product Rule to show that if $y = x^2$, then $dy = 2x\,dx$.

Even though they could not fully explain their methods, both Newton and Leibniz could see that their methods gave answers that made sense physically and which agreed with the results of their predecessors. That is, their methods worked.

For example, in Problem 20 you used Fermat's method for tangents to show that at the point $(1, 1)$ the slope of the curve $y = x^2$ is 2 and that at the point $(-2, 4)$ the slope of the curve is -4. Recall from Example 9 that the differential ratio $\frac{dy}{dx}$ represents the slope of the curve. With this in mind we rewrite the formula $dy = 2x\,dx$ from Problem #43 as $\frac{dy}{dx} = 2x$, from which we see that the Product Rule easily recovers Fermat's results.

But what can it mean to say that the slope of the graph of $y = x^2$ is $2x$? The expression $2x$ changes with x but slope is supposed to be constant isn't it? Moreover, slopes have always been associated with straight lines in the past, but there is not a straight line to be seen anywhere in this problem.

Or is there?

The notion of a differential is essentially an extension of the following observation: If you look very closely at a curve it looks like a straight line. You can confirm this with any graphing technology. Graph a curve and zoom in repeatedly at any point on the curve. Eventually the curve will look like a straight line, and the slope of that line will be the value of $\frac{dy}{dx}$ at that point. If we extend this observation to the infinitely small scale we get differentials.

The idea that at the infinitely small scale lines and curves are indistinguishable is known as the **Principal of Local Linearity**, and it is a fundamental principle underlying all of Calculus. We will formally define the Principle of Local Linearity in Section 4.2. For now, the informal idea is that when you look at a very small section of a curve it looks like a straight line. When we choose to simply ignore the term $dx\,dy$ in our development of the Product Rule we are invoking the Principle of Local Linearity[7].

Again, Newton and Leibniz relied on the fact that their methods produced solutions that made sense physically and which agreed with known solutions to old problems. Snell's Law is an example of the latter. The following problem is an example of the former.

---

[7]This is true but it is is not at all obvious.

Problem #44:

When a rock is tossed into a quiet lake it generates an expanding, circular wave, as in the diagram below.

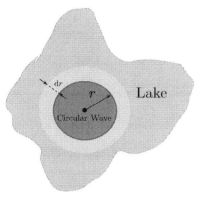

The area enclosed by the wave at any time is given by the formula: $A = \pi r^2$, where r is the expanding radius of the circle. As time advances the radius of the circular wave expands and, as a consequence, the area enclosed by the wave also grows.

(a) Use the Constant Multiple Rule and the Product Rule to show that

$$\mathrm{d}A = \mathrm{d}(\pi r^2) = 2\pi r\,\mathrm{d}r.$$

(b) Explain why be the area of the yellow ring in the diagram is also equal to $\mathrm{d}A$.

(c) Find $\mathrm{d}A$ by cutting the yellow region at the dotted line, reshaping the ring into a rectangle. How does this compare with what we obtained using our Calculus rules. Do you see any logical issues with this solution? Specifically, why is it important that $\mathrm{d}r$ must be infinitely small?

Digression #3: Differential Notation

We will pause here for a moment to take explicit notice of the notational convenience we used in part (a) of Problem 44 because it will be useful later. We have used the expression $\mathrm{d}x$ to represent an infinitesimal displacement of x, but it will be useful to think of the "d" as meaningful in itself. That is, in the expression $\mathrm{d}(\pi r^2)$ we think of the "d" as "operating on" the expression πr^2. Thus when d "operates on" the expression πr^2 it returns the expression $2\pi r\,\mathrm{d}r$ and we have

$$\mathrm{d}A = \mathrm{d}(\pi r^2) = 2\pi r\,\mathrm{d}r.$$

This is actually consistent with our previous usage if we think of $\mathrm{d}(A)$ as "operating on" the area A and returning the differential $\mathrm{d}A$.

This is akin to the way we think about the square root symbol. The symbol $\sqrt{}$ "operates on" the expression underneath it so we have $\sqrt{4} = 2$. Just as $\sqrt{}$ is always reserved for the square root *of some quantity*, d is always reserved for the differential *of some quantity*. In both cases the quantity needs to be named. It is as meaningless to write πr^2 d as it is to write $\pi r^2 \sqrt{}$. It is important to use the notation as it was designed to be used.

Also, notice that on the left side of $dA = d(\pi r^2) = 2\pi r\, dr$ we have the infinitesimal quantity, dA. Since the two sides of the equation are equal it follows that the quantity on the right side is also an infinitesimal. The obvious conclusion is that the ordinary real number $2\pi r$ multiplied by the infinitesimal dr must result in an infinitesimal quantity. Dividing both sides by dr we have $\frac{dA}{dr} = 2\pi r$, which seems to indicate that the quotient of two differentials will be an ordinary real number. Does this make intuitive sense to you?

Notice that we asked if it makes *intuitive* sense. When working with differentials it frequently happens that a statement feels right (makes intuitive sense) but begins to fall apart when examined more carefully.

================ End Of Digression #3 ================

Problem #45:
We mentioned earlier that the Constant Rule, the Sum Rule, and the Product Rule are fundamental, and that the other three can be proved using these three. Show that the Constant Multiple Rule follows from the Constant Rule and the Product Rule.

Problem #46: Find the pattern

(a) Compute each of the following differential:

  (i) $d(x+1)$

  (ii) $d\left[(x+1)(x+2)\right]$

  (iii) $d\left[(x+1)(x+2)(x+3)\right]$

  (iv) $d\left[(x+1)(x+2)(x+3)(x+4)\right]$

  (v) $d\left[(x+1)(x+2)(x+3)(x+4)(x+5)\right]$

  (vi) $d\left[(x+1)(x+2)(x+3)(x+4)(x+5)(x+6)\right]$

(b) Do you see a pattern in the computations you did in part (a)? Assume n is an unknown positive integer and use the pattern to compute:

$$d\left[(x+1)(x+2)(x+3)(x+4)\cdots(x+n)\right].$$

Problem #47: Find the Pattern

By custom, differentials are written at the end of each term where they appear in a given computation so the Product Rule is usually written as

$$d(xy) = x(\,dy) + y(\,dx).$$

But this is just a custom so it is not strictly necessary. We could also use the Product Rule in the form

$$d(xy) = x(\,dy) + (\,dx)y.$$

(a) Use the Product Rule twice to show that
$$d(xyz) = xy(\,dz) + x(\,dy)z + (\,dx)yz,$$
(**Hint:** The Product Rule requires two factors. But we have three: x, y, and z. We can fix this with the substitution $\alpha = yz$. Then $d(xyz) = d(x\alpha)$. Now use the Product Rule.)

(b) Emulate part (a) to show that.
$$d(xyzw) = xyz(\,dw) + xy(\,dz)w + x(\,dy)zw + (\,dx)yzw.$$

(c) What does the Product Rule look like for $d(x_1 x_2 x_3 \cdots x_n)$?

(d) Use the result of part (c) with $x_1 = x_2 = \cdots = x_n = x$ to show that $d(x^n) = nx^{n-1}\,dx$. This is called the **Power Rule for Positive Integers**.

The Power Rule for Positive Integers: For any positive integer n, $d(x^n) = nx^{n-1}\,dx$.

Let's try out our differentiation rules on a relatively simple example. We will include every single step so that you can see how the differentiation rules are used in concert.

Example #10:

From the Sum Rule we have,

$$d\left(5x^6 - 3x^4 + 21x^2 - 7\right) = d\left(5x^6\right) - d\left(3x^4\right) + d\left(21x^2\right) - d(7).$$

Next, Constant Rule, and the Constant Multiple Rule give,

$$= 5\,d\left(x^6\right) - 3\,d\left(x^4\right) + 21\,d\left(x^2\right) - 0,$$

and by the Power Rule for Positive Integers we have,

$$= 5\left(6x^5\,dx\right) - 3\left(4x^3\,dx\right) + 21\left(2x^1\,dx\right)$$
$$= 30x^5\,dx - 12x^3\,dx + 42x\,dx.$$

Finally, factoring out the differential of x gives,

$$d\left(5x^6 - 3x^4 + 21x^2 - 7\right) = \left(30x^5 - 12x^3 + 42x\right)\,dx.$$

Did you notice that the differential dx appeared in every term allowing us to factor it out at the end? When there is only one independent variable involved (x in this case) that will *always* happen. So it provides an easy way to check your computations.

If you end with an expression where the differential of the independent variable cannot be factored out then you have made a mistake in your computations. You should find your mistake before going on. Or just begin again.

End Of Example #10

As you become more skilled you will probably do many of the steps from Example 10 in your head. But for now, notice how the rules work together and are applied as they are needed.

Example #11:

Here is another example without all the details spelled out. Make sure you see which rule is being invoked at each step.

$$
\begin{aligned}
d((2x+5)(3x-7)) &= (2x+5)\,d(3x-7) + (3x-7)\,d(2x+5) \\
&= (2x+5)(3)\,dx + (3x-7)(2)\,dx \\
&= (6x+15+6x-14)\,dx \\
&= (12x+1)\,dx.
\end{aligned}
$$

End Of Example #11

Drill #48: Identify each of the rules used in each step of Example 11.

Of course, in Example 11 we could have multiplied the factors together before differentiating and obtained the same answer:

$$
\begin{aligned}
d((2x+5)(3x-7)) &= d(6x^2 + x - 35) \\
&= 6(2x\,dx) + dx - 0 \\
&= (12x+1)\,dx.
\end{aligned}
$$

Either procedure will work. You are at liberty to do whichever you prefer.

Drill #49:
Compute each of the following:

(a) $d(5x+3)$

(b) $d(\pi^2)$

(c) $d(x^3 - 5x^2 + 7)$

(d) $d(\pi^2 + 2)$

(e) $d((3x+4)(2x-5)(2-6x))$

(f) $d\left((x-3)^2\right)$

(g) $d\left((x-r)^2\right)$
　　　Assume that r is a constant.

Drill #50:

Compute each of the following:

(a) $d((x^2 + 3x + 1)(5x - 7x^{20} + x^{12} - 6))$

(b) $d((5x^2 - 7x + 1)(2x^{10} - 4x^7 + 3x^3 - 2x + 8))$

(c) $d(a_0 + a_1x + a_2x^2 + a_3x^3 + \ldots + a_nx^n)$
Assume that $a_0, a_1, \ldots,$ and a_n are all constant.

(d) $d(x^4(3x^2 - 2x + 45))$

Drill #51:

Compute dy for each of the following:

(a) $y = 4.9x^2 + 15x + 6$

(b) $y = 3.14$

(c) $y = 3.1416$

(d) $y = \pi$

(e) $y = x^2 - 2x + 4$

(f) $y = 3(x^3 - 4x + 2)$

(g) $y = \frac{7x^5 - 3x^3 + x^2}{x}$

(h) $y = 5x^2 + 2x - 3$

(i) $x^2 - y^2 = 1$

(j) $x^2 + y^2 + z^2 = 1$

(k) $xy^2 = z^3$

(l) $xyz = 2$

Example #12:

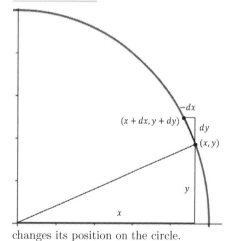

Differentiating both sides of an ordinary algebraic equation yields a **Differential Equation** – an equation which relates the differentials of the quantities involved. For example, suppose we have a point (x, y) lying on the unit circle so that the quantities x and y are related by the equation $x^2 + y^2 = 1$.

Differentiating, we have the differential equation

$$2x\,dx + 2y\,dy = 0 \text{ or}$$
$$y\,dy = -x\,dx. \qquad (3.3)$$

Let's look at this geometrically and focus on the first quadrant. The sketch at the left shows what happens to the quantities x and y as the point changes its position on the circle.

The smaller triangle is called a **differential triangle**[8] and it is infinitely small. Differential triangles were a favorite tool of Leibniz. He assumed without justification (as we will, for now) that they are just like ordinary (finite) triangles.

---

[8]Because all three sides are differentials, obviously.

Notice that $\mathrm{d}x$ is negative since the x coordinate is moving to the left, and that $\mathrm{d}y$ is positive since the y coordinate is moving upward. We need positive quantities to represent the length of the triangle's legs. Therefore we use $-\mathrm{d}x$ to represent a positive length for the horizontal leg of our differential triangle.

A little more mysterious is the (correct) observation that the smaller triangle isn't really a triangle at all. Because it is part of the circle the line connecting (x, y) and $(x + \mathrm{d}x, y + \mathrm{d}y)$ – the hypotenuse of the triangle – is curved. But there is nothing lost by thinking of the hypotenuse as a straight line because according to the Principle of Local Linearity at an infinitely small scale lines and curves are indistinguishable. At least in part, this why Newton, Leibniz, and their contemporaries worked with differentials. At that scale they could replace curves with straight lines.

End Of Example #12

Problem #52:

(a) Show that the two triangles in the diagram above are similar. Use this to show that

$$y \, \mathrm{d}y = -x \, \mathrm{d}x.$$

(**Comment:** Notice that this problem specifically asks you to use the triangles, not differentiation to show that $y \, \mathrm{d}y = -x \, \mathrm{d}x$.)

(b) After Problem #43 we observed that the ratio $\frac{\mathrm{d}y}{\mathrm{d}x}$ must represent the slope of both the curve and its tangent line at a given point.

Notice that the differential equation for the circle can be written as

$$\frac{\mathrm{d}y}{\mathrm{d}x} = -\frac{x}{y}.$$

Explain how this is related to the geometric fact that the tangent to a circle at a point is perpendicular to the radius through that point.

Example #13: Brute Force Computation

Suppose and we wish to find $\mathrm{d}y$ when $y = 5(x^2 + x)^3$ One way to do this is simple brute force. That is, we compute

$$y = 5(x^2 + x)^3 = 5(x^6 + 3x^5 + 3x^4 + x^3) = 5x^6 + 15x^5 + 15x^4 + 5x^3.$$

Applying the Sum Rule we see that

$$\mathrm{d}y = \mathrm{d}\left(5x^6\right) + \mathrm{d}\left(15x^5\right) + \mathrm{d}\left(15x^4\right) + \mathrm{d}\left(5x^3\right).$$

Next we use the Constant Multiple Rule, to get

$$\mathrm{d}y = 5\,\mathrm{d}\left(x^6\right) + 15\,\mathrm{d}\left(x^5\right) + 15\,\mathrm{d}\left(x^4\right) + 5\,\mathrm{d}\left(x^3\right).$$

Finally, we use the Power Rule four times to get

$$dy = 30x^5\,dx + 75x^4\,dx + 60x^3\,dx + 15x^2\,dx.$$
$$dy = (30x^5 + 75x^4 + 60x^3 + 15x^2)\,dx.$$

In the end we have,

$$dy = (30x^5 + 75x^4 + 60x^3 + 15x^2)\,dx.$$

Brute force works but expanding an expression like $(x^2 + x)^3$ is dull (and error prone) and mathematicians are like Nature: We are lazy. We'd really rather avoid doing all of that dull computation if we possibly can. Wouldn't you?

Suppose, we make this problem a little "easier on the eyes" with a substitution like we did in Section 1.2. Let $z = x^2 + x$. Then our original problem becomes $y = 5z^3$ which is much easier to look at. And now $dy = 15z^2\,dz$. Substituting $x^2 + x$ back in for z we get $dy = 15(x^2 + x)^2\,d(x^2 + x)$. After computing $d(x^2 + x) = (2x + 1)\,dx$ we see that

$$dy = 15(x^2 + x)^2(2x + 1)\,dx.$$

Problem #53:

(a) Complete Example 13 by showing that we get the same dy both ways.

(b) Compute dy if $y = 5(x^2 + x)^{30}$ and then solve the equation $dy = 0$ for x.
(**Comment:** This problem is completely contrived. There is no obvious reason that we would want or need to solve this equation. However, in the near future this will be the next step in many of the problems we will encounter.)

End Of Example #13

Example #14: Making Things "Easier on the Eyes"

Suppose we wish to find dy when $y = (x + 2)^2(2x - 3)^3$ Once again we could just apply brute force by multiplying out the expression $(x + 2)^2(2x - 3)^3$. But this is a lot of work and it is very error prone.

Instead notice that y is the *product* of $(x + 2)^2$ and $(2x - 3)^3$, so the Product Rule seems a likely place to begin. But first we make it "easier on the eyes" with the substitutions, $z = x + 2$, and $w = 2x - 3$. Thus:

$$y = \underbrace{(x + 2)}_{=z}^2\underbrace{(2x - 3)}_{=w}^3$$
$$y = z^2 w^3.$$

Using the Product Rule we now have

$$dy = z^2 \, d(w^3) + w^3 \, d(z^2)$$
$$= (x+2)^2 \, d(w^3) + (2x-3)^3 \, d(z^2)$$
$$= (x+2)^2 (3w^2) \, dw + (2x-3)^3 (2z) \, dz$$
$$= (x+2)^2 (3)(2x-3)^2 \, d(2x-3) + (2x-3)^3 (2)(x+2) \, d(x+2)$$
$$= (x+2)^2 (3)(2x-3)^2 (2) \, dx + (2x-3)^3 (2)(x+2) \, dx.$$

and so

$$dy = \left[6(x+2)^2 (2x-3)^2 + 2(2x-3)^3 (x+2) \right] \, dx.$$

Not only does this involve considerably less Algebra (and is thus less prone to error) it also gives us dy in a form that is easy to factor. This is important because, as we mentioned in our comment to Problem #53, many of the problems to come will involve finding a differential, setting it equal to zero, and then solving the resulting equation. If we had computed this by brute force we would have to find the roots of a fully expanded fourth degree polynomial. That would be hard. The form given above is much easier to work with. Let's go ahead and set $dy = 0$ and solve the resulting equation:

$$6(x+2)^2 (2x-3)^2 + 2(2x-3)^3 (x+2) = 0.$$

just for practice.

The prospects for solving the equation, even in this form seem pretty glum at first, but it really isn't so bad once we notice that $(x+2)$ and $(2x-3)^2$ appear as factors in both terms on the left hand side. Factoring these out gives

$$(x+2)(2x-3)^2 \left[6(x+2) + 2(2x-3) \right] = 0$$

so that

$$(x+2)(2x-3)^2 \left[6x+12 + 4x-6 \right] = 0$$
$$2(x+2)(2x-3)^2 (5x+3) = 0. \qquad (3.4)$$

Drill #54: Complete this example by finding all solutions of the last equation.

End Of Example #14

Drill #55: Compute the differential of $y = (x^2 - 4)^3 (x^2 + 3)^5$ and solve $dy = 0$ for x.

As you become more comfortable using these differentiation rules together, you will probably do many of the steps in a long differentiation more informally, perhaps even in your head.

However, most of the time differentiation will only be one part of much larger problems. If you don't differentiate correctly whatever you do after that is wasted time and effort. It is better to proceed slowly to be sure you are right. If it helps to write out each step in detail then you should certainly do that.

At this point we can find the differentials of a large number of algebraic expressions. But not all. For example suppose $y = \sqrt{x}$. Nothing we've done so far tells us what dy is.

Example #15:

However, you are surely aware that the radical symbol, $\sqrt{}$, can be expressed as a fractional exponent. For example, $\sqrt{x} = x^{\frac{1}{2}}$. It is tempting to simply assert that, by the Power Rule, $d(x^{1/2}) = \frac{1}{2} \cdot x^{1/2-1}\,dx = \frac{1}{2} \cdot \frac{1}{x^{1/2}}\,dx = \frac{1}{\sqrt{2x}}\,dx$. In fact this is true, but it doesn't follow from the way we developed the Power Rule because we depended quite explicitly on the assumption that the exponent of x^n is a positive integer.

Here's one way to prove that the Power Rule works when $n = 1/2$. If $y = \sqrt{x}$ then $y^2 = x$. Computing the differential of both sides gives:

$$d(y^2) = dx$$
$$2y\,dy = dx$$
$$dy = \frac{1}{2y}\,dx = \frac{1}{2x^{1/2}}\,dx = \frac{1}{2} \cdot \frac{1}{x^{1/2}}\,dx$$

or $dy = \frac{1}{2}x^{1/2-1}\,dx$ which is the Power Rule with $n = \frac{1}{2}$.

End Of Example #15

This example is more important than it appears to be. What it shows is that the Power Rule can be extended to include at least the case where the exponent is $1/2$. In fact, the Power Rule is easily extended to allow the exponent to be any positive fraction, say $2/3$ for example.

Example #16:

You should be a little bit surprised at this. After all, $y = x^{2/3}$ is a complicated thing, compared to $y = x^2$, or even $y = x^{1/3}$. Nevertheless, essentially the same procedure works here too. If $y = x^{2/3}$, then $y^3 = x^2$. Differentiating both sides gives

$$3y^2\,dy = 2x\,dx$$

and solving for dy leaves us with

$$dy = \frac{2}{3}\frac{x}{y^2}\,dx.$$

This is not yet recognizable as the Power Rule primarily because we need to express the right side entirely in terms of x. But recall that $y = x^{2/3}$ so that $y^2 = x^{4/3}$. Making that substitution gives

$$dy = \frac{2}{3}\frac{x}{x^{4/3}\,dx} = \frac{2}{3}x^{-\frac{1}{3}}\,dx = \frac{2}{3}x^{\frac{2}{3}-1}\,dx$$

which is the Power Rule with $n = 2/3$.

End Of Example #16

Problem #56: The Power Rule for Positive, Rational Numbers

(a) Mimic the process in Examples 15 and 16 to show that $\mathrm{d}\left(\sqrt[3]{x^4}\right) = \frac{4}{3}x^{\frac{1}{3}}\,\mathrm{d}x$.

(b) Now suppose $y = x^{\frac{p}{q}}$, where p and q are positive integers and show that $\mathrm{d}\left(x^{\frac{p}{q}}\right) = \frac{p}{q}x^{\frac{p}{q}-1}\,\mathrm{d}x$.

Example #17:

Having seen that the Power Rule can be extended to include positive, fractional exponents it is natural to ask if it can be extended to negative exponents Can we find the differential of $y = 1/x = x^{-1}$.

Of course we can.

If $y = 1/x$ then $xy = 1$. By the Product Rule we have

$$\mathrm{d}(xy) = \mathrm{d}(1)$$
$$x\,\mathrm{d}y + y\,\mathrm{d}x = 0$$
$$x\,\mathrm{d}y = -y\,\mathrm{d}x$$
$$\mathrm{d}y = -\frac{y}{x}\,\mathrm{d}x = -\frac{\frac{1}{x}}{x}\,\mathrm{d}x$$
$$= -\frac{1}{x^2}\,\mathrm{d}x$$

and thus

$$\mathrm{d}y = \mathrm{d}\left(x^{-1}\right) = (-1)x^{(-1)-1}\,\mathrm{d}x.$$

So the Power Rule works for $n = -1$ as well.

End Of Example #17

Problem #57:

Let r be a positive rational number and $y = x^{-r} = 1/x^r$. As in Example #17 clear the fraction and use the Product Rule to obtain the Power Rule for negative rational numbers:

$$\mathrm{d}y = -rx^{-r-1}\,\mathrm{d}x.$$

Drill #58:

Use the formula you found in Problem#57 to show that $d\left(\frac{1}{\sqrt[3]{x^4}}\right) = -\frac{4}{3}x^{-\frac{7}{3}}\,dx$.

Thus we see that the Power Rule holds for any rational number, positive or negative, which gives us the following.

The Power Rule for Rational Numbers: Let p, and q be any integers, positive or negative, with $q \neq 0$. Then $d\left(x^{\frac{p}{q}}\right) = \frac{p}{q}x^{\frac{p}{q}-1}\,dx$.

We can now differentiate some pretty complicated expressions. Frequently an appropriate substitution will make this "easier on the eyes" but otherwise at each step only need to invoke one of the General Differentiation Rules. When the expression is complicated the key is to be methodical and do one step at a time even if you are doing some of them in your head.

Example #18:

To differentiate $\left(\sqrt{x^2-2}\right)\left(\sqrt{x}-2\right)$ we begin by re-expressing the radicals as exponents because we have no differentiation rules for radicals.

$$
\begin{aligned}
d\left[\left(\sqrt{x^2-2}\right)\left(\sqrt{x}-2\right)\right] &= d\left[\left((x^2-2)^{1/2}\right)\left(x^{1/2}-2\right)\right] \\
&= (x^2-2)^{\frac{1}{2}}\,d\left(x^{\frac{1}{2}}-2\right) + \left(x^{\frac{1}{2}}-2\right)\,d(x^2-2)^{\frac{1}{2}} \\
&= (x^2-2)^{\frac{1}{2}}\left(\frac{1}{2}x^{-\frac{1}{2}}\right)\,dx + \left(x^{\frac{1}{2}}-2\right)\left(\frac{1}{2}(x^2-2)^{-\frac{1}{2}}\right)\,d(x^2-2) \\
&= (x^2-2)^{\frac{1}{2}}\left(\frac{1}{2}x^{-\frac{1}{2}}\right)\,dx + \left(x^{\frac{1}{2}}-2\right)\left(\frac{1}{2}(x^2-2)^{-\frac{1}{2}}\right)2x\,dx \\
&= \left[(x^2-2)^{\frac{1}{2}}\left(\frac{1}{2}x^{-\frac{1}{2}}\right) + \left(x^{\frac{1}{2}}-2\right)\left(\frac{1}{2}(x^2-2)^{-\frac{1}{2}}\right)2x\right]\,dx
\end{aligned}
$$

Be sure you can follow all the computations at each step in Example #18. You may want to make some substitutions as you go. With practice, you will be able to do most of this in your head.

Drill #59:

Show that the formula above "simplifies" to

$$
d\left[\left(\sqrt{x^2-2}\right)\left(\sqrt{x}-2\right)\right] = \frac{3x^2 - 4x^{\frac{3}{2}} + 2}{2\sqrt{x}\sqrt{x^2-2}}\,dx
$$

Does this seem simpler to you?

End Of Example #18

Drill #60:

Compute dy in terms of x and dx.

(a) $y = z^3$, where
$z = x^2 + 3x - 7$

(b) $y = \sqrt{w} + 3x$, where
$w = x^2 + x$

(c) $y = z^{-\frac{1}{4}}$, where
$z = 3w^5 + w^{-5}$, and
$w = x^4 - 5x^{-3}$

Drill #61:

Compute each of the following:

(a) $d(2x + 2x^{-1})$

(b) $d\left(3x + \frac{1}{\sqrt[3]{x^2}}\right)$

(c) $d\left(\frac{5\sqrt{x} - x^4}{\sqrt[5]{x}}\right)$

(d) $d\left(\frac{1}{\sqrt{3x}} - 5x^2 + \sqrt{5}x^4\right)$

(e) $d\left(\frac{1}{\pi} + \sqrt{\pi}\right)$

(f) $d\left(\sqrt[3]{x^2 - \frac{7}{x} + 4}\right)$

(g) $d\left((t^2 + 24t - 3)^{-7}\right)$

(h) $d\left((x^2 - \sqrt{x})\left(3x^{-\frac{1}{4}} + 5x\right)\right)$

(i) $d\left((2x - 3\sqrt{x})^5(x^2 - x + 1)^9\right)$

(j) $d\left(\sqrt{x^{-3} + 2x - 1} \cdot \sqrt[3]{x^{4/3} + x^{-1}}\right)$

(k) $d\left(\sqrt[3]{x^{-3} + 2x - 1} \cdot \sqrt[3]{x^{4/3} + x^{-1}}\right)$

Drill #62:

Compute dy for each of the following:

(a) $y = \frac{x^2 - 2x + 4}{x}$

(b) $y = x^2 - \sqrt{x}$

(c) $y = (\sqrt[3]{x})^2 - (\sqrt{x})^3$

(d) $y = \left(\frac{1}{x^2} + \frac{1}{x^3}\right)(x^2 + x^3)$

(e) $y = \sqrt{3x^4 - 7x^3 + 3}$

(f) $y = \sqrt{1 + \sqrt{1 + \sqrt{1 + x}}}$

(g) $y = \sqrt{x} + \sqrt{z}$

(h) $y = \sqrt{x + z}$

(i) $y = \sqrt{xz}$

(j) $c^2t^2 - x^2 - y^2 - z^2 = 0$,
where c is a constant[9].

---

[9]If x, y, and z are spatial coordinates, t is time, and the constant c is the speed of light then the expression on the left-hand side represents the square of the distance between the origin and the point (x, y, z, t) in 4 dimensional, relativistic, spacetime. Setting this equal to zero allows us to identify all of the events that an observer at the origin is observing at a given instant. For example, if there is a solar flare happening on the sun 93 million miles away from the earth, then we observe it 8 minutes later. The spacetime distance is zero to allow for the simultaneity of the event happening and us observing it. The closest galaxy to the Milky Way Galaxy is the Andromeda Galaxy which is approximately 2.5 million light-years away. This means that the light we are observing now originated 2.5 million years ago but the spacetime distance between the two events (called the Minkowski distance) is still zero.

In most of Drill #62 y is given explicitly in terms of x. But in part (j) y is given implicitly. We've seen this before. Almost everyone's first impulse in this situation is to try to solve this for y explicitly and then differentiate, but (a) it isn't necessary, (b) it isn't always possible, and (c) even when it is possible it is often harder that simply differentiating the formula we're given. Our differentiation rules remain unchanged. After completing the differentiation we simply need to solve for dy.

Example #19:

For example, how can we compute dy given that

$$2x^2 - xy + z^3 y^2 = 1 + y? \tag{3.5}$$

It is possible to solve this explicitly for y but it is difficult and the complexity of the computations tends to hide the underlying simplicity of the larger problem. Since Equation (3.5) is quadratic in y (the highest power of y is 2) we need only use the Quadratic Formula to get y explicitly in terms of x and z and then differentiate. Try that some time when you have time to kill. Lots of time.

Instead, we'll just apply our differentiation rules to Equation (3.5) as it is. Differentiating we have

$$4x\,dx - (x\,dy + y\,dx) + \left(z^3(2y\,dy) + y^2(3z^2\,dz)\right) = dy. \tag{3.6}$$

At first this may look very difficult to solve for dy but look again. This differential equation is actually linear in each of the differentials, dx, dy, and dz. That is, each differential only appears raised to the first power. This will always happen. When we differentiate any expression the result will always be linear in the differentials involved.

We can rearrange our equation algebraically so that it has the following form.

$$\text{(stuff)}\,dy = \text{(more stuff)}\,dx + \text{(even more stuff)}\,dz.$$

Solving for dy gives

$$dy = \frac{\text{(more stuff)}\,dx + \text{(even more stuff)}\,dz}{\text{(stuff)}}.$$

For this example the specific computations are:

$$4x\,dx - x\,dy - y\,dx + 2yz^3\,dy + 3y^2z^2\,dz = dy$$
$$2yz^3\,dy - x\,dy - dy = y\,dx - 4x\,dx - 3y^2z^2\,dz$$
$$(2yz^3 - x - 1)\,dy = (y - 4x)\,dx - 2y^2z^2\,dz$$
$$dy = \frac{(y - 4x)\,dx - 2y^2z^2\,dz}{2yz^3 - x - 1}.$$

At this point we have solved our problem so we needn't do any more. But notice that we could also write this as

$$dy = \frac{(y - 4x)}{2yz^3 - x - 1}\,dx - \frac{2y^2z^2}{2yz^3 - x - 1}\,dz$$

.

Some problems are legitimately hard, and some only look hard. So remember that as bleak as things may look sometimes, you should always keep your goal in view. In this case we were trying to isolate dy, so we gathered all of the terms that had dy in them, put all the other terms on the other side of the equation, factored out the dy and divided by the "stuff" that formed the coefficient of dy. This process is often easier than trying to solve for y before differentiating.

Drill #63:
Solve Equation (3.6) for dx and dz.

End Of Example #19

Drill #64:
Compute dy for each of the following. (You will see these formulas again in Problem 82.)

(a) $x^{\frac{2}{3}} + y^{\frac{2}{3}} = 4$

(b) $y^2 = x^3 - x + 1$

(c) $\left(x^2 + y^2\right)^2 + 4x(x^2 + y^2) = 4y^2$

(d) $(y-2)^2(x^2 + y^2) = 2y^2$

(e) $(x^2 + y^2 + 1)^2 - 4x^2 = \frac{3}{2}$

(f) $y^2\left(1 - x^2\right) = \left(x^2 + 2y - 1\right)^2$

(g) $x^4 = x^2 + y^2$

(h) $(x^2 + y^2)(y^2 + x(x+4)) = 4xy^2$

The General Power Rule

It the title of his 1684 paper Leibniz claimed that his *Calculus Differentialis* was "... *Impeded Neither by Fractional nor Irrational Quantities*, ... ". But notice that nothing we've done so far allows us to differentiate, say $y = x^{\sqrt{2}}$, since $\sqrt{2}$ is irrational and cannot be represented as a fraction. Having an irrational exponent is a bigger problem than it seems to be.

Take a moment and ask yourself what an expression like $x^{\sqrt{2}}$ could even mean.

> No! No! No! Wait!
> Don't keep reading. We're serious. Take a moment and think about this. How do you multiply $\sqrt{2}$ copies of x together? Does that even mean anything? If so, what?

We clearly have no way (so far) to interpret the meaning of an expression like $x^{\sqrt{2}}$. So trying to find its differential using the techniques we have is hopeless. In Chapter 7 we will find[10] a way to give meaning to $x^{\sqrt{2}}$ and other such expressions. When we do we will find that the Power Rule still works. In the meantime, *for now* we will assume *for now* that the Power Rule always works, even when the exponent is irrational.

---

[10] Actually, we will invent it. Meaning is not something we find, it is something we create.

The General Power Rule: Let α be any real number. Then $\mathrm{d}(x^\alpha) = \alpha x^{\alpha-1}\,\mathrm{d}x$.

<u>Example #20:</u>

Suppose we wish to find $\mathrm{d}y$ when $y = \frac{2-3x^2}{\sqrt{x}}$. Rewriting this slightly we have $y = \frac{2-3x^2}{\sqrt{x}} = x^{\frac{1}{2}}\left(2 - 3x^2\right) = 2x^{-\frac{1}{2}} - 3x^{\frac{3}{2}}$. From the General Differentiation Rules we have:

$$
\begin{aligned}
\mathrm{d}y = \mathrm{d}\left(\frac{2-3x^2}{x^{\frac{1}{2}}}\right) &= \mathrm{d}\left(2x^{-\frac{1}{2}} - 3x^{\frac{3}{2}}\right)\\
&= \left[2\left(-\frac{1}{2}x^{-\frac{3}{2}}\,\mathrm{d}x\right) - 3\left(\frac{3}{2}x^{\frac{1}{2}}\,\mathrm{d}x\right)\right] = \left(-x^{-\frac{3}{2}} - \frac{9}{2}x^{\frac{1}{2}}\right)\mathrm{d}x.
\end{aligned}
$$

Now suppose we have $z = 1/y = \frac{\sqrt{x}}{2-3x^2}$. Can we compute[11]: $\mathrm{d}z$?

There are actually two different approaches to this problem that use the Product Rule. The first is to rewrite z as $x^{\frac{1}{2}}(2-3x^2)^{-1}$ then apply the Product Rule followed by the Power Rule.

The second approach is to clear the fraction so that $z(2 - 3x^2) = \sqrt{x}$. From here we can compute the differential of both sides (using the Product Rule on the left side) and solve the result for $\mathrm{d}z$.

Problem #65:

Compute $\mathrm{d}\left(\frac{\sqrt{x}}{2-3x^2}\right)$ by each of the two methods indicated in Example #20. Verify that your results are equivalent either way.

<u>End Of Example #20</u>

Both of the techniques in Example #20 are straightforward and can be applied to any fractional expression. Because this can become a bit cumbersome we will calculate $\mathrm{d}\left(\frac{x}{y}\right)$ once and for all. This will give us a convenient shortcut to handle fractional expressions called the Quotient Rule.

The Quotient Rule: $\mathrm{d}\left(\dfrac{x}{y}\right) = \dfrac{y\,\mathrm{d}x - x\,\mathrm{d}y}{y^2}$.

Problem #66:

Derive the Quotient Rule, $\mathrm{d}z = \dfrac{y\,\mathrm{d}x - x\,\mathrm{d}y}{y^2}$, in two ways:

(a) By writing $\mathrm{d}\left(\frac{x}{y}\right) = \mathrm{d}(xy^{-1})$ and applying the Product Rule.

(b) By making the substitution $z = \frac{x}{y}$, so that $yz = x$. Apply the Product Rule and solve for $\mathrm{d}z$.

---

[11] Be sure you see why the previous approach won't work.

Applying the Quotient Rule directly to Problem 65 we have

$$d\left(\frac{\sqrt{x}}{2-3x^2}\right) = \frac{(2-3x^2)\,d\left(x^{1/2}\right) - x^{1/2}\,d(2-3x^2)}{(2-3x^2)^2}$$

$$= \frac{(2-3x^2)(\frac{1}{2}x^{-1/2})\,dx - x^{1/2}(-6x)\,dx}{(2-3x^2)^2}$$

$$= \frac{(2-3x^2)(\frac{1}{2}x^{-1/2}) - x^{1/2}(-6x)}{(2-3x^2)^2}\,dx.$$

Drill #67: Show this is the same as your solution of Problem #65.

Drill #68:
Compute dy for each of the following:

(a) $y = \frac{x+1}{x}$

(b) $y = \frac{x}{x+1}$

(c) $y = x + \frac{1}{x}$

(d) $y = \frac{x^3+2x^2}{x^{-1}+7x^{15}}$

(e) $y = \frac{x}{y^2+1}$

(f) $\frac{xy}{x+z} = x^2 + \frac{x}{y+1}$

(g) $\frac{xy^2}{y^2+1} = 1$

(h) $y = (x^2-3)(3x^4+6x+2)^{-1}$

(i) $y = \frac{(3x^2+2x-1)(4x^8-x^{-9}+2)}{\sqrt{x}+\frac{2}{\sqrt{x}}}$

Problem #69:

(a) Use the Quotient Rule to show that the differential of each of the following is: $dy = \frac{-1}{(x+2)^2}\,dx$.

    (i) $y = \frac{1}{x+2}$ **(ii)** $y = \frac{x+3}{x+2}$ **(iii)** $y = \frac{2x+5}{x+2}$ **(iv)** $y = \frac{-3x-5}{x+2}$

    Can you explain this?

(b) Show that each of the expressions in part (a) is of the form $\frac{1}{x+2} + a$ for some constant a. Now can you explain it?

(c) Compute the differential of $y = \frac{7x+13}{x+2}$. Can you explain why this one is different?

Problem #70:

Assume that neither x nor y is zero. Show that each of the following statements is true.

(a) The Product Rule can be rearranged as: $\mathrm{d}\left(xy\right) = xy\left(\dfrac{\mathrm{d}x}{x} + \dfrac{\mathrm{d}y}{y}\right).$

(b) The Quotient Rule can be rearranged as: $\mathrm{d}\left(\dfrac{x}{y}\right) = \dfrac{x}{y}\left(\dfrac{\mathrm{d}x}{x} - \dfrac{\mathrm{d}y}{y}\right).$

(c) Why must we assume that neither x nor y is zero?

Of the six General Differentiation Rules, the Quotient Rule is the most complicated to use. Many people try to avoid it when possible. In certain situations you can get around using the Quotient Rule by finding algebraic simplifications of the original expression, as demonstrated by the next problem.

Problem #71:

First compute each of the following using the Quotient Rule, and then find an algebraic simplification that makes the differentiation easier. Verify that you get the same answer either way.

(a) $\mathrm{d}\left(\dfrac{x^2+x}{x}\right) = \mathrm{d}x$

(b) $\mathrm{d}\left(\dfrac{x^2-1}{x+1}\right) = \mathrm{d}x$

(c) $\mathrm{d}\left(\dfrac{x^3-x}{x-1}\right) = \mathrm{d}x$

(d) $\mathrm{d}\left(\dfrac{x^2+x-2}{x+2}\right) = \mathrm{d}x$

(e) $\mathrm{d}\left(\dfrac{x^3+2x^2-x-2}{x+2}\right) = 2x\,\mathrm{d}x$

(f) $\mathrm{d}\left(\dfrac{x^3+2x^2-x-2}{(x+2)(x-1)}\right) = \mathrm{d}x$

(g) $\mathrm{d}\left(\dfrac{x^3+3x^2-x}{x^2+3x-1}\right) = \mathrm{d}x$

(h) $\mathrm{d}\left(\dfrac{x^3-x^2-2x+2}{x-1}\right) = 2x\,\mathrm{d}x$

(i) $\mathrm{d}\left(\dfrac{x^3-x^2-x-2}{x-2}\right) = (2x+1)\,\mathrm{d}x$

(j) $\mathrm{d}\left(\dfrac{x^3-x^2-x-2}{x^2+x+1}\right) = \mathrm{d}x$

We now have all six of the General Differentiation Rules in our toolbox:

The Constant Rule: If a is a constant, then $\mathrm{d}a = 0$.

The Sum Rule: $\mathrm{d}(x + y) = \mathrm{d}x + \mathrm{d}y$.

The Constant Multiple Rule: If a is a constant, then $\mathrm{d}(ax) = a\,\mathrm{d}x$.

The Product Rule: $\mathrm{d}(xy) = x\,\mathrm{d}y + y\,\mathrm{d}x$.

The Power Rule: If n is any real number then, $\mathrm{d}(x^n) = nx^{n-1}\,\mathrm{d}x$.

The Quotient Rule: $\mathrm{d}\left(\dfrac{x}{y}\right) = \dfrac{y\,\mathrm{d}x - x\,\mathrm{d}y}{y^2}.$

We have not yet shown that the Power Rule works when n is irrational but we will do that in Chapter 7. So we have stated the full version here.

Of these, the Constant Multiple Rule, the Power Rule and the Quotient Rule are really just conveniences. They can all be derived from the other three.

We remind you that the General Differentiation Rules only tell you how to compute differentials. They do not tell you what differentials you need to compute or why. Algebra, Geometry, Arithmetic, and Trigonometry are still important tools as well. Tools are only useful if you are skillful with them, and can use them in a coordinated fashion. This requires practice. Lots of practice.

Chapter 4

Slopes, Tangents, and Rates of Change

"A Vulgar Mechanick can practice what he has been taught or seen or done, but if he is in an error he knows not how to find it out and correct it, and if you put him out of his road, he is at a stand; Whereas he that is able to reason nimbly and judiciously about figure, force and motion, is never at rest till he gets over every rub."

– Isaac Newton (1642-1727)

4.1 Slopes and Tangents

As we observed in Chapter 3.2 Newton, Leibniz, and their contemporaries extended the Principle of Local Linearity to its logical limit. They said if you cut out an infinitely small section of a curve then the section actually is an infinitely short straight line segment. Of course we are quite familiar with infinitely short line segments. We call them differentials.

Leibniz called a triangle whose sides are differentials, like the blue triangle in the figure at the right, a **differential triangle**[1]. In the figure dy and dx are differentials in the vertical and horizontal directions, respectively. But ds is a differential at the point (a, a^2) in the direction of the curve or, what comes to the same thing, in the direction tangent to the curve. Thus ds is a differential along the curve, and simultaneously along the line tangent to the curve[2].

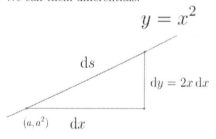

---

[1] Because, what else would you call it?

[2] The idea that ds is a straight line segment on the curve and also on its tangent line is a bit troubling. It

94

Notice that from the Pythagorean Theorem we have

$$(\mathrm{d}s)^2 = (\mathrm{d}x)^2 + (\mathrm{d}y)^2. \tag{4.1}$$

We will find Equation 4.1 very useful.

The differentials $\mathrm{d}x$, and $\mathrm{d}y$, don't really tell us much about the graph of $y = x^2$, but the **differential ratio**, $\frac{\mathrm{d}y}{\mathrm{d}x}$, does. At each point, (a, a^2), $\frac{\mathrm{d}y}{\mathrm{d}x}$ gives us the slope of $\mathrm{d}s$ and the line tangent to the curve at that point. Loosely speaking, the differential ratio $\frac{\mathrm{d}y}{\mathrm{d}x}$ gives the slope of the curve at each point.

If we want to find the slope of the curve $y = x^2$ at the point (a, a^2) we simply find $\mathrm{d}y$ as usual: $\mathrm{d}y = 2x\,\mathrm{d}x$. Then we take the extra step of dividing through by $\mathrm{d}x$ to get $\frac{\mathrm{d}y}{\mathrm{d}x} = 2x$. Evaluating this at the point $x = a$, $y = a^2$, and $\frac{\mathrm{d}y}{\mathrm{d}x} = 2a$ which will give us the slope of the line tangent to the graph of $y = x^2$ at the point (a, a^2).

Drill #72:
Find an equation of the line tangent to the graph of $y = x^2$ at each of the following points.

(a) $(-2, 4)$ **(b)** $(-1, 1)$ **(c)** $(0, 0)$ **(d)** $(1, 1)$ **(e)** $(2, 4)$

Compare these results to those obtained using Fermat's Method in Problem #20

Digression #4: Evaluation Notation

We will frequently need to evaluate the expression $\frac{\mathrm{d}y}{\mathrm{d}x}$ at different points. This can quickly become very confusing unless we have some way of indicating which point is under consideration. To avoid confusion, we use the notation

$$\left.\frac{\mathrm{d}y}{\mathrm{d}x}\right|_{(x,y)=(a,b)} \quad \text{or} \quad \left.\frac{\mathrm{d}y}{\mathrm{d}x}\right|_{(a,b)}.$$

This notation is very flexible. Frequently the y coordinate will not be in play. In that case we write

$$\left.\frac{\mathrm{d}y}{\mathrm{d}x}\right|_{x=a}$$

to indicate that we are evaluating $\frac{\mathrm{d}y}{\mathrm{d}x}$ at the point $x = a$.

End Of Digression #4

Example #21:

For example to compute the slope of the graph of $y = 3x^2 - 5x$ at $(3, 12)$ we use the following three-step process.

1. First differentiate $y = 3x^2 - 5x$ to obtain the differential equation $\mathrm{d}y = (6x - 5)\,\mathrm{d}x$. This relates $\mathrm{d}y$ and $\mathrm{d}x$.

2. Second, from this differential equation we find the ratio $\frac{\mathrm{d}y}{\mathrm{d}x} = 6x - 5$. This differential ratio tells us the slope of the curve at every point on the curve.

---

is one of many bizarre consequences of the notion of differentials.

3. Third, if we need the value of $\frac{dy}{dx}$ at a single point like $(3, 12)$, for example[3], we compute

$$\frac{dy}{dx}\bigg|_{(x,y)=(3,12)} = 6x - 5\bigg|_{(x,y)=(3,12)} = 6 \cdot 3 - 5 = 13.$$

In this case we could just write: $\frac{dy}{dx}\big|_{x=3} = 13$, since the y coordinate never comes into play.

Finally, we emphasize that Leibniz' notation is *deliberately* evocative of the notion of slope because when we evaluate the differential ratio at a point it tells us the slope of the curve at that point. In view of the **Principle of Local Linearity**, this is equivalent to finding the slope of the line tangent to the curve at that point.

End Of Example #21

This notation probably seems unnecessarily cumbersome and honestly, in some ways it is. But be assured we have not made this choice lightly, and this notation has certain advantages that will become apparent later.

It can be easy to get careless or simply confused and write $\frac{dy}{dx}$ when you mean $\frac{dy}{dx}\big|_{x=a}$, and *vice versa*, so it is important that you have the distinction between them clear in your mind.

Problem #73:

(a) Explain the difference between $\frac{dy}{dx}$ and $\frac{dy}{dx}\big|_{x=a}$ carefully and clearly.

(b) We (the authors) have sometimes had students assert that since $\frac{dy}{dx} = 2x$, the equation of the line tangent to the graph of $y = x^2$ at the point (a, a^2) is

$$y - a^2 = 2x(x - a). \tag{4.2}$$

Set $a = 3$. Is this the equation of a line?

(c) Find the correct formula for line tangent to the graph of $y = x^2$ at the point (a, a^2).

Drill #74:

Find $\frac{dy}{dx}\big|_{(x,y)=(2,2)}$ if $y = \sqrt{2x}$ and compare this with the slope we obtained in Drill #25 using Descartes' Method of Normals.

---

[3]Obviously this makes no sense if the point $(3, 12)$ is not a point on the curve. You should always make sure the problem makes sense before you try to solve it.

Problem #75:

Evaluate $\left.\dfrac{\mathrm{d}y}{\mathrm{d}x}\right|_{x=a}$ for each of the following functions at each of the given values of x.

(a) $y = x^3$, $a = 0, \pm1, \pm2$ (Compare with Problem #20.)

(b) $y = x^3 + 2x^2$, $a = 0, \pm1, \pm2$ (Compare with Problem #21.)

(c) $y = \sqrt{x}$, $a = 4$ (Compare with Problem #26.)

There is real temptation at this point to cut corners and compute the differential ratio $\dfrac{\mathrm{d}y}{\mathrm{d}x}$ all in one step. On purely practical grounds, we urge you to differentiate first and then divide by $\mathrm{d}x$ in two separate steps. Our reasons are two-fold. First, the rules we've learned are *differentiation* rules. They were designed to compute differentials, not differential ratios. Second, in applications to come we will see that dividing by $\mathrm{d}x$ will not always move the solution process forward. It can sometimes even get in the way, depending on the problem.

Nonetheless, as you gain more experience and a deeper understanding you will find yourself gravitating toward the differential ratio more and more. This is a normal progression. As we have said before differentials are an intermediate step, a convenient fiction. You don't want to become tied to them for life.

4.2   Defining the Tangent Line

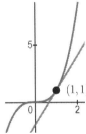

The word tangent comes from the Latin word *tangere* (to touch). So you'd think it would be easy to define what we mean by "tangent line." When asked, most people will come up with something like, "The line tangent to a curve is the line that touches the curve at exactly one point." Does this seem like a reasonable definition to you? Stop and think about it for a few minutes. We're obviously offering a plausible sounding definition that we know won't work. Do you see the problem?

It certainly *seems* OK, and if we check it with a few simple examples everything looks reasonable. But consider a small segment of the graph of $y = x^3$ at the point $(1, 1)$ and its corresponding tangent line as seen at the left.

While this certainly fits our notion of a tangent line touching a curve only once, look what happens if we zoom out (see the sketch at the right). This supposed tangent line will cross (touch) the graph of the curve a second time. In fact, there is only one point on the graph of $y = x^3$ where the tangent line touches the graph only once. Do you see which point that is? Give this a few minutes thought.

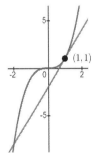

In view of what we've just seen, what do you think the definition of a tangent line *ought* to be?

In the figure at the right it is clear that the "touching" is different at the two points. At $(1, 1)$ the blue tangent line "grazes" the graph of $y = x^3$ at $(1, 1)$ exactly as we would expect. But at the other point it actually cuts through the graph.

The difficulty seems to be that we said "touch" when we meant "graze". How about this definition instead: "The line tangent to a curve is the line that *grazes* the curve at exactly one point."

If it is not possible for a line to "graze" a curve at more than one point this could be a workable definition. Unfortunately the next drill shows that this is not true.

Drill #76:

Show that $y = \frac{1}{2}x + \frac{1}{4}$ is the equation of the line tangent to the graph of

$$y = \frac{1}{2}x + \frac{1}{4} + (x-1)^2(x-2)^2(x-3)^2(x-4)^2.$$

at $x = 1, 2, 3$, and $x = 4$ as seen in the sketch at the right.

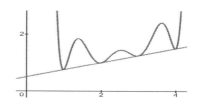

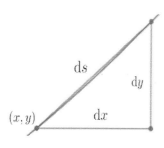

It appears that clearly defining what we mean by "tangent line" is not as simple as it seemed to be at first. This is frustrating because we all have a pretty clear intuitive idea of what we mean. The difficulty seems to be capturing in words the mental image we all share.

Recall that we have informally stated the **Principle of Local Linearity** as: "Locally any curve is indistinguishable from a straight line."

But which straight line?

The answer to that question is visible in the differential triangle at the left. It is clear that, *locally* (near a given point (x, y) on the curve) a curve will look like the hypotenuse of the differential triangle ds at the point (x, y). So we make the following definition.

Definition 2: **The Line Tangent to a Curve at a Point**

The **line tangent to a curve**, at the point (a, b) is the line which passes through the point (a, b) with slope $m = \left. \frac{dy}{dx} \right|_{(x,y)=(a,b)}$.

Do you see what we did here? Intuitively we know what properties we want a tangent line to have. We want it to "touch" or "graze" our curve at a particular point but we've seen that neither of those words quite captures everything we need. And what we need is for the tangent line to pass through the tangent point and have the same slope as the function at that point. So we've removed the words "touch" and "graze" in favor of the more precise, quantifiable language of Calculus.

Since we *defined* the tangent line to be the extension of ds to the finite scale we have essentially defined it to have exactly that property we will need to make Differential Calculus useful. Moreover with this definition in place the **Principle of Local Linearity** can be formalized a bit more.

<u>Definition 3:</u> **The Principle of Local Linearity**

Sufficiently close to a given point every smooth curve is indistinguishable from the line tangent at that point.

The history of mathematics is riddled with this sort of backward looking definition and we will see it again. For example Newton and Leibniz both knew what they wanted their *Calculus Differentialus* (Leibniz) and *Method of Fluxions* (Newton) to do. They worked out their computational procedures intuitively – just as we started with an intuitive understanding of "tangent line." But coming up with precise definitions and a solid logical foundation was harder. It took about 200 years for the mathematical community to devise definitions that gave back what intuition had led us to. This is part of why we are not yet overly concerned about our inability to precisely define a differential. When we finally address this issue in Chapter 12 we will not be devising any new differentiation techniques. We will be providing logical underpinnings for the techniques our intuition has led us to and that our experience has shown to be useful.

<u>Drill #77:</u>

Find an equation of the line tangent to the given curve at the indicated values of x.

(a) $y = \frac{2x}{x+1}$
when $x = 1$.

(b) $y = \frac{1}{1 + x^2}$
when $x = -1$

(c) $y = x + \sqrt{x}$
when $x = 1$

(d) $y^2 = x^3$
when $x = 1$

(e) $y^3 = x^2$
when $x = 1$

(f) $y = \frac{\sqrt{x}}{x + 1}$
when $x = 4$

(g) $y = 3x$
when $x = 10$

(h) $y = -7x$
when $x = -100$

(i) $y = -\frac{x^2}{\pi}$
when $x = \sqrt{\pi}$

(j) $y = (3x - 1)^{-6}$
when $x = 0$

(k) $y = x^3 - \frac{1}{x}$
when $x = 1$

(l) $y = \sqrt{1 + x^2}$
when $x = 2$

(m) $y = \frac{x}{x - 2}$
when $x = 0$

(n) $y = \frac{x}{x - 2}$
when $x = \frac{1}{4}$

(o) $y = \frac{1}{1 + x^2}$
when $x = \frac{1}{2}$

(p) $y = \frac{1}{1 - x^2}$
when $x = 1$

(q) $y = \frac{1}{\sqrt{x}}$
when $x = 9$

(r) $y = \frac{1}{\sqrt[3]{x^2}}$
when $x = 4$

(s) $y = \sqrt{2x + \sqrt[3]{64 - x}}$
when $x = 0$

(t) $y = \pi x^2$
when $x = \frac{1}{\sqrt{\pi}}$

Problem #78:

Show that the only point on the graph of $y = x^3$ where the tangent line touches the curve *only* at the point of tangency is the point $(0,0)$ and that the tangent is horizontal.

Now graph the curve and the line tangent at $(0,0)$ on the same set of axes. Does this *look* like a tangent line to you?

Does the graph help you see the significance of Problem #78? The line tangent to the graph of $y = x^3$ at the point $(0,0)$ actually crosses the graph at that point. This is weird. And it is exactly counter to our original understanding of what it means for a line to be tangent to a curve isn't it?

The next problem will probably strike you as equally weird. But in both problems the weirdness is a logical consequence of our definition of tangent line, so we will accept it as long as it doesn't lead to inconsistencies.

Weirdness is acceptable. It is inconsistency that we need to avoid.

Problem #79:

Use Definition 2 to find the equation of the line tangent to the graph of the straight line $y = mx + b$ at the point $(a, y(a))$. Show that this is in fact, the original line.

Problem #80:

(a) Find the equations of all lines tangent to the graph of $4x^2 + 4y^2 = 25$ that are also parallel to the line $2x - 3y = 7$.

(b) Find the equations of all lines tangent to the graph of $16x^2 + 9y^2 = 144$ that are also parallel to the line $8x + 6y = 8$.

(c) Find the equations of all lines tangent to the graph of $16x^2 - 9y^2 = 144$ that are also parallel to the line $8x + 6y = 8$.

Problem #81:

Find those points on the graph of the curve $y = x^3 + 5$ where the tangent line is

(a) Parallel to the line: $12x - y = 17$.   (b) Perpendicular to the line: $x + 3y = 2$.

Problem #82: (continued on the next page.)

Find an equation of the line(s) tangent to and normal to each of the given curves at the specified points. (You have seen all of these curves previously in Drill #64)

(a) Astroid:
$$x^{\frac{2}{3}} + y^{\frac{2}{3}} = 4$$
at $\left(1, 3\sqrt{3}\right)$ and $\left(-1, -3\sqrt{3}\right)$.

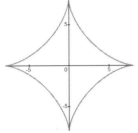

(b) An Elliptic Curve:
$$y^2 = x^3 - x + 1$$
at $(0, 1)$ and $(0, -1)$.

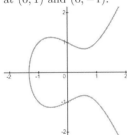

(c) Cardioid:
$$\left(x^2 + y^2\right)^2 + 4x(x^2 + y^2) = 4y^2$$
at $(0, 2)$ and $(0, -2)$.

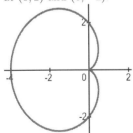

(d) Conchoid of Nicomedes:
$$(y - 2)^2(x^2 + y^2) = 2y^2$$
at $(1, 1)$ and $(3, 3)$.

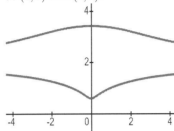

(e) Cassini oval:
$$(x^2 + y^2 + 1)^2 - 4x^2 = \frac{3}{2}$$
at $\left(\frac{\sqrt[4]{2}}{2}, \frac{\sqrt[4]{2}}{2}\right)$

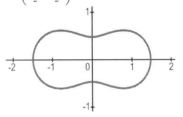

(f) The Bicorn:
$$y^2\left(1 - x^2\right) = \left(x^2 + 2y - 1\right)^2$$
at $\left(\frac{1}{2}, \frac{12 \pm 3\sqrt{3}}{26}\right)$

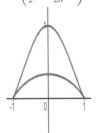

Problem #82: (continued from the previous page)

(g) The Kampyle of Eudoxus:
$$x^4 = x^2 + y^2$$
at $\left(\pm 2, \pm 2\sqrt{3}\right)$

(h) The Folium:
$$(x^2 + y^2)(y^2 + x(x + 4)) = 4xy^2$$
at $(-1, -1)$ and $(-1, 1)$

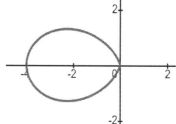

Problem #83: Find the Pattern

Find all points where the line tangent to the curve passes through the indicated points. If no such points exist, explain how you know.

(a) $y = x^2 + 2$ through the points

    (i) $(0, 0)$ **(ii)** $(-5, 0)$ **(iii)** $(2, 6)$ **(iv)** $(1, 6)$

(b) $y = \frac{x+1}{x-1}$ through the points

    (i) $(0, 0)$ **(ii)** $(0, -5)$ **(iii)** $(5, 5)$ **(iv)** $(-1, 0)$

(c) $y = \frac{x^2-1}{x+2}$ through the points

    (i) $(0, 0)$ **(ii)** $(0, -1/2)$ **(iii)** $(-5, -10)$ **(iv)** $(-5, 10)$

Digression #5: Dividing by Zero

Drill #84: Show that if $y^2 = x^3 - 3x + 1$ then $\frac{dy}{dx} = \frac{3x^2-3}{2y}$.

In Drill #84 it is tempting to to say that $\frac{dy}{dx} = \frac{3x^2-3}{2y}$ will give us the slope of the tangent line tangent to the curve at *any* point (x, y). Typically this would be correct. But not always.

For example the tangent line of this curve is horizontal (has slope equal to zero) when

$$0 = \frac{dy}{dx} = \frac{3x^2 - 3}{2y}.$$

Solving this gives $x = \pm 1$. It is plainly visible on the graph at the right that there is a horizontal tangent line when $x = -1$. But notice that there is no point on the graph where $x = 1$! Obviously it is meaningless to ask for the slope of a curve at a point that isn't on the curve.

Even if we didn't have the graph to look at we could still tell that at $x = 1$ there is no tangent line. Setting $x = 1$ and trying to solve for the corresponding y values we get $y^2 = 1 - 3 + 1 = -1$. Since there is no real number that satisfies the equation $y^2 = -1$ we conclude that there is no point on the graph with x-coordinate equal to 1.

On the other hand, there are three values of x that correspond to $y = 0$. These would be difficult to compute but from the graph we can see that the tangent line is most likely vertical at all three points. To compute $\frac{dy}{dx} = \frac{3x^2-3}{2y}$ at each of these points we would have to divide by $y = 0$.

Obviously when we divide a number by zero we get infinity, and just as obviously the slope of a vertical line is also infinity so everything fits. Right? No, of course not. This is just a very deceptive coincidence.

Many students come into a Calculus with the impression that dividing by zero results in either zero or infinity. It does not. Division by zero is not meaningful.

Mathematicians say that division by zero is an **undefined operation** or simply that it is **undefined**. At first it is not at all clear why this is, so let's take look at this question.

What does it mean to divide by any number? To take a very concrete example, what does it mean to divide a length of five units[a] by seventeen? It means we want to divide the length into seventeen equally sized pieces, right? But if we want to divided 5 units by zero, obviously we can't divide five into zero pieces. So in this very concrete example the phrase "five divided by zero" is simply and utterly without meaning.

From a slightly more abstract viewpoint we could ask for the length of each piece when we divide a length of five into seventeen pieces. We get $\frac{5}{17}$ of course. That's what the fraction notation means[b]. But what number do we get when we divide five into zero pieces. Once again the idea has no meaning.

Taking an even more abstract point of view, observe that multiplication and division are inverse operations (they undo each other). Twelve divided by three is four $\left(\frac{12}{3} = 4\right)$ precisely because when we multiply three times four we get twelve $(3 \times 4 = 12)$.

Now don't think of five as a length to be divided, think of it instead as simply a number. So what number can we multiply by zero to get five? Obviously there isn't any such number so this is a meaningless question.

No matter what we try or how we look at it we cannot find any way to make division by zero meaningful.

---

[a]The units could be inches, picometers, or light-years. We don't care.

[b]Just as $\frac{1}{2}$ is the number we get when we divide one into two pieces.

━━━━━━━━━━ **End Of Digression #5** ━━━━━━━━━━

Since we can't divide by zero we will need to be a bit more careful about how we interpret the symbol $\frac{dy}{dx}$. It will give us the slope of the curve (equivalently, the slope of the tangent line) as long as $\frac{dy}{dx}$ has meaning. But when y is zero $\frac{dy}{dx} = \frac{3x^2-3}{2y}$ is meaningless. Thus it appears that for this particular curve we can draw no conclusions whatsoever from our formula about the tangent line when $y = 0$. In this case we say that the differential quotient is **undefined**. In general, the differential quotient is **undefined** at any point where evaluating $\frac{dy}{dx}$ requires a division by zero.

Does this mean we can draw no conclusions at all? Certainly not. In fact those values of x or y where $\frac{dy}{dx}$ is undefined will often turn out to be the most useful. But we are not yet quite prepared to see how to deal with them properly so we will defer this discussion until a later point.

At the very least this warns us that there are subtleties that must be dealt with when using a powerful tool like Calculus. We will avoid these subtleties for a bit longer, but you need to know that they exist. Don't try to force matters by, for example, blindly dividing by zero as if it is meaningful. We will return to these matters when we have a better understanding of the underlying principles.

Problem #85:

Suppose that the two blue line segments in the figure at the right are parallel. Show that c is exactly halfway between a and b.

(**Comment:** That is, show that $c = \frac{a+b}{2}$.)

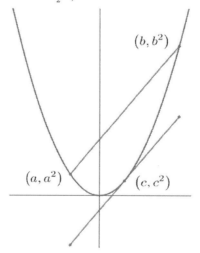

Problem #86: Find the Pattern

Suppose that a and n are positive numbers. In the following sketch the line AB is tangent to the curve $x^n y = 1$ at the point $\left(a, \frac{1}{a^n}\right)$.

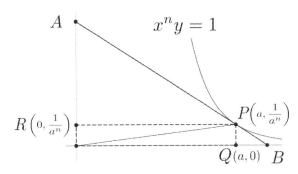

(a) For $n = 1$ first show that the coordinates of points A and B are $\left(0, \frac{2}{a}\right)$ and $(2a, 0)$, respectively, and then confirm that:

    (i) area$(\triangle AOB) = 2$ **(iii)** area$(\triangle BPQ) = 1/2$

    (ii) area$(\triangle OPQ) = 1/2$ **(iv)** area$(\triangle PAR) = 1/2$

(b) For $n = 2$ first show that the coordinates of points A and B are $\left(0, \frac{3}{a^2}\right)$ and $\left(\frac{3}{2}a, 0\right)$, respectively, and then confirm that:

    (i) area$(\triangle AOB) = \frac{9}{4a}$.   **(iii)** area$(\triangle BPQ) = \frac{1}{4a}$.

    (ii) area$(\triangle OPQ) = \frac{1}{2a}$.   **(iv)** area$(\triangle PAR) = \frac{1}{a}$.

(c) For $n = 3$ first show that the coordinates of points A and B are $\left(0, \frac{4}{a^3}\right)$ and $\left(\frac{4}{3}a, 0\right)$, respectively and then confirm that:

    (i) area$(\triangle AOB) = \frac{8}{3a^2}$.   **(iii)** area$(\triangle BPQ) = \frac{1}{6a^2}$.

    (ii) area$(\triangle OPQ) = \frac{1}{2a^2}$.   **(iv)** area$(\triangle PAR) = \frac{3}{2a^2}$.

(d) Find a formula for the coordinates of points A and B for any value of n and then:

    (i) Find the the area of $\triangle AOB$ **(iii)** Find the the area of $\triangle BPQ$
        for any value of n.   for any value of n.

    (ii) Find the the area of $\triangle OPQ$ **(iv)** Find the the area of $\triangle PAR$
        for any value of n.   for any value of n.

Problem #87:

Consider the equation $y = x\sqrt[3]{x - 8}$.

(a) Find the equation of the line tangent to the graph of when $x = 0$.

(b) Does a line tangent to the graph of this function at $x = 8$ exist? If so, find the equation of the line. If not, explain why not.
(**Hint:** Have you looked at the graph yet?)

These last three problems illustrate that while many otherwise difficult computations can be done "in these lines, as if by magic" (to quote Leibniz) there are still a great many subtleties to be accounted for. There is still plenty of room for creative, analytical problem solving.

We will come back to some of these subtleties later. For now keep in mind that while Calculus is a very powerful tool it does not allow us to solve all problems blindly, by simply moving the pebbles.

4.3   The Vomit Comet

To acclimate astronaut trainees to the effects of weightlessness, NASA uses the following training regimen: It has an airplane perform a series of steep climbs and sharp dives. At the top of each climb passengers will experience weightlessness for about 25 seconds. During a training flight the pilot will repeat this maneuver about 40 times.

Because this "roller coaster" ride sometimes causes nausea for the passengers the planes used for the maneuver have been christened "Vomit Comets." One of these airplanes was used to film the weightless scenes in the 1995 film Apollo 13.

It is well known that the path of an object moving only under the influence of the Earth's gravity[4] at the surface of the earth is parabolic. To simulate weightlessness[5] inside the plane the Vomit Comet is flown so that its flight path matches such a parabolic flight. That is, its shape will be the graph of a curve having the form

$$y = Ax^2 + Bx + C.$$

We'd like to find the values of the unknown parameters A, B, and C that match the path of an object moving under the influence of Earth's gravity. Once these are known we will also be able to determine the peak altitude of the flight and how far (horizontally) it will go before coming back to the altitude where the maneuver began. That is, we can find the point where the pilot should pull out of the dive. Finally we'd like to confirm the claim that this maneuver takes about 25 seconds.

Can we find A, B, and C? No. Unfortunately we don't yet have enough information to determine A, but we can find B and C.

---

[4]That is, we're ignoring air resistance.
[5]More precisely, to create neutral buoyancy.

Problem #88:
Suppose the following graph depicts the parabolic flight path followed by the Vomit Comet as it starts its maneuver at an altitude of 7000 meters and an initial angle of elevation of 45°.

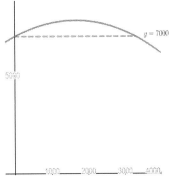

If the equation of this parabola is $y = Ax^2 + Bx + C$, then determine the values of B and C.

Ultimately to find A, we'll need to have a better model of the motion. Fortunately, Calculus is exactly the right tool for building such a model but we don't yet have all of the pieces we need. We will return to the Vomit Comet problem once we have them.

The pilot of a Vomit Comet seeks to simulate weightlessness, but the pilot of a commercial airliner works hard to avoid subjecting its passengers to extreme effects like weightlessness or, at the other end, of extreme gravity so it must descend more gradually. This situation is a little easier to understand so we will explore it in the next couple of problems and examples before returning to the Vomit Comet.

Example #22: Modeling the flight path of an airliner

We want to model the flight path of a plane as it lands and determine the distance from the runway the plane should be when it starts its descent.

A fundamental tenet of mathematically modeling real world phenomena is to keep things as simple as possible. So, the first thing we'd be likely to try for is a parabolic descent path:

$$y = Ax^2 + Bx + C.$$

But it is pretty clear that this won't work because the plane should be traveling horizontally at the beginning and at the end of its descent. At the end, because at that point it should be on the ground, and at the beginning because we don't want to terrify the passengers.

Drill #89:
Show that there is only one point on any parabola where the line tangent to the curve is horizontal. Explain why this proves that the flight path of the airliner in Example #22 cannot be parabolic.
(**Hint:** Wherever the flight path is horizontal its slope will be zero.)

The next simplest curve we could use would be a cubic polynomial

$$y = Ax^3 + Bx^2 + Cx + D. \tag{4.3}$$

Problem #90:

Below is a section of a cubic polynomial depicting a flight path with the plane starting initially at the point $P(l, h)$ and ending at the airport Q which we will arbitrarily designate as the origin.

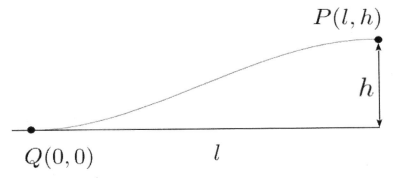

(a) Assuming that the flight path is the graph of Equation 4.3, compute dy. Then divide by dx to obtain $\frac{dy}{dx}$.

(b) Show that $D = 0$ in Equation (4.3).
    (**Hint:** The point $(0, 0)$ is on the graph of Equation 4.3.)

(c) Show that $C = 0$ in Equation (4.3).
    (**Hint:** The flight path is horizontal at $(0, 0)$.)

(d) Determine the values of A and B in Equation (4.3) in terms of l and h.
    (**Hint:** The point P is on the flight path and the flight path is horizontal at P.)

End Of Example #22

We've taken our analysis of the flight paths of both the Vomit Comet and our airliner as far as we can using slopes alone. The problem is that a flight path is like a road. A road doesn't go anywhere. It just sits there. But an object traveling along a road (or a flight path) is moving. It has a velocity and an acceleration.

Analyzing a static path does not allow us to model either the velocity or the acceleration of an object moving along that path. Fortunately for us, Newton's formulation of Calculus is just what we need to do attack these problems.

But since the Vomit Comet aims to replicate the path of a body falling freely under the influence of gravity we will also need to consider the influence of gravity.

4.4   Galileo Drops the Ball

In the previous section we asserted – with no justification whatsoever – that the flight path of the Vomit Comet would be parabolic. Then, in Problem 88, we gave you the task of finding the constants B, and C for which the graph of the curve

$$y = Ax^2 + Bx + C$$

is the flight path of the Vomit Comet with an initial angle of elevation of $45°$. You should have obtained

$$y = Ax^2 + x + 7000.$$

Galileo Galilei
1564-1642

Inside the airplane, we want what is called **neutral buoyancy**. This means that we don't want any forces pushing us up or down, side to side, or back and forth relative to the airplane[6]. The way to assure this is to force the airplane to fly along the same path it would take if it were unpowered and falling freely. At first it might seem like all we have to do is shut down the engine, but that won't work because air resistance will prevent the plane from falling freely. The engines must be engaged to force the plane along the path it would follow naturally if there were no atmosphere[7], and thus, no resistive forces. In this section we'll see why this path must be in the shape of a parabola.

Newton very famously said, "If I have been able to see further, it is by standing on the shoulders of giants," and, in his 1684 paper on Calculus, Leibniz remarked that "Other very learned men have sought in many devious ways what someone versed in this calculus can accomplish in these lines as by magic."

As we've seen Fermat, Descartes, and Roberval were three of the learned giants Newton and Leibniz were indebted to. Another was Professor Galilei (1564-1642) of the University of Pisa, who is universally known and referred to by his first name, Galileo. As a professor of mathematics at Pisa, Galileo studied, among other things, how objects moved under the influence of gravity.

We will be following Galileo's lead to address such questions as:

- Suppose you throw a ball straight up into the air. How high will the ball go?

- How long will it take for it to hit the ground and what will its velocity be at impact?

- If you throw the ball up twice as hard. Will it go twice as high?

Since Galileo had neither the technology nor the mathematics to account for air resistance he ignored it. For the moment we will ignore it too.

---

[6]Naturally, if the plane and everything in it are falling towards the earth then the force of gravity is in play. But if everything falls together there is no force inside (relative to) the plane.

[7]Also, it is incredibly dangerous to turn off the engines of an airplane while it is flying.

Problem #91:

We all know from experience that if you throw a ball straight up in the air, it will reach some maximum height. But suppose you throw the ball up twice as hard, would it go twice as high? (**Comment:** We're asking you to guess. Don't worry about being wrong. Just take your best guess.)

The accepted theory of motion in Galileo's time was Aristotle's assertion that a heavier object would fall faster than a lighter object. Our common experience is that a hammer falls faster than a feather so this was an entirely reasonable thing to believe at the time. But we now know that this is because the resistance of the air slows the feather more than it does the hammer.

In 1971, Apollo Astronaut David Scott confirmed this experimentally (see the video at the right) by dropping both a hammer and a feather on the surface of the moon. Because there is no air on the surface of the moon there is no air resistance, so the hammer and feather hit the surface of the moon at the same time.

Since he didn't have access to the moon Galileo had to be clever instead. But Galileo was one of the group of new scientists who gathered experimental data and applied mathematical principles to theories. As a result of his experimental investigations Galileo proposed that in the absence of air all objects would fall at the same rate[8].

How did he surmise that all objects would fall at the same rate?

Well actually, he didn't. We need to be very careful in our use of language here. To say that "all objects fall at the same rate" is a bit sloppy. Since velocity is the rate of change of position it seems to say that all objects fall at the same velocity.

But we know that's not true because the velocity of a falling object depends on how long it has been falling. At the moment you drop a ball its velocity is zero. Thereafter it gains velocity – it accelerates. Thus an object that has just been dropped is moving slowly while an object that has been falling for a while is moving at a faster rate.

What Galileo actually proposed was that the rate of change of the velocity – the **acceleration** – of all falling bodies is constant. But an object falling freely under the influence of Earth's gravity gets moving pretty quickly and in Galileo's day the tools available for measurement were very limited. So he slowed things down by letting small balls roll down a ramp as shown below.

---

[8]Galileo could be quite argumentative and this eventually got him into hot water with the Vatican. In the last years of his long life he was threatened with excommunication and and risked execution for espousing Copernicus' heliocentric theory of planetary motion. It was only because he was well known and respected as a scientist that he was only confined to his home instead.

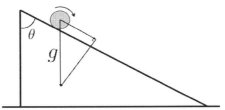

Galileo assumed (correctly) that friction with the ramp would not significantly influence his measurements. When he did this he noticed that the balls always seemed to accelerate at a constant rate which depended only on the steepness of the ramp. More precisely, the acceleration of the rolling ball varied with the angle of descent. In modern terms we would say that the acceleration is a function of the angle of descent.

θ (in radians)	Acceleration in $\left(\frac{\text{meters}}{\text{second}^2}\right)$
$\pi/3 \approx 1.05$	4.9
$\pi/4 \approx 0.79$	6.93
$\pi/6 \approx 0.52$	8.49
$\pi/12 \approx 0.26$	9.47
$\pi/24 \approx 0.13$	9.72
$\pi/48 \approx 0.07$	9.78
$\pi/100 \approx 0.03$	9.795
$\pi/200 \approx 0.02$	9.799
$\pi/300 \approx 0.01$	9.799

Referring to the diagram above, it is clear that when[9] $\theta = \pi/2$ the ball won't move at all. So its acceleration is zero. When $\theta = 0$ the ball accelerates downward freely under the influence of gravity with no resistance[10]. Galileo measured the acceleration associated with steeper and steeper ramps (that is for θ closer and closer to zero) obtaining a table of values similar to the one at the left.

From the table it is clear that as θ gets closer and closer to zero the acceleration is getting closer and closer to 9.8. Thus Galileo deduced that when there is no ramp (when $\theta = 0$) the velocity will increase each second by $9.8\frac{\text{meters}}{\text{second}}$.

That is, the velocity of an object falling under the influence of the earth's gravity increases by 9.8 meters per second, each second. This is usually abbreviated as $9.8\frac{\text{meters}}{\text{second}^2}$, is commonly denoted by g, and is called the **constant of acceleration due to gravity**

Drill #92:

With a little Trigonometry you can deduce that $g = 9.8\frac{\text{meters}}{\text{second}^2}$ with only one measurement. Use the diagram and the first line of the table above to deduce that $g = 9.8$.
(**Hint:** $\cos(\pi/3) = 1/2$.)

If we drop the object from some height, then its initial velocity is zero. After one second it will be falling at a rate of $9.8\frac{\text{meters}}{\text{second}}$, after two seconds, its velocity will be $9.8 \times 2 = 19.6\frac{\text{meters}}{\text{second}}$, etc. That is, as an object falls, its velocity increases at the constant rate of $9.8\frac{\text{meters}}{\text{second}}$ every second: $v = 9.8t$.

The specific number that Galileo found, $9.8\frac{\text{meters}}{\text{second}^2}$, is an artifact of the units we use to measure distance (meters) and time (seconds) and the fact that we are on the surface of a particular planet. If we measure distance in feet instead then at the surface of the earth a falling object will accelerate at $32\frac{\text{feet}}{\text{second}^2}$. If we go to the surface of the moon, it will accelerate

---

[9]Notice that we are using radians to measure the angle. If you are unsure what a radian is we have a brief review of Trigonometry in Section (5.1).
For scientific computation radian measure is usually simplest, so we will use fairly consistently throughout this text. But degree measure is also common so it will occasionally make an appearance, like it did in Problem #88.

[10]Or at least, very little.

at $1.6\frac{\text{meters}}{\text{second}^2}$.

Drill #93: Show that if we measure distance in feet, the acceleration constant on the moon is approximately $5.2\frac{\text{feet}}{\text{second}^2}$.

The general situation is this: If a falling object's velocity, in meters per second $\left(\frac{\text{meters}}{\text{second}}\right)$, is changing at a constant rate of r meters per second per second $\left(\frac{\text{meters}}{\text{second}^2}\right)$, and t is the number of elapsed seconds then $v = rt$. From Galileo's work we know that at the surface of the Earth $r = g = 9.8$ so

$$v = 9.8t \tag{4.4}$$

We can check that this is reasonable by looking at the units of measurement. Since the acceleration r, is measured in $\frac{\text{meters}}{\text{seconds}^2}$ and time is measured in seconds, when they are multiplied a symbolic cancellation gives

$$\frac{\text{meters}}{\text{second}^2} \cdot \text{second} = \frac{\text{meters}}{\text{second} \cdot \cancel{\text{second}}} \cdot \cancel{\text{second}} = \frac{\text{meters}}{\text{second}}$$

or meters per second; the units used to measure velocity. Notice that Equation 4.4 is independent of the weight of the falling object. Under the influence of gravity alone all objects accelerate downward at the same rate.

Galileo's hypothesis that all objects falling solely under the influence of Earth's gravity accelerate at the same rate came from both his experimental evidence and a famous thought experiment he described in his book *On Motion* (1590). The experiment runs as follows:

Imagine that two objects, one light and one heavy, are connected to each other by a string and we drop them from a great height, say the top of the Tower of Pisa. If we assume heavier objects do indeed fall faster than lighter ones the string will soon pull taut as the lighter object retards the fall of the heavier object.

So, the system taken as a whole will fall more slowly than the heavier object alone. But the system as a whole is heavier than either individual object. So, the system taken as a whole will fall faster than the heavier object.

This contradiction leads inexorably to the conclusion that our initial assumption – that heavier objects accelerate faster – must be false.

According to legend Galileo tested his hypothesis by dropping balls of different weights from the top of the Tower of Pisa, but that is almost certainly pure legend. He never actually did this. Probably.

Galileo set out his ideas about falling objects in his last book *Discorsi e Dimostrazioni Matematiche intorno à due nuoue Scienze* (Discourses and Mathematical Demonstrations Concerning Two New Sciences) (1638). This was the last of Galileo's many scientific works[11]. The two sciences referred to in the title were the science of motion, which became the foundation of modern physics, and the science of materials and construction, an important contribution to engineering.

Suppose an object falls 56 meters from the top of the Tower of Pisa to the ground. Can we determine how fast it is moving when it strikes the ground?

Recall that the formula $v = gt$ tells us the ball's velocity at any time t. So if t_g is the amount of time it takes for the ball to reach the ground then the velocity at the end would be $v = gt_g$. But how do we find out exactly when the ball strikes the ground?

To see the difficulty, suppose we dropped the ball from a height of 9.8 meters. Would it take 1 second for the ball to hit the ground?

Clearly not.

To reach the ground after 1 second the ball would have to average $9.8 \frac{\text{meters}}{\text{second}}$ during the entirety of that first second. But at first it is not moving at all (velocity = 0). After one second its velocity has increased to $9.8 \frac{\text{meters}}{\text{second}}$. So for the entire duration of that first second the ball's velocity is less than $9.8 \frac{\text{meters}}{\text{second}}$. Thus after 1 second it has not yet hit the ground because it was never going fast enough to do so. Exactly how far it has fallen isn't clear.

Reasoning similarly, at the beginning of the next second the ball is already falling at $9.8 \frac{\text{meters}}{\text{second}}$ and thereafter it's velocity increases, so it falls at least 9.8 meters during the next second, in addition to the distance it fell during the first. So, while we cannot yet tell exactly how far it falls during either second, we can say that, (1) it will not hit the ground during the first second, and (2) it definitely will hit the ground sometime during the next second.

If we had an expression for the ball's position, p, similar to Equation (4.4), we would be in much better shape. Galileo was able to determine the distance the ball fell without the tools of Calculus, but since learning to use those tools is why we're here, we will use them.

Bringing in Calculus

Let $p(t)$ represent the position at time t of a ball under the influence of gravity. That is, $p(t)$ tells us how far the ball has moved from its starting position, $p(0)$, after t seconds. Our goal is to use Galileo's discovery that $g = 9.8 \frac{m}{s^2}$ to find a formula for $p(t)$.

During an (infinitesimal) instant of time, dt, the velocity is virtually constant so during that instant of time, dt, the infinitesimal change in position, dp is given by

$$dp = \text{velocity} \times \text{change in time} = v\, dt.$$

But from Equation (4.4) we also know that $v = 9.8t$, so $dp = 9.8t\, dt$.

---

[11] Toward the end of his life the Inquisition of the Catholic Church placed Galileo under house arrest in his home. His crime what that he had openly supported Copernicus's theory that the earth revolves around the sun. Rather than remain idle during his imprisonment he revisited his unpublished research from when he was younger and used that as a foundation for his final opus.

Problem #94:

Thus finding the position of the ball at any time reduces to finding an expression for $p(t)$ that satisfies the differential equation

$$\mathrm{d}p = 9.8t\,\mathrm{d}t. \tag{4.5}$$

We begin with an educated guess. From the Power Rule the differential of a quadratic expression like kt^2 will be the linear term $2kt\,\mathrm{d}t$, so $p(t) = kt^2$ seems like a reasonable guess.

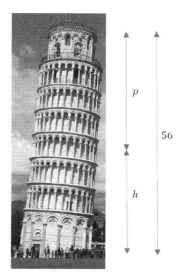

(a) Show that $p(t) = kt^2$ satisfies Equation (4.5) when

$$k = 4.9 = \frac{g}{2}.$$

(b) Earlier we reasoned that a ball dropped from a height of 9.8 meters would strike the ground between one and two seconds after being dropped. Use $p(t)$ to find out exactly how long it takes.

(c) How long would it take the ball to hit the ground if dropped from the top of the Tower of Pisa (a height of 56 meters?

(d) Evaluate $\left.\frac{\mathrm{d}p}{\mathrm{d}t}\right|_{p=56}$. What does this represent physically?

(**Hint:** Remember that $\mathrm{d}p$ is a change in position and $\mathrm{d}t$ is a change in time.)

To summarize the results of Problem #94 we see that if $p = p(t) = \frac{g}{2}t^2$ denotes the position of a dropped ball at time t, the following statements are true.

1. The velocity of the ball is given by $v = \frac{\mathrm{d}p}{\mathrm{d}t}(= gt)$,

2. The rate of change of the velocity (acceleration) is then.

$$\frac{\mathrm{d}v}{\mathrm{d}t} = \frac{\mathrm{d}\left(\frac{\mathrm{d}p}{\mathrm{d}t}\right)}{\mathrm{d}t} = g. \tag{4.6}$$

Notice that in our diagram we also introduced the variable h which represents the height of the ball from the ground. The way we choose to define our variables can have a considerable impact on the way we understand a given problem. Here for example both p and h give us the position of the ball but if $p(t) = 4.9t^2$, then $p = 0$ represents the top of the tower and the positive direction is down. Conversely, if $h(t) = 56 - 4.9t^2$, then $h = 0$ represents ground level and the positive direction is up.

Our examination of Galileo's work affords us the opportunity to broaden our understanding of the meaning and use of differentials and differential notation. In Problem #94 we used $p(t)$ to represent the distance that the ball has fallen at time t. In that case it turned out that $\frac{dp}{dt}$ represents the velocity with which the ball is falling at time t. This is at once mundane and profound.

It is mundane because velocity has always been defined as distance (dp) divided by elapsed time (dt), and this remains true even when the distance and the time are infinitesimals.

It is profound because the (instantaneous) velocity $v(t)$, of the ball is always some finite quantity, but we compute it using the quotient of two differentials, $\frac{dp}{dt}$ in this case.

This **differential ratio** is a fundamental concept. In general if some quantity, say y is changing in time then $\frac{dy}{dt}$ represents the (instantaneous) rate of change of y.

In Problem #94 we saw that the velocity of the falling ball is also changing in time, just like its position. Thus we can turn around and compute the instantaneous change in velocity (the acceleration) by computing the differential of the velocity $d\left(\frac{dp}{dt}\right)$, and dividing by dt, giving $\frac{d\left(\frac{dp}{dt}\right)}{dt}$. This very awkward notation is often abbreviated as $\frac{d^2p}{dt^2}$. Notice that the acceleration is the result of the following set of computational steps:

1. Differentiate p.

2. Divide by dt.

3. Differentiate $\frac{dp}{dt}$.

4. Divide by dt again.

As you become more fluent with these computations you will inevitably begin to combine these steps. Your teacher probably already does. However, the computation of a differential ratio always involves finding the differential of some *finite* quantity and then dividing by another differential. If your instructor computes a differential ratio and you don't see how it was done, ask them to show you each differentiation and division.

If we read the abbreviated notation $\frac{d^2p}{dt^2}$ literally it seems to suggest that $d^2p = d(dp)$ is meaningful but it is not. The notion of taking the differential of a differential is fraught with logical difficulties which we will address in Chapter 12. For now we can avoid pitfalls by recognizing that the expression $\frac{d^n y}{dx^n}$ is the result of differentiating and dividing by dx n times. We will explore this bit further in the next section.

Problem #95:

(a) Consider a ball moving vertically so that its height at time t seconds is given by
$$h(t) = 56 + 49t - 4.9t^2 \text{ meters}$$

(i) Determine the ball's initial

(A) Position: $h(0)$,   **(B)** Velocity: $\frac{dh}{dt}\big|_{t=0}$,   **(C)** Acceleration: $\frac{d^2h}{dt^2}\big|_{t=0}$

(**Comment:** Remember to go through the two step process of differentiating and then dividing by dt. We insist.)

(ii) Is "up" the positive or the negative direction?

(iii) How high will the ball go?

(iv) When will the ball hit the ground?

(v) What is the impact velocity?

(vi) Describe in words the physical situation being modeled by the formula $h(t) = 56 + 49t - 4.9t^2$ meters?

(b) In general the height of an object falling near the surface of the earth is given by
$$h(t) = h_0 + v_0 t - 4.9t^2 \text{ meters}$$

    (i) Show that the initial height is h_0, the initial velocity is v_0, and the acceleration is $= -9.8$.

    (ii) For simplicity, assume $h_0 = 0$. How high will the ball go?

    (iii) Suppose we double our initial velocity. Would the ball go twice as high? Compare this to your guess in Problem #91?

Since the graph of $h(t) = h_0 + v_0 t - 4.9t^2$ is a parabola it is tempting to conclude that we have shown that an object falling under the influence of gravity alone must be a parabola. But this not correct. We have consistently assumed that the ball is falling vertically so its flight path is a straight vertical line, not a parabola. The graph of $h(t)$ is not the flight path of the ball.

4.5 The Derivative

Differentials are helpful for learning and using the differentiation rules, but otherwise they are not very useful. Moreover as we have frequently pointed out, using differentials brings up certain logical and philosophical questions (Like, "What are they?") that are very difficult to address. When we come back to these matters in Chapter 12 you'll see what we mean. For all of these reasons and more the concept of differentials should be regarded as a convenient fiction and nothing more.

On the other hand as we've just seen the *ratio* of differentials, $\frac{dy}{dx}$, is extremely useful as it can be used to represent either the slope of a graph or the velocity of a moving object, depending on the context. Moreover the differential ratio is an ordinary real number.

Because of concerns regarding the validity of differentials, mathematicians in the 18th and 19th centuries, had a strong motivation to skip over the differential concept and jump immediately to the more useful, and finite, differential ratio.

Joseph Louis Lagrange
1736-1813

In his 1797 work *Théorie des Fonctions Analytiques* (*The Theory of Analytic Functions*), Joseph Louis Lagrange (1736 − 1813) attempted to make Calculus more rigorous. He even coined a new term for the differential ratio. He called it the *fonction dérivée* (meaning a function *derived* from another function). He also replaced the differential ratio $\frac{dy}{dx}$ with the more modern **function** notation $y'(x)$ (read "y prime of x").

Lagrange's attempt to make Calculus rigorous was very clever, but ultimately unsuccessful. Full rigor had to wait for another hundred years, so we will not say much about Lagrange's efforts here. But we will adopt his terminology and his notation.

Digression #6: Function Notation, and Prime Notation

The French phrase *fonction dérivée* has come into English as "derived function," the **derivative function**, or (most commonly) just the **derivative**.

Suppose that $y = x^3$. It is clear that y depends on x, so we denote this functional dependence with the notation

$$y(x) = x^3.$$

Lagrange called the differential ratio $\frac{dy}{dx}$, a **derived function**. The "derived" part seems clear enough. After all, if $y = x^3$ them $\frac{dy}{dx}$ is obtained (derived) from y as follows:

$$y = x^3$$
$$dy = 3x^2\,dx$$
$$\frac{dy}{dx} = 3x^2.$$

Since $\frac{dy}{dx}$ depends on $3x^2$ as a function it would not be wrong to denote this functional dependence as

$$\frac{dy}{dx}(x) = 3x^2$$

but it would be awkward. Moreover, Lagrange was trying to get away from the use of differentials so instead he used

$$y'(x) = 3x^2$$

and called $y'(x)$ the **derivative** (derived function) of $y(x)$.

In some contexts Lagrange's prime notation has several advantages over the differential notation we've been using. Over time it has become the most common notation for the **derivative** in mathematics. But the fact that it took over 100 years to develop suggests that something more than mere notation is in play here.

Our current task is to master the differentiation rules so we will stick to Leibniz's differential notation as much as possible because using multiple equivalent notations can be very confusing. But there will come a time when Lagrange's prime notation will be much more convenient. At that point we will casually use the two expressions $\frac{dy}{dx}$ and $y'(x)$ interchangeably and we will think of them both as a function *derived from* the function $y(x)$.

When we do this the differential notation we're currently emphasizing will take on two distinct "personalities." On the one hand $\frac{dy}{dx}$ represents a ratio of the differentials dy, and dx which are distinct infinitesimal quantities. On the other hand $\frac{dy}{dx}$ is the name of a function

– it is all one symbol. You cannot detach the pieces of $\frac{dy}{dx}$ any more than you can delete the letter "n" from $\sin(x)$ because $\mathrm{si}(x)$ has no meaning.

Eventually the differentials we've been using so casually will become a guilty secret. Given $y = y(x)$ we'll use them as a helpful aid while we *compute*. But as soon as we have $\frac{dy}{dx}$ in hand we will view it as a single, complete symbol representing the (finite) derivative function. Often we will simply replace it with $y'(x)$ as if we are ashamed of having used differentials at all.

This more advanced viewpoint will become commonplace later, but to give you a preview, consider the following problem.

Problem #96: Hudde's Rule:

Recall that in Descartes' Method of Normals, we had to find a double root of a polynomial. To deal with this problem, Johann van Waveren Hudde (1628-1704) developed an algebraic tool for determining such double roots. Calculus allows a development of Hudde's Rule that does not require the complex algebraic reasoning that Hudde used and is much easier to follow[a].

Consider any polynomial $p(x) = a_0 + a_1 x + \cdots + a_n x^n$. Let a and b be any real numbers and form the following "Hudde Polynomial."

$$H(x) = aa_0 + (a + b)\,a_1 x + (a + 2b)\,a_2 x^2 + (a + 3b)\,a_3 x^3 + \ldots + (a + nb)\,a_n x^n$$

Hudde showed that if r is a double root of $p(x)$, then r is a root of the Hudde polynomial $H(x)$.

(a) Show that if r is a double root of the polynomial $p(x)$ then it is a root of $p'(x) = \frac{dp}{dx}$. (**Hint:** If r is a double root of $p(x)$, then $p(x) = (x - r)^2 q(x)$ for some polynomial $q(x)$.)

(b) Show that $H(x) = ap(x) + bxp'(x)$ and use this to prove Hudde's Rule.

---

[a]Actually Hudde did considerably more than this. His method for finding double roots was a part of what has been called the "Lost Calculus" of algebraic functions. If you are interested you can read more about this in Jeff Suzuki's award winning article *The Lost Calculus (1637-1670): Tangency and Optimization without Limits*

===== End Of Digression #6 =====

The bottom line is that we will adopt the name **derivative** to indicate the result of dividing one differential by another. So the expression $\frac{dy}{dx}$ is "the derivative of y with respect to x."

When computing a derivative you will eventually become sufficiently proficient that you will jump directly to the derivatives. But for now we urge you to go through the two-step process of differentiating to obtain a differential and then dividing by another differential to obtain a derivative because the computational rules you've learned are differentiation rules, not derivative rules. If you do this, you will avoid some difficulties created by trying compute too much too soon. This can be illustrated in the following example, where we purposely use prime notation to highlight the difficulties involved in the computation.

Example #23:

Given $y(x) = (1 + x^2)^{\frac{1}{2}}$ we wish to compute $y'(x)$. Setting $z = 1 + x^2$ we see that

$$y(x) = z^{\frac{1}{2}}.$$

By the Power Rule we have

$$y'(x) = \frac{1}{2} z^{-\frac{1}{2}}. \tag{4.7}$$

This would seem to be correct but it is not. Do you see the problem?

The left side of equation (4.7) indicates that the variable is x but there is no x on the right side, only z. So this can't be right. But what went wrong?

We can avoid problems like this by using differentials:

$$dy = \frac{1}{2} z^{-\frac{1}{2}} \, dz. \tag{4.8}$$

At this point if we divide by dz we recover equation (4.7 in the form:

$$\frac{dy}{dz} = \frac{1}{2} z^{-\frac{1}{2}}.$$

Thus we see the left side of equation (4.7) should have been $y'(z)$ not $y'(x)$.

Drill #97:
Starting with equation (4.7) complete the computation of $y'(x)$.

End Of Example #23

Example #24:

Of course, using differentials does not address all of the difficulties.
For example, let $y = x^3$. Then

$$dy = d(x^3) = 3x^2 \, dx \left(\text{First Derivative:} \frac{dy}{dx} = 3x^2 \right)$$

So far, so good. Next we apply the Product Rule,[12]

$$d(\,dy) = d(3x^2 \, dx) = 3x^2 \underbrace{d(\,dx)}_{=0} + 6x \, dx \, dx$$

so

$$d(\,dy) = 6x \, dx \, dx \left(\text{Second Derivative: } \frac{d(\,dy)}{dx \, dx} = 6x = \frac{d^2 y}{dx^2}. \right) \tag{4.9}$$

The glaring question here is why is $d(\,dx)$ equal to zero but $d(\,dy)$ is not equal to zero? Or, at a more fundamental level, what do we mean by "the infinitely small change of an infinitely small change?" As we will see in Chapter 12 the early critics of Calculus cited this question specifically to argue that Calculus was invalid.

------

[12] To see why $d(\,dx) = 0$ we need to know that Leibniz always considered the differential dx to be a constant. And the differential of any constant is zero, by the Constant Rule.

We will address these issues beginning in Chapter 12. For now we will make the following compromise: We will only differentiate finite quantities, be they functions, or derivatives. Since our ultimate goal is to compute some derivative this will suit our needs without getting caught up in the very problematic question of the nature of higher order differentials. So for this example we have

$$y = x^3$$

$$\mathrm{d}y = 3x^2\,\mathrm{d}x$$

$$\text{(First Derivative)}\quad \frac{\mathrm{d}y}{\mathrm{d}x} = 3x^2$$

$$\mathrm{d}\left(\frac{\mathrm{d}y}{\mathrm{d}x}\right) = 6x\,\mathrm{d}x$$

$$\text{(Second Derivative)}\quad \frac{\mathrm{d}^2 y}{\mathrm{d}x^2} = \frac{\mathrm{d}\left(\frac{\mathrm{d}y}{\mathrm{d}x}\right)}{\mathrm{d}x} = 6x$$

$$\text{(Third Derivative)}\quad \frac{\mathrm{d}^3 y}{\mathrm{d}x^3} = \frac{\mathrm{d}\left(\frac{\mathrm{d}^2 y}{\mathrm{d}x^2}\right)}{\mathrm{d}x} = 6.$$

End Of Example #24

Example #25:

Consider the expression $y = \frac{1}{x} = x^{-1}$. Differentiating we have

$$\frac{\mathrm{d}y}{\mathrm{d}x} = (-1)x^{-2},$$

$$\frac{\mathrm{d}^2 y}{\mathrm{d}x^2} = (-1)(-2)x^{-3},$$

$$\frac{\mathrm{d}^3 y}{\mathrm{d}x^3} = (-1)(-2)(-3)x^{-4},$$

and finally

$$\frac{\mathrm{d}^4 y}{\mathrm{d}x^4} = (-1)(-2)(-3)(-4)x^{-5}$$

You've probably been taught all of your life to "simplify" complex looking expressions like $(-1)(-2)(-3)(-4)$ and you probably do it without thinking. So you may be wondering why we left the coefficients above in the form we did.

The reason is simple. We were looking for patterns not numbers. Writing the above formulas as $\frac{\mathrm{d}^2 y}{\mathrm{d}x^2} = 2x^{-3}$, $\frac{\mathrm{d}^3 y}{\mathrm{d}x^3} = -6x^{-4}$, and $\frac{\mathrm{d}^4 y}{\mathrm{d}x^4} = 24x^{-5}$ obscures the pattern. Keep this in mind as you proceed. Algebraic or arithmetical "simplifications" often get in the way of recognizing patterns. Don't do them until there is a compelling reason to.

Drill #98: Find the pattern in Example #25. Use this pattern to find $\frac{\mathrm{d}^{50} y}{\mathrm{d}x^{50}}$ directly, without computing all fifty derivatives.

End Of Example #25

Example #26:

Consider the circle $x^2 + y^2 = 1$. Differentiating, we have $2x\,dx + 2y\,dy = 0$, or $\frac{dy}{dx} = -\frac{x}{y}$. Differentiating again we have

$$d\left(\frac{dy}{dx}\right) = -\frac{y\,dx - x\,dy}{y^2}.$$

Problem #99:

(a) Continue this example to show that $\frac{d^2y}{dx^2} = -\frac{1}{y^3}$.

(b) Solve for $y = \pm\sqrt{1-x^2}$ and use this to compute $\frac{d^2y}{dx^2}$.

(c) Do you get the same answer? Which method do you prefer?

End Of Example #26

Drill #100:

For each of the following find $\frac{d^2y}{dx^2}$ in terms of x and y:

(a) $y = 3x^4 - x^3 + 2x - 7$

(b) $x = y^2$

(c) $y = \sqrt{x}$ Compare this with part (b).

(d) $xy = 1$ Compare this with Example #25. Which method do you prefer?

(e) $\frac{x^2+y}{3x+y^2} = x - y$

Problem #101: Find the pattern

We know that it is not generally true that $a^b = a \cdot b$ even though there are certain exceptions, like $a = b = 1$, $a = 4$ and $b = 1/2$, or $a = b = 2$. In the same way, even though the Product Rule makes it very clear that

$$\frac{d(y \cdot z)}{dx} \neq \frac{dy}{dx} \cdot \frac{dz}{dx}. \tag{4.10}$$

there are certain pairs of functions which are exceptions; for which Equation (4.10) *is* true.

For example, show that for each of the following it is true that $\frac{d(y \cdot z)}{dx} = \frac{dy}{dx} \cdot \frac{dz}{dx}$.

(a) (i) $y = x$ $z = \frac{1}{1-x}$ (ii) $y = x^2$ $z = \frac{1}{(2-x)^2}$ (iii) $y = x^3$ $z = (3-x)^{-3}$

(b) Find the general pattern in part (a).

(c) Those pairs of functions which fit the pattern you found in part (b) are not the only exceptional pairs. Can you find others?

Adopting Lagrange's terminology, but not his notation, we see that if the position of a point moving in a straight line (like the x axis) is given by $x = x(t)$, then the first derivative, $\frac{dx}{dt}$, will give its velocity, and its second derivative, $\frac{d^2x}{dt^2}$, will give its acceleration.

Drill #102:
Each of the following represents the position of a point on the x-axis at time t. Find the velocity and acceleration.

(a) $x(t) = 12t^3$

(b) $x(t) = -4t^4 + 3t^2 + 1$

(c) $x(t) = 5 - 2\sqrt{t} + t^3$

(d) $x(t) = \frac{1}{2}t^{1/2} + t^{-1/2}$

(e) $x(t) = \dfrac{1}{\sqrt{t^2 + t + 1}}$

(f) $x(t) = t^{2/3}$

Problem #103:
For each of the following, determine if a point moving along the x-axis is slowing down or speeding up at the instant t_0.

(a) $\left.\frac{dx}{dt}\right|_{t=t_0} > 0$, $\left.\frac{d^2x}{dt^2}\right|_{t=t_0} > 0$

(b) $\left.\frac{dx}{dt}\right|_{t=t_0} > 0$, $\left.\frac{d^2x}{dt^2}\right|_{t=t_0} < 0$

(c) $\left.\frac{dx}{dt}\right|_{t=t_0} < 0$, $\left.\frac{d^2x}{dt^2}\right|_{t=t_0} > 0$

(d) $\left.\frac{dx}{dt}\right|_{t=t_0} < 0$, $\left.\frac{d^2x}{dt^2}\right|_{t=t_0} < 0$

4.6 Thinking Dynamically

If $s(t)$ represents the position of an object moving in a straight line we have seen that its velocity is given by $\frac{ds}{dt}$. When the object is falling vertically we will use $y(t)$ to represent its vertical position, so that $\frac{dy}{dt}$ is its vertical velocity. Similarly if it is moving horizontally we will use $x(t)$ and $\frac{dx}{dt}$.

Recall that in Problem 34 we imagined releasing an object from a helicopter which is flying horizontally horizontally with a speed of $\frac{dx}{dt} = 1\frac{meter}{second}$. From Galileo's work we now know that its vertical velocity will be $\frac{dy}{dt} = 9.8t\frac{meters}{second}$.

After its release the ball will fall neither horizontally, nor vertically. It won't even fall along a straight line. If we ignore air resistance then combination of the ball's horizontal velocity (inherited from the helicopter) and its vertical velocity (due to the force of gravity) will cause the flight

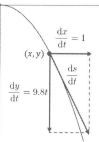

path, $s(t)$, to curve into an arc similar to that shown in the figure at the right.

Drill #104:

Since $\frac{dx}{dt} = 1$ we have $x = t$. Since $\frac{dy}{dt} = -9.8t$ and we know that $y = -4.9t^2$. Use this to find a formula for $y = y(x)$ and confirm that the arc is a parabola.

As the ball falls there are three distinct quantities we are interested in: the horizontal velocity of the ball, $\frac{dx}{dt}$, the vertical velocity of the ball, $\frac{dy}{dt}$, and its speed in the direction of travel.

We'd like to find the *speed* of the object in the direction it is moving. Referring to the differential triangle in our sketch it is clear that this will be[13] $\left| \frac{ds}{dt} \right|$. But how do we find $\frac{ds}{dt}$?

Since dx and dy are perpendicular (they are displacements in the horizontal and vertical directions, respectively) by the Pythagorean Theorem we have

$$(ds)^2 = (dx)^2 + (dy)^2.$$

Thus the displacement of $s(t)$, in the direction of travel is

$$|ds| = \sqrt{(dx)^2 + (dy)^2}.$$

Dividing by $|dt|$ we see that the speed in the direction of travel at any time t is

$$\left| \frac{ds}{dt} \right| = \frac{\sqrt{(dx)^2 + (dy)^2}}{dt}$$
$$= \sqrt{\left(\frac{dx}{dt} \right)^2 + \left(\frac{dy}{dt} \right)^2}$$
$$= \sqrt{1 + (9.8t)^2}.$$

Recall that we stopped analyzing in Problem 90 because we needed to be able to account for both the velocity and the acceleration of the craft. We now have everything we need to finish the analysis of the flight path of the commercial airliner which we started in Example #22.

Problem #105:

Recall that in Problem 90 we asked you find the equation of this flight path from the data in the figure at the right. You should have found that

$$y = \frac{-2h}{l^3}x^3 + \frac{3h}{l^2}x^2.$$

As we said when we suspended our earlier efforts, the problem with this picture is that it is static. It is a picture of the path the airliner has flown after the flight is finished. We now have the tools we need to address the characteristics of the flight as it occurs.

[13]The absolute value bars here are correct. This has more to do with our vocabulary (speed vs. velocity) than with this physical problem. In general speed is always a positive number, while velocity can be negative or positive. We will discuss this in more depth in Chapter 5.

(a) Use the differential triangle in our figure to show that airspeed of the airplane in its direction of motion, $\left|\frac{ds}{dt}\right|$, its horizontal velocity, $\frac{dx}{dt}$, and slope of its flight path, $\frac{dy}{dx}$, are related by the formula:

$$\left|\frac{ds}{dt}\right| = \left|\frac{dx}{dt}\right| \sqrt{1 + \left(\frac{dy}{dx}\right)^2}. \tag{4.11}$$

(**Hint:** Recall that $\frac{dx}{dt}$, and $\frac{dy}{dt}$ are the horizontal and vertical velocities respectively)

(b) Assume that the plane's horizontal velocity is constant.

   (i) Use Equation (4.11) to explain how we know that the plane is traveling fastest when it is at the point where the curve is steepest (about where the red dot is in our sketch[14]).

   (ii) What is the slowest speed attained by the plane, and where on the flight path does this occcur?

Drill #106:

Suppose (x, y) are the coordinates of a ball moving along the given curves. If the ball is moving with a constant horizontal velocity of $\frac{dx}{dt} = 2\frac{\text{units}}{\text{second}}$ for each curve find the following.

(a) The vertical velocity of the ball at the points indicated.

(b) The horizontal and vertical acceleration of the ball at the points indicated.

(c) The speed in the direction of travel of the ball at the points indicated.

Curve 1:	**Curve 2:**	**Curve 3:**	**Curve 4:**
$y = x^2$,	$y = x^3$,	$x^2 - y^2 = 3^2$	$x^2 + y^2 = 5^2$
at $(-1, 1)$	at $(-1, -1)$	at $(-5, 4)$	at $(3, 4)$
and $(1, 1)$	and $(1, 1)$	and $(-5, -4)$	and $(3, -4)$

The next problem will complete our analysis of the flight path of our commercial airliner.

Problem #107:

The flight path obtained in Problem #90 was $y = \frac{-2h}{l^3}x^3 + \frac{3h}{l^2}x^2$. We need to put some limitations on the vertical acceleration, $\frac{d^2y}{dt^2}$, experienced by the passengers in a commercial airliner. For simplicity assume that the pilot must maintain a constant horizontal speed of $v\frac{\text{meters}}{\text{second}}$. (That is, set $\frac{dx}{dt} = -v$.)

---

[14]It is possible to find the numerical coordinates of this point but it is rather difficult to see how to proceed at this point. It is worth taking a few minutes to ponder how this might be done.

(a) Use the above equation to show that the vertical acceleration is given by

$$\frac{d^2y}{dt^2} = \frac{6hv^2}{l^2}\left(1 - \frac{2x}{l}\right).$$

(b) On the interval $0 \le x \le l$, what is the largest vertical acceleration and what is the smallest vertical acceleration and where do they occur? Does this make sense physically?

(c) Suppose we put a restriction on the vertical acceleration so that

$$-k\frac{\text{meters}}{\text{second}^2} \le \frac{d^2y}{dt^2} \le k\frac{\text{meters}}{\text{second}^2}$$

for some constant k. Show that with this restriction, $l \ge \sqrt{\frac{6Hv^2}{k}}$.

(d) Suppose that initially $h = 10000$ meters, $v = 100\frac{\text{meters}}{\text{second}}$, $k = 0.1\frac{\text{meters}}{\text{sec}^2}$ (which is approximately 1% of the acceleration due to gravity). Find what l must be (in kilometers).

In Section 4.3 we mentioned that NASA claims that the Vomit Comet can make passengers experience weightlessness for about 25 seconds. Let's check on that claim.

To simulate weightlessness (neutral buoyancy) the pilot must execute a parabolic flight path $y = Ax^2 + Bx + C$. In Problem #88 you should have found that B and C were 1 and 7000, respectively, so the flight path is

$$y = Ax^2 + x + 7000 \qquad (4.12)$$

with A yet to be determined.

The pilot is climbing at angle of elevations $45°$ to an altitude of about 7000 meters and then follows this parabolic path to produce a vertical acceleration of $\frac{d^2y}{dt^2} = -9.8\frac{m}{s^2}$ (matching the acceleration due to gravity) and horizontal acceleration of $\frac{d^2x}{dt^2} = 0$. This will provide neutral buoyancy inside the plane. On the way back down the pilot pulls out of this dive when the altitude returns to 7000 meters.

For training purposes this is repeated 40 times.

Problem #108:

(a) To determine A we need one more fact. At the beginning of the maneuver, the initial airspeed is about $180\frac{\text{meters}}{\text{second}}$ (approximately 400 mph). Use the initial airspeed to determine $\frac{dx}{dt}$. In turn use this result and the fact that $\frac{d^2y}{dt^2} = -9.8$ to show that $A = -\frac{9.8}{180^2} \approx -0.0003$.
(**Comment:** Notice that you are not asked to find A. The problem is to show that the value we've given is correct.)

(b) Now that we've determined all of the coefficients, Equation 4.12 describes the flight path of the Vomit Comet. Use Equation 4.12 to determine the value of x when the pilot pulls out of the dive at 7000 meters.

(c) Next find the value of t when the pilot pulls out of the dive. How does this compare with the 25 second claim?
(**Hint:** You may find it helpful to review, part (b) of Problem #95.)

(d) If the pilot wants to maintain a constant horizontal speed what must the airspeed of the plane be in terms of t ($t = 0$ representing the start of the maneuver)?

4.7   Newton's Method of Fluxions

"The method of Fluxions is the general key by help whereof the modern mathematicians unlock the secrets of Geometry, and consequently of Nature."

– George Berkley, from *The Analyst* (1685-1753)

Through experimentation Galileo had accurately described the motion of objects falling near the surface of the earth. At about the same time Johannes Kepler (1571 − 1630) had accurately described the motion of the planets by analyzing the vast catalog of astronomical observation made by Tycho Brahe (1546 − 1601). But these two descriptions of motion did not appear to be related.

It was left to Newton to unify them, but the mathematics for this did not exist at the time. So he invented Calculus, which he called *The Method of Fluxions*. Galileo studied motion on the surface of the Earth. Kepler studied the motion of the planets, but the underlying theme for both was motion.

Through experimentation Galileo had accurately described the motion of falling objects near

For Newton everything was in motion. When he used the variable x he thought of it as representing something "flowing in time" (moving). Such quantities he called **fluents**, from *fluere*, the Latin word which means "to flow." As he put it himself in his book *Quadratura Curvarum* (On the Quadrature of Curves), *I sought a method of determining quantities from the velocities of the motions or [of the] increments, with which they are generated; and calling*

Tycho Brahe
1546-1601

Johannes Kepler
1571-1630

these velocities of the motions, or [of the] increments, fluxions, *and generated quantities* fluents, *I fell by degrees, in the years 1665 and 1666, upon the method of fluxions, which I have made use of here in the quadrature of curves.*

For a given fluent x, Newton used the "dotted letter," $\dot{x}$, to refer to its *instantaneous velocity* or **fluxion**. Whereas for Leibniz the static differential was the fundamental concept, for Newton the dynamic fluxion (velocity) was fundamental. On the surface fluxions seem quite different from differentials.

In Newton's view the only independent variable is time. So all fluxions were velocities, or rates of change with respect to time. To see how fluxions are connected to the differential ratios we've been using, we need only ask ourselves how Leibniz would express the fluxion, $\dot{x}$, of the fluent, x. In Leibniz' notation the rate of change of x *with respect to t* is the differential ratio $\frac{dx}{dt}$. Since Newton *defines* $\dot{x}$ to be the rate of change of x with respect to (t)ime (velocity),

$$\dot{x} = \frac{dx}{dt}.$$

From Newton's point of view differentiating the spatial coordinate y with respect to the spatial coordinate x to get $\frac{dy}{dx}$ is simply not meaningful. On the other hand, if $P = (x, y)$ is a point moving along some curve in the plane then both x and y are fluents with corresponding fluxions $\dot{y}$ and $\dot{x}$.

What Leibniz's notation expresses as $\frac{dy}{dx}$ Newton's notation expresses as $\frac{\dot{y}}{\dot{x}}$. But they are the same thing. since

$$\frac{\dot{y}}{\dot{x}} = \frac{\frac{dy}{dt}}{\frac{dx}{dt}} = \frac{dy}{dt}\frac{dt}{dx} = \frac{dy}{dx}.$$

Although the two formulations are equivalent Leibniz' notation has become dominant in mathematics. But in fields where velocity is a fundamental concept, like physics and engineering, Newton's dot notation is often still used. For example, suppose we are considering a point P on the curve $y = x^2$ and we want the slope of the curve at P. Using our differentiation rules, we have

$$dy = 2x\,dx.$$

To get the slope, we divide by dx to get

$$\frac{dy}{dx} = 2x.$$

Using his Method of Fluxions, Newton would have considered both x and y to be fluents and $P = (x, y)$ to be a point moving along a curve. His version of Calculus would have started with the same governing equation $y = x^2$ and determined that their fluxions were related by the equation

$$\dot{y} = 2x\dot{x}.$$

To get the slope of the curve $y = x^2$, we simply need to recognize that this is the same as

$$\frac{\dot{y}}{\dot{x}} = 2x = \frac{\frac{dy}{dt}}{\frac{dx}{dt}} = \frac{dy}{dx}.$$

Although Newton's dot notation has fallen out of favor in mathematics you will likely see it being used in your physics or engineering courses (if you take any). We would be remiss if we failed to recognize this fact. So when appropriate, we will sometimes couch our problems in the dynamical language and dot notation of Newton. We will even sometimes refer to the derivatives $\frac{dy}{dt}$, or $\frac{dx}{dt}$ as fluxions. After all when t represents time that's what they are. Only the notation has changed.

If you prefer the Leibnizian terms and notation it is easy to translate between Newton and Leibniz. If x is changing in time then $\dot{x} = \frac{\mathrm{d}x}{\mathrm{d}t}$ is the fluxion of x.

Drill #109:
For each of the following equations, find an equation relating their differentials and use this to relate their fluxions (instantaneous rates of change with respect to time).

(a) $x^{\frac{1}{2}} + y^{\frac{1}{2}} = 1$

(b) $\dfrac{y}{x} = z^2$

(c) $\sqrt{z^3} = x^2 + y^2$

(d) $xyz = 1$

Example #27:
Consider two carts joined by a 100 foot length of rope passing through a pulley P, which is held at a fixed height of 10 feet above where the rope attaches to the carts.

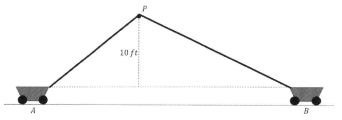

Suppose cart A is being pulled to the left at a constant speed of $1\frac{\text{foot}}{\text{second}}$.

Drill #110: Make a guess: Is cart B moving at a constant speed?

Let's check your guess. The general approach is to find the relationships between all of the fluents involved then differentiate and divide by $\mathrm{d}t$ to see how their fluxions are related. Below we have redrawn the essential features of the problem schematically and labeled all of the fluents.

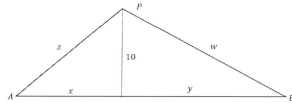

We have the following relationships between the fluents:

$$x^2 + 10^2 = z^2, \quad y^2 + 10^2 = w^2, \text{ and } z + w = 100.$$

Problem #111:

(a) Differentiate the above equations to obtain relationships between the differentials dx, dy, dz, and dw.

(b) Determine the relationship between the fluxions $\frac{dx}{dt}$ and $\frac{dy}{dt}$. Recall that $\frac{dx}{dt} = 1\frac{\text{foot}}{\text{second}}$. Is $\frac{dy}{dt}$ constant? How does this compare with your guess earlier?

(c) Translate your solution into Newton's dot notation.

End Of Example #27

Problem #112:

(a) In the following diagram suppose the point P is moving on the x-axis from left to right with horizontal velocity $\frac{dx}{dt} = 1\frac{\text{unit}}{\text{second}}$.

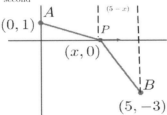

Find the distance, D from A to P to B as a single function of x and use this to compute

$$\left.\frac{dD}{dt}\right|_{\frac{dx}{dt}=1}.$$

(b) As an alternative approach, we re-label the diagram as follows:

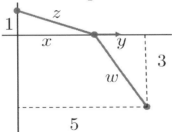

Define $D - z + w$. From this diagram we have

$$w^2 = 9 + y^2,$$
$$5 = x + y, \text{ and}$$
$$z^2 = 1 + x^2.$$

(c) Differentiate each of these equations and use the results to show that

$$dD = \left(\frac{x}{z} - \frac{y}{w} \right) dx.$$

(d) Compute $\left. \frac{dD}{dt} \right|_{x=1}$.

Problem#112 demonstrates that you have alternatives when solve any problem. Consciously try to avoid getting locked in to a single solution scheme. One alternative is to try to determine a single function of a single variable before differentiating. At the other extreme we can just assign variable names to all of the important quantities in our problem and differentiate the equations relating these variables.

The best approach will depend upon the problem. In fact, most of the time you'll find yourself using a mixture of the two. Keep in mind that it is always good to have alternatives.

Problem #113:

(a) Suppose the length of a rectangle is increasing at a rate of $1\frac{\text{unit}}{\text{second}}$ and the width is decreasing at a rate of $1\frac{\text{unit}}{\text{second}}$. Make a guess: Will the area remain constant?

(b) Let the length be denoted by the fluent L and the width denoted by the fluent W. The fluxions of L and W are $\frac{dL}{dt} = 1$ and $\frac{dW}{dt} = -1$, respectively. Let A denote the area of the rectangle and compute the fluxion $\frac{dA}{dt}$.

(c) How does your solution in part (b) compare to your guess in part (a)?

(d) Translate your solution into Newton's dot notation.

Problem #114:

The sketch at the right represents a 15 foot long ladder leaning against a vertical wall. Suppose that the bottom is sliding to the right at a constant rate.

(a) Make a guess: Is the top sliding down at a constant rate?

(b) Find $\frac{da}{dt}$ in terms of $\frac{db}{dt}$, and use this to check your guess in part (a).

(c) Translate your solution into Newton's dot notation.

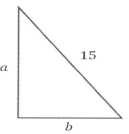

Problem #115:

Suppose that at a certain instant of time the price of a certain commodity is increasing at a rate of 5% per month and the quantity sold is decreasing at a rate of 3% per month. Would the revenue increase at a rate of 2% per month? Explain.

Problem #116:

The strength of a signal from a cell tower, measured in decibels[15] is inversely proportional to the square of the distance between the tower and the cell phone. Suppose you have a 200 foot tall cell tower and a car driving away from the tower at a rate of $100\frac{\text{ft}}{\text{second}}$ (approximately 68 mph).

(a) Find a formula for the rate at which the signal is decreasing in terms of the distance x from the car to the base of the tower. (Use k to denote the constant of proportionality.)

(b) Plot a graph of the formula in part (a) with $x \geq 0$ and use this to approximate the distance from the base of the tower where the signal decreases fastest. (Use $k = 1000000$. You'll see why we chose this scale once you've plotted it.)

(c) Based on the graph, what is happening to the rate at which the signal is decreasing as the car moves farther away from the tower?

Problem #117:

It is reasonable to assume that the rate at which the volume of a spherical raindrop is increasing as it forms is proportional to the surface area of the raindrop. Show that under this assumption, the radius (surprisingly?) grows at a constant rate.

Problem #118:

Suppose we have a rectangular box whose length is increasing by $3\frac{\text{centimeters}}{\text{second}}$, whose width is increasing by $2\frac{\text{centimeters}}{\text{second}}$ and whose height is decreasing by $3\frac{\text{centimeters}}{\text{second}}$. How fast are the volume and surface area of the box changing when the length is 25 centimeters, width is 20 centimeters, and height is 10 centimeters? Are they increasing or decreasing?

Problem #119:

Suppose a point P is moving along the curve $y = x^2$ so that its horizontal velocity is $\frac{dx}{dt} = 1\frac{\text{unit}}{\text{second}}$. For which values of x is the distance from P to the point $(0, 1)$ increasing and for what values is it decreasing? What can you say about the points where the distance transitions from increasing to decreasing or decreasing to increasing?

---

[15]The icon on your cell phone probably uses bars, but there is no universally agreed upon standard for what "one bar" means. There is a standard for decibels.

Problem #120:

The ideal gas law (Boyle's Law) states that the pressure P (in pascals), volume V (in cubic meters), and temperature T (in degrees Kelvin) of an ideal gas are related by the formula $PV = kNT$ where N is the number of gas molecules and k is the Boltzmann constant. What this says is that for a fixed amount of gas, if the volume is held fixed, then the pressure is proportional to the temperature and if the temperature is held fixed, then the pressure is inversely proportional to the volume.

(a) Assuming that we have an enclosed gas, and that N is held constant. Find an equation that relates dP, dV, and dT, and use this to find $\frac{dT}{dt}$ in terms of $\frac{dP}{dt}$ and $\frac{dV}{dt}$.

(b) Suppose we have a piston compressing the gas in a cylinder as in the following sketch.

$h\ meters$

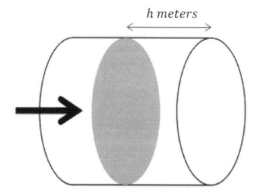

Show that for the pressure to be held fixed $\frac{dT}{dt}$ must satisfy

$$\frac{dT}{dt} = \frac{T}{h}\frac{dh}{dt}.$$

(**Comment:** Notice that this is independent of the radius of the cylinder.)

(c) Suppose that when $h = 0.2$ meters the temperature is $300°K$. If the piston is moving to the right at a rate of $0.001\frac{\text{meters}}{\text{second}}$, how fast should the temperature be decreasing at that instant to maintain a constant pressure?

Problem #121:

A streetlamp is mounted at the top of a 20 foot pole. A 6 foot tall person is walking away from the base of the pole at a constant speed.

(a) Make a guess: Is the length of this person's shadow increasing at a constant rate?

(b) Now compute the rate at which the person's shadow is increasing.

Problem #122: Find the Patterns

Suppose the position of a point, P_x, on the x-axis is given by $(x(t), 0)$ and the position of another point, P_y, on the y-axis is given by $(0, y(t))$. Let $S(t)$ represent the distance between P_x and P_y.

(a)   **i.** If $x(t) = t$, and $y(t) = t$ show that $\frac{\mathrm{d}S}{\mathrm{d}t} = \sqrt{2}$.

   ii. If $x(t) = 2t$, and $y(t) = 2t$ show that $\frac{\mathrm{d}S}{\mathrm{d}t} = \sqrt{8}$.

   iii. If $x(t) = t$, and $y(t) = 3t$ show that $\frac{\mathrm{d}S}{\mathrm{d}t} = \sqrt{10}$.

   iv. If $x(t) = 5t$, and $y(t) = 3t$ show that $\frac{\mathrm{d}S}{\mathrm{d}t} = \sqrt{34}$.

   v. Do you see a pattern yet? If you do, write it down and try to show that it always holds. If you don't, make up some more simple examples and solve them to gather more evidence. when you believe you have see it conjecture a pattern and then show that the pattern always holds.

(b)   **(i)** Show that if $x(t) = t^{\frac{1}{2}}$, and $y(t) = t^{\frac{1}{2}}$ then $\dfrac{\mathrm{d}S}{\mathrm{d}t} = \dfrac{1}{\sqrt{2t}}$. Does this make intuitive sense to you?

   (ii) Show that if $x(t) = t^{\frac{1}{3}}$, and $y(t) = t^{\frac{1}{3}}$, then $\dfrac{\mathrm{d}S}{\mathrm{d}t} = \dfrac{\sqrt{2}}{3\sqrt[3]{t^2}}$.

   (iii) Show that if $x(t) = t^{\frac{1}{4}}$, and $y(t) = t^{\frac{1}{4}}$, then $\dfrac{\mathrm{d}S}{\mathrm{d}t} = \dfrac{\sqrt{2}}{4\sqrt[4]{t^3}}$.

   (iv) Do you see a pattern yet? If you do, write it down and try to show that it always holds. If you don't make up some more, simple examples, and solve them to gather more evidence. when you believe you have see it conjecture a pattern and then show that the pattern always holds.

(c) Finally, given *any* $x(t)$ and *any* $y(t)$, find a completely general formula for $\frac{\mathrm{d}S}{\mathrm{d}t}$.

4.8   Self-intersecting Curves and Parametric Equations

In Problem #82 we asked you to find the line tangent to several interesting curves. However, we were careful to ask only about relatively simple curves. In particular, none of the curves in Problem #82 intersected themselves. We avoided self-intersecting curves earlier because we didn't have the techniques necessary to address the problem of tangent lines at points where a curve crosses itself. We do now.

But we need to broaden our thinking a bit.

Drill #123:

(a) For the Folium of Descartes: $x^3 + y^3 = 3xy$

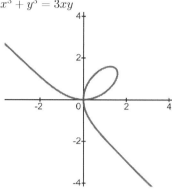

(i) Show that $\frac{\mathrm{d}y}{\mathrm{d}x} = \frac{y - x^2}{y^2 - x}$.

(ii) Locate all of the points $(x, y) \neq (0, 0)$ where the line tangent to the Folium of Descartes is horizontal.

(iii) Locate all of the points $(x, y) \neq (0, 0)$ where the line tangent to the Folium of Descartes is vertical.

(b) The Tschirnhausen cubic: $27y^2 = (1 - x)(8 + x)^2$

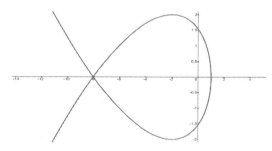

(i) Show that $\frac{\mathrm{d}y}{\mathrm{d}x} = \frac{-(8 + x)(3x + 6)}{54y}$.

(ii) Locate all of the points $(x, y) \neq (-8, 0)$ where the line tangent to the Tschirnhausen cubic is horizontal.

(iii) Locate all of the points $(x, y) \neq (-8, 0)$ where the line tangent to the Tschirnhausen cubic is vertical.

If we try to compute $\left. \frac{\mathrm{d}y}{\mathrm{d}x} \right|_{(x,y)=(0,0)}$ for the Folium of Descartes we find that $\left. \frac{\mathrm{d}y}{\mathrm{d}x} \right|_{(x,y)=(0,0)} = \frac{0}{0}$ which is very strange. We can see in the graph that at $(0, 0)$ there is both a horizontal and a vertical tangent line, so it seems to make some sort of sense.

You might be thinking that we have stumbled upon a new rule about tangent lines: If we ever obtain $\frac{dy}{dx} = \frac{0}{0}$, at some point then the curve has both a vertical and horizontal tangent at that point. It would be nice if things were that simple, but they aren't.

But now consider the Tschirnhausen Cubic at the self-intersection point $(-8, 0)$. As long as we stay away from the self-intersection point there are no difficulties. But from the graph we can see that any sort of tangent line at the point of self-intersection would be neither vertical nor horizontal despite the fact that once again we have

$$\left.\frac{dy}{dx}\right|_{(x,y)=(-8,0)} = \frac{0}{0}.$$

If nothing else, these examples illustrate that using Calculus is much more subtle than simply computing a derivative. A cavalier attitude can lead to some very strange anomalies. As is true of any powerful tool, to avoid disaster we must be careful.

The safest approach is to avoid points of self-intersection and fractions such as $\frac{0}{0}$. But we won't be able to avoid them forever so we might as well address the issue now. Adopting Newton's dynamic approach will give us the crucial insight. Think of the horizontal and vertical coordinates as Newton's fluents; things changing in time.

Using the static approach to find a tangent line at a self-intersection point is very much like standing in the center of the intersection of two roads and trying to decide if the road goes north-south or east-west. Obviously the road doesn't go anywhere. It just sits there. Likewise, a curve is not dynamic. It just sits there, like a road.

It is the travelers on the road and the point that traces a curve which move.

If instead we ask, "Which way are we going as we *pass through the intersection*?" there is only one answer. We're going in the direction we were traveling when we entered the intersection. If we think about the situation dynamically rather than statically, we always have both a position on the curve and a direction we are traveling.

So if we adopt Newton's viewpoint and think of the curve as being generated by the motion of a point things change.

If we are traveling along a curve our direction of travel is always tangent to the curve. By changing our question from "What is the tangent line at this point?" to "What is the tangent line at this time?" the concept of two (or more) tangent lines at a single point in space becomes meaningful. Each tangent is obtained by passing through the point of tangency at distinct moments in time.

Problem #124:

(a) Show that if $x(t)$ and $y(t)$ satisfy

$$x(t) = 1 - 3t^2$$
$$y(t) = t(3 - t^2)$$

then x and y satisfy the equation of the Tschirnhausen Cubic: $27y^2 = (1 - x)(8 + x)^2$.

(b) Compute the fluxions of x and y.

(c) If we think of t as time, with $t < 0$, representing time in the past, will the point $(x(t), y(t))$ traverse the clockwise or counterclockwise as t increases?

(**Hint:** Consider the values of t for which x and y are moving in the positive and negative directions.)

(**d**) Find the values of t for which $(x(t), y(t)) = (-8, 0)$. Use the result of part (b) to compute $\frac{dy}{dx} = \frac{\dot{y}}{\dot{x}}$ at these times. Are your answers consistent with what you obtained in part (c)? Explain.

(**e**) Show that the equations of the two lines which are tangent to the Tschirnhausen cubic at $(-8, 0)$ are

$$y = \pm \frac{1}{\sqrt{3}}(x + 8).$$

Problem #125:

Recall that the Folium of Descartes, $x^3 + y^3 = 3xy$, crosses itself at the origin.

(**a**) Show that if $x(t) = \frac{3t}{1+t^3}$ and $y(t) = \frac{3t^2}{1+t^3}$ then x and y satisfy the equation of the Folium.

(**b**) Compute the fluxions of x and y.

(**c**) For which values of t is $y \geq 0$?

(**d**) Find the value of t for which $(x(t), y(t)) = (0, 0)$. use the result of part (b) to compute $\frac{dy}{dx} = \frac{\dot{y}}{\dot{x}}$ at this time. Is this consistent with the graph?

(**e**) Can you explain why we only found one tangent line at $(0, 0)$ when it is quite clear from the graph that there must be two?

What comes along with this change in interpretation is this: We no longer want to think of a differential ratio *only* as a slope. If y and x happen to represent the vertical and horizontal coordinates of a graph, then the change of y with respect to x, $\frac{dy}{dx}$, will be the slope of the curve $y = y(x)$.

If y represents the vertical position of an object and t represents the time when the object is at position $y(t)$, then the change of y with respect to t, $\frac{dy}{dt} = \dot{y}$, is the vertical velocity of the object as it passes through y. Likewise, if $x(t)$ represents the horizontal position of an object then $\frac{dx}{dt} = \dot{x}$ is the horizontal velocity of the object as it passes through x.

In general, if α and β are two related quantities then $\frac{d\alpha}{d\beta}$ is the **rate of change of α with respect to β.** The physical (or geometric) interpretation of $\frac{d\alpha}{d\beta}$ will necessarily depend on what α and β represent physically (or geometrically).

Parametric Functions

When we switched to Newton's dynamical viewpoint, we changed the nature of our representations of the curves. For example the Folium of Descartes can be represented by the formula as

$$x^3 + y^3 = 3xy.$$

This formula is complex and can be hard to work with, mainly because the relationship between x and y is difficult to see and understand.

In the representation

$$x(t) = \frac{3t}{1 + t^3}, \quad y(t) = \frac{3t^2}{1 + t^3}$$

the relationship between x and y is still difficult but since $x(t)$ and $y(t)$ are both functions the relationship between x and t and between y and t is a bit simpler. We know how to work with functions.

This second representation is usually called the **parametric functions** or **parametric equation** representation, because the x and y coordinates are given in terms of a parameter. In this case the parameter t represents time. This is common but by no means required. The parameter might represent anything, just as any variable might.

In fact, you might be wondering where we got the parameterization for the Folium. It may not seem obvious, but as long as $(x, y) \neq (0, 0)$, the parameter t actually represents the slope of the line joining the origin to the point (x, y) on the Folium.

Problem #126:

Let (x, y) represent any point on the Folium $x^3 + y^3 = 3xy$ which is not the origin. Let t represent the slope of the line joining the origin to (x, y); that is, $\frac{y}{x} = t$ or $y = tx$. Use this to show[16] that

$$x = \frac{3t}{1 + t^3}, \text{ and } y = \frac{3t^2}{1 + t^3}.$$

Of course, it is not wrong to also think of this parameter as time. We are just stipulating that the point is moving so that its position at time t is such that the slope of the line joining the origin to the point matches t. Mathematically, what the parameter represents is usually not at issue. It is just a parameter.

Recall that when we looked at Roberval's treatment of the conic sections in Section 2.6 we found it handy to think of our curves as being traced out by the motion of a point and we created the notation $\begin{Bmatrix} x(t) \\ y(t) \end{Bmatrix}$ to reflect that point of view. With one slight modification this notation suits our current needs as well.

First, since the coordinates of our point are, individually, functions of t it follows that the position of the point P itself depends on (is a function of) t as well:

$$P(t) = \begin{Bmatrix} x(t) \\ y(t) \end{Bmatrix}.$$

Second, it is useful for us to have a convenient way to specify the domain of the function. So we add a third component to do that. For example, if the domain of our function is all

---

[16]The difference between this problem and Problem 125 is this: In Problem 125 we gave you $x(t)$ and $y(t)$ and asked you to show that it satisfies the equation of the Folium. Here we start with the equation of the Folium and you need to find $x(t)$ and $y(t)$.

values of t strictly between zero and one we would write.

$$P(t) = \left\{ \begin{array}{c} x(t) \\ y(t) \\ 0 < t < 1 \end{array} \right\}.$$

"Dynamic" and "static" are only words we use to describe the way we're thinking about a problem. There is nothing inherently dynamic or static in either representation so there is no *a priori* reason to prefer one over the other. They describe the same set of points in the plane.

For example if $y = x^2$ then $dy = 2x\,dx$. Time (t) does not appear in these formulas so we tend to think of them statically. However if we want to think of them dynamically we divide by dt to get $\frac{dy}{dt} = 2x\frac{dx}{dt}$ and interpret this to say that at any given time t, the position of a point is $\left\{ \begin{array}{c} x(t) \\ y(t) \end{array} \right\}$ and the vertical velocity, $\frac{dy}{dt}$ is twice the value of the x coordinate times the horizontal velocity, $\frac{dx}{dt}$.

Problem #127:

  (a) Use your favorite graphing technology to show that the parameterization

$$P(t) = \left\{ \begin{array}{c} t^2 + 1 \\ t^4 + 2t^2 + 1 \\ -\infty < t < \infty \end{array} \right\}$$

  traces out part of the parabola $y = x^2$. Which part?

  (b) The parameterization $P(t) = \left\{ \begin{array}{c} -(t^2 + 1) \\ t^4 + 2t^2 + 1 \\ -\infty < t < \infty \end{array} \right\}$ traces out different part of the same parabola. How else is this parameterization different from the one in part (a)?

  (c) Explain why neither of these parameterizations traces the part of the curve $y = x^2$ where $-1 < x < 1$.

Example #28:

Moving between the equation and parametric forms can be very hard to do depending on the complexity of the equation. The simplest situation is when you have y as a function of x; for example $y(x) = x^2$. To find a parametric representation we observe that we need to specify both x and y as functions of a third parameter, t. This can be puzzling until we realize that x is completely free. All we need to do is ensure that $y = x^2$. So if we take $x(t) = t$ and $y = x^2 = t^2$ we *almost* have our parameterization.

When faced with a formula like $y = x^2$ you have learned to always assume that x could be any real number that makes sense in the formula. But with parametric equations this assumption can lead to problems. We'll need to specify the allowable values of the parameter t

explicitly. This is why we said we *almost* have our parameterization. A complete parameterization must specify the values of t that are available to us, so in this case

$$P(t) = \left\{ \begin{array}{c} x(t) = t \\ y(t) = t^2 \\ -\infty < t < \infty \end{array} \right\}.$$

We can *always* parameterize the graph of a function the same way we just parameterized $y = x^2$. A parameterization of $y = y(x)$, with domain $a \leq x \leq b$ is

$$P(t) = \left\{ \begin{array}{c} x(t) = t \\ y(t) = y(t) \\ t \in [a, b] \end{array} \right\}.$$

This parameterization is equivalent to working with the function $y = y(x)$ so it may or may not be particularly useful, but it can always be done.

End Of Example #28

Problem #128:

(a) Use your favorite graphing technology to show that each of the following is a parameterization of part of the graph of $y = x^2$.

(i) $P(t) = \left\{ \begin{array}{c} 3t \\ 9t^2 \\ t > 0 \end{array} \right\}$ (v) $P(t) = \left\{ \begin{array}{c} 1/t \\ 1/t^2 \\ |t| > 0 \end{array} \right\}$

(ii) $P(t) = \left\{ \begin{array}{c} -t \\ t^2 \\ t \leq 0 \end{array} \right\}$ (vi) $P(t) = \left\{ \begin{array}{c} t^{1/3} \\ t^{2/3} \\ t > 0 \end{array} \right\}$

(iii) $P(t) = \left\{ \begin{array}{c} \sqrt{t} \\ t \\ t \geq 0 \end{array} \right\}$ (vii) $P(t) = \left\{ \begin{array}{c} t^3 - 1 \\ t^6 - 2t^3 + 1 \\ -\infty < t < \infty \end{array} \right\}$

(iv) $P(t) = \left\{ \begin{array}{c} -\sqrt{t} \\ t \\ t \geq 0 \end{array} \right\}$ (viii) $P(t) = \left\{ \begin{array}{c} t + 1 \\ t^2 + 2t + 1 \\ -20 < t < 20 \end{array} \right\}$

(b) Sketch only the part of the curve included in each parameterization in part (a). Be sure to indicate the direction of travel in each case, assuming t is increasing.

(c) Compute $\frac{\dot{y}}{\dot{x}}$ and show that this yields $\frac{dy}{dx} = 2x$ for each of the parameterizations in part (a).

Problem #129:

(a) Show that each of the following is a parameterization of part of the unit circle.

$$\textbf{(i)} \ \ P(t) = \left\{ \begin{array}{c} t \\ \sqrt{1-t^2} \\ -1 \le t < 1 \end{array} \right\} \quad \textbf{(iii)} \ \ P(t) = \left\{ \begin{array}{c} \sqrt{1-t^2} \\ t \\ -1 \le t < 1 \end{array} \right\} \quad \textbf{(v)} \ \ P(t) = \left\{ \begin{array}{c} t^2 \\ \sqrt{1-t^4} \\ -1 \le t < 1 \end{array} \right\}$$

$$\textbf{(ii)} \ \ P(t) = \left\{ \begin{array}{c} t \\ -\sqrt{1-t^2} \\ 0 \le t < 1 \end{array} \right\} \quad \textbf{(iv)} \ \ P(t) = \left\{ \begin{array}{c} \sqrt{1-t^2} \\ t \\ 0 \le t < 1 \end{array} \right\} \quad \textbf{(vi)} \ \ P(t) = \left\{ \begin{array}{c} t - 2 \\ \sqrt{4t - (3+t^2)} \\ 1 \le t < 2 \end{array} \right\}$$

(b) Sketch *only* the part of the curve included in each parameterization in part (a). Be sure to indicate the direction of travel in each case.

(c) Compute $\frac{\dot{y}}{\dot{x}}$ and show that this yields

$$\frac{\mathrm{d}y}{\mathrm{d}x} = -\frac{x}{y}$$

for each of the parameterizations in part (a).

As we've seen we can always parameterize the graph of a function, but the reverse is not true. A parameterized curve will not always be the graph of some function. For example the curves in Problem #82 are not graphs of functions, but all of these curves can be parameterized.

Because it can't always be accomplished there is no general strategy for expressing a parameterized curve as the graph of a function. One strategy that sometimes works[17] is to find $\frac{\mathrm{d}y}{\mathrm{d}x}$ and "undifferentiate" as in the following example.

Problem #130:

The red curve in the sketch at the right is parameterized by

$$P(t) = \left\{ \begin{array}{c} \frac{1}{\sqrt{t^2-1}} \\ \frac{t^2 - 2\sqrt{t^2-1}}{\sqrt{t^2-1}} \\ 1 < t < \infty \end{array} \right\}.$$

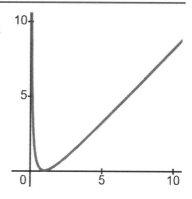

Differentiating x and y gives

$$\frac{\mathrm{d}x}{\mathrm{d}t} = \frac{-t}{(t^2-1)^{\frac{3}{2}}}$$

and

$$\frac{\mathrm{d}y}{\mathrm{d}t} = \frac{t^3 - 2t}{(t^2-1)^{\frac{3}{2}}}$$

so that $\frac{\mathrm{d}y}{\mathrm{d}x} = 1 - (t^2 - 1)$.

---

[17]Not necessarily the best. In general there is no best way.

(a) Fill in the details of the computation of $\frac{dx}{dt}$, $\frac{dy}{dt}$, and show that $\frac{dy}{dx} = 1 - \frac{1}{x^2}$.

(b) Let $y = x + \frac{1}{x}$ and show that $\frac{dy}{dx} = 1 - \frac{1}{x^2}$.

(c) Sketch the graph of $y(x) = x + \frac{1}{x}$ to see that this is *not* the same as the parameterized curve above. Can you tell what went wrong?

(d) Show that the point $(1, 0)$ is on our parameterized curve. Use this to find the function, $y(x)$, that has the same graph as $P(t)$).

Problem #131:

For each of the given parameterizations find $\frac{dy}{dx}$ two different ways:

(i) Compute dx and dy and find their ratio, $\frac{dy}{dx}$.

(ii) Solve for t in terms of x (or y). Substitute this into y (or x). Compute $\frac{dy}{dx}$ directly.

And then find $y(x)$.

(a) $P(t) = \begin{Bmatrix} t - 1 \\ t + 1 \\ t \in \mathbb{R} \end{Bmatrix}$

(b) $P(t) = \begin{Bmatrix} 3t - 2 \\ -5t + 7 \\ t \in \mathbb{R} \end{Bmatrix}$

(c) $P(t) = \begin{Bmatrix} 1/\sqrt{t} \\ \sqrt{t} \\ 0 < t \end{Bmatrix}$

4.9 Bridges, Chains, Domes, and Telescopes

Bridges

In the previous section all of the quantities we were looking at were time dependent – they were in motion – so it was useful to think of the derivative, $\frac{dy}{dt}$, as a velocity (fluxion). In other applications, where the quantities involved are not time dependent, the derivative is still a useful tool but thinking of it as a velocity may not be as useful.

For example, consider the shape of the support cable on a stable suspension bridge as seen in the picture below. The shape of the suspension cable appears to be parabolic, but how can we be sure of this?

Golden Gate Bridge,
photo by
Modestas Urbonas

At any given moment there are a lot of forces acting on a bridge, but most are insignificant most of the time. The mantra of mathematical modeling is to keep things as simple as possible (at least in the beginning) by focusing on the dominant parameter first[18] In this case the dominant force involved is clearly the weight of the bridge itself.

We assume that the weight density of the deck of the bridge is W newtons/meter[19]. The cable adds to the weight of the bridge as well, but it is relatively small compared to the weight of the deck. So we will ignore it to keep the model simple. Assuming the deck is horizontal, we can take it to be the x axis

Now suppose the graph of $y = y(x)$ represents the cable between two upright towers located at $x = -U$ and $x = U$. Remember, though we suspect that $y(x)$ is a parabola we don't yet know if this is true.

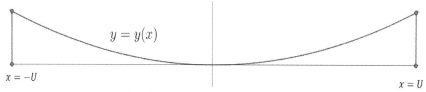

$y = y(x)$

$x = -U$ $x = U$

We choose an arbitrary point (x, y) on the curve with $0 < x < U$ and focus on the portion of the bridge between $(-x, y)$ and (x, y).

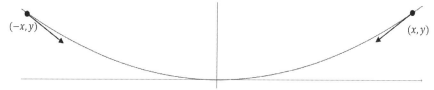

$(-x, y)$ (x, y)

These are the two points that are holding up the section of the bridge on the interval from $-x$ to x. The arrows represent the tangential forces felt on the cable at the points.

We'll examine the the horizontal and vertical components of the tangential force at various

---

[18]Or, equivalently, we set the secondary parameters equal to zero.
[19]A *newton* is a unit of force, named after Isaac Newton.

points on the bridge.

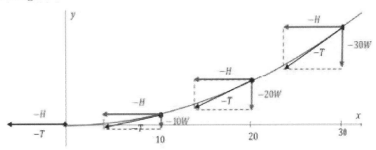

Since the curve is symmetric, we only draw the half where $x \geq 0$.

Notice the tangential force at $x = 0$, which we have labeled $-T$, is horizontal. This reflects the fact that at that point the vertical force would be the weight for the deck from $x = 0$ to $x = 0$ which is zero[20]. (You'll see why we used negatives momentarily.) Hence the tangential force is equal to the horizontal tension, $-H$.

As we move away from the center of the cable to some point x_1, there is more of the deck to support. Since we are ignoring the weight of the cable, the vertical force is equal to the weight of the deck from $x = 0$ to x_1 so the tangential tension gets larger as we move to the right. The horizontal tension at every single point will be the same as the tension at the origin. What varies is the vertical component of the force.

The cumulative effect can also be thought of this way. The point on the cable at $x = 20$ meters must not only support the weight of the deck from $x = 10$ meters to $x = 20$ meters, but must bear the brunt of the load at the point $x = 10$ meters as well. This leads to the vertical force at $x = 20$ meters being $-10W$ newtons $- 10W$ newtons $= -20W$ newtons. The point at $x = 30$ meters must support whatever weight there is at $x = 20$ meters along with the extra weight from $x = 20$ meters to $x = 30$ meters which totals $-20W$ newtons $- 10W$ newtons $= -30W$ newtons. If you were hoisting a person carrying a bucket of sand, then you would be bearing the weight of both the person and the sand even though that person is only bearing the weight of the sand. This is the same idea.

The conclusion of this analysis is that at any point (x, y) on the curve, the tangential force pulling against the cable has a horizontal component of $-H$ and a vertical component of $-Wx$. To stabilize the bridge, we need the cable to be pulling with the same force in exactly the opposite direction. This leads to the sketch at the right. (Now you see why we used negatives before.)

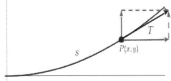

Problem #132:

(a) Use the above analysis and schematic drawing of the forces involved to show that the curve representing the cable must satisfy the differential equation

$$\frac{dy}{dx} = \frac{Wx}{H}.$$

---

[20]This is why it's the lowest point, there is no vertical pull.

(**Hint:** Notice that T is pulling in the direction tangent to the cable.)

(**b**) Show that the parabola $y = \frac{W}{2H}x^2 + b$, where b is an arbitrary constant, satisfies this differential equation

(**c**) Let $W = 1$, $b = 0$ and plot the parabola for $H = 1, 2, 3$. Does this agree with the idea that H indicates how tightly we are winching the cable?

With our simplifying assumptions in place it appears that the cable on a suspension bridge does indeed hang in the shape of a parabola. But the suspension bridge has to hold up the deck beneath it. After all, that is its purpose.

Chains

What shape do you think a chain takes on if it is pinned at both ends, and allowed to hang freely in between? Take your best guess and don't worry about guessing correctly. We'll solve this problem shortly.

If you guessed that the curve is a parabola, then you are in good company. Galileo also believed that a hanging chain assumed a parabolic shape as we see in the following passage from his book Dialogue Concerning Two New Sciences (1638).

"Drive two nails into a wall at a convenient height and at the same level; make the distance between these nails twice the width of the rectangle upon which it is desired to trace the semiparabola. Over these two nails hang a light chain of such length that the depth of its sag (curve or sacca) is equal to the length of the prism. This chain will assume the form of a parabola, so that if this form be marked by points on the wall we shall have described a complete parabola which can be divided into two equal parts by drawing a vertical line through a point midway between the two nails . . . Any ordinary mechanic will know how to do it."

Problem #133: The Hanging Chain

This problem is very similar to finding the shape of the suspension bridge cable. The difference here is that since there is no deck to support, the only vertical force will be the weight of the chain itself, so we can't ignore the weight of the chain the way we ignored the weight of the cable in the suspension bridge.

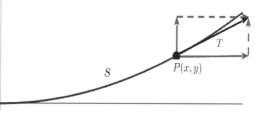

Let w represent the weight density of the chain in newtons per meter and s represent the length of the chain from the lowest point

to a point $P = (x, y)$ on the chain. Show that the curve represented by the chain must satisfy the differential equation

$$\frac{\mathrm{d}y}{\mathrm{d}x} = \frac{ws}{H}. \tag{4.13}$$

OK, but so what? All Equation (4.13) says is that the proportion $\frac{\mathrm{d}y}{\mathrm{d}x}$ is equal to the proportion $\frac{ws}{H}$.

If we could *solve* this equation for $y(x)$ then the graph of y would be the shape of the chain, but sadly we don't have the tools to do that (yet).

So why did we bother writing down Equation (4.13) at all? Does this tell us anything about the shape of the hanging chain?

Yes. Actually it does.

The fact is that in our attempts to describe the world around us using mathematics we can't actually solve *most* of the equations we write down. Real world phenomena are just too complex. But just writing them down is a step forward. Although we can't (yet) solve Equation (4.13), and thereby find the shape of a hanging chain, we can use it to eliminate some shapes. In particular, we can now show that Galileo was wrong about the shape of a hanging chain.

Problem #134: Galileo was wrong!

The difficulty is that we have the wrong variable on the right side of Equation 4.13. Since y depends on x we'd like to have only the variables x and y, appearing in our equation. Instead we have x, y, and s. And we really don't know anything about s.

However, recall that we do know something about $\mathrm{d}s$.

(a) Use a differential triangle to show that the hanging chain curve must satisfy the differential equation

$$\frac{\mathrm{d}^2 y}{\mathrm{d}x^2} = \frac{w}{H}\frac{\mathrm{d}s}{\mathrm{d}x} = \frac{w}{H}\sqrt{1 + \left(\frac{\mathrm{d}y}{\mathrm{d}x}\right)^2}. \tag{4.14}$$

(**Hint:** Recall the $\mathrm{d}s$ represents a differential along the direction of the curve. How is it related to $\mathrm{d}x$ and $\mathrm{d}y$?)

(b) Show that the general parabola $y = ax^2 + bx + c$ does *not* satisfy this differential equation (and so Galileo was mistaken!) .

(c) Show that, in fact no nonzero polynomial $y = a_0 + a_1 x + a_2 x^2 + \ldots + a_n x^n$ satisfies Equation 4.14.
   (**Hint:** Suppose it did satisfy the equation. If we were to square both sides of the equation, what would be the degree of each side?)

Galileo's brilliance is not at all diminished by this error. As we said in Chapter 1, smart people make mistakes! This is how they get to be smart. You should follow the example of

Galileo (and Newton, and Leibniz) by making and embracing lots of mistakes. But don't forget to learn from them as well. Also, in fairness to Galileo, he did not have access to the Calculus tools that make this problem tractable. We do.

Domes

In Problem #134 we saw that the shape of a hanging chain is not a parabola as Galileo believed. But it actually shows much more than that. It shows that the shape of a hanging chain is not the graph of any polynomial regardless of its degree. (A parabola is the graph of a polynomial of degree 2.) This result tell us that the set of polynomials is too small to model all of the phenomena we observe in the world. The solution of the hanging chain problem will require a larger class of functions.

The curve which *does* satisfy equation (4.13), and thus is the shape of a hanging chain is called the catenary. This is not especially illuminating since the word "catenary" is derived from the Latin word *catena* which simply means chain.

The structural properties of the catenary have been known and used since ancient times The Pantheon in Rome was completed during the reign of Hadrian and dedicated around 126 AD. It is not known who

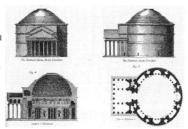
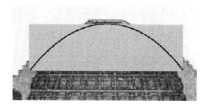

Drawings of the Pantheon and a cross section of the dome with an inverted catenary superimposed on the arch.

designed it, but there is evidence[21] which suggests that a catenary design was employed.

The architect Filippo Brunelleschi (1377 − 1446) used a hanging chain to develop the shape of the dome of the Cathedral of Santa Maria del Fiore in Florence, Italy in the Middle Ages.

A number of modern architects and masons have used the catenary to design arches and domes (a rotated arch) as well.

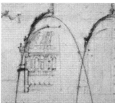

St. Paul's Cathedral,
London, UK

For example, the mathematician and architect Sir Christopher Wren (1632 − 1723) used the shape of the catenary arch in the design and construction of the structural part of the dome on St Paul's Cathedral in London.

Wren was assisted in designing St. by his good friend Robert Hooke (1635 − 1703), who[22] advised him that the cross section of the dome should be an inverted catenary: "As hangs a flexible cable so, inverted, stand the touching pieces of an arch."

---

[21] For example, its shape.

[22] Hooke is also famous for showing that the contracting force of a stretched spring is proportional to the amount of stretching. This is known as "Hooke's Law." We will examine this in more depth in Section 5.3.

The idea to use catenaries in building design was most likely originally motivated by experimentation and intuition. But, after Calculus was invented, it became possible to explain why they are so stable. When the forces involved in causing a hanging chain to fall into the shape of a catenary are inverted (turned upside down) then the weight of the catenary arch is directed tangentially along the arch toward the base. Catenary arches are still in use today in part because they have this property.

Because of its inherent strength and stability the catenary arch is still a common choice for arches and domes today. For example, the roof of the East Rail Station in Budapest, Hungary is also a catenary. We've seen that a catenary is not a parabola, but we do not yet have a formula for the catenary curve. We will address, this question in Problem #276.

East Rail Station
Budapest, Hungary

Telescopes

Though he didn't invent the telescope, Galileo is usually cited as the first person[23] to use a telescope to discover, for example, craters and mountains on the surface of the Moon, the phases Venus, and the moons of Jupiter. This work helped convince Galileo of the validity of Nicolaus Copernicus's heliocentric (sun-centered) model of the solar system, for which he (Galileo) was eventually condemned by the Inquisition.

All telescopes follow one of two basic designs, refractive and reflective. Refractive telescopes us the refractive property of light described by Snell's Law (see Section 2.7) to reduce the large image entering the telescope to a smaller area, thus focusing the image for the observer. Galileo used a refractive telescope

Refractive telescopes work well for relatively close objects, but since refraction separates light into its various color components (think of light passing through a prism) it tends to create little rainbows (usually called chromatic aberrations) in the image.

Because of his work in optics, Newton realized that he could use the reflective properties of the parabola to achieve greater magnification with a smaller physical device while simultaneously avoiding the chromatic aberrations. All modern research telescopes are built on Newton's original design, which uses parabolic mirrors to reflect light toward the focus of the parabola, where a secondary mirror reflects it to the eyepiece.

The Large Binocular Telescope
Mt. Graham, Arizona

For example the each mirror of the two large mirrors required by the Large Binocular Telescope at Mt. Graham, Arizona is 8.4 meters in diameter. The image below gives a sense of the size of one of these mirrors.

---

[23]Thomas Harriot did it before Galileo but Harriot didn't publish his observations.

To produce a large, perfectly parabolic mirror the Richard F. Caris Mirror Laboratory uses a process called spin casting, where high quality borosilicate glass is place into a revolving furnace. As the furnace spins the glass liquefies and the rotational forces push the surface of the glass into a parabolic shape.

As the molten glass spins the middle goes down and the sides go up. As we will see momentarily the surface generated must be a parabola. The shape of the mirror, and hence its focal length, will be affected by the rotational speed of the glass. The question is, how fast must we spin the furnace to produce a particular focal length?

To begin to answer that question we will need to think about a typical point mass at a point on the surface of the molten glass as shown below. Suppose the glass is spinning at an angular velocity of ω $\frac{\text{radians}}{\text{second}}$. Our task is to find the function $y = y(x)$ whose graph is shape of a cross-section of the surface of the liquid glass.

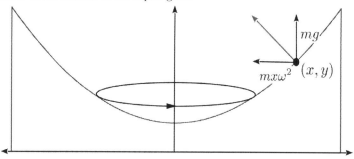

The red arrow in the diagram depicts the force keeping the point mass elevated and spinning in a circle. It will be perpendicular to the surface of the liquid, as shown. (Think about a hose with a hole in it. The water sprays out in a stream perpendicular to the hose.)

If we separate that force into its vertical and horizontal components, as shown in the diagram, the magnitude of the vertical component of the force is mg, where g is the acceleration due to gravity. This is the force needed to counter the weight of the particle. The only horizontal force is the centripetal force due to the spinning of the furnace, which is $mx\omega^2$. (We will derive this formula analytically in Chapter 5 when we have extended the scope of our differentiation rules. For now we will assume this is correct and proceed.)

Problem #135:

(a) Use the diagram above to show that the curve $y = y(x)$ must satisfy the differential equation

$$\frac{dy}{dx} = \frac{\omega^2}{g}x.$$

(**Hint:** The slope of the line tangent to the parabola at (x, y) will be $\frac{dy}{dx}$. This will be perpendicular to the force acting at that point, represented by the red arrow.)

(b) Show that $y(x)$ must be a parabola to satisfy this differential equation.

(c) Using the value $g = 9.8 \frac{\text{meters}}{\text{second}^2}$, graph the parabola from part (b). for $\omega = 1, 2, 3$. Do these graphs coincide with your intuition about what should happen as the liquid rotates faster?

In antiquity the reflective properties of all of the conic sections (parabola, ellipse and hyperbola) were worked out via very laborious geometric arguments. In Chapter 2 we saw that Roberval reestablished these properties using his more dynamic (if somewhat questionable) approach. The next two problems will reestablish the reflective property of the parabola once more using a combination of Geometry and Calculus.

Recall from Chapter 2 that any light ray parallel to the axis of a parabola will reflect to a single point (the focus of the parabola).

Problem #136:

A parabola may be defined geometrically as the set of points equidistant from a given point, the focus, and a given line, the directrix as shown below. Suppose that the point (x, y) lies on the parabola with focus $F = (0, p)$ and directrix $y = -p$ as in the diagram at the right.

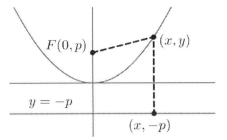

(a) Show that (x, y) must satisfy the equation: $x^2 = 4py$.

(b) In Problem #135, show that in order to spin a mirror with a focus[24] at $(0, p)$ the angular velocity must be $\omega = \sqrt{\frac{g}{2p}}$.

---

[24] Having the correct focus (and thus the correct focal length) is of paramount importance in the performance of the telescope. To give you a notion of the precision required, it took 3 months to polish the surface of one of the primary mirrors in the Large Binocular Telescope to a precision of 30 nanometers (3,000 times thinner than a human hair).

Problem #137: Parabolic Reflectivity

Consider the parabola with equation $y = \frac{x^2}{4p}$ focus $F = (0, p)$, and directrix $y = -p$ as in Problem 136.

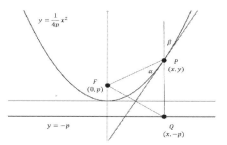

(a) Show that the tangent line (in red) is perpendicular to line segment FQ.

(b) Show that $\angle \alpha = \angle \beta$.
(**Hint:** What do you know about $\triangle FPQ$?)

Chapter 5

Calculus and Trigonometry

 See also the TRIUMPHS Primary Source Project in Appendix A.6.

Recall in Problem 135 we told you that the centripetal force was $mx\omega^2$. We didn't explain how we know, saying only that after extending the scope of our differentiation rules we would be able to show that this is the correct formula for the centripetal force. According to Newton, *Force = mass × acceleration*, so to verify the centripetal force formula the task is to show that centripetal acceleration is given by $x\omega^2$. We will finally do this in Problem #170 but first, we'll need to be able to differentiate both the sine and the cosine functions. In fact, since acceleration is the second derivative of position, we will need the second derivatives of both. Once the derivatives of the sine and cosine are known, computing the derivatives of the other four trigonometric functions is straightforward.

But before we begin we will remind you of some useful facts from Trigonometry.

5.1   A Trigonometric Interlude

Radian Measure

You are probably accustomed to measuring angles in degrees. We hope to convince you that **radian measure** actually is much more natural. It doesn't feel natural simply because it is new and unfamiliar.

Suppose two children ride on a merry-go-round through an angle θ, one child is 2 meters from the center, the other 4 is meters from the center. However we choose to measure the angle θ, it is pretty clear that the child who is 4 meters away from the center will travel farther than the child who is 2 meters away from the center, even though both of their paths have swept out the same angle, θ.

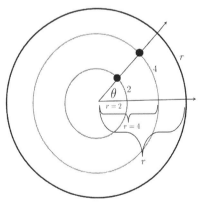

This tells us is that the distance traveled for a fixed angle along a circle will be proportional to the radius of the circle. To find the actual distance traveled is harder as the following drill shows.

Drill #138:

Now suppose[1] $\theta = 57°$. Use the sketch above to show that the first child travels slightly less than 2 meters along the red circle while the second travels slightly less than 4 meters along the blue circle.

(**Hint:** If we travel 57° around a circle, what fraction of the circumference of the circle have we traversed?)

Drill #138 was not particularly hard, but it was complicated by the use of degree measure. Radian measure removes that complication.

If on a circle with radius 2 meters, like the red circle in the figure above, we trace out a circular arc equal to the length of its radius we say that the arc-length is 2 meters. If we trace out a distance equal to the length of its radius on the blue circle then this is an arc-length of 4 meters.

But notice that the same central angle subtends both of these arcs. We defince the measure of this angle to be one **radian** because it is the angle associated with a single radius. An angle of two radians is thus the angle subtended when we measure out an arc length two times the radius of the circle.

In general we have the following result:

$$\text{arclength} = (\text{length of radius}) \times (\text{number of radians in } \theta).$$

More succinctly, if we let s represent the arclength and measure θ in radians we have

$$s = r\theta. \tag{5.1}$$

In Drill 138, if we had measured θ in radians rather than degrees, the computations for each of the arclengths would be $s = 2\theta$ (when $r = 2$) and, $s = 4\theta$ (when $r = 4$). We chose an angle of 57° because 57° is slightly less than an angle of one radian. So we know that the first child traveled slightly less than the radius, 2 meters. Similarly the second child traveled slightly less than 4 meters.

Rather than constantly translating between degrees and radians it will be simplest if you learn to think in radians directly. You should start trying to do that immediately. But breaking old habits is difficult so we need to see how to convert between them. Fortunately this is not hard.

Since the circumference of a circle is $2\pi r$, one full transit around the circle subtends an angle of 2π radians. In degrees, a full circle is 360°, so we have

$$360° = \frac{2\pi r}{r} = 2\pi \text{ radians.}$$

---

[1]Why do you suppose we chose $\theta = 57°$ rather than something more familiar like $\theta = 45°$ or $\theta = 30°$? It seems an odd choice, doesn't it?

This leads to the conversion, π radians $= 180°$ and the identities:

$$\pi/2 \text{ radians} = 180°/2 = 90°,$$
$$\pi/3 \text{ radians} = 180°/3 = 60°,$$
$$\pi/4 \text{ radians} = 180°/4 = 45°,$$
$$\pi/6 \text{ radians} = 180°/6 = 30°.$$

Thus, as we mentioned earlier, 1 radian $= (180°)/\pi \approx 57.296°$.

You may find it simpler to just remember that 2π radians is one full rotation around a circle, so π radians (a straight angle) is halfway around a circle, and a right angle is half of that, ($\pi/2$ radians). Three quarters of the way around a circle would thus be $\pi + \pi/2 = 3\pi/2$ radians, etc.

Use whatever works for you but do start thinking in radians rather than degrees as quickly as you can. It will make what's coming up easier for you.

We adopt the custom that positive angles are counterclockwise and negative angles are clockwise.

Drill #139:
For each angle, determine the number of revolutions and direction around the circle. Do not convert to degrees first.

(a) 45π radians

(b) $-\frac{7\pi}{2}$ radians

(c) $-\frac{20\pi}{3}$ radians

Drill #140:
Find the radian measure of each angle described. Do not convert to degrees first.

(a) $\frac{1}{6}$ of a circle in the positive direction.

(b) $\frac{5}{6}$ of a circle in the negative direction.

(c) Twice around the circle in the positive direction.

(d) $\frac{7}{8}$ times around the circle in the negative direction.

(e) α times around the circle where α can be any real number.

So far in this chapter we've only considered static angles. If an object is moving in a circle as in the sketch then the rate of change of the central angle is called the **angular velocity**.

Angular velocity is $\frac{d\theta}{dt}$, the rate of change of the central angle, θ with respect to time. Of course the object still has both a vertical velocity, $\frac{dy}{dt}$ and a horizontal velocity, $\frac{dx}{dt}$.

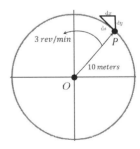

In the diagram at the right the angular velocity,

$$\frac{d\theta}{dt} = 3\frac{\text{revolutions}}{\text{minute}} \times 2\pi\frac{\text{radians}}{\text{revolution}} = 6\pi\frac{\text{radians}}{\text{minute}},$$

measures how fast our object is revolving about the point O in the positive (counterclockwise) direction. The sign of angular velocity indicates its direction: Positive means counterclockwise and negative means clockwise. The absolute value of the angular velocity, $\left|\frac{d\theta}{dt}\right|$, is the **angular speed**.

As we saw in Section 4.6 the velocity in the direction of motion is denoted, $\frac{ds}{dt}$ where the length of ds is the (infinitesimal) hypotenuse of the differential triangle in our diagram. Thus $\frac{ds}{dt}$ denotes the **linear velocity** of the object. Because ds is tangent to the path of the object, $\frac{ds}{dt}$ is also called the **tangential velocity**.

The direction of the linear velocity is the direction the object is moving as it passes through the point P, but notice that the direction cannot be specified with a plus or a minus because the object can travel in more than two directions. During a single circumnavigation the object is traveling in a different direction at every point in its path.

We will continue to use the symbol $\frac{ds}{dt}$ to denote the tangential velocity. But be aware that this a rather clumsy notation because it doesn't provide a simple way to indicate the direction of travel. This deficiency in our notation will eventually need to be addressed. For now we will be primarily be interested in the **linear (tangential) speed**: $\left|\frac{ds}{dt}\right|$.

The tangential speed tells us how fast the object would move in a straight line if the force holding it in a circular path were suddenly released – think of an object swinging on a string if the string breaks.

Conversion from angular velocity to linear speed is essentially a change of units, but we need to remember that velocity has direction and speed does not. So we must first convert angular velocity to angular speed by taking its absolute value. In our diagram above the angular velocity of the point P about the point O is 3 revolutions/minute. We compute the linear speed of P as follows:

$$\left|\frac{3 \text{ revolutions}}{1 \text{ minute}}\right| \cdot \left(\frac{2\pi \text{ radians}}{1 \text{ revolution}}\right) \cdot \left(\frac{10 \text{ meters}}{1 \text{ radians}}\right) \cdot \left(\frac{1 \text{ minute}}{60 \text{ second}}\right) = \frac{\pi \text{ meters}}{1 \text{ second}} \approx 3.14\frac{\text{meters}}{\text{second}}.$$

In the computation above the absolute value was superfluous since the angular velocity was positive. However if the object were traveling clockwise it would have been essential to take the absolute value first because a negative speed is meaningless[2].

Drill #141:

Suppose a point P is revolving in a circle with angular velocity $\frac{d\theta}{dt}$. For each situation find the linear speed of the point in the units indicated.

(a) Find the linear speed of P in meters/second if $r = 5$ meters and $\frac{d\theta}{dt} = 2$ radians/second.

(b) Find the linear speed of P in centimeters/second if $r = 3$ centimeters and $\frac{d\theta}{dt} = 720$ degrees/minute.

(c) Find the linear speed of P in centimeters/second if $r = 7$ feet and $\frac{d\theta}{dt} = 720$ degrees/hour. (**Hint:** The units are mixed in this problem.)

---

[2]In ordinary speech the words speed and velocity are often used interchangeably, which can make the distinction we are stressing here difficult to absorb. The distinction is this: Velocity has a magnitude and a direction. The magnitude of velocity is speed.

(d) Find the linear speed of P in mph (miles per hour) if $r = 4000$ miles and $\frac{d\theta}{dt} = 1\,\frac{\text{revolution}}{\text{day}}$.
   (**Comment:** This problem describes a physical phenomenon you see every day. Can you identify it?)

(e) Find the linear speed of P in mph if $r = 238,900$ miles and $\frac{d\theta}{dt} = \frac{1}{28}\,\frac{\text{revolution}}{\text{day}}$.
   (**Comment:** This problem describes a physical phenomenon you see every month. Can you identify it?)

(f) Find the linear speed of P in mph if $r = 93,496,000$ miles and one revolution is completed every 365 days, 5 hours, 59 minutes, and 16 seconds.
   (**Comment:** Can you identify the physical phenomenon this problem represents?)

(g) Our sun appears to revolve around the earth once per day. If that were actually happening, what would the sun's linear speed need to be in miles per second? Assume that the distance from the sun to the earth is 93 million miles.

The Trigonometric Functions

You are probably most familiar with right triangle Trigonometry, where the functions are defined in terms of the sides of a triangle. This is the simplest way to introduce these functions but historically Trigonometry emerged from the geometry of a circle. Ancient astronomers found it useful to have a **Table of Chords** to refer to. A chord is the line segment that cuts off part of a circle.

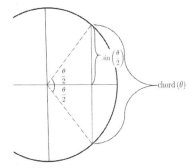

The Sine Function

The name of the sine function has a colorful history. In *The Words of Mathematics*, Steven Schwartzman explains:

"In dealing with spherical trigonometry used to study astronomy, Hindu mathematicians determined that it was often convenient to deal with half-chords. The Hindu mathematician Aryabhata ($476 - 550$ A.D.) frequently used the abbreviation *jya* for the word *jya-ardha* (half chord). This was phonetically translated into *jiba* by subsequent Arabic mathematicians. Since Arabic is written without vowels then this was written as *jb*. When Arabic works were translated into Latin, *jb* posed a problem as there is no such word as *jiba* in Arabic (recall it was translated phonetically). The closest 'real' Arabic word is *jaib* which means 'cove' or 'bay.' The Latin word for this is *sinus* which becomes our modern sine."

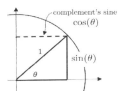

In the above picture we see that $\sin\left(\frac{\theta}{2}\right)$ is the length of the half chord.

In the unit circle in the figure at the left, because the two acute angles in a right triangle are **complementary** (they add up to $\pi/2$ radians or $90°$) we see that the term **cosine** actually makes sense as it is an abbreviation for complement's sine.

Etymology also helps to explain where the names of the other trigonometric functions came from. When $0 \leq \theta \leq \frac{\pi}{2}$ the sine, tangent, and secant functions can be represented as the length of a particular line segment and their names are descriptive of these segments. Let $0 \leq \theta \leq \frac{\pi}{2}$ be an angle in standard position (with its vertex at the origin and its initial side along the x-axis). On the positive x-axis mark off the line segment OA that is 1 unit long. On the terminal side of the angle, mark off the line segment OB so that the line segment AB is tangent to the unit circle. Then the length of the tangent line segment $\overline{AB}$ is $\tan(\theta)$, while the length of the other line segment $\overline{OB}$ is $\sec(\theta)$. As we've already seen the word "tangent" comes from the Latin *tangere*

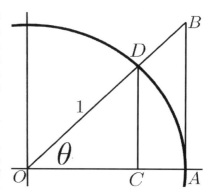

meaning "to touch." Similarly the word "secant" comes from the Latin *secare* meaning "to cut."

The "co" prefix in front of the other trig functions is an abbreviation of the the word "complement". The six **trigonometric functions** are thus the sine (sin), cosine (cos), tangent (tan), cotangent (cot), secant (sec), and cosecant (csc).

Drill #142:

In the diagram at the right arc ADF is the unit quarter-circle in the first quadrant.

(a) For the angle θ on the diagram above match the trigonometric function value with the appropriate line segment.

    (i) $\sin(\theta)$ **(iv)** $\cot(\theta)$

    (ii) $\cos(\theta)$ **(v)** $\sec(\theta)$

    (iii) $\tan(\theta)$ **(vi)** $\csc(\theta)$

(b) You may have wondered why secant is the reciprocal of cosine and not sine. Use the diagram, similar triangles, and the observation that $\overline{OD} = \overline{OA} = 1$ to show that

    (i) $\tan(\theta) = \frac{\sin(\theta)}{\cos(\theta)}$ **(ii)** $\sec(\theta) = \frac{1}{\cos(\theta)}$

Since the cotangent and cosecant literally mean "complement's tangent" and "complement's secant" we also have $\cot(\theta) = \frac{\cos(\theta)}{\sin(\theta)}$ and $\csc(\theta) = \frac{1}{\sin(\theta)}$.

Drill #143:
Use a unit circle to illustrate and explain the following identities:

(a) $\sin^2(\theta) + \cos^2(\theta) = 1$ **(c)** $\sin(-\theta) = -\sin(\theta)$ **(e)** $\sin(\theta + \pi) = -\sin(\theta)$

(b) $\tan^2(\theta) + 1 = \sec^2(\theta)$ **(d)** $\cos(-\theta) = \cos(\theta)$ **(f)** $\cos(\theta + \pi) = -\cos(\theta)$

When we graph the points $(\theta, \sin(\theta))$ we get the "sine wave." This follows from the fact that on a unit circle the radian measure of a central angle, θ, is equal to the length of the arc it cuts. So we get the "sine wave" when we roll the arc length out as a straight line on the x-axis.

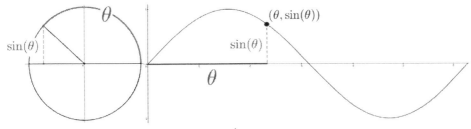

Notice that as the angle (arc) sweeps around the unit circle from 0 to 2π, the graph of $\sin(\theta)$ cycles from 0 (at $\theta = 0$), to 1 (at $\theta = \pi/2$), to 0 (at $\theta = \pi$), to -1 (at $\theta = 3\pi/2$), and back to 0 (at $\theta = 2\pi$).

Drill #144:
A similar development gives us the graph of $y = \cos(\theta)$.

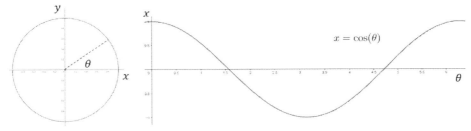

Use the diagram above to explain why the cosine cycles from 1, to 0, to -1, to 0 to 1. for $0 \le \theta \le 2\pi$. What are the precise values of θ where the cosine takes on those values?

Modeling with Trigonometric Functions

The sine and cosine functions are **periodic** functions. As such they are useful for modeling phenomena which are cyclical in nature; that is, phenomena which repeat the same pattern periodically. This periodicity is reflected in the formulas:

$$\cdots = \sin(\theta - 2\pi) = \sin(\theta) = \sin(\theta + 2\pi) = \sin(\theta + 4\pi) = \cdots$$
$$\cdots = \cos(\theta - 2\pi) = \cos(\theta) = \cos(\theta + 2\pi) = \cos(\theta + 4\pi) = \cdots$$

The rationale for the term **periodic** is very evident when we graph $\sin(\theta)$ on a set of (θ, y) axes.

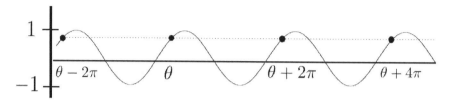

As you can see a full cycle is completed over every interval of length 2π. Thus the sine and cosine functions are said to be 2π-periodic. We can start our cycle for any value of θ, but you are probably accustomed to graphing one complete cycle over the interval $[0, 2\pi]$ as in the graphs below.

Drill #145:
Because $\sin(t)$ and $\cos(t)$ complete one cycle on an interval of 2π they are called 2π-**periodic** functions. Suppose that A, B, and C are constants. Choose several non-zero values for A, B, and C (at least three of each) and graph the function

$$z(t) = A\sin(t) + B\cos(t) + C$$

to show graphically that $z(t)$ is also a 2π-periodic function.

Notice that on any interval of length 2π the function $y = \sin(\theta)$ takes on every possible value between -1 and 1, so the **amplitude** of this sine wave is 1. Changing the amplitude of a periodic function is easy. If we want an amplitude of 5 then we just multiply by 5: $y = 5\sin(\theta)$. This new function will oscillate between -5 and 5.

If we are modeling some real-world phenomenon then the amplitude will correspond to some physical attribute of the phenomenon. For example increasing the amplitude of a sound wave will increase the volume of the sound.

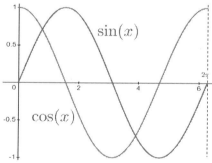

The sinusoidal axis is the horizontal line in the center of the range. So, for $y = \sin(\theta)$ the sinusoidal axis is horizontal axis ($y = 0$) because the graph of $y = 0$ is at the center of the range $-1 \leq y \leq 1$. Likewise the horizontal axis is the sinusoidal axis for $y = 5\sin(\theta)$. But if we have $y = 3 + 5\sin(\theta)$, this would shift the sinusoidal axis to the line $y = 3$, because this line would be at the center of the range and the wave would oscillate between $3 - 5 = 2$ and $3 + 5 = 8$.

Drill #146:

Suppose we had a sinusoidal wave oscillating between -4 and 12. What would be the amplitude and what would be the sinusoidal axis of this wave?

Example #29:

The pitch of a sound wave is regulated by how fast the wave is oscillating. Faster oscillations mean higher pitches. Suppose we want a wave that oscillates once per second. Our base function, $y = \sin(\theta)$, oscillates once over the interval $0 \le \theta \le 2\pi$. Divide θ by 2π, so that we have one oscillation occurring when $0 \le \frac{\theta}{2\pi} \le 1$. If we let $t = \frac{\theta}{2\pi}$ so that $\theta = 2\pi t$ then $y = \sin(2\pi t)$ oscillates at a rate of one cycle per second as in the following graph.

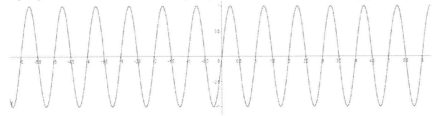

Now suppose we want to double the frequency to 2 oscillations per second. Again our base function $y = \sin(\theta)$ oscillates once for $0 \le \theta \le 2\pi$. We want two oscillations per second or one oscillation per half second. So, we want $0 \le \frac{\theta}{4\pi} \le \frac{1}{2}$. Letting $t = \frac{\theta}{4\pi}$ we see that $y = \sin(4\pi t)$ oscillates once every half second (or twice every second) as in the following graph.

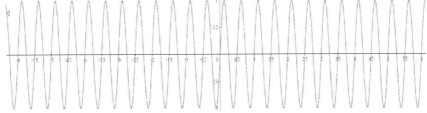

The number of cycles per second is referred to as the number of **Hertz**[3] (Hz). So $y = \sin(2\pi t)$ oscillates at 1 Hz and $y = \sin(4\pi t)$ oscillates at 2 Hz.

End Of Example #29

Problem #147:

(a) Mimic the derivation above to determine ω so that $y = \sin(\omega t)$ oscillates at h Hz.

(b) The standard musical pitch is the $A440$ or A_4, the musical note A above middle C. A_4 has a frequency of 440 Hz. Determine ω so that an A_4 note can be modeled by $y = \sin(\omega t)$. Do the same with each of the following notes.

---

[3] Named for Heinrich Rudolf Hertz, (1857 - 1894).

(i) C_4, (261.63 Hz)   **(iii)** E_4, (329.63 Hz)   **(v)** G_4, (392 Hz)

(ii) D_4, (293.66 Hz)   **(iv)** F_4, (349.23 Hz)   **(vi)** B_4, (493.88 Hz)

(c) Musical notes an octave higher have frequencies that are doubled. So, A_5 (one octave higher than A_4) has a frequency of 880 Hz. Repeat part (b) for A_5, C_5, D_5, E_5, F_4, G_5, and B_5, each one octave higher than the corresponding note in part (b).

Phase Shifts

There is one more aspect of periodic functions we need to address before we put all of this together, and that is the **phase shift**. To illustrate phase shift, consider the graph at the right. We last saw this graph when we introduced Fermat's Method of Adequality in Section 2.4. It represents the number of hours of daylight in Santa Barbara, CA over a given year. The graph of $y(t)$ represents a full cycle (one year) but it is not quite the graph of $y(t) = 12 + 2.26 \sin\left(\frac{2\pi t}{365}\right)$ as we would expect from our discussion

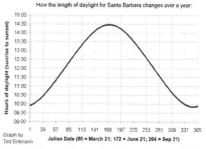

of period and amplitude. The graph of $y(t)$ gives the correct sinusoidal axis of $y = 12$, and the correct maximum ($12 + 2.26 = 14.26$) and minimum ($12 - 2.26 = 9.74$) but it does not quite match the blue graph.

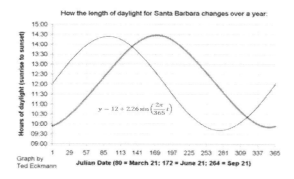

We can easily see the problem if we compare our original graph (above) to the graph of $y(t)$ as seen in the figure at the left. The two graphs clearly have the same shape but our guess has been shifted to the left by about 80 days. Since the red graph represents the typical graph of a single cycle for a sine curve, we say that the blue graph has undergone a **phase shift** of 80 days. Let's make this a bit more precise.

The red sine wave $y(t) = 12 + 2.6 \sin\left(\frac{2\pi t}{365}\right)$, shows that at day 1 (January 1) we have 12 hours of daylight, and immediately thereafter the number of hours of daylight increases. But we know that this actually happens at the spring equinox, March 21 or day 80. For the red graph to coincide with the blue graph we need for it to shift to the right so that it shows 12 hours of daylight on day 80 and completes one cycle in the interval $[80, 445]$.

To obtain the proper equation, we go back to basics. Our basic sine wave $y = \sin(\theta)$ oscillates once for $0 \leq \theta \leq 2\pi$. To get the proper period, we have

$$0 \leq \frac{365\theta}{2\pi} \leq 365.$$

To get our phase shift, we add 80 to each term to obtain

$$80 \leq \frac{365\theta}{2\pi} + 80 \leq 445.$$

Problem #148:

Let $t = \frac{365\theta}{2\pi} + 80$. Solve this for θ and use this to find a formula for the number of hours of daylight per day in Santa Barbara, CA on any given day with $t = 0$ representing January 1. Graph this and compare your graph with the original graph.

Problem #149:

Suppose we have a sine wave whose amplitude is given by a, period is given by p, sinusoidal axis is given by $y = b$, and whose phase shift is given by s. Show that the equation of this wave is

$$y = b + a \sin\left(\frac{2\pi}{p}(t - s)\right).$$

Drill #150:

For each of the following waves find the amplitude, period, sinusoidal axis, and phase shift.

(a) $y = -1 + 3\sin(\pi(t + 2))$

(b) $y = 12 + 2\sin(t - \pi)$

(c) $y = \frac{\sin(3t-1)}{2}$

(d) $y = \frac{\sin(3(t-1))}{2}$

(e) $y = \frac{\sin(3t-1)}{2} - 1$

(f) $y = \frac{\sin(3\pi t-1)}{2} - \frac{\pi}{3}$

Drill #151:

Do you see that the cosine curve is basically the sine curve with a phase shift? What is the value of the phase shift?

We usually restrict the phase shift to values between 0 and 2π. Explain why this restriction is useful.

5.2 Polar Coordinates

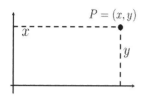

When we say that the coordinates of point P in the plane are (x, y). These coordinates are called **Cartesian (or rectangular) coordinates** in honor of René Descartes who, as we mentioned in Section 2.6, was one of the pioneers in applying algebra to geometry. The geometric picture that goes with this is shown at the right.

Using rectangular coordinates is one way to to translate geometry problems into algebra problems and *vice versa*. This simple idea changed forever how mathematics is done. Really.

But Cartesian coordinates are not the only way we can locate points in the plane. If we superimpose a right triangle on the diagram above, as shown at the left, we can find another way to locate P. Since P is the endpoint of the ray starting at the origin and ending at P the ordered pair of numbers (r, θ) works just as well as the ordered pair (x, y). The numbers r and θ are called the **polar coordinates** of P.

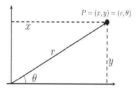

There are advantages and disadvantages to either coordinate system. For example the coordinates in the Cartesian system are unique. There is only point with rectangular coordinates, $(3, 4)$ (where $x = 3$ and $y = 4$). This is not true of polar coordinates. The point with polar coordinates $(2, \pi)$ (where $r = 2$ and $\theta = \pi$) is the same as the point with polar coordinates $(2, -\pi)$ (where $r = 2$ and $\theta = -\pi$). It is also the same as the point with polar coordinates $(-2, \pi)$, where $r = -2$ (gasp!). The idea of a negative value for r is a little jarring because we usually think of the negative sign as denoting negative numbers. Instead, think of it as meaning "go the opposite direction[4]."

Drill #152:

Explain why the polar coordinates (r, θ), $(r, \theta + 2\pi)$, $(-r, \theta + \pi)$ all locate the same point in the plane. Find at least three other sets of polar coordinates that identify the same point. How many are there?

Drill #153:

The following pairs of points are given in polar coordinates. Plot them all on the same set of axes and then check your answers using your favorite graphing software.

(a) $(r, \theta) = (1, 0)$ and $(1, \pi)$

(b) $(r, \theta) = (2, \pi/4)$ and $(2, -\pi/4)$

(c) $(r, \theta) = (1, \pi/2)$ and $(1, 5\pi/2)$

(d) $(r, \theta) = (2, 7\pi/4)$ and $(2, -5\pi/4)$

(e) $(r, \theta) = (0, -\pi/2)$ and $(0, \pi/2)$

(f) $(r, \theta) = (1, \pi/3)$ and $(-1, \pi/3)$

---

[4]Thinking this way also explains why the negative of a negative must be positive. The number 2 is at the endpoint of a ray pointing to the right along the x-axis. If we put a negative sign in front we "go the opposite direction" to -2. Another negative will reverse the direction again.

Drill #154:

Of course, we'll need to be able to translate from one coordinate system to the other.

(a) Use the diagram above to show that if $P = (r, \theta)$ in polar coordinates, and $P = (x, y)$ in rectangular coordinates then,

    (i) $x = r\cos(\theta)$,   **(ii)** $y = r\sin(\theta)$,   **(iii)** $\tan(\theta) = \frac{y}{x}$.

(b) In Cartesian coordinates the equation of a circle centered at the origin with radius $a > 0$ is $x^2 + y^2 = a^2$. What is the equation of the same circle in polar coordinates? (**Hint:** Use the result from part (a).)

    Just like the Cartesian coordinates the order of polar coordinates matters. The radius r comes first, and the angle θ comes second. Notice that there is nothing in the ordered pair notation that tells you which system is in play. This will usually be clear from the context but if you are ever unsure whether the ordered pair (a, b) represents Cartesian or polar coordinates ask your instructor.

Drill #155:

Plot the points $(1, \pi/4)$ and $(2, 3)$ twice. First assume that they are polar coordinates and then assume that they Cartesian coordinates.

Drill #156:

The graph of an equation given in polar coordinates is quite different from one given in Cartesian coordinates. To get a sense of this sketch the graph of each of the following functions in polar coordinates.

(**Comment:** Most graphing software has a built-in polar mode which will do this for you. This can be helpful once you are thoroughly familiar with the polar coordinate system but in the beginning you should do the graphing without the use of graphing software. Use technology to verify your graph after you've drawn it by hand.)

(a) $r = \sin(\theta)$ **(e)** $r = 1 + \cos(\theta)$ **(i)** $r = \sin(\theta) + \cos(\theta)$

(b) $r = \cos(\theta)$ **(f)** $r = 1$ **(j)** $r = \sin(\theta) - \cos(\theta)$

(c) $r = \sin(2\theta)$ **(g)** $\theta = \pi/4$ **(k)** $r = \tan(\theta)$

(d) $r = \sin(3\theta)$ **(h)** $r = \sin(\theta)\cos(\theta)$ **(l)** $r = \sec(\theta)$

    An advantage of using polar coordinates is that the formula that describes a curve can be extraordinarily complicated if we give y as a function of x but extraordinarily simple if we give

r as a function of θ. For example, consider the following Spiral of Archimedes:

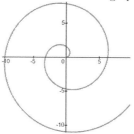

Drill #157:

In polar coordinates the Spiral of Archimedes is the graph of the equation $r = \theta, \theta \geq 0$. Convert this to an equation in Cartesian coordinates.
(**Hint:** Use the results of Drill#154.)

5.3   The Differentials of the Sine and Cosine Functions

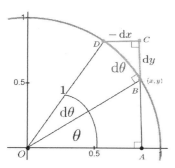

Recall that when a central angle θ, of a unit circle is measured in radians then the arclength subtended by that angle will also be θ as seen in the sketch at the left. Similarly, when we increase the angle θ by $d\theta$ the blue arc is also of length $d\theta$. Moreover, by the Principle of Local Linearity the blue arc length can be thought of as an infinitely small straight line. Thus it is the hypotenuse of the blue triangle.

Notice that when θ is increased by $d\theta$, y is increased by dy, but x is decreased by dx which makes dx negative. But the sides of a triangle must be positive so the label on the blue triangle is $-dx$.

Drill #158:   Show that: $AB = \sin(\theta)$, $OA = \cos(\theta)$, and that $\triangle OAB$ and $\triangle BCD$ are similar.

The relevant portion of the diagram above are the two similar triangles shown in the diagram below.

Using the two similar triangles we have

$$\frac{d(\sin(\theta))}{d\theta} = \frac{\cos(\theta)}{1}, \text{ and } -\frac{d(\cos(\theta))}{d\theta} = \frac{\sin(\theta)}{1}.$$

And so we have the following Differentiation Rules. Memorize them.

Derivative of Sine: $d(\sin(\theta)) = \cos(\theta)\,d\theta$

Derivative of Cosine: $d(\cos(\theta)) = -\sin(\theta)\,d\theta$.

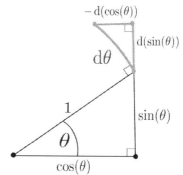

Example #30:

We can now use the new rules in conjuction with the General Differentiation Rules from Chapter 3

(a) Suppose $y = 3\theta + 2\sin(\theta)$. Then $dy = d(3\theta + 2\sin(\theta)) = (3 + 2\cos(\theta))\,d\theta$.

(b) Suppose $y = (t^3 - 2t^2)\cos(t^2 - t)$. Letting $\theta = t^2 - t$ we have

$$dy = (t^3 - 2t^2)\,d(\cos(\theta)) + \cos(\theta)\,d(t^3 - 2t^2)$$
$$= (t^3 - 2t^2)(-\sin(\theta))\,d\theta + \cos(\theta)\,d(t^3 - 2t^2)$$
$$= (t^3 - 2t^2)(-\sin(t^2 - t))(2t - 1)\,dt + \cos(t^2 - t)(3t^2 - 4t)\,dt$$
$$= -\left[(t^3 - 2t^2)(2t - 1)\sin(t^2 - t) + (3t^2 - 4t)\cos(t^2 - t)\right]\,dt.$$

(c) Suppose $y = \sin(2\theta)$. Then $dy = \cos(2\theta)\,d(2\theta) = 2\cos(2\theta)\,d\theta$.

(d) Suppose $y = \sin(\theta^2)$. Then $dy = \cos(\theta^2)\,d(\theta^2) = 2\theta\sin(\theta^2)\,d\theta$.

(e) Suppose $y = \sin(k - \theta)$, where k is constant. Then

$$dy = d(\sin(k - \theta)) = \cos(k - \theta)\,d(k - \theta) = -\cos(k - \theta)\,d\theta$$

End Of Example #30

Problem #159:

Part (e) of Example #30 is more useful than is immediately apparent because the complementary angle identities: $\cos(\theta) = \sin(\pi/2 - \theta)$ and $\sin(\theta) = \cos(\pi/2 - \theta)$ allow us to obtain the differential of either $\sin(\theta)$ or $\cos(\theta)$ provided only that we have the differential of the other.

Use these identities to show the following:

(a) If $d(\sin(\theta)) = \cos(\theta)\,d\theta$, then $d(\cos(\theta)) = -\sin(\theta)\,d\theta$.

(b) If $d(\cos(\theta)) = -\sin(\theta)\,d\theta$, then $d(\sin(\theta) = \cos(\theta)\,d\theta$.

Drill #160:

Compute the differential, dy, for each of the following functions:

(a) $y = \cos(-3\theta)$

(b) $y = \sin(\theta)\cos(\theta)$

(c) $y = \cos^2(\theta)$

(d) $y = \cos(\theta^2)$

(e) $y = \cos^2(\theta) + \sin^2(\theta)$

(f) $y = \cos^2(\theta) - \sin^2(\theta)$

(g) $y = \cos^4(\theta) - \sin^4(\theta)$

(h) $y = \cos(5\theta^3 - 2\theta^2 - 3\theta + 12)$

(i) $y = \sin^2(7\pi\theta) + \cos^2(7\pi\theta)$

Drill #161:

Assume that $x = x(t)$ and $y = y(t)$. Find an equation relating dx and dy. Use this to compute $\frac{dy}{dx}$, $\frac{dy}{dt}$, $\frac{dx}{dy}$, and $\frac{dx}{dt}$

(a) $\sin(xy) = \cos^2(x+y)$

(b) $\sin(y) = x$

(c) $y^2\sqrt{1+\sin^2(x)} = \cos(y)$

(d) $\sin(2y) = \sin^2(xy^2)$

(e) $\sin(x^2+y) = y\cos(x)$

(f) $y^2\sqrt{1+\cos^2(x)} = y^2 + x$

Problem #162:

(a) For a fixed value of k, what are the largest and smallest possible values for the slope of the tangent line to the curve $y = kx + \sin(x)$?

(b) For which values of k will the graph of $y = kx + \sin(x)$ have horizontal tangent lines?

(c) For which values of k will the graph of $y = kx + \sin(x)$ not have horizontal tangent lines?

(d) Find the values of x where the lines tangent to $y = \frac{x}{2} + \sin(x)$ are horizontal. Graph the function to verify your answers.

Problem #163:

(a) Show that for $0 \leq x \leq 2\pi$, the x coordinates of the points where the tangent line of $y = \sin(x) + \cos(x)$ is horizontal are $\frac{\pi}{4}, \frac{3\pi}{4}, \frac{5\pi}{4}$ and $\frac{7\pi}{4}$.

(b) What are the corresponding y coordinates?

Problem #164:

(a) Show that, if a is constant then $y(\theta) = a\sin(\theta)$ satisfies the equation

$$\frac{d^2y}{d\theta^2} = -y. \tag{5.2}$$

(b) Show that, if b is constant then $y(\theta) = b\cos(\theta)$ also satisfies Equation 5.2

Problem #165:

One of the authors once heard a television weatherperson remark that, "We gain and lose daylight faster at the equinoxes than at the solstices." Recall that in Problem #148 you were asked to find a formula for the number of hours of daylight in Santa Barbara, CA. You should have obtained the solution

$$y = 12 + 2.26 \sin\left(\frac{2\pi(t-80)}{365}\right).$$

Use this to explain why the weatherperson's claim does, or does not, make sense.

Problem #166:

The following sketch represents a Ferris wheel rotating counterclockwise at a rate of one revolution every two minutes.

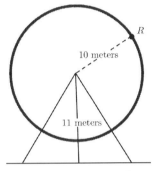

How fast is a rider R rising when his seat is 16 meters above the ground? What is the height of the rider when he is rising the fastest?

Polar Coordinates and Calculus

In Section 5.2 we introduced the polar coordinates and the equations

$$x = r\cos(\theta), \tag{5.3}$$
$$y = r\sin(\theta) \tag{5.4}$$

which allow us to convert from polar to rectangular coordinates.

Given a functional relation between r and θ like those we saw in Drill #156 it should be clear that the differential ratio $\frac{dr}{d\theta}$ is not the slope of the tangent line. However it is still the rate of change of r with respect to θ.

Regardless of which coordinate system we use, the slope of the line tangent to a curve is still given by $\frac{dy}{dx}$ for the same reason that $\frac{\Delta y}{\Delta x}$ gives the slope of the line: Both $\frac{dy}{dx}$ and $\frac{\Delta y}{\Delta x}$ represent a displacement in the vertical direction divided by a displacement in the horizontal direction. But $\frac{dr}{d\theta}$ is the rate of change of distance from the origin, r, with respect to a change of the angle, θ.

Problem #167:

(a) Use equations (5.3) and (5.4) to find dx and dy in terms of dr and $d\theta$.

(b) Show that the slope of the line tangent to the graph of $r = r(\theta)$ (in polar coordinates) is given by

$$\frac{dy}{dx} = \frac{r\cos(\theta) + \sin(\theta)\frac{dr}{d\theta}}{-r\sin(\theta) + \cos(\theta)\frac{dr}{d\theta}}.$$

(c) Find an equation of the line tangent to the Spiral of Archimedes, $r = \theta$, $\theta \geq 0$, at $\theta = \frac{\pi}{6}$, $\theta = \frac{\pi}{4}$, $\theta = \frac{\pi}{3}$, $\theta = \frac{\pi}{2}$, and $\theta = \pi$. Graph the Spiral and your tangent lines together to confirm your computations.

(d) Show that the line tangent to the Spiral of Archimedes is horizontal when $\tan(\theta) = -\theta$. Explain why this will only ever happen when the terminal side of the angle θ is in the second or fourth quadrants.

(e) Show that the line tangent to the Spiral of Archimedes is vertical when $\tan(\theta) = \frac{1}{\theta}$. Explain why this will only ever happen when the terminal side of the angle θ is in the first or third quadrants.

Drill #168:

Find the equation of the line tangent to the following curves at the given value of θ.

(a) $r = \theta^2, \theta \geq 0$

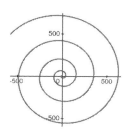

(i) $\theta = 0$ (iii) $\theta = \frac{\pi}{4}$ (v) $\theta = \frac{\pi}{2}$

(ii) $\theta = \frac{\pi}{6}$ (iv) $\theta = \frac{\pi}{3}$ (vi) $\theta = \frac{37\pi}{6}$

(b) $r = 2 + \sin(3\theta)$.

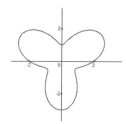

(**i**) $\theta = 0$ (**iii**) $\theta = -\frac{\pi}{4}$ (**v**) $\theta = -\frac{\pi}{2}$

(**ii**) $\theta = \frac{\pi}{6}$ (**iv**) $\theta = \frac{\pi}{3}$ (**vi**) $\theta = \frac{37\pi}{6}$

(**c**) $r = \cos\left(\frac{\theta}{2}\right)$.

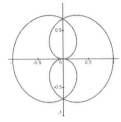

(**i**) $\theta = \frac{\pi}{6}$ (**iii**) $\theta = \frac{\pi}{4}$ (**v**) $\theta = \frac{\pi}{3}$

(**ii**) $\theta = -\frac{\pi}{6}$ (**iv**) $\theta = -\frac{\pi}{4}$ (**vi**) $\theta = -\frac{\pi}{3}$

The Brachistochrone Problem

Suppose a bead is sliding down a frictionless wire from point A to point B as seen at the left. Assuming that the bead starts at rest and slides down the wire under only the influence of gravity, what shape do you think the wire must have if the bead descends from A to B in the least possible time. Galileo thought the path of least time had to be a circular arc as we've drawn it here, but he could not prove it. Think about this for a moment before reading on. What does your intuition tell you the solution must be?

This question is known as the Brachistochrone Problem[5]. In 1696 the Swiss mathematician Johann Bernoulli published the statement of the Brachistochrone Problem along with the following challenge:

> *I, Johann Bernoulli, address the most brilliant mathematicians in the world. Nothing is more attractive to intelligent people than an honest, challenging problem, whose possible solution will bestow fame and remain as a lasting monument. Following the example set by Pascal, Fermat, etc., I hope to gain the gratitude of the whole scientific community by placing before the finest mathematicians of our time a problem which will test their methods and the strength of their intellect. If someone communicates to me the solution of the proposed problem, I shall publicly declare him worthy of praise.*

At the time an acrimonious rivalry existed between Continental and British mathematicians concerning whether Newton's *Method of Fluxions* or Leibniz' *Calculus Differentialis* was the better approach to Calculus. Bernoulli didn't believe Newton would be able to solve the

---

[5]From two Greek words meaning "least time."

Brachistochrone Problem so the challenge was intended in part to show that Leibniz' approach was better.

At that point in his life Newton had stopped doing science. He had been appointed England's Warden of the Mint and was given the Herculean task of recalling and replacing all of the country's coinage. He had nothing to gain by attempting the problem but the challenge probably irritated him because he later complained,

> *I do not love . . . to be . . . teezed by forreigners about Mathematical things.*

According to his niece, Catherine Conduitt,

> *When the problem in 1696 was sent by Bernoulli Sir I. N. was in the midst of the great recoinage and did not come home till four from the Tower very much tired, but did not sleep till he had solved it, which was by four in the morning.*

Newton submitted his solution anonymously but the presentation was so uniquely in his style of written mathematics that when he received it Bernoulli immediately recognized that the solution had come from Newton because, as he put it,

> *I know the lion by his claw.*

Johann Bernoulli also received solutions from his student, the Marquis de L'Hôpital (whom we will meet again in Chapter 11), his older brother Jacob Bernoulli, and Leibniz. Of course Johann had a solution of his own as well.

It turned out that the path of least time is an inverted **cycloid**. A cycloid is the curve generated by tracing the path of a point on the edge of a wheel as it rolls in a straight line without slipping, like the bicycle wheel at the right.

We will not be solving the Brachistochrone Problem ourselves because it is a bit beyond the scope of this course. But the solution, the cycloid curve had been studied long before the invention of Calculus. Naturally, the invention of Calculus gave us a new window on the properties of cycloids.

For example, if you make a bowl whose cross section is an inverted cycloid then objects sliding to the center (again, we ignore friction) will take the same length of time to reach the bottom regardless of their starting position. This is known as the Tautochrone Problem. Christiaan Huygens used this fact to design a better pendulum clock than had previously existed. This is explored in more depth in Appendix A.5.

It would be difficult to express the cycloid as the graph of some curve: $y = y(x)$. But it is fairly simple to parameterize it, as we will see in Problem #169. In our parameterization θ will still represent an angle but this time the vertex of the angle is at the center of the wheel, which is in motion. This makes the parameterization a little more interesting[6]. The placement of θ is shown schematically in the next problem.

---

[6]Often, "interesting" also means "more challenging."

Problem #169:

Let ρ be a point on a circle of radius a that is rolling on the x-axis and let $P(\theta) = \begin{Bmatrix} x(\theta) \\ y(\theta) \end{Bmatrix}$ be the position of ρ when the ball has rolled through an angle of θ.

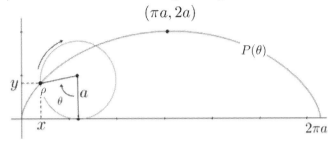

$(\pi a, 2a)$

$P(\theta)$

$2\pi a$

(a) (i) Use the diagram above to show that the parameterization of $P(\theta)$ is given by

$$P(\theta) = \begin{Bmatrix} x(\theta) \\ y(\theta) \\ -\infty < \theta < \infty \end{Bmatrix} = \begin{Bmatrix} a\theta - a\sin(\theta) \\ a - a\cos(\theta) \\ -\infty < \theta < \infty \end{Bmatrix}. \tag{5.5}$$

(ii) Compute dx and dy in terms of $d\theta$.

(iii) Find the slope of the tangent line to the cycloid at an arbitrary point P in terms of θ and use this to confirm that the tangent line is horizontal at the apex of the cycloid, point P in our diagram.

(iv) Show that

$$\frac{dy}{dx} = \frac{1 + \cos(\theta)}{\sin(\theta)},$$

and use this to examine the slope of the cycloid near the points where it touches the x-axis.

(b) (i) Suppose the circle is rolling at an angular speed of $2\frac{\text{units}}{\text{second}}$ and compute the tangential speed,

$$\left| \frac{ds}{dt} \right| = \frac{\sqrt{(dx)^2 + (dy)^2}}{dt}$$

of P. What do you notice about the speed of P in relation to the circle's radius? Do you find this surprising?
(**Hint:** Consider using Equation 4.1.)

(ii) When is P moving the fastest and when is it moving the slowest? Does this make sense physically?

Spin Casting, Redux

In Section 4.8 we saw how Newton's fluxional approach to Calculus led us naturally to the notion of parametric equations, $P(t) = \begin{Bmatrix} x = x(t) \\ y = y(t) \\ a < t < b \end{Bmatrix}$.

Recall that in the Problem #135 we asserted, without justification, that the centripetal force holding the spinning, molten glass in its circular path is given by the formula $mr\omega^2$. We now have the tools we need to justify this claim.

If an object having mass m, is revolving in a circle of radius r meters around an axis with an angular velocity of ω radians/second, the centripetal force that keeps it moving in a circle is directed toward the center of the circle. Anything moving in a circular path is held on course by a centripetal or "center seeking" force.

Recall that force and acceleration are related by Newton's Second Law of Motion: force = mass × acceleration. Thus to show that the force is what we said it was we'll need to show that the centripetal acceleration is given by $r\omega^2$.

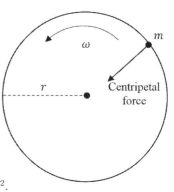

Problem #170: Centripetal Force

To compute centripetal acceleration, we will consider the point P traveling around the circle, with radius r, so that its position at time t is given by

$$P(t) = \begin{Bmatrix} x(t) \\ y(t) \end{Bmatrix} = \begin{Bmatrix} r\cos(\theta(t)) \\ r\sin(\theta(t)) \end{Bmatrix}.$$

The velocity in the direction of motion, $v = \frac{ds}{dt}$, is tangent to the circle and is composed of the velocity in the x direction $\left(\frac{dx}{dt}\right)$ and the velocity in the y direction $\left(\frac{dy}{dt}\right)$: $v = \begin{Bmatrix} \frac{dx}{dt} \\ \frac{dy}{dt} \end{Bmatrix}$ as seen below.

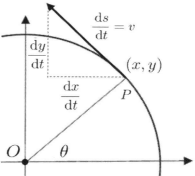

(a) The magnitude of the velocity (speed) in the direction of motion is the length of v. Show that the speed of P is given by:

$$\sqrt{\left(\frac{\mathrm{d}x}{\mathrm{d}t}\right)^2 + \left(\frac{\mathrm{d}y}{\mathrm{d}t}\right)^2} = \left| r\frac{\mathrm{d}\theta}{\mathrm{d}t} \right|.$$

(**Hint:** Use the Pythagorean Theorem.)
(**Comment:** This also follows directly from the definition of radian measure. We want you to do it this way in this problem because you will do a similar computation for acceleration in part (b) below.)

(b) Assume that the angular velocity is constant: $\frac{\mathrm{d}\theta}{\mathrm{d}t} = \omega$. Acceleration, like velocity, consists of a magnitude and a direction. In this case, the centripetal acceleration, represented by a in our diagram below, is composed of the vertical acceleration $\frac{\mathrm{d}^2 y}{\mathrm{d}t^2}$, and horizontal acceleration $\frac{\mathrm{d}^2 x}{\mathrm{d}t^2}$.

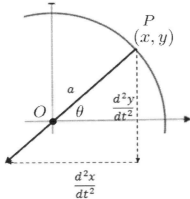

The length of the arrow, a is the magnitude of the centripetal acceleration.

Compute $\frac{\mathrm{d}^2 x}{\mathrm{d}t^2}$ and $\frac{\mathrm{d}^2 y}{\mathrm{d}t^2}$, and show that the length of the centripetal acceleration is given by

$$\sqrt{\left(\frac{\mathrm{d}^2 x}{\mathrm{d}t^2}\right)^2 + \left(\frac{\mathrm{d}^2 y}{\mathrm{d}t^2}\right)^2} = r\omega^2,$$

which is what we said it was in Problem #135.

Digression #7: The Centripetal and Tangential Forces

In Problem #170 we assumed the angular velocity, $\left(\frac{\mathrm{d}\theta}{\mathrm{d}t} = \omega\right)$ was constant, so that we could focus our attention on the centripetal force that keeps the point P moving in a circle.

In Problem #170 only the centripetal force was in play. But consider a model airplane flying at the end of a cord, as in the sketch below.

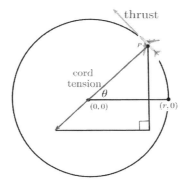

Now we have two forces to contend with. The tension in the cord (shown in red) supplies the centripetal (center seeking) force, while the force of the engine (thrust) will always be in the direction of motion, tangential to the path at P (shown in blue). Since the airplane will speed up or slow down depending on the magnitude of the thrust the airplane is no longer constrained to fly at a constant angular velocity.

Finding an expression for the centripetal and tangential acceleration is a straightforward, though somewhat daunting, exercise in differentiation.

Problem #171:

Show that if a point, $P = \begin{Bmatrix} x(t) \\ y(t) \end{Bmatrix}$, is constrained to move in a circle (so that $x = r\cos(\theta)$ and $y = r\sin(\theta)$) but that $\frac{d\theta}{dt}$ is no longer constant, then the horizontal acceleration $\left(\frac{d^2x}{dt^2}\right)$ and the vertical acceleration $\left(\frac{d^2y}{dt^2}\right)$ are given by,

$$\frac{d^2x}{dt^2} = -r\frac{d^2\theta}{dt^2}\sin(\theta) - r\left(\frac{d\theta}{dt}\right)^2\cos(\theta) \tag{5.6}$$

$$\frac{d^2y}{dt^2} = r\frac{d^2\theta}{dt^2}\cos(\theta) - r\left(\frac{d\theta}{dt}\right)^2\sin(\theta). \tag{5.7}$$

From Newton's Second Law of Motion, (force = mass × acceleration), we see that the horizontal and vertical forces acting on the airplane are $m\frac{d^2x}{dt^2}$ and $m\frac{d^2y}{dt^2}$. We'd like to resolve these into their centripetal and tangential components.

Drill #172:

Show that the red terms in equations 5.6 and 5.7 are the horizontal and vertical components of the centripetal acceleration by confirming that they are the same as the $\frac{d^2x}{dt^2}$ and $\frac{d^2x}{dt^2}$ that you computed for part (b) of Problem #170.

Drill #172 suggests that the red terms in equations 5.6 and 5.7 are the horizontal and vertical components of the centripetal acceleration. If that is true (it is) then the blue terms must represent the tangential acceleration. Thus, by Newton's Second Law, we obtain the horizontal and vertical components of the tangential force by multiplying the horizontal and vertical accelerations by m. This gives us

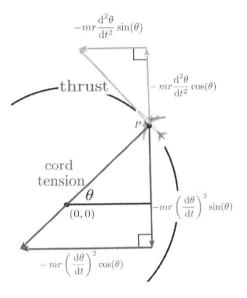

Horizontal Force: $-mr\frac{\mathrm{d}^2\theta}{\mathrm{d}t^2}\sin(\theta)$

Vertical Force: $mr\frac{\mathrm{d}^2\theta}{\mathrm{d}t^2}\cos(\theta)$

All of our results so far are depicted in the sketch at the right.

Finally, we let $s(t)$ represent the length of the circular arc traced by P at time t. Since θ is measured in radians we know that the length of a circular arc, s is $s = r\theta$. Applying the Constant Multiple Rule we see that $\mathrm{d}s = r\frac{\mathrm{d}\theta}{\mathrm{d}t}\,\mathrm{d}t$. Since $\mathrm{d}s$ represents an infinitesimal displacement tangent to the circle we see that

$$\frac{\mathrm{d}s}{\mathrm{d}t} = r\frac{\mathrm{d}\theta}{\mathrm{d}t}$$

is the tangential velocity of the airplane.

Differentiating again using the Constant Multiple Rule we see that

$$\frac{\mathrm{d}^2 s}{\mathrm{d}t^2} = \frac{\mathrm{d}^2(r\theta)}{\mathrm{d}t^2} = r\frac{\mathrm{d}^2\theta}{\mathrm{d}t^2}.$$

is the tangential acceleration.

So equations 5.6 and 5.7 can be expressed as

$$\frac{\mathrm{d}^2 x}{\mathrm{d}t^2} = -\frac{\mathrm{d}^2 s}{\mathrm{d}t^2}\sin(\theta) - r\left(\frac{\mathrm{d}\theta}{\mathrm{d}t}\right)^2\cos(\theta)$$

$$\frac{\mathrm{d}^2 y}{\mathrm{d}t^2} = \frac{\mathrm{d}^2 s}{\mathrm{d}t^2}\cos(\theta) - r\left(\frac{\mathrm{d}\theta}{\mathrm{d}t}\right)^2\sin(\theta).$$

In this form these equations express the relationship between the various accelerations in play (horizontal, vertical, centripetal, and tangential). The forces are obtained from Newton's Second Law by multiplying both sides of both equations by the mass, m. We, the authors, think of this as "uncancelling" m.

Use the diagram above to show that the magnitude of the thrust, $m \left| \frac{\mathrm{d}^2 s}{\mathrm{d}t^2} \right|$, is given by

$$\sqrt{\left(-m \frac{\mathrm{d}^2 s}{\mathrm{d}t^2} \sin(\theta) \right)^2 + \left(m \frac{\mathrm{d}^2 s}{\mathrm{d}t^2} \cos(\theta) \right)^2}.$$

End Of Digression #7

Simple Harmonic Oscillation

Much of what occurs in the real world recurs periodically. As we saw in Problem #149 the number of hours of daylight in Santa Barbara, California (and everywhere else) changes regularly over the course of a year The sun, moon, and stars rise and set regularly ever 24 hours. The compression of your heart muscle repeats periodically every few seconds. Can you think of other examples of periodic behavior in the natural world?

The usefulness of the trigonometric functions, especially the sine and cosine, comes from the fact that they are also periodic. With enough effort the sine and cosine functions can be used to model any periodic behavior, but the phrase "with enough effort" covers a lot. It is possible to model the compression of your heart using only sines and cosines, but the required theory and methods are beyond the scope of this text. We'll keep things simple.

A function $y(t)$ is said to be a **Simple Harmonic Oscillator (SHO)** if it satisfies the **second order differential equation**

$$\frac{\mathrm{d}^2 y}{\mathrm{d}t^2} = -\omega^2 y, \tag{5.8}$$

for some constant ω. Equation 5.8 is a little scary at first but it really isn't that bad. To simplify things suppose for a moment that $\omega = 1$. Then we have $\frac{\mathrm{d}^2 y}{\mathrm{d}t^2} = -y$ which says simply that $y(t)$ is a function whose second derivative is equal the negative of y itself.

Of course, you already know two such functions. Since

$$\frac{\mathrm{d}^2 (\sin(x))}{\mathrm{d}x^2} = -\sin(x) \quad \text{and} \quad \frac{\mathrm{d}^2 (\cos(x))}{\mathrm{d}x^2} = -\cos(\theta),$$

$\sin(x)$ and $\cos(x)$ are both SHOs.

Find two more SHOs.
(**Hint:** Don't overthink this. Build on the two that you already know.)

Equation 5.8 is used to model vibrations of buildings, acoustics, AC circuits, molecular, and crystal vibrations; basically anything that oscillates, but where the effects of air resistance are negligible. In Section (7.6), after we have expanded our repertoire of functions a bit, we will look at one way we can incorporate the role of air resistance into our computations so that we can extend the usefulness of our analysis.

Problem #175:

(a) Show that $y = A\sin(\omega t) + B\cos(\omega t)$ satisfies Equation (5.8). for any constants A and B.

(b) Determine the values of the constants A and B if $y(0) = -2$ and $\left.\dfrac{dy}{dt}\right|_{t=0} = 0$. plot the graph of $y(t)$ for these values of A and B.

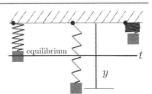

The classical physical example of a simple harmonic oscillator is an object with mass, m, hanging from one end of a spring, as shown at the right. In this sketch the horizontal axis is time so it shows the same bouncing spring at three different times. Assume that our spring is anchored in some way at the top. When the weight of the object and the restoring force of the spring balance exactly we say that they are in equilibrium as illustrated by the leftmost spring in our sketch.

Robert Hooke (1635 − 1703), who we encountered back in Section 4.9, was a leading elder scientist when Newton was young and a rising star in English science. Hooke was the first to show that the restoring force exerted by a spring (the force back toward equilibrium) is directly proportional to the length of its extension beyond equilibrium. This is known today as **Hooke's Law for Springs** (or just **Hooke's Law**) and it is true whether the spring is stretched or compressed.

If we let $y = y(t)$ denote the vertical displacement of the mass from equilibrium then Hooke's Law says that the restoring force of the spring is given by $-ky$, for some positive constant k (called the **spring constant**). For a relatively weak spring, k would have a small value. For a relatively strong spring, the value of k would be large. If we let F represent the restoring force acting on the hanging mass then we have

Robert Hooke
(1635-1703)

$$F = -ky.$$

Since the spring constant, k, is positive the negative sign in front of k is necessary. But it is easy to misinterpret this. The negative sign does not mean that the force F is always negative (upward in our diagram). In the analysis above the sign of F will be the negative (opposite) of the direction of the displacement of y. If the spring is displaced in the positive direction (stretched downward in our diagram) then the $-k$ in front guarantees that the force, F, will be negative (upward). Conversely if we displace the spring in the negative direction (compressed upward in the diagram) then the $-k$ guarantees that F is positive.

As we have seen the acceleration of an object is the second derivative of its position with respect to time, or $\dfrac{d^2 y}{dt^2}$. Thus according to Newton's Second Law, the force acting on our mass will satisfy $F = m\dfrac{d^2 y}{dt^2}$. Finally, since F represents the same force in both Hooke's Law and Newton's Second Law, we see that the vertical displacement of our mass must satisfy the equation

$$m\frac{d^2 y}{dt^2} = -ky \tag{5.9}$$

which is equivalent to Equation (5.8).

Drill #176:
Show that Equation 5.8 and equation 5.9 are equivalent as we've claimed.
(**Hint:** What is ω in Equation 5.9?)

Digression #8:

You may be wondering why we've neglected the force due to gravity (which will be the weight of the object or mg where m is it's mass and $g = 9.8\frac{\text{meters}}{\text{second}^2}$) in Equation (5.9). Actually, this was accounted for when we chose our coordinate system so that $y = 0$ at the equilibrium point. At equilibrium the upward force from the spring exactly balances the downward force of gravity (that's why it's called equilibrium) so we can proceed as if those forces are not there. This does not say that there are no other forces acting on the object, only that such forces as exist are exactly in balance; they add to zero.

If you buy this intuitive argument, then fine. If not, work through the following problem.

Problem #177:
Remember that the positive direction is downward. Assume that the weight of the object extends the spring a distance of y_0 as shown, and that y is the vertical displacement of the object from equilibrium.

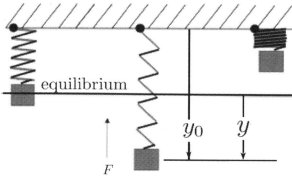

Notice that the downward force is the weight of the object and the upward force is the pull of the spring.

(**a**) Show that the vertical displacement of the object satisfies the equation

$$m\frac{\mathrm{d}^2 y}{\mathrm{d}t^2} = mg - k(y - y_0).$$

(**b**) Use the fact that when the object is at rest, $y = 0$ to conclude that $ky_0 = mg$ and use this to conclude that the spring-object system still satisfies Equation 5.9

━━━━━━━━━━ **End Of Digression #8** ━━━━━━━━━━

Problem #178:

Show that $y(t) = 2\cos\left(\sqrt{k/m} \cdot t\right)$ will satisfy Equation (5.9).

(a) Compute $y(0)$ and $\left.\dfrac{dy}{dt}\right|_{t=0}$. If we are modeling a mass-spring system, what do these values represent physically?

(b) Compare the graphs of $y(t)$ for each of the following choices of k and m.

   (i) $k = 1$, $m = 1$,

   (ii) $k = 4$, $m = 1$,

   (iii) $k = 1$, $m = 4$.

In particular, how do the values of k and m affect the frequency of the oscillation? Is this consistent with what k and m represent physically?

(c) For which values of y do the greatest and smallest velocities occur? What is the acceleration at each of these points? Is this consistent with the idea that the mass is transitioning from speeding up to slowing down and *vice versa*? Explain.

(d) For which values of y is the acceleration the largest and the smallest? Is this consistent with both Newton's Second Law and Hooke's Law? Explain.

5.4   The Differentials of the Other Trigonometric Functions

Once the differential of $\sin(x)$ is known, the differentials of the other trigonometric functions are easily computed. Since our current goal is simply to develop the tools we will need later we will not spend any more time on this than necessary.

Observe that by definition $\tan(x) = \frac{\sin(x)}{\cos(x)}$, so the Quotient Rule applies:

$$
\begin{aligned}
\mathrm{d}\left(\tan(x)\right) &= \mathrm{d}\left(\frac{\sin(x)}{\cos(x)}\right) \\[2mm]
&= \frac{\cos(x)\,\mathrm{d}(\sin(x)) - \sin(x)\,\mathrm{d}(\cos(x))}{\cos^2(x)} \\[2mm]
&= \frac{\cos^2(x)\,\mathrm{d}x + \sin^2(x)\,\mathrm{d}x}{\cos^2(x)} \\[2mm]
&= \frac{1}{\cos^2(x)}\,\mathrm{d}x
\end{aligned}
$$

and since $\sec(x) = 1/\cos(x)$ we have

$$d\left(\tan(x)\right) = \sec^2(x)\,dx.$$

Drill #179: Use the Quotient Rule to show that $d(\cot(x)) = -\csc^2(x)\,dx$.

Observe that by definition $\sec(x) = \frac{1}{\cos x} = (\cos(x))^{-1}$. Differentiating, we have

$$d(\sec(x)) = d\left(\underbrace{(\cos(x))^{-1}}_{=z}\right),$$

and making the substitution $z = \cos(x)$ as indicated we have $d(\sec(x)) = d(z^{-1})$. By the Power Rule this is

$$d(\sec(x)) = -z^{-2}\,dz = -(\cos(x))^{-2}\,d(\cos(x)) = -(\cos(x))^{-2}(-\sin(x))\,dx.$$

Simplifying gives

$$d(\sec(x)) = \frac{\sin(x)}{\cos^2(x)}\,dx = \frac{1}{\cos(x)} \cdot \frac{\sin(x)}{\cos(x)}\,dx$$

so that, finally we have

$$d(\sec(x)) = \sec(x)\tan(x)\,dx.$$

Drill #180: By similar means show that $d(\csc(x)) = -\csc(x)\cot(x)\,dx$.

Remember all of those identities you had to memorize in Trigonometry? You can reduce that memorization burden a bit by using Calculus. If two variable quantities are equal then their differentials must be equal too. So if you differentiate both sides an identity you get another identity!

Example #31:

Consider the double angle formula for the sine function: $\sin(2x) = 2\sin(x)\cos(x)$. Differentiating gives $\cos(2x)\,dx = \cos^2(x)\,dx - \sin^2(x)\,dx$ or

$$\cos(2x) = \cos^2(x) - \sin^2(x). \tag{5.10}$$

which is the double angle formula for the cosine function.

End Of Example #31

Example #32:

We know that $\sin^2(x) + \cos^2(x) = 1$ no matter what value x has, so we'd expect that differential of $\sin^2(x) + \cos^2(x)$ to be zero. Let's check.

By the Sum Rule $\mathrm{d}(\sin^2(x) + \cos^2(x)) = \mathrm{d}(\sin^2(x)) + \mathrm{d}(\cos^2(x))$ and by the Power Rule we have

$$\begin{aligned}
&= 2\sin(x)\,\mathrm{d}(\sin(x)) + 2\cos(x)\,\mathrm{d}(\cos(x)) \\
&= 2\sin(x)\cos(x)\,\mathrm{d}x + 2\cos(x)(-\sin(x))\,\mathrm{d}x \\
&= 2(\sin(x)\cos(x) - \sin(x)\cos(x))\,\mathrm{d}x \\
&= 0.
\end{aligned}$$

End Of Example #32

Drill #181:
Since the sine and cosine functions are both differentiable and $\mathrm{d}(\sin^2(x) + \cos^2(x)) = 0$ we can conclude that $\sin^2(x) + \cos^2(x)$ is (probably) equal to some constant. If we didn't already know, how could we conclude that the constant is 1?

We now know the differentials of all of the trigonometric functions. These are shown in the table below. Memorize them.

Function	Differential
$\sin(x)$	$\cos(x)\,\mathrm{d}x$
$\cos(x)$	$-\sin(x)\,\mathrm{d}x$
$\tan(x)$	$\sec^2(x)\,\mathrm{d}x$
$\cot(x)$	$-\csc^2(x)\,\mathrm{d}x$
$\sec(x)$	$\sec(x)\tan(x)\,\mathrm{d}x$
$\csc(x)$	$-\csc(x)\cot(x)\,\mathrm{d}x$

Drill #182:
Differentiate both sides of each trigonometric identity to get another identity. Verify each identity (including the one you compute) by graphing the expression on both sides of the equals sign.

(a) $\cos(2\theta) = \cos^2(\theta) - \sin^2(\theta)$

(b) $\tan(2\theta) = \frac{2\tan(\theta)}{1 - \tan^2(\theta)}$

(c) $\sec(2\theta) = \frac{1}{\cos^4(\theta) - \sin^4(\theta)}$

(d) $\cos^2\left(\frac{\theta}{2}\right) = \frac{1}{2}(1 + \cos(\theta))$

(e) $\sin^2\left(\frac{\theta}{2}\right) = \frac{1}{2}(1 - \cos(\theta))$

(f) $\tan\left(\frac{\theta}{2}\right) = \frac{\sin(\theta)}{1 + \cos(\theta)}$

Drill #183:

If possible find an equation of the line tangent to the graphs of $y = \tan(x)$ and $y = \sec(x)$ at each of the points below. If no such line exists explain why not.

(a) $x = 0$

(b) $x = \pm\frac{\pi}{6}$

(c) $x = \pm\frac{\pi}{4}$

(d) $x = \pm\frac{\pi}{3}$

(e) $x = \pm\frac{\pi}{2}$

(f) $x = \pm\frac{2\pi}{3}$

Problem #184:

Show that differentiating each of the identities below leads to the other. Assume A is a constant.

(a) $\sin(\theta + A) = \sin(\theta)\cos(A) + \cos(\theta)\sin(A)$

(b) $\cos(\theta + A) = \cos(\theta)\cos(A) - \sin(\theta)\sin(A)$

Problem #185:

Compute the differential, dy, for each of the following functions:

(a) $y = \tan(10x)$

(b) $y = \cot(\pi x)$

(c) $y = \sec(2\pi x)$

(d) $y = \csc(-\pi x)$

(e) $y = \sqrt{x^2 + 1}\sec(x^2 + x)$

(f) $y = \csc\left(\sqrt{x} + \frac{1}{\sqrt{x}}\right)$

(g) $\sin(y) = \tan(x)$

(h) $\sec^2(y) = \frac{1}{x^{3/2}} + \cos(y)$

(i) $y = \sqrt{\csc^2(x) - 1}$

(j) $y = \tan\left(\sqrt{3x - 7}\right)\cot\left(\sqrt{3x - 7}\right)$

Problem #186:

Assume that $x = x(t)$ and $y = y(t)$. Find an equation relating dx and dy. Use this to compute $\frac{dy}{dx}$, $\frac{dy}{dt}$, $\frac{dx}{dy}$, and $\frac{dx}{dt}$.

(a) $\tan(x^2 + y) = y\sec(x)$

(b) $y^2\sqrt{1 + \csc^2(x)} = y^2 + x$

(c) $\cot(y) = x$

(d) $\sec^2(y + x) = y\csc(x^2)$

Problem #187:

Find an equation of the tangent line to each curve at the indicated point.

(a) $\tan(y) = x^2 - x + 1$ at $(1, \pi/4)$ **(c)** $\csc(y) = x^2 + x + 2$ at $(0, \pi/6)$

(b) $\cot^2(y) = x^2 + x + 3$ at $(0, \pi/6)$

Problem #188:

(a) Show that the line tangent to the curve $y = \tan(x)$ at (x_0, y_0) is parallel to the line tangent to the curve at $(-x_0, -y_0)$.

(b) Show that the line tangent to the curve $y = \cot(x)$ at (x_0, y_0) is parallel to the line tangent to the curve at $(-x_0, -y_0)$.

Problem #189:

(a) Show that there is no line tangent to the graph of $y = \tan(x)$ which is parallel to any tangent line of the graph of $y = \cot(x)$.

(b) Show that this is not true of the graphs of $y = x^3$ and $y = -x^3$.

Problem #190:

A camera located at C at ground level is tracking a rocket R which is traveling vertically and took off from a spot 500 meters from the camera.

(a) How fast is the angle of elevation of the camera changing (in radians per second) when the rocket is 1000 meters high and traveling at 250 m/sec?

(b) Now suppose the rocket is climbing at an angle $\pi/6$ radians off of vertical as shown in the diagram below.

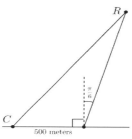

How fast is the angle of elevation of the camera changing (in radians per second) when the rocket is 1000 meters high and traveling at $250\frac{m}{sec}$?

Problem #191:

(a) Use the Difference formulas for the sine and cosine from Trigonometry:

$$\sin(\alpha - \beta) = \sin(\alpha)\cos(\beta) - \cos(\alpha)\sin(\beta)$$
$$\cos(\alpha - \beta) = \cos(\alpha)\cos(\beta) + \sin(\alpha)\sin(\beta),$$

to show that

$$\tan(\alpha - \beta) = \frac{\tan(\alpha) - \tan(\beta)}{1 + \tan(\alpha)\tan(\beta)}.$$

(b) Consider two points, P and Q, moving upward on the line $x = 1$, with P above Q as seen in the sketch below:

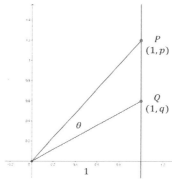

(i) Suppose P is moving up at a rate of 5 units per second and Q is moving up at a rate of 3 units per second. How fast is θ increasing when $p = 20$ and $q = 10$?

(ii) Suppose Q is moving up at a rate of 3 units per second and we wanted the value of θ to remain constant. How fast must P move?

5.5   The Inverse Tangent and Cotangent Functions

If x is the tangent of y, $x = \tan(y)$, then we say that y is the **arctangent** of x, $y = \arctan x$. Speaking loosely, we'd like for the arctangent to be a function which "undoes" the tangent.

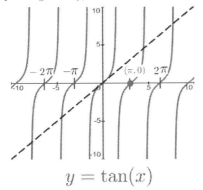

$$y = \tan(x)$$

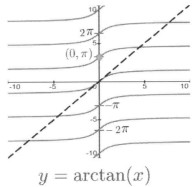

$$y = \arctan(x)$$

The sketch above shows the graph of $y = \tan(x)$ (in red) and the same graph (in blue) reflected about the graph of the line $y = x$ (dashed, in black). Reflecting in this manner swaps the coordinates of each point. For example, the point $(\pi, 0)$ is on the graph of $y = \tan(x)$, because $\tan(\pi) = 0$. Similarly, the point $(0, \pi)$ is on the graph of $y = \arctan(x)$.

But is it true that $\arctan(0) = \pi$? If we are to believe our graph, it could be true. But couldn't it also be true that $\arctan(0) = 2\pi$, or even $\arctan(0) = -\pi$? The blue graph above is clearly the graph of the arctangent as we have defined it but we seem to have a choice for the output of $\arctan(x)$. Many choices, in fact.

Having more than one output for a given input clearly violates what we mean when we use the word "function." A mathematical function returns exactly one output for a given input. There is no choice. The sketch of the arctangent (in blue) is not the graph of a **function**. It is the graph of the **multifunction** $\arctan(x)$. Each of the blue curves on the right is one **branch** of the multifunction[7], $\arctan(x)$. In fact all of the "arc" functions from trigonometry are multifunctions. Mult-functions are interesting objects and are well worth studying. But this is not the time for that study. Right now we are only interested in the properties of the **inverse function** of $\tan(x)$. Since $\arctan(x)$ is not a function, it can't be the inverse function of $\tan(x)$ so we will stop thinking about it as soon as we can.

But if $\arctan(x)$ is not the inverse of $\tan(x)$ what is? Since we only allow one output for a given input, could it be as simple as choosing just one of the branches of the $\arctan(x)$, say the one that lies between $y = -\frac{\pi}{2}$ and $y = \frac{\pi}{2}$, shown below, and calling it the the inverse of $\tan(x)$?

---

[7]Note that by itself, any single branch of the arctangent is a function.

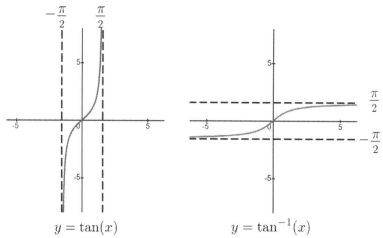

$$y = \tan(x) \qquad\qquad y = \tan^{-1}(x)$$

Actually, yes. It is just that simple. And the usual choice is the one we've indicated. In this text we will designate this branch of $\arctan(x)$ with $\tan^{-1}(x)$. Thus $\tan^{-1}(x)$ denotes the **inverse tangent** function. Because the multifunction arctangent is not a function we will henceforth ignore it as much as possible.

Digression #9: Inverse Function Notation

The use of -1 as an exponent is probably the most common notation used to indicate function inversion. Unfortunately, from the standpoint of a student it is also probably the worst possible notation we could have invented because It is so very easily confused with reciprocation. While it is true that

$$2^{-1} = \frac{1}{2}, \tag{5.11}$$

it is important to remember that

$$\tan^{-1}(x) \text{ is not equal to } \frac{1}{\tan(x)}. \tag{5.12}$$

That the "-1" notation is used for both comes from the fact that both 2^{-1} and $\sin^{-1}(x)$ really are inverses. But they are different kinds of inverses: 2^{-1} is the multiplicative inverse of 2, which means simply that

$$\frac{1}{2} \cdot 2 = 1 \text{ and that } 2 \cdot \frac{1}{2} = 1.$$

On the other hand $\tan^{-1}(x)$ is the functional inverse of $x = \tan(y)$, which means that if $-\frac{\pi}{2} < x < \frac{\pi}{2}$ then

$$\tan^{-1}(\tan(x)) = x,$$

and that

$$\tan(\tan^{-1}(x)) = x.$$

In Equation 5.11 you can think of the -1 in the exponent as an operator. It operates on 2 by taking its reciprocal: $2^{-1} = \frac{1}{2}$. In Equation 5.12 the -1 is not an operator. It is part of the symbol, $\tan^{-1}$, that we use to denote the inverse tangent.

With practice this all gets easier, but in the beginning it is very troublesome. Be careful.

Drill #192:
Evaluate each of the following:

(a) $\left(\frac{2}{3^{-1}}\right)^{-1}$ (b) $\tan^{-1}\left(\frac{\sqrt{3}}{2}\right)$ (c) $\left(\cot\left(\frac{\pi}{3}\right)\right)^{-1}$ (d) $\left(\tan^{-1}(1)\right)^{-1}$

═══════ End Of Digression #9 ═══════

But what, exactly, is $\tan^{-1}(x)$ the inverse of? From the sketch above it should be clear that restricting the **range** of $\tan^{-1}(x)$ to values in the interval $(-\pi/2, \pi/2)$ forced us to restrict the **domain** of $\tan(x)$. So

$$\tan^{-1}(x) \text{ with domain all real numbers, } (\mathbb{R})$$

is the inverse of $\tan(x)$ with domain, $(-\pi/2, \pi/2)$, and it is not the inverse of $\tan(x)$ with domain, $\mathbb{R}$ because that function has no inverse.

An easy way to remember what $\tan^{-1}(x)$ means is to read the symbol $\tan^{-1}(x)$ as
"the angle whose tangent is x."
The advantage of this phrasing is that it emphasizes that x is the tangent of some angle, and $\tan^{-1}(x)$ is that angle. Similarly the inverse functions of the other trigonometric functions should be read as
"the angle whose {sine, cosine, secant, whatever} is x".
Each of these will also come with suitable restrictions on its range.

We should point out that reserving the "arc" notation for the trigonometric multifunctions is actually a conceit of the authors of this text. Most of the world uses $\arctan(x)$ and $\tan^{-1}(x)$ interchangeably, and eventually you will too. But for now it will be helpful for you to keep in mind that the difference between them is that restricting the range of $\tan^{-1}(x)$ to $-\frac{\pi}{2} < x < \frac{\pi}{2}$ guarantees that it is a function. But since the range of $\arctan(x)$ is not similarly restricted it is not a function.

Drill #193:
Suppose we had chosen $\frac{\pi}{2} < \tan^{-1}(x) < \frac{3\pi}{2}$. What function (with domain) is that the inverse of?

All of this fussiness is really just about making our abstract definitions useful and consistent. It would be nice if these details only impinged on us in an abstract setting but unfortunately some practical difficulties do come up, as the following drill shows.

Problem #194:

Find all solutions of $\tan(x) = 1$ and $x = \tan^{-1}(1)$. Do they have the same set of solutions?
(**Hint:** Obviously, they do not. Otherwise we wouldn't have asked the question. What is the difference between the two sets of solutions?)

Digression #10: $\tan(x)$ Has No Inverse

The function $\tan(x)$ is not invertible. This is because, by custom, its domain is all real numbers (except $\frac{\pi}{2}, \pm\pi, \pm 2\pi, \pm 3\pi, \cdots$.) . Thus it is **not** the same function as

$$\tan(x) \text{ with domain } -\frac{\pi}{2} < x < \frac{\pi}{2}.$$

A function has two parts: (1) The set of inputs (domain) and (2) the rule associating input with output. Most of the time the domain is the set of all real numbers ($\mathbb{R}$), so we don't bother to explicitly state that the domain of, say $f(x) = x^2$ is $\mathbb{R}$. Unless otherwise specified we simply assume that it is. Properly speaking, we should always specify the domain of our functions, but typically we don't. The custom is to assume that the domain of a function is $\mathbb{R}$ unless otherwise stated. Thus the function, $\tan(x)$ cannot be inverted because on its domain ($\mathbb{R}$) it has more than one branch.

Because we both want and need an inverse tangent function we restrict the range of $\tan^{-1}(x)$. But this is the inverse of $\tan(x)$, with domain $-\frac{\pi}{2} < x < \frac{\pi}{2}$, which has only one branch. It is **not** the inverse of $\tan(x)$, because it has too many branches.

To use our notation as it was intended to be used we should say that $\tan^{-1}(x)$ is the inverse of $\tan(x)$, with domain $-\frac{\pi}{2} < x < \frac{\pi}{2}$, which is true. But instead, we typically just say that it is the inverse of $\tan(x)$, which strictly speaking, is not true.

When we (mathematicians) talk amongst ourselves this is not a problem. We all understand what we mean. But it can be very confusing for students who usually have a more tenuous grasp of these distinctions. It is a bit unfair of us (mathematicians) to speak to students in what amount to incomplete sentences, but we tend to do it anyway, mostly out of habit.

We (the authors) apologize.

══════════ **End Of Digression #10** ══════════

The definition of the arccotangent is similar to the definition of the arctangent: If x is the cotangent of y, $x = \cot(y)$, then we say that y is the **arccotangent** of x, and write

$$y = \text{arccot}(x).$$

The arccotangent is also a multifunction with multiple branches so, just as before, we will have to decide which branch to use to define the inverse cotangent: $\cot^{-1} x$.

We obtained our branch for the single-valued function $y = \tan^{-1}(x)$ from the multifunction $y = \arctan(x)$ by restricting its range to $-\frac{\pi}{2} < y < \frac{\pi}{2}$. A similar restriction would allow us to obtain the single-valued function $\cot^{-1}(x)$ from the multifunction $\text{arccot}(x)$, but it is a bit simpler to once again use a trigonometric identity.

Drill #195:
Use the identity

$$\cot^{-1}(x) = \frac{\pi}{2} - \tan^{-1}(x)$$

to choose an appropriate range for the function $y(x) = \cot^{-1}(x)$.

5.6   The Witch of Agnesi and the Inverse Tangent Function

Maria Gaëtana Agnesi
(1718-1799)

In a time when women had very few options in life Maria Gaëtana Agnesi (1718-1799) was both exceptional and very lucky. Her brilliance and talent were recognized early and nurtured by her wealthy father, who encouraged her studies and provided her with the best possible tutors to develop her talents. She mastered the Calculus of Newton and Leibniz and in 1748 wrote a series of textbooks on the topic titled *Instituzioni Analitiche ad Uso Della Gioventù Italiana*[8]. It was immediately recognized as a masterpiece of mathematical exposition and was used throughout Europe during eighteenth century. It was by far the most popular Calculus textbook in use at the time. An Englishman, John Colson, was so impressed with Agnesi's work that in 1760 he took it upon himself to learn Italian specifically so that he could translate her text into English.

In her text Agnesi[9] collected many of the known results of the time and organized them for the instruction of students. The Latin name of one of the curves that she used for instruction is *versoria* ("rope that turns a sail") because of its shape. Agnesi correctly translated this into Italian as "la versiera." Unfortunately Colson mistook this for "l'aversiera" which means "witch." As a result this particular curve has been known ever since as the Witch of Agnesi.

As modern function notation was yet to be invented Agnesi understood this curve geometrically as a particular set of points. In the diagram at the right think of P as moving from left to right. For each value of x_0, draw the line from the origin to P and locate the vertical coordinate y_0 where this line in-

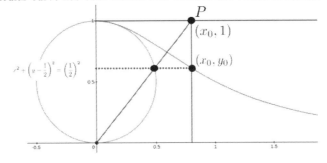

---

[8]This is usually translated as *Analytical Methods for the use of Italian Youth*

[9]Her name is pronounced "Awn-yes-ee," not "Ag-nes-ee."

tersects the circle

$$x^2 + \left(y - \frac{1}{2}\right)^2 = \left(\frac{1}{2}\right)^2,$$

centered at $\left(0, \frac{1}{2}\right)$, with radius $r = \frac{1}{2}$. Every point (x_0, y_0) is a point on the Witch of Agnesi. The Witch itself is the curve shown in red.

Problem #196: In the diagram above show that the coordinates x_0 and y_0 satisfy the equation, $y_0 = \dfrac{1}{1 + x_0^2}$. Thus the Witch is the graph of

$$y(x) = \frac{1}{1 + x^2}.$$

Whenever you encounter a new curve an important question to ask is, "What is its derivative?" In this case you already have everything you need to find the answer.

Problem #197: Show that if $y = \frac{1}{1+x^2}$, then $\frac{dy}{dx} = \frac{-2x}{(1+x^2)^2}$.

Computing the derivative of a function as a formula is very useful. This has in fact been our primary focus so far in this text. However to truly understand the relationship between a function and its derivative nothing can replace seeing both of them graphed together. Look closely at the relationship between the Witch and its derivative in the sketch at the right. Is it clear how these graphs are related?

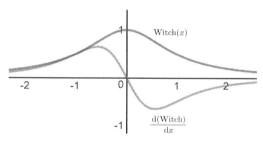

Notice in particular that when $x = 0$ the y coordinate of the Witch is at its highest point (maximum value), whereas the y coordinate of $\frac{d(\text{Witch})}{dx}$ is zero.

We know that the derivative of a curve at a given point gives us the slope of the line tangent at that point. Thus at its highest point the line tangent to the Witch will be horizontal. That is, its derivative will be zero. This is exactly what these two graphs are showing us.

When x is just to the right of zero, the slope of the Witch is close to zero and negative. Similarly just to the left of zero the slope of the Witch is close to zero and positive. At the extreme right end of the graph above the slope of the Witch is close to zero and negative and at the extreme left it is close to zero and positive. And all of this is reflected in the shape of the blue (derivative) curve.

It is a little more interesting to reverse this process. That is, suppose we could see only the derivative of the Witch (blue curve). Could we figure out the shape of the Witch from this?

Sure we can. Well, almost.

Consider: From the extreme left of the graph to $x = 0$ the y–coordinate of the (blue) derivative curve is above the x–axis. Therefore the slope of the Witch is positive. Clearly wherever the slope of a function is positive the function is increasing, so we can deduce that the Witch increases from left to right until we reach $x = 0$ where the blue derivative function crosses the x-axis.

Thereafter the y-coordinate of the blue derivative curve is below the x-axis. That is, the slope of the Witch is negative, so the Witch is decreasing.

Just by looking at the derivative curve we can see that the Witch of Agnesi increases from left to right until we reach $x = 0$, and after that it decreases. Although this shows us the shape of the Witch it is not enough to completely describe the Witch of Agnesi. We can tell a lot about a curve by looking at the graph of its derivative but we can't tell everything.

Drill #198:

In the sketch below the red curve is the graph of the Witch and the blue curve is the graph of its derivative. Convince yourself that the blue curve could also be the graph of the derivative of any of the other curves shown as well. As clearly as you can, explain what this suggests about the relationship between a function and its derivative.

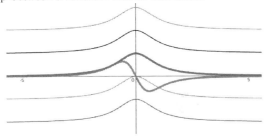

Next we'd like to apply this same sort of reasoning to the Witch itself. We'd like to answer the question, "What curve is the Witch of Agnesi the derivative of?" Whatever that curve is, we'll call it the **antiderivative** of the Witch for obvious reasons.

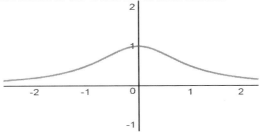

As before, by simply looking at the graph of the Witch we can see that: (1) At the extreme ends of its graph the antiderivative will have a positive slope which gets closer and closer to zero as we go farther from the origin, but (2) since the Witch never crosses the x-axis the antiderivative will never have a horizontal slope, and (3) at $x = 0$ the slope of the antiderivative will be equal to one. A sketch of the antiderivative of the Witch begins to emerge when we put these three observations into our graph:

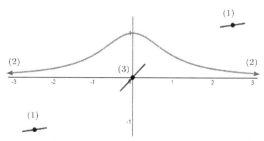

Continuing to fill between the black segments in the same fashion the sketch becomes even clearer:

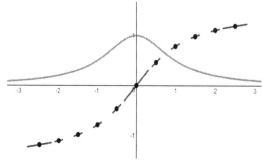

Finally, connecting the dots with a smooth curve we see the the graph of the antiderivative of the Witch of Agnesi must look like this:

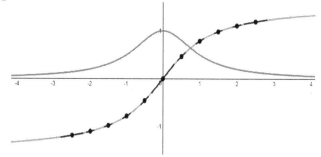

We've been a little lazy with our use of language. As we saw in Drill #198, the antiderivative is not unique, so it is improper to speak of the antiderivative. Any one of the curves shown below could be an antiderivative of the Witch of Agnesi. (Except the black one, of course. That's the Witch.)

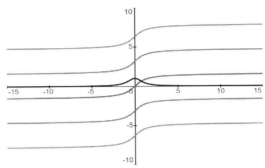

This graph should look very familiar to you. It looks very much like the graph of the arctangent function we discussed in Section 5.5, doesn't it? Do you suppose it is possible that the derivative of the arctangent function is the Witch of Agnesi?

Of course it is. Why else would we have led you down this path? But there are some subtleties here that we shouldn't ignore. For example we will want to find a function that is the antiderivative of the Witch. We will proceed cautiously.

The following exercise is not directly related to the Witch of Agnesi. We include it so that you can get practice relating the graphs of functions, there derivatives, and their antiderivatives, as this is a very useful skill. We will need it in a far more substantial way in Section #9.2 when we get there.

Problem #199:
Sketch the graph of the derivative and the antiderivative of each of the following curves on the same set if axes,

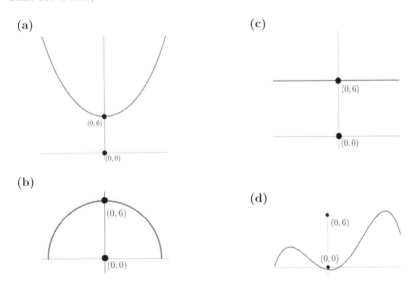

5.7 The Differentials of the Inverse Tangent and Inverse Cotangent Functions

Since we want to find a function whose derivative is the Witch of Agnesi and we are pretty sure that each of the branches of the arctangent multifunction takes the shape of the Witch's antiderivative it is tempting to assume that the branch of the arctangent shown at the right is the function we are looking for.

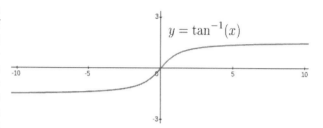

But we must be careful. Reasoning from pictures, as we've just done, can be very useful. but the most we can hope for when reasoning from pictures is an intuitive feel for the problem. We always need to confirm our intuition analytically. Always.

So we will verify, analytically, our conjecture that the derivative of the inverse tangent function is the Witch of Agnesi.

From our definition of $\tan^{-1}(x)$ we know that $y = \tan^{-1}(x)$ precisely when[10] $\tan(y) = x$. Differentiating $\tan(y) = x$ gives:

$$\mathrm{d}(\tan(y)) = \mathrm{d}x$$
$$\sec^2(y)\,\mathrm{d}y = \mathrm{d}x$$
$$\mathrm{d}y = \frac{1}{\sec^2(y)}\,\mathrm{d}x.$$

This is a correct formula for the differential of the arctangent function. However, there are two problems: (1) it does not seem to match our conjecture, and (2) even if it is correct this formula will not be very useful to us in this form since we have $\mathrm{d}y$ in terms of y itself. We can address both of these problems by finding $\mathrm{d}y$ in terms of x and $\mathrm{d}x$.

Referring to the diagram at the right, recall from Section 5.1 that $\tan(y) = \frac{x}{1} = x$ so $y = \tan^{-1}(x)$. The hypotenuse in the diagram at the right is $\sec(y)$ so from the Pythagorean Theorem we see that $\sec^2(y) = 1 + x^2$. Thus

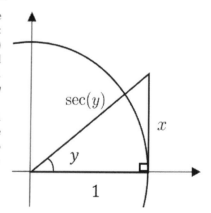

$$\mathrm{d}y = \frac{1}{\sec^2(y)}\,\mathrm{d}x = \frac{1}{1 + x^2}\,\mathrm{d}x,$$

---

[10]Notice how cavalierly we've ignored the necessary constraints on the domain of the tangent. The function $\tan^{-1}(x)$ is not the inverse of $\tan(x)$ because the domain of $\tan(x)$ is $\mathbb{R}$. It is the inverse of $\tan(x)$, with domain, $\frac{-\pi}{2} < x < \frac{\pi}{2}$. The domain is part of the definition of the function.

or
$$\frac{dy}{dx} = \frac{1}{1 + x^2}$$

So our intuition was correct. The Witch is indeed the derivative of the arctangent function. A similar derivation can be used for the arccotangent.

Problem #200:

(a) The inverse cotangent function is defined as $y = \cot^{-1}(x)$ if and only if $\cot(y) = x$. Proceed as we did above to show that
$$d\left(\cot^{-1}(x)\right) = \frac{-1}{1 + x^2}\, dx.$$

(b) Derive the same result from the identity $\cot^{-1}(x) = \pi/2 - \tan^{-1}(x)$.

Problem #201:

(a) Show that if $y = \tan^{-1}(x)$ then y satisfies the differential equation
$$(1 + x^2)\frac{d^2 y}{dx^2} + 2x\frac{dy}{dx} = 0.$$

(b) The function $y = \cot^{-1}(x)$ satisfies the same differential equation. Show this in two different ways.

    (i) By direct computation, just as you did part (a).

    (ii) By direct computation, after first observing that $\cot^{-1}(x) = \frac{\pi}{2} - \tan^{-1}(x)$.

Problem #202:
Show that each of the following statements is true.

(a) $d\left(\tan^{-1}\left(\dfrac{1 + x}{1 - x}\right)\right) = \dfrac{1}{1 + x^2}\, dx$ (c) $d\left(\tan^{-1}\left(\dfrac{10 + x}{1 - 10x}\right)\right) = \dfrac{1}{1 + x^2}\, dx$

(b) $d\left(\tan^{-1}\left(\dfrac{2 + x}{1 - 2x}\right)\right) = \dfrac{1}{1 + x^2}\, dx$ (d) $d\left(\tan^{-1}\left(\dfrac{2543 + x}{1 - 2543x}\right)\right) = \dfrac{1}{1 + x^2}\, dx$

(e) This is weird isn't it? None of the functions on the left is $\tan^{-1}(x)$ but they all have the same derivative as $\tan^{-1}(x)$. Can you explain this?
    (**Hint:** Let $y_1 = \tan^{-1}(x)$ and $y_2 = \tan^{-1}(\kappa)$. What is $\tan(y_1 + y_2)$?)

(f) Now show that $d\left(\tan^{-1}\left(\dfrac{\kappa + x}{1 - \kappa x}\right)\right) = \dfrac{1}{1 + x^2}\, dx$ where κ is an arbitrary constant.

5.8 The Other Inverse Trigonometric Functions

Despite how much time we spent talking about them, the single valued branches for $y = \tan^{-1}(x)$ and $y = \cot^{-1}(x)$, were actually fairly apparent from the graphs of $x = \tan(y)$ and $x = \cot(y)$. All we had to do was choose one continuous branch from either graph. We described the process carefully because for the other inverse trigonometric functions things are a little more problematic. For those we will have to use the derivatives of our "arc" multifunctions as a guide, rather than the multifunctions themselves.

In general, we define an arc[function] as $\text{arcfunction}(x) = y$ precisely when $\text{function}(y) = x$. So, $\arcsin(x) = y$ when $\sin(y) = x$ and $\arccos(x) = y$ when $\cos(x) = y$.

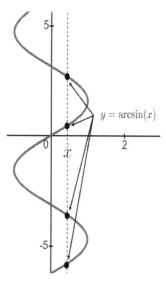

The Inverse Sine Function: $\sin^{-1}(x)$

When we graph $\arcsin(x)$ by flipping the graph of $\sin(x)$ across the graph of the line $y = x$ we get the sketch at the right. For the value of x shown in the sketch the arrows point to a few of the possible values of $\arcsin(x)$. There are infinitely many, so obviously $\arcsin(x)$ is also a multifunction, not a function.

To find the differentials of $y = \arcsin(x)$ and $y = \arccos(x)$ we proceed just as we did with the $\arctan(x)$ and $\text{arccot}(x)$. If $y = \arcsin(x)$ then $x = \sin(y)$ so:

$$d(\sin(y)) = dx$$
$$\cos(y) = dx$$
$$dy = \frac{1}{\cos(y)}\, dx$$

Drill #203:
Use the diagram below,

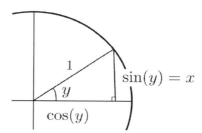

to show that

$$d(\arcsin(x)) = \frac{\pm 1}{\sqrt{1 - x^2}}\, dx. \tag{5.13}$$

Problem #204:

(a) Use the fact that $y = \arccos(x)$ if and only if $\cos(y) = x$ and proceed as we did in Drill #203 to show that

$$d\left(\arccos(x)\right) = \frac{\mp 1}{\sqrt{1-x^2}}\, dx. \tag{5.14}$$

(**Comment:** Notice how this formula differs from the one you found in Drill 203.)

(b) Derive the same result from the identity: $\arccos(x) = \frac{\pi}{2} - \arcsin(x)$.

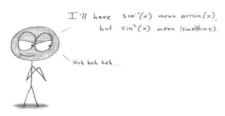

The World's Most Evil Mathematician
from Math With Bad Drawings
by Ben Orlin

The plus/minus and minus/plus that appear in equations 5.13 and 5.14, respectively, are present because, $\arcsin(x)$ and $\arccos(x)$ are both multifunctions like $\arctan(x)$.

Since $\arcsin(x)$ is not a function at all it can't be the inverse function of $\sin(x)$. Once again, to *create* an inverse sine function (which we will call $\sin^{-1}(x)$) we will have to restrict the range of $\sin^{-1}(x)$ just like we restricted the range of $\tan^{-1}(x)$. The question is, what restriction should we impose?

When we were looking to restrict the range of the $\tan^{-1}(x)$ there was a natural choice that was clearly visible in the graph. Notice that the derivative of $\arctan(x)$ (and thus the derivative of $\tan^{-1}(x)$) is always positive while the derivative of the $\text{arccot}(x)$ (and thus the derivative of $\cot^{-1}(x)$) is always negative. This happens naturally for the tangent and cotangent, but not for the arcsine, the arccosine or the other trigonometric functions.

But this does suggest how we might proceed. As you can see in the sketch at the right the slope of $\arcsin(x)$ is sometimes positive and sometimes negative. Since we must restrict the range of $\sin^{-1}(x)$, we may as well make a convenient choice. We'd like to constrain the range of the inverse sine in such a way that its derivative is always positive, and we'd like to constrain the range of the inverse cosine in such a way that its derivative is always negative.

From the sketch we see that if we restrict the range of $\sin^{-1}(x)$ to the interval $[-\pi/2, \pi/2]$ the graph of $\sin^{-1}(x)$ (in blue) will always[11] have a positive slope, and therefore a positive derivative.

With this restriction in place we define the derivative of the inverse sine as follows.

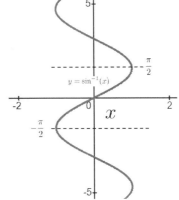

---

[11]Except at the endpoints of course. What do you think the slope of $\sin^{-1}(x)$ is at $x = \frac{\pi}{2}$?

<u>Definition 4:</u> **The Derivative of the Inverse Sine**

The derivative of the inverse sine function is defined to be,

$$\frac{d(\sin^{-1}(x))}{dx} = \frac{1}{\sqrt{1-x^2}},$$

where $-\frac{\pi}{2} < \sin^{-1}(x) < \frac{\pi}{2}$.

Problem #205:

What function is $\sin^{-1}(x)$, as defined in Definition 4 the inverse off?

(**Hint:** Naturally, $\sin^{-1}(x)$ is the inverse of $\sin(x)$, but with which domain?)

Similarly, if we restrict the range of $\cos^{-1}(x)$ to $0 < x < \pi$ its derivative will always be negative.

<u>Definition 5:</u> **The Derivative of the Inverse Cosine**

The derivative of the inverse sine function is defined to be,

$$\frac{d(\cos^{-1}(x))}{dx} = \frac{-1}{\sqrt{1-x^2}},$$

where $0 < x < \pi$.

Problem #206:

(**a**) Show that if $y = \arcsin(x)$ then y satisfies the differential equation

$$\frac{d^2y}{dx^2} + x\frac{dy}{dx} = 0.$$

(**b**) The function $y = \arccos(x)$ satisfies the same differential equation. Show this in two different ways.

   (**i**) By direct computation, just as you did part (a).

   (**ii**) By direct computation, after first observing that $\arccos(x) = \frac{\pi}{2} - \arcsin(x)$.

The Inverse Secant and Inverse Cosecant

To find the differential of $\arcsec(x)$ we refer to the sketch at the right and we proceed exactly as before. If $y = \arcsec(x)$, then $x = \sec(y)$ so

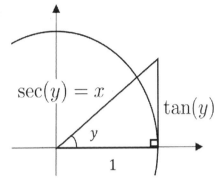

$$d(\sec(y)) = dx$$
$$\sec(y)\tan(y)\,dy = dx$$

so that

$$dy = \frac{1}{\sec(y)\tan(y)}\,dx.$$

Drill #207: Show that: $d\left(\arcsec(x)\right) = \frac{\pm 1}{x\sqrt{x^2-1}}\,dx$.

Problem #208:

(a) Use the fact that $y = \arccsc(x)$ if and only if $\csc(y) = x$ and proceeding as we did above, show that
$$d\left(\arccsc(x)\right) = \frac{\mp 1}{x\sqrt{x^2-1}}\,dx.$$

(b) Derive the same result from the identity: $\arccsc(x) = \frac{\pi}{2} - \arcsec(x)$.

Problem #209:

(a) Show that if $y = \arcsec(x)$ then y satisfies the differential equation
$$x(x^2-1)\frac{d^2y}{dx^2} + (2x^2-1)\frac{dy}{dx} = 0.$$

(b) The function $y = \arccsc(x)$ satisfies the same differential equation. Show this in two different ways.

(i) By direct computation, just as you did part (a).

(ii) By direct computation, after first observing that $\arccsc(x) = \frac{\pi}{2} - \arcsec(x)$.

Again we will want to define the inverse secant, $y = \sec^{-1}(x)$ by restricting the range of the multifunction $y = \arcsec(x)$ in such a way that the derivative of $\sec^{-1}(x)$ will always be positive. Similarly for the inverse cosecant function.

But forcing the derivative of the inverse secant to always be positive is a bit harder for a couple of reasons. The first is just that these functions are used less and thus we are not as familiar with them. The other is the nature of the derivative formula itself. Recall that

$$\frac{d(\mathrm{arcsec}(x))}{dx} = \frac{\pm 1}{x\sqrt{x^2 - 1}}.$$

This time it is the presence of the x in the denominator along with the ± 1 in the numerator that is troublesome. By choosing the range constraint judiciously we can control whether the plus or the minus is chosen in the numerator but any reasonable constraint on the range of $\sec^{-1}(x)$ will always include both positive and negative numbers in its domain. So the x in the denominator will make the derivative of $\sec^{-1}(x)$ positive for some values and negative for others. We don't want that. We want it to be positive.

Usually when we want things in the world to be simple, Nature just laughs at us. But not this time. This time the problem is simply that we have too many choices. Both the ± 1 in the numerator and the x in the denominator will influence the sign (positive or negative) of the expression $\frac{\pm 1}{x\sqrt{x^2 - 1}}$. If they are both in play it is hard to control the sign. So to simplify things we just declare, by fiat, that the x in the denominator will be positive. Specifically, we'll replace the x in the denominator with $|x|$. Now we can control the sign of the derivative of the $\sec^{-1}(x)$ by simply constraining its range.

Problem #210:
The sketch below

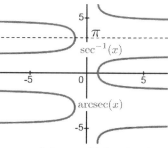

shows that if we constrain the range of the $\sec^{-1}(x)$ to be the interval $(0, \pi/2) \cup (\pi/2, \pi)$ then

$$\frac{d(\sec^{-1}(x))}{dx} = \frac{1}{|x|\sqrt{x^2 - 1}}.$$

(a) Use the identity $\csc^{-1}(x) = \frac{\pi}{2} - \sec^{-1}(x)$ to show that $\frac{d(\csc^{-1}(x))}{dx} = \frac{-1}{|x|\sqrt{x^2-1}}$.

Until now there has been a pattern to differentiation that we have not remarked on. But you may have noticed that when we differentiate a function we usually get back another function of the same type. That is,

1. The derivative of a polynomial is another polynomial,

2. The derivative of a quotient of polynomials is another quotient of polynomials,

3. The derivative of a trigonometric function is another trigonometric function.

The inverse trigonometric functions break this pattern. The derivative of an inverse trigonometric function is not another inverse trigonometric function. Nor is it a trigonometric function, a polynomial, or a quotient of polynomials[12].

Do you suppose there is any significance to this?

The inverse trigonometric functions will not have a significant role in our story for a while. However they will be very useful in some topics that will come up next semester. We've introduced them here simply because it makes sense to develop all of the differentiation rules at more or less the same time.

We now have differentiation formulas for all of the inverse trigonometric functions. These, along with the constraints on their ranges are given in the table below. **Memorize them! You will need them.**

Function	Domain	Range	Derivative
$y = \tan^{-1}(x)$	Any real number	$-\frac{\pi}{2} < y < \frac{\pi}{2}$	$\dfrac{dy}{dx} = \dfrac{1}{1 + x^2}$
$y = \cot^{-1}(x)$	Any real number	$0 < y < \pi$	$\dfrac{dy}{dx} = \dfrac{-1}{1 + x^2}$
$y = \sin^{-1}(x)$	$-1 \le x \le 1$	$-\frac{\pi}{2} \le y \le \frac{\pi}{2}$	$\dfrac{dy}{dx} = \dfrac{1}{\sqrt{1 - x^2}}$
$y = \cos^{-1}(x)$	$-1 \le x \le 1$	$0 \le y \le \pi$	$\dfrac{dy}{dx} = \dfrac{-1}{\sqrt{1 - x^2}}$
$y = \sec^{-1}(x)$	$x \le -1$ or $x \ge 1$	$0 \le y < \frac{\pi}{2}$ or $\frac{\pi}{2} < y \le \pi$	$\dfrac{dy}{dx} = \dfrac{1}{|x|\sqrt{x^2 - 1}}$
$y = \csc^{-1}(x)$	$x \le -1$ or $x \ge 1$	$0 \le y < \frac{\pi}{2}$ or $-\frac{\pi}{2} < y \le 0$	$\dfrac{dy}{dx} = \dfrac{-1}{|x|\sqrt{x^2 - 1}}$

Drill #211:
Compute each of the following:

(a) $\mathrm{d}\left(\sin^{-1}(x^{1/2})\right)$

(b) $\mathrm{d}\left(\tan^{-1}(x^{1/2})\right)$

(c) $\mathrm{d}\left(\sec^{-1}(x^{1/2})\right)$

(d) $\mathrm{d}\left(\left(\sin^{-1}(x)\right)^{-1}\right)$

(e) $\mathrm{d}\left(\left(\tan^{-1}(x)\right)^{-1}\right)$

(f) $\mathrm{d}\left(\left(\sec^{-1}(x)\right)^{-1}\right)$

---

[12]Well, actually that's not quite true. The derivative of the inverse tangent is a quotient of polynomials, and a particularly simple one at that. But it is not an inverse trigonometric function

Problem #212: Find the Pattern

Show that for any constant $a > 0$,

(a) $d\left(\dfrac{1}{a}\tan^{-1}\left(\dfrac{x}{a}\right)\right) = \dfrac{1}{x^2 + a^2}\,dx$

(d) $d\left(\dfrac{1}{a}\cot^{-1}\left(\dfrac{a}{x}\right)\right) = \dfrac{1}{x^2 + a^2}\,dx$

(b) $d\left(\dfrac{1}{a}\sin^{-1}\left(\dfrac{x}{a}\right)\right) = \dfrac{1}{a\sqrt{a^2 - x^2}}\,dx$

(e) $d\left(\dfrac{1}{a}\cos^{-1}\left(\dfrac{a}{x}\right)\right) = \dfrac{1}{|x|\sqrt{x^2 - a^2}}\,dx$

(c) $d\left(\dfrac{1}{a}\sec^{-1}\left(\dfrac{x}{a}\right)\right) = \dfrac{1}{|x|\sqrt{x^2 - a^2}}\,dx$

(f) $d\left(\dfrac{1}{a}\csc^{-1}\left(\dfrac{a}{x}\right)\right) = \dfrac{1}{a\sqrt{a^2 - x^2}}\,dx$

Identify and describe any patterns you see in the forms of these derivatives.

Problem #213:

Show that

$$d\left(\dfrac{\sin^{-1}(x) + x\sqrt{1 - x^2}}{2}\right) = \sqrt{1 - x^2}\,dx.$$

Problem #214: Find the Pattern

(a) Show that each of the following statements is true.

(i) $d\left(\sin^{-1}\left(\dfrac{x}{\sqrt{x^2+1}}\right)\right) = \dfrac{1}{x^2+1}\,dx$

(iii) $d\left(\sin^{-1}\left(\dfrac{x}{\sqrt{x^2+9}}\right)\right) = \dfrac{3}{x^2+9}\,dx$

(ii) $d\left(\sin^{-1}\left(\dfrac{x}{\sqrt{x^2+4}}\right)\right) = \dfrac{2}{x^2+4}\,dx$

(iv) $d\left(\sin^{-1}\left(\dfrac{x}{\sqrt{x^2+5}}\right)\right) = \dfrac{\sqrt{5}}{x^2+5}\,dx$

(b) Now compute $d\left(\sin^{-1}\left(\dfrac{x}{\sqrt{x^2+a^2}}\right)\right)$, where $a > 0$. Does this problem change if a is negative? How?

Problem #215:

Show that each of the following statements is true.

(a) $d\left(x\sin^{-1}(x) + \sqrt{1 - x^2}\right) = \sin^{-1}(x)\,dx.$

(b) $d\left(x\cos^{-1}(x) - \sqrt{1 - x^2}\right) = \cos^{-1}(x)\,dx.$

Problem #216:

(a) Show that $d\left(\cot^{-1}\left(\frac{1-x}{1+x}\right)\right) = d\left(\tan^{-1}(x)\right)$.

(b) Part (a) says that the graphs of $y = \cot^{-1}\left(\frac{1-x}{1+x}\right)$ and $y = \tan^{-1}(x)$ have the same slope when $x \neq -1$ and that their graphs should differ by a constant. Substitute $x = 0$ into both to see what this constant should be.

(c) Now plot the graphs of both. Do they differ by a constant? Explain why or why not.

5.9   Curvature

 See also the TRIUMPHS Primary Source Project in Appendix A.5.

Intuitively speaking, the **curvature** of a plane curve is how quickly a curve turns. It is an important property to understand when designing, for example, a road or a roller-coaster where the sharpness of a curve determines the safe speed limit for that curve. Also, the stresses imposed on the physical structure of a moving object during any high speed maneuver are directly related to the curvature of their paths.

One of the first people to study the notion of curvature was Nicole Oresme[13] $(1323 - 1382)$. Oresme defined the curvature of a straight line to be zero (no surprise), and he defined the curvature of a circle to be the reciprocal of its radius. For example, a circle with radius 2 is $\frac{1}{2}$ whereas the curvature of a circle with radius 1 is 1. This makes intuitive sense. A circle with a smaller radius is "more curved" that one with a larger radius. The radius of the earth is so large that the curvature of say, the equator, is so close to zero as to be completely imperceptible, at least for someone standing on the surface.

Oresme's definition of curvature works just fine for circles and straight lines but we'd like to extend it to more general curves. Specifically, given a curve, we'd like to associate a number with each point on the curve which tells us the curvature at that point. Ideally, this should also generalize Oresme's results for straight lines and circles.

The sketch at the right shows three circles in the first quadrant with radii, $\frac{1}{3}$, 1, and 2, respectively. Notice that on the unit circle, the point of tangency travels $\frac{\pi}{2}$ units along the circumference while the the red tangent line rotates through an angle of $\frac{\pi}{2}$ radians. On the

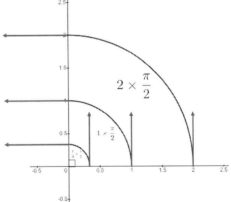

---

[13]Pronouced "Or-em," not "Or-es-me."

circle of radius 2, the point of tangency travels $2 \times \frac{\pi}{2}$ units to turn the tangent line the same $\frac{\pi}{2}$ radians, whereas on the circle of radius $1/3$, the point of tangency travels $\frac{1}{3} \times \frac{\pi}{2}$ units to turn the tangent line the same $\frac{\pi}{2}$ radians. This suggests that a possible definition for **curvature** might be the number of radians the tangent line rotates through as it travels along the curve divided by the distance traveled along the curve while making the turn. In other words, the curvature for a circle of radius r would be

$$\frac{\theta \text{ radians}}{r\theta \text{ units}} = \frac{1}{r} \text{ radians per unit.}$$

This seems to make intuitive sense too. A circle with a radius of 0.0000001 meters certainly seems to be "more curved" than a circle with radius $1,000,000,000$ meters.

By the same reasoning, the curvature of a straight line would be zero. (Why?)

This definition works fine for circles and straight lines which have constant curvature, but what about a more general curve. What if the curvature changes from point to point along the curve such as a long and winding road.

Clearly we'll need a definition of curvature that also changes from point to point on the curve. So it seems reasonable to consider infinitely small changes in both the angle θ and in arclength s. More precisely, we make the following definition.

Definition 6:

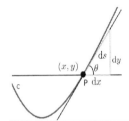

Suppose the point $P = (x, y)$ lies on a curve C as in the sketch at the left. Let θ represent the angle formed in the figure at the left by the line tangent to curve C at point P, with some fixed line.

Then the curvature is defined to be

$$\kappa = \left| \frac{d\theta}{ds} \right|. \tag{5.15}$$

To keep things simple we will always designate θ to be the angle the tangent line forms with a horizontal line.

It can be difficult at first to see how formula 5.15 measures curvature but think carefully for a moment about the meaning of the expression $\frac{d\theta}{ds}$. Loosely put "the rate of change of θ (the angle of our curve with the horizontal) with respect to the change of s (the arclength of our curve)" is the ratio of how much a point moving on the curve has changed direction to how far it has moved. The more our curve changes direction in a given distance the more it is curved and so the more curvature it has.

Don't let the absolute value bars in this formula disturb you. They are there simply because we don't want to consider whether a curve bends to the right or to the left (whether θ is increasing or decreasing), but just how fast it bends.

Also note, for later reference, that

$$\tan(\theta) = \frac{dy}{dx}. \tag{5.16}$$

A good test of the value of a new definition is whether or not it produces the same results that the earlier, more intuitive musings that led you to it. It should be clear that with this definition, the curvature of a straight line would still be zero. (Why?)

Problem #217:

Use the sketch at the right of a quarter-circle with radius r to show that Definition 6 yields a curvature of $\kappa = \frac{1}{r}$.

In problem (217) it was helpful to know that the line tangent to a circle is always perpendicular to its radius. But for an arbitrary curve this is not necessarily true. Let's look at the general situation.

First recall from Equation (5.16) that $\tan(\theta) = \frac{dy}{dx}$. Rewrite this as $\theta = \tan^{-1}\left(\frac{dy}{dx}\right)$ and differentiate so that

Dividing both sides of Equation 5.17 by ds we have,

$$d\theta = \frac{1}{1 + \left(\frac{dy}{dx}\right)^2} \cdot d\left(\frac{dy}{dx}\right). \tag{5.17}$$

$$\frac{d\theta}{ds} = \frac{1}{1 + \left(\frac{dy}{dx}\right)^2} \cdot \frac{d\left(\frac{dy}{dx}\right)}{ds}.$$

Next we "uncancel" a $\frac{1}{dx}$

$$\frac{d\theta}{ds} = \frac{1}{1 + \left(\frac{dy}{dx}\right)^2} \cdot \frac{d\left(\frac{dy}{dx}\right)}{ds} \cdot \frac{\frac{1}{dx}}{\frac{1}{dx}}$$

which gives

$$\frac{d\theta}{ds} = \frac{1}{1 + \left(\frac{dy}{dx}\right)^2} \cdot \frac{\frac{d\left(\frac{dy}{dx}\right)}{dx}}{\frac{ds}{dx}} \tag{5.18}$$

or

$$\frac{d\theta}{ds} = \frac{\frac{d^2 y}{dx^2}}{\left[1 + \left(\frac{dy}{dx}\right)^2\right]\frac{ds}{dx}}. \tag{5.19}$$

Problem #218:

Use Equation (5.19) to show that

$$\kappa = \frac{\left|\frac{d^2 y}{dx^2}\right|}{\left[1 + \left(\frac{dy}{dx}\right)^2\right]^{\frac{3}{2}}}.$$

(5.20)

(**Hint:** $ds = \sqrt{(dx)^2 + (dy)^2}$.)

Digression #11: *Hic Sunt Dracones* (Here Be Dragons)

The time has come for us to begin understanding why differentials were abandoned as a foundational concept for Calculus. We are entering uncharted waters but we won't dive into the deep part just yet. We'll only wade in a little way.

To indicate that uncharted waters were the most dangerous medieval mapmakers would fill in the unexplored regions of their maps with illustrations of dragons and other mythological beasts. The Lennox Globe, in the Rare Book Division of the The New York Public Library (1510 CE, seen at the right), even has the inscription "*Hic Sunt Dracones*" (Here Be Dragons) along the eastern Asian coast.

The Lennox Globe

The concept of the differential of a differential, like $d^2 x$ or $d^2 y$, is a mathematical dragon of sorts.

We will proceed carefully.

If the entire development from Equation (5.17) to Equation (5.19) feels contrived, it's because it is contrived. In particular the "uncancelling" step is clearly a trick in the sense that nothing we did before that step seems to motivate the uncancelling. We just pulled it out of the air, and it worked. Clearly we knew that it would work, but why do you suppose we used a trick rather than explaining what we were doing?

Since everything we did hinged on the observation that $\frac{d^2 y}{dx^2} = \frac{d\left(\frac{dy}{dx}\right)}{dx}$ (from Equation (5.18) and Equation 5.19) it would seem more natural to simply apply the Quotient Rule to $d\left(\frac{dy}{dx}\right)$, wouldn't it?

Let's try that and see what happens. First we get

$$d\left(\frac{dy}{dx}\right) = \frac{dx\, d(dy) - dy\, d(dx)}{(dx)^2}.$$

Next we simplify the notation a bit. Let[a] $d(dy) = d^2 y$ and $d(dx) = d^2 x$ so that,

$$d\left(\frac{dy}{dx}\right) = \frac{dx\, d^2 y - dy\, d^2 x}{(dx)^2}.$$

But the expressions $d(dx) = d^2x$ and $d(dy) = d^2y$ are a problem because to get Equation (5.19) when we are finished we need to have $d^2x = 0$, but $d^2y \neq 0$, which seems inconsistent. Why would d^2y be something, but d^2x be nothing? This is very troubling.

We have observed regularly beginning in Chapter 3 that the concept of a differentials is questionable. But if differentials are problematic, second differentials – the differential of a differential – is even more moreso, if that is possible.

The problem here is conceptual, not computational. That is, there is no computation we can do to see what the value of d^2x must be zero. Rather, we need to think carefully about the meanings of our symbols.

Leibniz' Conception

When we use Leibniz' differential notation we think of dy and dx as infinitesimal increments in the x and y coordinates. Specifically, $dx = x_2 - x_1$ where x_2 and x_1 are infinitely close together. This is already a difficult thing to accept.

But if we stick with Leibniz then it must be that $d(dx) = dx_2 - dx_1$, right? We can write this down and we can read these symbols easily enough. But what they seem to mean is that $d(dx)$ is the infinitely small difference of two infinitely small differences. So does that mean that $d(dx)$ just another differential? Or is smaller than dx? But dx is infinitely small so how could dx be smaller than that?

Down that path be dragons. We won't go there.

Newton's Conception

Instead we'll adopt Newton's viewpoint and hope that it gives us a meaningful interpretation of our symbols.

For Newton, time was the only variable, and time always flows forward at a constant rate. He thought of a variable, x for example, as moving, or flowing (*fluent*) in time and $\dot{x}$ was the rate of flow (*fluxion*) of the *fluent* x. In the simplest example, if x is the position of a point then $\dot{x}$ is its velocity.

Newton only applied his dot notation to something that was changing in time; something that has a rate of change with respect to time. Can we apply it to time itself?

Sure we can. Time itself is "changing in time", isn't it? Time flows at a rate of 1 second per second, or one day per day, or one century per century. The units don't really matter. Loosely speaking (and mixing the Newtonian and Leibnizian viewpoints a bit), an increment of time now has the same magnitude as an increment of time later, has the same magnitude as an increment of time in the past. That is, every increment of t is the same size. If we let t represent elapsed time then this means that the infinitesimal increment dt is constant, so the fluxion of dt is zero: $d(dt) = d^2t = \dot{dt} = 0$. However, keep in mind that this is not true of a quantity that is flowing at a variable rate. For example, if $y = t^2$ then $dy|_{t=1} = 2\,dt$ whereas $dy|_{t=2} = 4\,dt$.

This solves our problem. If dt is constant then by the Constant Rule

$$d^2t = d(dt) = 0.$$

Moreover we always have the option of adopting Newton's convention that the only independent variable is time so that when we write $\frac{dy}{dx}$ we are thinking of the independent variable x as time (although we rarely say so out loud), and we are thinking of y as functionally dependent on time (represented by x in this case). Therefore

$$d^2x = d(dx) = 0 \text{ and } d^2y = d(dy) \neq 0.$$

As a practical matter we will rarely be interested in second order differentials like d^2x or d^2y. As we indicated in Section 3.1 differentials are really just an aid to computation; a convenient fiction. They are a helpful aid but the more important and useful concept is the derivative. Differentials only serve as a step along the way to finding derivatives.

But we will be very interested in second order derivatives: $\frac{d}{dx}\left(\frac{dy}{dx}\right) = \frac{d^2y}{dx^2}$ because these often represent real, physical quantities like velocity or acceleration.

But now there is another difficulty that can't be ignored. In order to make sense of the expression d^2x we had to abandon Leibniz' conception altogether. It is nice that Newton's viewpoint gives us a way to make sense of the notation but what this tells us is that taking either viewpoint (Newton's or Leibniz') does not get us to the logical heart of the matter. A viewpoint is just a manner of thinking. We adopt a viewpoint in order to build intuition.

When two viewpoints are at odds it means that we need something more general. In this case we need a theory that subsumes, and can replace, the views of both Leibniz and Newton. This issue must, eventually, be addressed. But for now we will continue to work intuitively. When we are done, when we stand at the top of the Calculus mountain we will be able to see the paths that Newton and Leibniz each took to get to the top. We will begin our own trek to the summit in Chapter 12.

---

[a]Note this very carefully, $d(dy) \neq (dy)^2$, because the latter is $(dy) \times (dy)$ whereas the former is the second difference of y.

━━━━━ **End Of Digression #11** ━━━━━

Since the equation of a straight line is $y = mx + b$ it is clear that formula (5.20) recovers Oresme's assertion that the curvature of a straight line must be zero. (Why?)

Example #33:

Let's apply formula (5.20) to a circle to see if this agrees with Oresme's definition of the curvature of a circle. Consider the circle of radius r given by the graph of $x^2 + y^2 = r^2$. Differentiate to obtain $2x\,dx + 2y\,dy = 0$ so that

$$\frac{dy}{dx} = -\frac{x}{y}.$$

Differentiate both sides again to see that

$$d\left(\frac{dy}{dx}\right) = \frac{-y\,dx + x\,dy}{y^2}$$

or, after dividing both sides by dx

$$\frac{d^2y}{dx^2} = \frac{-y + x\frac{dy}{dx}}{y^2}.$$

Drill #219:

Use the values for $\frac{dy}{dx}$ and $\frac{d^2y}{dx^2}$ we just computed to show that for a circle of radius r, the curvature $\kappa = 1/r$.

End Of Example #33

As we said earlier, the curvature of a general curve need not be constant, but we can still apply formula (5.20).

Problem #220:

(a) Show that the curvature of the parabola $y = x^2$ is given by $\kappa = \dfrac{2}{\left(1 + 4x^2\right)^{\frac{3}{2}}}$.

(b) Where does the greatest curvature occur? Does this agree with what you can see on the graph of $y = x^2$?

Problem #221:

Consider the ellipse given by $\frac{x^2}{a^2} + \frac{y^2}{b^2} = 1$, $a > b > 0$.

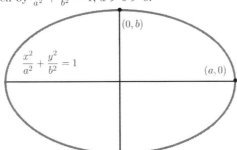

(a) Show that the curvature is given by $\kappa = \dfrac{a^4 b^4}{\left(a^4 y^2 + b^4 x^2\right)^{\frac{3}{2}}}$.
   (**Hint:** Rewrite $\frac{x^2}{a^2} + \frac{y^2}{b^2} = 1$ as $b^2 x^2 + a^2 y^2 = a^2 b^2$.)

(b) Looking at this graph it appears that the curvature at $(a, 0)$ should be greater than at $(0, b)$. Use the formula you just derived to verify this.

(c) A circle is the special case of an ellipse when $a = b$. Use the formula from part (a) to compute the curvature of a circle.

Problem #222: Descartes' Method of Normals and Curvature
Recall that in exercise #25 of Section 2.5 we used Descartes's Method of Normals to find the line tangent to the graph of $y = \sqrt{2x}$ at the point $(2, 2)$ by finding a circle with its center on the x-axis which touches the graph exactly once, as seen in the sketch below.

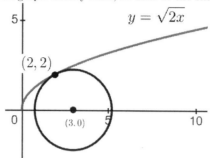

(a) Compute the curvatures of the parabola and the circle seen in the diagram at the right at their point of intersection to show that they are not the same.

(b) Find the equation of the circle which passes through the point $(2, 2)$, and also has the same slope and curvature as $y = \sqrt{2x}$ at the point $(2, 2)$. This is known as the **osculating circle**, or "kissing circle".

(c) Show that the center of the osculating circle is on the line which passes through $(2, 2)$ and $(3, 0)$.

We observed earlier that if we define curvature using Equation (5.15) then the curvature of a straight line will be zero as Oresme said it should be. The converse is also true. Specifically, if $\left| \frac{d\theta}{ds} \right| = \kappa = 0$ then θ must be a constant and so $\frac{dy}{dx} = \tan(\theta)$ must also be a constant. (For simplicity we'll ignore the case where $\theta = \pm \frac{\pi}{2}$.)

Drill #223:
Assume that $-\frac{\pi}{2} < \theta < \frac{\pi}{2}$ and that θ is constant. Complete the line of reasoning we began in the previous paragraph to show that

$$y = (\tan(\theta)) \, x + b$$

for some number b. Explain how you know that this is this the equation of a line.

We've also shown that the curvature of a circle is also constant (specifically, it is the reciprocal of the circle's radius). The converse of this is also true[14]. This is shown in much the same manner as the straight line but, naturally, the computations are more complex.

---

[14]But only if we confine our attention to curves in the plane. It turns out that there are many curves in three-dimensional space, (that is, curves that are not constrained to a two-dimensional plane) with constant curvature which are neither circles nor lines.

To see this recall the diagram that we used to define curvature, shown at the right. If we suppose that $\left|\frac{d\theta}{ds}\right| = \kappa$ then we see that $\frac{d\theta}{ds} = \pm\kappa$. From our diagram we also see that

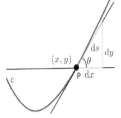

$$\sin(\theta) = \frac{dy}{ds}, \text{ and }$$

$$\cos(\theta) = \frac{dx}{ds}.$$

Problem #224:

(a) Complete the line of reasoning we began in the previous paragraph to show that $dy = \pm\frac{1}{\kappa}\sin(\theta)\,d\theta$ and $dx = \pm\frac{1}{\kappa}\cos(\theta)\,d\theta$.

(b) Next show that

$$x = \pm\frac{1}{\kappa}\sin(\theta) + x_0$$

$$y = \mp\frac{1}{\kappa}\cos(\theta) + y_0$$

for some constants x_0 and y_0.

(c) And finally, show that the point (x, y) lies on a circle of radius $\frac{1}{\kappa}$. What is the equation of the circle?

Chapter 6

Approximation Methods

"Although this may seem a paradox, all exact science is dominated by the idea of approximation. When a man tells you that he knows the exact truth about anything, you are safe in inferring that he is an inexact man. Every careful measurement in science is always given with the probable error . . . every observer admits that he is likely wrong, and knows about how much wrong he is likely to be."

– Bertrand Russell (1872-1970)

"I think that it is a relatively good approximation to truth—which is much too complicated to allow anything but approximations—that mathematical ideas originate in empirics."

– John von Neumann (1903-1957)

In a world where you can take your phone out of your pocket, ask it for the square root of two (≈ 1.4142135624) or the fifth root of seven (≈ 1.47577316159), and instantly obtain those numbers accurate to eleven decimal places it is difficult to convey the profound importance of having good methods of approximation. There appears to be no need for approximations.

But stop and think about this for a moment. Both $\sqrt{2}$ and $\sqrt[5]{7}$ are irrational numbers so neither can be completely represented by a terminating decimal. That is, the decimal form of both numbers is infinitely long. So if all we have is a value accurate to only eleven decimal places what we really have is an approximation, right? It's not even a particularly good approximation in the sense that most of the information we need to completely specify $\sqrt{2}$ or $\sqrt[5]{7}$ in decimal form is missing.

The fact is that the modern world could not exist without good approximation methods because very little of the information necessary to functioning in the modern world can be computed precisely. Moreover in those cases where it can be computed precisely the exact number is often less useful than the approximation. For example, if you are driving to Cincinnati your GPS will tell you that you are 2 hours and 25 minutes away, not 145.22434554656546456 minutes away, even if the latter number is exactly correct.

Based on the audio signal your phone receives it constantly approximates what signal to send to the speaker for you to hear. Because processing an audio signal is such a ubiquitous problem, many very sophisticated approximation techniques have been developed and they are used all of the time. We don't see them because they are usually embedded in software on our many electronic devices. Because they are so accurate, we tend not to see them as approximations.

Every scientific, engineering, or financial computation involves approximations because it is almost always impossible to get perfect information. We must approximate and we do it all of the time. Well, actually most of the time our technology does it for us. But our technology is simply the realization of ideas that begin with paper, pencil, and thought[1]. Without these no new technology is possible.

After the invention of Calculus – and especially in the twentieth century – the number of very good approximation techniques ballooned. We will look, very briefly, at two pre-Calculus methods of approximation. Then we will consider two early approximation methods that came from Calculus, Newton's Method and Euler's Method.

6.1   Root Finding: Two Pre-Calculus Approaches

The Bisection Method

The Bisection Method is what nearly everyone would think of first when faced with an approximation problem. It sounds very complicated when written out in words and symbols, as we're about to do, but it is really quite simple. It will help if you do the computations along with us, rather than just reading them.

Example #34:

For the sake of having a definite problem to work with suppose we want to compute a decimal approximation to $\sqrt{2}$. The Bisection Method works like this: First pick two numbers, one less than $\sqrt{2}$, and one greater than $\sqrt{2}$, In this example we'll choose 1 and 2.

Next, we take the midpoint of the interval $[1,2]$ as our first approximation to $\sqrt{2}$. The midpoint is the average of the endpoints so in this example $r_1 = \frac{1+2}{2} = \frac{3}{2}$. Since $\sqrt{2}$ and $\frac{3}{2}$ are both in the bracketing interval $[1,2]$ we see that the distance between $\sqrt{2}$ and $\frac{3}{2}$ is less than 1, the length of the interval.

Now $\sqrt{2}$ must either be in the interval $[1,3/2]$ or $[3/2,2]$. We need to decide which one. Since $2 < \frac{9}{4} = \left(\frac{3}{2}\right)^2$ we see that $\sqrt{2} < \frac{3}{2}$ so that $\sqrt{2}$ must be in the interval $[1,3/2]$.

We take our next approximation to be the midpoint of the (smaller) interval $[1,3/2]$. Thus, $r_2 = \frac{1+\frac{3}{2}}{2} = \frac{5}{4} = 1.25$. Since $\left(\frac{5}{4}\right)^2 \leq 2$ (confirm this) we have $\sqrt{2}$ bracketed by

$$\frac{5}{4} \leq \sqrt{2} \leq \frac{3}{2}.$$

---

[1]Ok, paper and pencil are not strictly necessary either because more modern technology is rapidly replacing even that. But the need for thought and a way to record our thoughts will never change.

This is really the whole idea. If we are approximating a number, α, we begin by bracketing α between two known numbers, say a and b. We take the average of these, $r_1 = \frac{a+b}{2}$, as our first approximation of α. We know that r_1 is within $|b - a|$ (the length of the interval $[a, b]$) of α. If this is sufficiently accurate we use r_1 as our approximation.

If not we determine if α is in the first half-interval, $\left[a, \frac{a+b}{2}\right]$ or the second, $\left[\frac{a+b}{2}, b\right]$, and repeat the process, finding a new approximation r_2 in an interval half the length of the first..

The Bisection Method generates a sequence of approximations, $r_1, r_2, r_3, \ldots$ of the root we seek. In our example we have $r_1 = \frac{3}{2}, r_2 = \frac{5}{4}$ and so on. At each step the new approximation is the midpoint of an interval whose length is one-half of the length of the previous interval. So our approximations can be made as close to the target as we would like.

Problem #225:

(a) Show that the next two iterations for this example are $r_3 = 1.375$ and $r_4 = 1.4375$.

(b) The starting interval matters.

  (i) For this example take the initial interval to be $[1, 10]$ and compute r_1, r_2, r_3 and r_4.

  (ii) Now take the initial interval to be $[1/4, 3/4]$ and compute r_1, r_2, r_3 and r_4.

  If you had to do these computations with paper and pencil would you use $[1, 2]$, $[1, 10]$, or $[1/4, 3/4]$ as your starting interval? Explain

End Of Example #34

Although we couched it as a purely arithmetic computation, when we compute $\sqrt{2}$ it should be clear that we found the positive root of the function $f(x) = x^2 - 2$. In fact the Bisection Method can be used to find the roots of any continuous function.

Problem #226:

Notice that for each of the functions below $f(4) > 0$. Find the largest positive integer r_1 such that $f(r_1) < 0$. This says that a positive root for the function lies in the interval $[r_1, 4]$. Use the Bisection Method to compute the next four approximations, r_2, r_3, r_4 and r_5.

(a) $f(x) = x^2 - 5$ (c) $f(x) = x^3 - 7$ (e) $f(x) = x^5 - x^2 - 8$

(b) $f(x) = x^2 - 10$ (d) $f(x) = x^9 - 11$ (f) $f(x) = x^3 + 3x^2 - 17x + 6$

The Bisection Method is simple, very general, and it always works. But, even in ideal circumstances, it is not an efficient algorithm. Despite all of our high-speed computational technology this is a drawback. We'd like something more efficient.

The Babylonian Method for Square Roots

As early as 1600 BC, the ancient Babylonians were using the approximation $\sqrt{2} \approx 17/12 \approx$ 1.41667, which is within $3/1000$ of the correct value. As with much ancient mathematics we don't really know how the Babylonians obtained this kind of accuracy. However Heron of Alexandria (circa 10 AD - 70 AD) described a method which may be the same as the Babylonian method. The method he described is as follows.

As with the Bisection Method we begin by making a guess for $\sqrt{2}$. We'll label our first guess r_1 as before. Just as with the Bisection Method we'd like to have $\sqrt{2}$ bracketed between two numbers. Drill #227 shows how to do that.

Drill #227: Show that if $r_1 < \sqrt{2}$ then $\frac{2}{r_1} > \sqrt{2}$, and that if $r_1 > \sqrt{2}$ then $\frac{2}{r_1} < \sqrt{2}$.

Here we will let $r_1 = 1$ be our guess and notice that $r_1 < \sqrt{2}$. In light of Drill #227 we see that $\frac{2}{r_1} = \frac{2}{1} > \sqrt{2}$ so, as before, we have $\sqrt{2}$ somewhere in the interval $[1, 2]$. Also as before, we take the average of these two numbers to get our second approximation,

$$r_2 = \frac{1}{2}\left(r_1 + \frac{2}{r_1}\right) = \frac{1}{2}\left(1 + \frac{2}{1}\right) = \frac{3}{2}.$$

In the Bisection Method we needed to determine if this was less than or greater than $\sqrt{2}$. In the Babylonian algorithm it doesn't matter for $\sqrt{2}$ will always be between r_2 and $\frac{2}{r_2}$ (by Drill #227). We average these together to get our third approximation,

$$r_3 = \frac{1}{2}\left(r_2 + \frac{2}{r_2}\right) = \frac{1}{2}\left(\frac{3}{2} + \frac{2}{\frac{3}{2}}\right) = \frac{1}{2}\left(\frac{3}{2} + \frac{4}{3}\right) = \frac{17}{12}.$$

This is the Babylonian approximation which we mentioned earlier is within $1/1000$ of the correct value.

It's pretty remarkable that we can get such a good approximation of $\sqrt{2}$ with so little arithmetic. If we were to apply the algorithm again, we would get an even closer approximation.

Drill #228:
Compute r_4. You should get an approximation within $3/1000000$ of the correct value. Do you?

Problem #229:

(a) Write down the Babylonian method, as described by Heron, as an algorithm.

(b) Choose and initial guess and then use your algorithm to compute an approximation of $\sqrt{5}$.

(c) Approximate $\sqrt{10}$ using the Babylonian method.

Problem #230:

(a) Suppose you wanted to use the Babylonian algorithm to approximate[2] $\sqrt{4}$ and started with an initial guess of 2. What would happen?

(b) What would happen in the general case for $\sqrt{N^2}$ if you ever got $r_n = N$?

Again, no one knows how the Babylonians discovered this algorithm[3], but some interesting questions arise from it: What about $\sqrt[3]{2}$? Is there some similar algorithm that approximates cube roots? Fourth roots? Fifth? Two hundred and eighty-seventh roots?

Of course the answer to all of these questions is yes, otherwise we wouldn't have asked. But to see why we'll have to step away from the Babylonians for a bit.

6.2 Newton's Method

When Calculus came along, Newton realized that his new invention could be used to approximate solutions to equations by a particularly simple method now called, reasonably enough, Newton's Method[4].

We will use Newton's Method to "re-invent" the Babylonian square root algorithm and, more importantly, to generalize it. Here's the essential idea: We know how to find the root of a **linear** equation like $ax + b = 0$. We want to use this knowledge to approximate the root of a nonlinear equation. As with the rest of Calculus this means that the **Principle of Local Linearity** is the postulate underlying Newton's Method.

For our purposes this means that we can approximate the coordinates of points on a curve with the coordinates of points on the line tangent to the curve when the the point of tangency is nearby. Moreover this approximation gets better as we get closer to the point of tangency.

Before we return the the square root problem we consider the problem of approximation more broadly.

Example #35:

Most mathematical software will accept the equation $x^3 - 3x^2 = 5x + 6$ as input and give back the approximate solution $x = 4.433$ at the click of a button. As a result it is easy to get the impression that this is a a simple problem. But, imagine yourself back in the late 17th century for a moment. The only computation technology available is paper and pencil. How would you solve this problem? How would you even generate an approximate solution?

One possibility is to graph $y = x^3 - 3x^2$ and $y = 5x + 6$ on the same set of axes and look for the value of x where

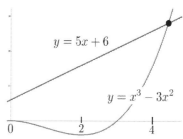

---

[2] Yes, we know this is 2. Work with us here.

[3] Not even Heron knew; look at the dates involved.

[4] This is sometimes also called the Newton-Raphson Method. Joseph Raphson $(1668 - 1712)$ was a younger contemporary of Newton who apparently invented this method independently.

the two graphs intersect as in the figure above at the right. This seems like a good idea until we actually try it. Immediately we realize that accurately graphing even simple equations would have been an almost insurmountable task in those days. We clearly used modern technology to draw the graph pictured. Drawing it by hand accurately enough to glean useful information from it would have been virtually impossible.

Here's another idea. If we rearrange the equation just a little we get

$$x^3 - 3x^2 - (5x + 6) = 0. \tag{6.1}$$

Now define $f(x)$ to be the expression on the left of Equation (6.1): $f(x) = x^3 - 3x^2 - (5x + 6)$. The graph of this function, seen at the left, will cross the x-axis (that is $f(x) = 0$) at the same x coordinate where the equation $x^3 - 3x^2 = 5x + 6$ is satisfied. This simple observation allows us to think of the problem in a slightly different way: We are looking for the x value which is a root of the function $f(x)$.

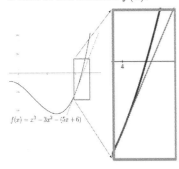

$f(x) = x^3 - 3x^2 - (5x + 6)$

You wouldn't think such a simple change would help. But it does. Now, instead of looking for both the x and y coordinates of an intersection point we need only search for the value of x where the graph of the function $f(x) = x^3 - 3x^2 - (5x + 6)$ crosses the x-axis. This gives us just a little more information because we know that the y coordinate is zero if a point is on the x-axis.

As before we will need an initial guess to get started. Since the root seems to be close to 4 we'll use $r_1 = 4$ as our first approximation. Now find and sketch the line tangent to $f(x)$ at $r_1 = 4$ as seen in the sketch at the left (in red).

If our first guess is close to the actual root the Principle of Local Linearity guarantees that the tangent line will cross the x-axis very near to the actual root. So the value of x, whatever it is, where the tangent line crosses seems like it would be a pretty good second approximation r_2, of the root of $f(x) = x^3 - 3x^2 - (5x + 6)$. If we zoom in on this part of our graph, as in the figure, this is easy to see.

Apparently all we have to do now is determine the slope of the line tangent to the graph at $r_1 = 4$, then find the equation of the line and its x-intercept.

Drill #231:

(a) Show that in this example an equation of the line tangent to $f(x)$ at $r_1 = 4$ is

$$y + 10 = 19(x - 4).$$

(b) Our second approximation (r_2) to the root we seek will be the x coordinate of the point where the line in part (a) crosses the x−axis. That is, where $y = 0$.

Set $y = 0$ and show that the line in part (a) crosses the x−axis at $r_2 = \frac{10}{19} + 4 \approx 4.526$.

The approximation we found in Drill #231 is better than our original guess of $r_1 = 4$, but it is still not great since $f(4.526) \approx 2.6$, whereas if we'd found the actual root, r, we'd have $f(r) = 0$.

But we don't have to stop there, and the pattern should be clear. If we wanted a more accurate approximation we could use r_2 to generate an r_3, and so on. We stop when our approximation is accurate enough for our purposes.

Problem #232:

(a) Find the equation of the line tangent to the function $f(x) = x^3 - 3x^2 - (5x + 6)$ at $r_2 = 4.526$ and use this to show that our third approximation to the root of $f(x)$ is $r_3 \approx 4.436$.

(b) Repeat part (a) using the line tangent at $r_3 = 4.436$ to obtain the next approximation r_4, but this time round it off to 6 decimal places.
   (**Comment:** You will need 6 digits for part (d).)

(c) If you've done it correctly, you will notice that $r_2 > r_3 > r_4$. Does this surprise to you? Explain.

(d) Use your favorite computational software to find an approximation to the root of $f(x) = x^3 - x^2 - (5x + 6)$ to 6 decimal places. Compare your r_4 to this approximation. How close did you come?

End Of Example #35

When computing approximations our goal is to compute good approximations efficiently, not to do a lot of arithmetic. We'd actually like to avoid doing arithmetic as much as possible. So it will be worth the effort needed to organize our computations as much as we can. Fortunately this is not hard to do.

In the diagram at the right we see the graph of a generic function $y = y(x)$. Suppose we have used Newton's Method repeatedly and found the nth approximation, r_n, of the the root (the nth iterate).

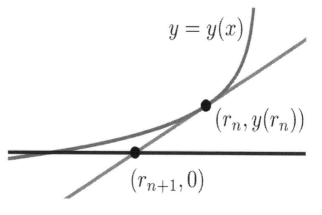

We'd like to find a formula to compute the next iterate, r_{n+1}, without having to draw the sketch and solve a new equation. Problem #233 leads you through this process.

Problem #233: Deriving Newton's Method

(a) Find the equation of the line tangent to the curve $y = y(x)$ at the point $(r_n, y(r_n))$. Show that it can be written in the form

$$y = y(r_n) + \left.\frac{dy}{dx}\right|_{x=r_n} (x - r_n).$$

(b) Use your answer to part (a) to show that

$$r_{n+1} = r_n - \frac{y(r_n)}{y'(r_n)}. \tag{6.2}$$

Equation (6.2) is the general formula for Newton's Method.

(c) If we get lucky and r_n is the actual root of the function $y(x)$ (not just an approximation) what happens at the next iteration.

(**Comment:** Most people can see intuitively what happens. If you can, good for you! But that is not enough. Now show your intuition is correct.)

Digression #12: Prime Notation

In Section 4.5 we introduced Lagrange's 'prime' notation for the derivative: If $y = y(x)$ then $\frac{dy}{dx} = y'(x)$. We also commented that when the differential form becomes cumbersome we would switch to Lagrange's notation. Such a time has come.

Lagrange had conceptual reasons for this change in notation, but we just want to streamline our notation a bit. Since we will be looking at tangent lines to curves it will be easier on the eyes to write

$$y = y(r_n) + y'(r_n)(x - r_n)$$

than

$$y = y(r_n) + \left.\frac{dy}{dx}\right|_{x=r_n} (x - r_n).$$

We still prefer differential notation for most purposes so in the next chapter we will switch back to it, but the prime notation is a little smoother for our present purpose.

======= End Of Digression #12 =======

We summarize the foregoing succinctly as follows:

Newton's Method

Given a differentiable function, $y = y(x)$, with a root at $x = r$ we can approximate r as follows.

1. Choose r_1.

2. For $n = 2, 3, 4, \ldots$ compute

$$r_{n+1} = r_n - \frac{y(r_n)}{y'(r_n)}$$

until the desired level of accuracy is obtained.

The reason we write down Newton's Method in this compact form is that this makes it easier to program into a computer.

As intimidating as the general formula might first appear, remember that ultimately we are simply constructing and solving a single linear equation. This is clear from the derivation of the formula. The apparent complexity appears only because we have arranged to construct and solve the equation in a single step.

Newton's Method works because the property of being the root of a function is a local, not a global property. If our approximation, r_n, is quite close to the root we seek then we can safely assume[5] that the curve and its tangent line are practically the same. This is, of course, the **Principle of Local Linearity** again.

At the end of step 2 we used the phrase "until the desired level of accuracy is obtained." Clearly we are being cagey. How can we tell when we have an estimate which is accurate to any level of precision, let alone the desired level? This is a harder question than it probably appears to be. For that reason we will not be looking into it very deeply. For our purposes it will be good enough to assume that if the first four digits to the right of the decimal have not changed from one iteration to the next then our estimate is accurate to four decimal places.

Drill #234:

Obviously, $f(x) = x - \sqrt{2}$ has a root at $x = \sqrt{2}$. But if we want to compute $\sqrt{2}$ this is not a good choice of function to apply Newton's Method to. Explain why not. What would be a good choice for $f(x)$ if we wish to approximate $\sqrt{2}$?

Problem #235:   Create a function which has a root at each of the following numbers and use your function to compute each to 5 decimals using Newton's Method.

(a) $\sqrt[5]{7}$ (c) $6^{2/3}$ (e) $\sqrt[7]{2}$

(b) $\sqrt[3]{5}$ (d) $\sqrt{27}$ (f) π

---

[5]Most of the time. See the discussion below.

Problem #236:
Start with $r_1 = 4$ and use Newton's Method to compute the next four approximations (r_2, r_3, r_4, and r_5) of the roots of each of the following functions. Compare these with your results in Problem #226. Which algorithm seems to be more accurate after four iterations?

(a) $f(x) = x^2 - 5$

(b) $f(x) = x^2 - 10$

(c) $f(x) = x^3 - 7$

(d) $f(x) = x^9 - 11$

(e) $f(x) = x^5 - x^2 - 8$

(f) $f(x) = x^3 + 3x^2 - 17x + 6$

Problem #237:
Use Newton's Method to approximate the root of each of the following functions to at least four decimal places on the interval given.

(a) $f(x) = \frac{x^2 - x + 2}{x^2(x-1)} - 3$ on $[0, 2]$

(b) $f(x) = x^{\frac{1}{3}} + \cos(2x) - 1/2$ on $[0, 3/2]$

(c) $f(x) = (x - 1/2)\cos(x^2 + 2x) + 1$ on $[-2, 0]$

Problem #238:

As you can see from the sketch at the right, the graphs of $y = x$ and $y = \cos(x)$ intersect exactly once. We want to use Newton's Method to find an approximation of the coordinates of the point of intersection.

First obtain the iteration formula:

$$r_{n+1} = \frac{r_n \sin(r_n) + \cos(r_n)}{\sin(r_n) + 1}.$$

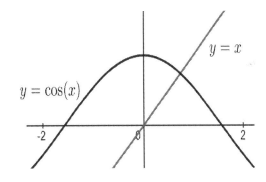

Then use this formula to approximate the coordinates of the point of intersection to 3 decimal places.

Problem #239: Find the pattern

(a) Apply Newton's Method to the function $f(x) = x^2 - a$ to determine the iteration formula for approximating $\sqrt{a}$. Show that this is precisely the $(n+1)$st iteration you get when using the Babylonian method. $\sqrt{a} : r_{n+1} = \dfrac{1}{2}\left(r_n + \dfrac{a}{r_n}\right)$.

(b) Use Newton's Method on the function $f(x) = x^3 - a$ to obtain the iteration formula:
$r_{n+1} = \dfrac{1}{3}\left(2r_n + \dfrac{a}{r_n^2}\right)$ for approximating $\sqrt[3]{a}$.

Notice that $\frac{1}{3}\left(2r_n + \frac{a}{r_n^2}\right)$ is the average of r_n, r_n, and $\frac{a}{r_n^2}$.

(c) Obtain the iteration scheme $r_{n+1} = \dfrac{1}{4}\left(3r_n + \dfrac{a}{r_n^3}\right)$ for approximating the fourth root of a.

Is this also an average? Of what?

(d) Now find an iteration scheme to find the kth root of a, if a is a positive number, and k is a positive integer.

If the initial guess is reasonably close to the root Newton's Method finds a very accurate approximation to the root of a function in just a few iterations most of the time. This made it extremely useful in the 17th century when such computations were done by hand. Indeed, it computes the square root of a number pretty quickly even if the initial guess is very bad. For example in the graph at the right the blue curve is the graph of $f(x) = x^2 - 2$. We start with an initial guess of $r_1 = 5$ (obviously a terrible guess) and find the x intercept of the red tangent line to find the next guess, $r_2 = 2.7$ which is better but still terrible. Repeating we generate the green tangent line at $(r_2, f(r_2))$ which crosses

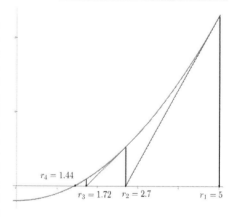

the x−axis at $r_3 = 1.72$. Finally we generate the orange tangent line at $(r_3, f(r_3))$ which crosses the x−axis at $r_4 = 1.44$ which is correct to one decimal. If we continue one more iteration (not shown) we get $r_5 = 1.4141$ which is correct to three decimals.

But this paper-and-pencil procedure is not as simple as handing the problem off to your favorite computational software so a natural question to ask is, "Why bother, why should we learn this?"

The answer is that whatever software you end up using will be performing either the computations above or something very like them. And these **Numerical Methods** are not 100% reliable.

However if you are familiar with the limitations of the algorithm(s) being used you will also be aware of the limitations of your software. Perhaps more importantly, you are less likely to believe a wrong answer when you get it. Depending on what you are computing an incorrect approximation could mean anything from a minor annoyance – if you are calculating $\sqrt{2}$ just for fun – to a deadly disaster – if you are designing a control procedure for a self-driving car.

Problem #240:

Even if you don't have any intuition into the problem a more than cursory understanding of the algorithm itself can be helpful. For example, show that when Newton's Method is used:

(a) If $y(r_n)$ and $y'(r_n)$ have the same sign then $r_{n+1} \leq r_n$.

(b) If $y(r_n)$ and $y'(r_n)$ have opposite signs then $r_{n+1} \geq r_n$.

(c) Suppose you are trying to compute a numerical approximation of $\sqrt{2}$ using an implementation of Newton's Method, but you accidentally enter $x^2 + 2$ as you're function (instead of $x^2 - 2$). Explain how you can use the results of (a) and (b) to know that the algorithm is failing at the third iteration.

So, how do you know if you should trust the approximation you get back from your favorite software? First, be aware of what a reasonable answer should be. In Example #35 it is clear that the root must be positive. If software tries to tell you that it is equal to -2.5 you know it is lying. Second be aware of the ways that an approximation method might fail.

For example, Newton's Method is not perfect. It can fail in two distinct ways: Subtle and Spectacular. Let's take a look at them.

Spectacular Failure

Newton's Method can fail spectacularly in two distinct, but related, ways. The first is very easy to spot.

Problem #241:

Suppose we want to find the root of $y = x^2 - 4x + 7$ and our initial guess is $r_1 = 2$. Investigate, both algebraically and graphically, what happens when we apply Newton's Method to this problem. Describe the results of your investigations.

Because Newton's Method requires that we divide by $y'(r_n)$ we will get an error if it happens that $y'(r_n) = 0$. We call this a spectacular failure because it is easy to spot whether we do the computation with a computer or with paper and pencil. Indeed, modern computer software is very adept at alerting us to division by zero errors.

The second kind of spectacular failure is exemplified by the following problem.

Problem #242:

The only root of the function $f(x) = x^{1/3}$ is zero.

(a) Use Newton's Method with the initial guess, $r_1 = 1$ to see if it converges to zero. (**Hint:** It won't.)

(b) Write down the iteration step (step 2) from Newton's Method for this function. Use this to explain why the method will not converge no matter what non-zero initial guess is used.

Obviously we don't need to use Newton's Method to compute the root of $f(x) = x^{1/3}$. The point of this example is that Newton's Method will not find the root no matter how close our initial guess is. Instead it will continue to generate alternately positive and negative "approximations" to zero, that are farther and farther from zero.

Subtle Failure

The other way Newton's Method fails can be quite subtle. That is, it can converge, but not to the number we seek. The best way to demonstrate this is with an example.

Example #36:

Suppose we wish to compute $\frac{\pi}{2}$ by finding the first positive root of $\cos(x)$. If we start with an initial guess of $r_1 = .1$ (not a great first guess, but it's not obviously horrible either) we get $r_2 = 10.07$, which certainly seems like it might be a problem since $\frac{\pi}{2} \approx 1.7$. If we ignore this and continue we get $r_3 = 11.4$, and $r_4 = 10.97$.

What's going on here? The numbers seem to be converging, but they are not converging to the answer we intended to find. The figure at the right shows what the difficulty is.

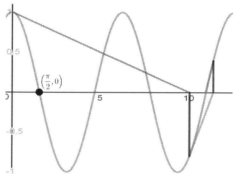

In a nutshell, our initial guess was too far away from the root. The slope of the tangent line at $(0.1, \cos(0.1))$ is $-\sin(0.1) \approx -0.1$ which means that the tangent line (in red) decreases from left to right, but also that its slope is very shallow. Thus the tangent line crosses the x−axis at about $r_2 = 10.07$, very far from the root we seek. Now it happens that 10.07 is actually pretty close to another root of our function: $7\pi/2$. So continued iterations of Newton's Method will settle in on the root at $7\pi/2$. But the damage has already been done. We've found a legitimate root but not he one we intended to find.

We call this a subtle failure because Newton's Method will converge without complaint. None of the computations will seem suspicious. A software implementation of Newton's Method for this problem using this initial guess will return a reasonable looking, but wrong, number. Although it is glaringly obvious what goes wrong when we draw a picture of each successive approximation the fact is if we use a software to compute the root most of the time there would be no pictures. Notice that, unlike the spectacular failure above there is nothing in the calculations being performed that could be detected in software to let the human in charge know that things have gone wrong. So, if you rely on software it is essential that you take the time to consider the "reasonableness" of the answer you obtain. If this is not understood there is a real risk that you could accept a ridiculous answer as correct.

End Of Example #36

The problem of converging to a wrong answer is particularly acute when a function has two roots which are very close together, for example if $f(x) = (10x^2 - 21x + 11)(x - 0.05)(x^3 + 7)$.

Problem #243: Find approximations to all real roots of

$$f(x) = (10x^2 - 21x + 11)(x - 0.05)(x^3 + 7).$$

From the previous examples it should be clear that it is important that the initial guess be sufficiently close to the root we seek that the iterations will converge to the desired root. This, of course, begs the question, "How close should our initial guess be?" This is actually a hard question. Since we don't yet possess all of the knowledge and skills needed we can't answer it in any definite way. So we'll just say that in general your initial guess should be as close as you can make it.

But take care. As we saw in Problem #242 sometimes even having a very accurate first guess is not sufficient.

Problem #244:

(a) Use Newton's Method to find approximations to the positive roots closest to zero of each of the following functions.
    (**Comment:** Yes, we know you can find them exactly using Algebra and Trigonometry. The point here is to see how good our guesses have to be sometimes for Newton's Method to work.)

   (a) $y(x) = x(x^2 - .01)$ **(c)** $y(x) = x^2 \sin(4x)$

   (b) $y(x) = (x^2 - 9)(x^2 - .01)$ **(d)** $y(x) = x^2 \cos(4x)$

(b) If we were to next ask you to find approximations of the negative roots closest to zero of each of these functions would you need to use Newton's Method again? Explain.

Problem #245:

Do not try to answer the questions in this problem analytically. Use a graphing calculator, or graphing software to explore these questions visually.

The function

$$f(x) = 4x^3 - 30x^2 + 72x - 52.$$

has exactly one real root and it is between one and two.

(a) Show that with an initial guess, $r_1 > 2$, Newton's Method almost never converges to the root.

(b) We said "almost never" in part (a) because there is a small interval of numbers greater than 2 with the property that Newton's Method will converge if r_1 is any number in the interval. Find an interval that works. (**Comment:** It doesn't have to be the largest possible interval.)

(c) Show that if you start with an initial guess of $r_1 = 2$ or $r_1 = 3$ Newton's Method will not even generate the first iterate: r_2. Explain.

Problem #246:

Suppose that a cubic polynomial has three real roots, a, b, and c and that two of them, a and b are known. We wish to approximate the third. Show that if we take the average of a and b as our initial guess, Newton's Method will find the exact value of the third root, c, in one iteration.

6.3   Euler's Method

Suppose B is a point on the graph of an unknown function $y(x)$ (in green in the figure at the right). Suppose further that if the line tangent to the graph at B (in red) crosses the x-axis at $(a, 0)$ as shown.

We wish to address the following question[6]: "Is there a curve which passes through the point $(0, 1)$ with the property that the distance from A to C is equal to 1 regardless of the location of B on the graph."

At B form the differential right triangle with the infinitesimal vertical displacement dy and the infinitesimal

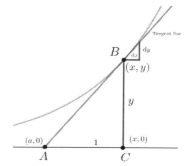

---

[6]The line segment AC is called the subtangent of the graph. In the seventeenth mathematics century was still strongly tied to Greek geometry so some of the early, pre-Calculus efforts to find the tangent lines were aimed at finding the length of the subtangent of a curve. Finding length of $\overline{CA}$ is equivalent to finding the derivative of y at B because if B and C are known then the slope of the curve at B is equal to $\frac{BC}{AC}$.

horizontal displacement dx, as shown. Then the right triangle with sides of length y and 1 is proportional to the differential triangle. By the properties of proportional triangles this curve must satisfy the differential equation: $\frac{dy}{dx} = y$.

Since we specified that the curve must pass through the point $(0, 1)$ we see that we need to find a function $y(x)$ that satisfies the following two conditions:

$$\frac{dy}{dx} = y, \text{ and } y(0) = 1. \tag{6.3}$$

A problem like the one stated in Formula 6.3 is called an **Initial Value Problem**, or IVP. We will give a formal definition below (Definition 7).

We do not know a formula for y which will satisfy IVP #6.3, nor do we have the tools to find such a formula, yet. We will return to this question in Chapter (7) where we will solve IVP (6.3) exactly. For the moment we will be satisfied if we can find an approximate graph of the solution. That will give us a general sense of its shape.

The initial value in IVP (6.3) shows that the curve passes through the point $(0, 1)$. From the differential equation in IVP (6.3) we see that

$$\left.\frac{dy}{dx}\right|_{x=0} = y(0) = 1.$$

which means that the curve passes through the point $(0, 1)$ with a slope equal to 1. So the equation of the line tangent to our curve is

$$y - 1 = \underbrace{\left[\left.\frac{dy}{dx}\right|_{x=0}\right]}_{=y(0)=1}(x - 0) \text{ or } y = x + 1.$$

This is not a lot to work with, but let's not set our sights too high.

By the Principle of Local Linearity, the line tangent to the curve and the curve itself are going to be nearly indistinguishable near to the point $(0, 1)$. Moreover, we can find any point on the tangent line since we have its equation. If we increment the x-coordinate just a little bit while staying on the tangent line then the corresponding $y-$coordinate on the tangent line will be close to the $y-$coordinate on the curve. So we can use the y-coordinate on the tangent line (which we know) to approximate the y-coordinate on the curve (which we don't know).

Let's say we increase x by 0.1 so that $x = 0.1$. The y-coordinate on the line tangent to the curve at $x = 0.1$ is 1.1 (since the equation of our tangent line is $y = x + 1$).

We now have two points on our curve: $(0, 1)$ and $(0.1, 1.1)$. The point $(0.1, 1.1)$ isn't on the curve, but it's close. Remember we're only trying to approximate the curve. Connecting these with a straight line we have the red segment on the graph at the right. So far, so good.

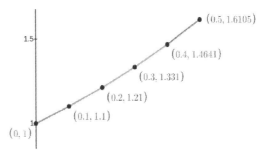

Next we increment x by 0.1 again, to $x = 0.2$. We would really like to have the equation of the line tangent to the curve at $(0.1, y(0.1))$ but we simply have no way to obtain it. All we have is the point $(0.1, 1.1)$. But we know that $y(0.1) \approx 1.1$ so the differential equation from IVP (6.3) tells us that $\left.\dfrac{\mathrm{d}y}{\mathrm{d}x}\right|_{x=0.1} \approx 1.1$ also. Thus we see that the curve will pass (approximately) through the point $(0.1, 1.1)$ with slope (approximately) equal to 1.1. Therefore the equation of the line tangent to the curve at (approximately) $(0.1, 1.1)$ will be $y - 1.1 = 1.1(x - 0.1)$ and as long as we don't move too far the Principle of Local Linearity guarantees that this line and the curve we seek are close together. So we use the blue line segment from $(0.1, 1.1)$ to $(0.2, 1.21)$ in our figure above to approximate the curve on the interval $(0.1, 0.2)$.

We now repeat this process to compute the points:$(0.3, 1.331)$, $(0.4, 1.4641)$, $(0.5, 1.61051)$, and so on. Plotting these points and connecting them with straight line segments gives us the rest of the sketch above.

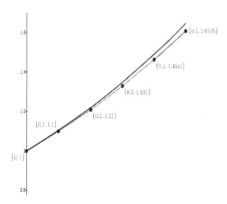

At each step we use the previous approximation to compute the next, so it would be miraculous if we actually found exactly the points on the graph of our curve. But it should be clear that the curve we've drawn will at least resemble the desired curve, as long as we don't stray too far from our initial point $x = 0$. The sketch below shows our approximation and the actual solution on the same set of axes[7].

The solution of this particular IVP turns out to be incredibly useful in mathematics, theoretical physics, engineering, and science and technology in general. We will be revisiting it in the next chapter.

The procedure we have just outlined is known as **Euler's Method**; named for the great eighteenth century mathematician Leonhard Euler. For now we'll focus on how to use Euler's Method to find an approximate solution of an arbitrary **Initial Value Problem**.

We define an Initial Value Problem formally as follows.

Definition 7: **Initial Value Problem**
An **Initial Value Problem** is a differential equation of the form

$$\frac{\mathrm{d}y}{\mathrm{d}x} = f(x, y),$$

along with an **Initial Value**

$$y(x_0) = y_0.$$

---

[7] In practice of course, we wouldn't know the actual solution – if we knew that there would be no reason to find an approximation – but in this case we (the authors) do know.

Don't let the formalism of this definition scare you. All it says is that at every point (x, y) the slope of $y(x)$, $\left(\frac{dy}{dx}\right)$, is given by some formula, $f(x, y)$, which may involve both x and y[8], and that we know the value of $y(x)$ for a single value of x. Specifically, at $x = x_0$.

To write down Euler's Method clearly we will need some notation.

We know that the equation of the tangent line to the curve $y = y(x)$ at the point (x_0, y_0) is given by

$$y = y_0 + \left(\frac{dy}{dx}\bigg|_{(x,y)=(x_0,y_0)} \right)(x - x_0)$$
$$= y_0 + f(x_0, y_0)(x - x_0).$$

So if we choose x_1 very close to x_0 and compute $y_1 = y_0 + f(x_0, y_0)(x_1 - x_0)$ then (x_1, y_1) would be approximately on the curve. In this way we can generate a sequence of points $(x_0, y_0), (x_1, y_1), (x_2, y_2), (x_3, y_3), \ldots$ which are approximately on the curve. Connecting them with straight line segments should provide an approximate graph of the curve.

Formalizing all of this we have:

Euler's Method

Given an IVP:

$$\frac{dy}{dx} = f(x, y), \quad y(x_0) = y_0.$$

approximate points $(x_1, y_1), (x_2, y_2), (x_3, y_3), \ldots$ on the graph of $y(x)$ by computing:

$$y_{n+1} = f(x_n, y_n)(x_{n+1} - x_n) + y_n \text{ for } n = 1, 2, 3, \ldots.$$

At each iteration the value of y has been approximated, so the next approximation is probably not as good. Thus, as we move further from our initial value (x_0, y_0) our approximation probably deviates further away from the actual curve. However, near to the initial value, (x_0, y_0) we should have a reasonable approximation to the curve $y = y(x)$. The next two problems demonstrate this.

Problem #247:

Observe that $y = \sin(x)$ satisfies the IVP

$$\frac{dy}{dx} = \cos(x), \quad y(0) = 0.$$

Use Euler's Method on this IVP to complete the table. Then plot the points you generated and the graph of $y = \sin(x)$ on the same set of axes so you can compare them.

---

[8]In our problem above we had $\frac{dy}{dx} = f(x, y) = y$.

n	x_n	$y_n = y_{n-1} + \cos(x_{n-1}) \cdot (x_n - x_{n-1})$	n	x_n	$y_n = y_{n-1} + \cos(x_{n-1}) \cdot (x_n - x_{n-1})$
0	0		8	0.8	
1	0.1		9	0.9	
2	0.2		10	1.0	
3	0.3		11	1.1	
4	0.4		12	1.2	
5	0.5		13	1.3	
6	0.6		14	1.4	
7	0.7		15	1.5	

Problem #248:

Observe that $y = \cos(x)$ satisfies the IVP

$$\frac{dy}{dx} = -\sin(x), \quad y(0) = 1.$$

Use Euler's Method on this IVP to complete the following table. Then plot the points you generated and the graph of $y = \cos(x)$ on the same set of axes so you can compare them.

n	x_n	$y_n = y_{n-1} - \sin(x_{n-1}) \cdot (x_n - x_{n-1})$	n	x_n	$y_n = y_{n-1} - \sin(x_{n-1}) \cdot (x_n - x_{n-1})$
0	0		8	0.8	
1	0.1		9	0.9	
2	0.2		10	1.0	
3	0.3		11	1.1	
4	0.4		12	1.2	
5	0.5		13	1.3	
6	0.6		14	1.4	
7	0.7		15	1.5	

Problem #249:

Use Euler's Method to approximate the solutions of the given IVPs by constructing a table like the ones in Problems (247) and (248). Then plot the points you found, connecting them with straight line segments.

(a) $\frac{dy}{dx} = y^2, \quad y(0) = 1$ **(c)** $\frac{dy}{dx} = y^4, \quad y(0) = 1$

(b) $\frac{dy}{dx} = y^3, \quad y(0) = 1$ **(d)** $\frac{dy}{dx} = y^5, \quad y(0) = 1$

Problem #250:

Use Euler's Method to approximate the solutions of the given IVPs by constructing a table like the ones in Problems (247) and (248). Then plot the points you found, connecting them with straight line segments.

(a) $\frac{dy}{dx} = \frac{1}{y}$, $y(1) = 1$ **(c)** $\frac{dy}{dx} = \frac{1}{y^3}$, $y(1) = 1$

(b) $\frac{dy}{dx} = \frac{1}{y^2}$, $y(1) = 1$ **(d)** $\frac{dy}{dx} = \frac{1}{y^4}$, $y(1) = 1$

Problem #251:

Use Euler's Method to approximate the solutions of the given IVPs by constructing a table like the ones in Problems (247) and (248). Then plot the points you found, connecting them with straight line segments.

(a) $\frac{dy}{dx} = xy$, $y(0) = 1$ **(d)** $\frac{dy}{dx} = x^2y^2$, $y(0) = 1$ **(g)** $\frac{dy}{dx} = \frac{x}{y^2}$, $y(1) = 1$

(b) $\frac{dy}{dx} = x^2y$, $y(0) = 1$ **(e)** $\frac{dy}{dx} = \frac{x}{y}$, $y(1) = 1$ **(h)** $\frac{dy}{dx} = \frac{x^2}{y^2}$, $y(1) = 1$

(c) $\frac{dy}{dx} = xy^2$, $y(0) = 1$ **(f)** $\frac{dy}{dx} = \frac{x^2}{y}$, $y(1) = 1$ **(i)** $\frac{dy}{dx} = \frac{x^2}{y^2}$, $y(1) = 2$

Problem #252:

Consider the top view of a tractor-trailer as it turns, as shown at the right. Initially, the center of the rear axle of the tractor is at the origin and the center of the rear axle of the trailer is at the point $(1,0)$. The tractor pulls the front wheels vertically up the y-axis and we assume that the rear wheels don't slip.

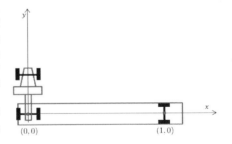

The path that the center of the rear axle follows is called a tractrix from the Latin verb *trahere*, meaning "to drag or pull."

(a) Show that the tractrix must satisfy the Initial Value Problem

$$\frac{dy}{dx} = -\frac{\sqrt{1-x^2}}{x} \quad y(1) = 0. \tag{6.4}$$

(**Hint:** Find a differential triangle and an ordinary triangle which are proportional..)

(b) Apply Euler's Method to complete the following table to approximate the tractrix.

n	x_n	$y_n = y_{n-1} + \left(\frac{dy}{dx}\Big|_{x_{n-1}} \right) \cdot (x_n - x_{n-1})$	n	x_n	$y_n = y_{n-1} + \left(\frac{dy}{dx}\Big|_{x_{n-1}} \right) \cdot (x_n - x_{n-1})$
0	1		5	0.5	
1	0.9		6	0.4	
2	0.8		7	0.3	
3	0.7		8	0.2	
4	0.6		9	0.1	

(c) Plot the points obtained in part b to see if this looks like the path the rear axle of the trailer would take.

We will re-visit this problem and find the exact solution in Section 10.2.

Problem #253:

Suppose a rocket R travels up the line $x = 1$ at a constant speed v. As the rocket passes through the point $(1,0)$, a missile M is fired from the origin directly at the rocket. Assume that the missile travels at a speed which is $\frac{3}{2}$ times the speed of the rocket and is always aimed directly at the rocket. At time t the missile is at the point $M(x,y)$ and the rocket is at the point $R(1, vt)$ We want to find the path the missile will follow. The diagram at the right shows the situation at time t.

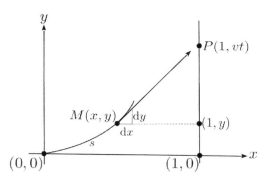

(a) Find s if s denotes the length of the the missile's path at time t.

(b) Show that the missile's path must satisfy the IVP

$$\frac{dy}{dx} = \frac{\frac{2s}{3} - y}{1 - x}, \quad y(0) = 0.r$$

(**Hint:** Find a triangle which is proportional to the differential triangle shown.)

(c) Apply Euler's Method to fill in the following table.

n	x_n	$y_n = y_{n-1} + \left(\frac{dy}{dx}\Big|_{x_{n-1}} \right) \cdot (x_n - x_{n-1})$	s	n	x_n	$y_n = y_{n-1} + \left(\frac{dy}{dx}\Big|_{x_{n-1}} \right) \cdot (x_n - x_{n-1})$	s
0	0	0	0	5	0.5		
1	0.1			6	0.6		
2	0.2			7	0.7		
3	0.3			8	0.8		
4	0.4			9	0.9		

(d) Plot the points obtained in part b to see if this resembles the path you think the missile would follow.

We will re-visit this problem and find the exact solution in Section 10.2

6.4   Higher Derivatives, Lagrange, and Taylor

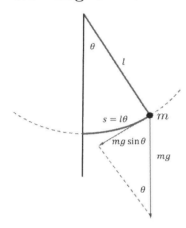

In the diagram at the left, we see a pendulum of length l with an object of mass m at the end. If the object is moved away from its equilibrium point the pendulum will begin to swing back and forth. If we disregard friction the angle θ, that the pendulum forms with a vertical line would oscillate in a manner very like the motion of the **Simple Harmonic Oscillators** (SHO) that we saw in Section 5.3.

If the motion of the pendulum actually is an SHO then it will necessarily satisfy Equation 5.8. In this case that means that

$$\frac{\mathrm{d}^2\theta}{\mathrm{d}t^2} = -\omega^2\theta,$$

for some constant value of ω. We'll investigate to see if that is true.

To keep our model simple we assume that $-\pi < \theta < \pi$ and we will ignore any sort of resistance. The only force we are considering is the (vertical) force due to gravity mg. As before this vertical force will resolve into the centripetal force along the length of the pendulum, and the tangential force in the direction of motion. We will focus our attention on the tangential force.

If θ is measured in radians then the length of the arc traced by the object is $s = l\theta$. Thus we see that the tangential component of the force due to gravity is given by $mg\sin(\theta)$ as shown. Notice that when $\theta > 0$ this tangential force points to the left and when $\theta < 0$ it points to the right (not shown). This says that the sign of the tangential force F is the opposite of the sign of θ. When θ is in the interval $[-\pi, \pi]$ θ and $\sin(\theta)$ have the same sign. Thus We have $F = -mg\sin(\theta)$. Using Newton's Second Law, Force = mass · acceleration, we see that the motion of a pendulum satisfies the equation

$$m\frac{\mathrm{d}^2 s}{\mathrm{d}t^2} = -mg\sin(\theta).$$

Finally, since $s = l\theta$ we have $\frac{\mathrm{d}^2 s}{\mathrm{d}t^2} = \frac{\mathrm{d}^2(l\theta)}{\mathrm{d}t^2}$. Using the Constant Rule (twice) we see that $\frac{\mathrm{d}^2 s}{\mathrm{d}t^2} = l\frac{\mathrm{d}^2\theta}{\mathrm{d}t^2}$. Thus

$$\frac{\mathrm{d}^2\theta}{\mathrm{d}t^2} = \frac{g}{l}\sin(\theta). \tag{6.5}$$

But it does not satisfy Equation (5.8). Therefore a swinging pendulum is not a Simple Harmonic Oscillator. Its motion is slightly more complex.

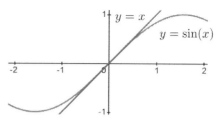

But only slightly.

By examining the graphs of $y = \sin(x)$ and $y = x$ we can see the that for values of x close to zero the graphs are nearly identical. Thus, when the angle θ is very small $\sin(\theta)$ and θ are very nearly equal. In that case if we replace $\sin(\theta)$ with θ in Equation (6.5) we see the the motion of a pendulum approximately satisfies the equation

$$\frac{\mathrm{d}^2\theta}{\mathrm{d}t^2} = -\frac{g}{l}\theta, \tag{6.6}$$

which we recognize as Equation (5.8) with $\omega^2 = \frac{g}{l}$.

Drill #254: Show that the equation of the line tangent to $y = \sin(x)$ at $x = 0$ is $y = x$.

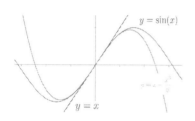

Approximating $\sin(x)$ by its tangent line at $x = 0$ works well for values of x close to zero. We have not been very precise about the meaning of "close to zero" but it should be clear that if θ is too large Equation (6.5) will no longer serve as a good model.

Notice that the function $y(x) = x$ is a first degree polynomial. Is it possible that a polynomial with a higher degree give us a better approximation? Can we find a polynomial with degree greater than one that approximates the graph of $y = \sin(x)$?

At the left we compare the graphs of $y = x$ (in red), $y = \sin(x)$ (in blue), and $y = x - \frac{x^3}{6}$ (in green) on the same set of axes. It should be clear $y = x - \frac{x^3}{6}$ is a better approximation to $y = \sin(x)$ than $y = x$ in the sense that the graph of $y = x - \frac{x^3}{6}$ stays closer to the graph of $y = x$ on a wider interval than the graph of $y = x$.

So it seems reasonable to suppose that the differential equation

$$\frac{\mathrm{d}^2\theta}{\mathrm{d}t^2} = -\frac{g}{l}\left(\theta - \frac{\theta^3}{6}\right), \; \theta(t) = 0, \tag{6.7}$$

if we can solve it, would serve as a better model for the motion of a pendulum than Equation 6.6. Unfortunately we do not yet have the tools to solve Equation 6.7, but the notion of approximating a complex function, like $\sin(x)$, with a polynomial will turn out to be very useful so we will explore it for a bit before we go on. We will again switch to Lagrange's prime notation because in this context Lagrange's notation really shines. Indeed, it was while he was looking at similar problems that Lagrange invented his prime notation in the first place.

The key is to look at higher derivatives of $\sin(x)$. Recall that for $y = f(x)$, Lagrange introduced the notation and terminology

$$\frac{\mathrm{d}y}{\mathrm{d}x} = f'(x) \text{ (first derivative)}$$

Extending this further, we have

$$\frac{d^2y}{dx^2} = f''(x) = f^{(2)}(x) \text{ (second derivative)}$$

$$\frac{d^3y}{dx^3} = f'''(x) = f^{(3)}(x) \text{ (third derivative)}$$

$$\frac{d^4y}{dx^4} = f''''(x) = f^{(4)}(x) \text{ (fourth derivative)}$$

$$\vdots$$

Drill #255:
Show that the equation of the line tangent to the graph of an arbitrary (differentiable) function $f(x)$ at $x = 0$ is given by
$$y(x) = f(0) + f'(0) \cdot x.$$

Applying the result of Drill 255 to $f(x) = \sin(x)$ we see that the equation of the line tangent to the graph of $y = \sin(x)$ at $(0,0)$ is given by

$$y(x) = \sin(0) + \cos(0) \cdot x = x.$$

Drill #256:
This drill demonstrates how we can obtain a first degree polynomial that approximates $f(x_0)$ near $x = 0$.

Suppose that $f(x)$ is some (differentiable) function and that $l(x) = A + Bx$.

(a) Show that if $f(0) = l(0)$ then $A = f(0)$.

(b) Show that if $f'(0) = l'(0)$ then $B = f'(0)$.

Next, suppose we want to find a second-degree (quadratic) polynomial, $q(x)$, for which $f(0) = q(0)$, $f'(0) = q'(0)$ and $f''(0) = q''(0)$. It is clear that we can simply extend what we did in the previous problem. That is, we start with a generic second-degree polynomial, $q(x) = A + Bx + Cx^2$.

First we insist that $f(0) = q(0)$. Evaluating both functions at $x = 0$ gives

$$f(0) = A + Bx + Cx^2 \big|_{x=0} = A + B \cdot 0 + C \cdot 0^2 = A,$$

so $A = f(0)$.

To obtain B, differentiate both functions and insist that the first two derivatives of $f(x)$ and $q(x)$ match at $x = 0$. That is,

$$f'(0) = \left.\frac{dq}{dx}\right|_{x=0}$$

$$= \left. B + 2Cx \right|_{x=0}$$

$$= B.$$

So $f'(0) = B$.

Problem #257:

(a) Differentiate again and set the second derivatives at $x = 0$ equal to one another to show that
$$C = \frac{f''(0)}{2}.$$

(b) Show that if the cubic $c(x) = A + Bx + Cx^2 + Dx^3$ has the same third derivative as $f(x)$ at $x = 0$ then
$$D = \frac{f'''(0)}{3 \cdot 2} = \frac{f^{(3)}(0)}{3 \cdot 2}.$$

(c) Show that if the quartic $q(x) = A + Bx + Cx^2 + Dx^3 + Ex^4$ has the same fourth derivative as $f(x)$ at $x = 0$ then
$$E = \frac{f^{(4)}(0)}{4 \cdot 3 \cdot 2}.$$

It seems clear that we could use this procedure in a "machine-like" way to produce a polynomial approximation of any degree. In fact, this "machine" for producing approximating polynomials was known long before Lagrange, but he made it more tractable by replacing differentials, which are very cumbersome to use here, with derivatives and his prime notation. In general this approximating polynomial is called a **Taylor Polynomial** named after the English mathematician Brook Taylor (1685 − 1731), but was known to mathematicians (including Newton and Leibniz) before Taylor.

Problem #258:
This is the process we used to generate our cubic approximation to the sine function just before Equation #6.7.

(a) Show that using this process on $y = \sin(x)$ will generate the polynomial that we showed you earlier: $\sin(x) \approx x - \frac{x^3}{6}$.

(b) Find the fourth degree Taylor Polynomial approximation for $f(x) = \sin(x)$.
(**Comment:** You may find this puzzling for a moment or two. Make sure you do all the calculations correctly and then believe your calculations.)

(c) Find the fifth degree Taylor Polynomial approximation for $f(x) = \sin(x)$ and graph both functions on the same set of axes.

(d) Find the sixth degree Taylor Polynomial approximation for $f(x) = \sin(x)$.

Problem #259:

Find the second and fourth degree Taylor Polynomial approximations for $f(x) = \cos(x)$ and graph them all on the same set of axes. Would it make any sense to use the fifth-degree Taylor Polynomial in this case? Explain.

In general the Taylor Polynomial, of degree n, that approximates a differentiable function $f(x)$ is given by:

$$T(x) = y(0) + \frac{y'(0)}{1!}x + \frac{y^{(2)}(0)}{2!}x^2 + \frac{y^{(3)}(0)}{3!}x^3 + \cdots + \frac{y^{(n)}(0)}{n!}x^n. \qquad (6.8)$$

As you might imagine Taylor Polynomials are incredibly useful approximation tools. At this point we have given you only the most basic of introductions. You will see this again in much more depth in the next course, Integral Calculus.

Chapter 7

Exponentials and Logarithms

> *"The extinction of the human race will come from its inability to emotionally comprehend the exponential function."*
>
> – Edward Teller (1908-2003)

Introduction

You are already familiar with fourteen of the so-called elementary functions in mathematics. These are:

1. **Polynomials:** Polynomials are functions of the form: $f(x) = c_0 + c_1 x + c_2 x^2 + c_3 x^3 + \ldots + c_{n-1} x^{n-1} + c_n x^n$, where $c_0, \ldots, c_n$ are constants.

2. **Rational Functions:** The rational functions are quotients of polynomials:

$$\frac{a_0 + a_1 x + a_2 x^2 + a_3 x^3 + \ldots + a_{n-1} x^{n-1} + a_n x^n}{b_0 + b_1 x + b_2 x^2 + b_3 x^3 + \ldots + b_{n-1} x^{m-1} + b_m x^m},$$

   where $a_1, \ldots, a_n, b_1, \ldots, b_m$ are constants.

3. **Trigonometric Functions:** There are six trigonometric functions: $\sin(\theta)$, $\cos(\theta)$, $\tan(\theta)$, $\cot(\theta)$, $\sec(\theta)$, and $\csc(\theta)$.

4. **Trigonometric Inverses:** Each of the trigonometric functions has an associated inverse: $\sin^{-1}(\theta)$, $\cos^{-1}(\theta)$, $\tan^{-1}(\theta)$, $\cot^{-1}(\theta)$, $\sec^{-1}(\theta)$, and $\csc^{-1}(\theta)$.

Algebraically combining this basic set of fourteen functions allows us to build almost all of the functions you have encountered so far in your mathematics education. Loosely speaking what makes these elementary is that we don't need Calculus to define them.

But Calculus gives us several different ways to define a multitude of new functions. Each such function is a new tool. New tools give us the means to solve new problems, and a new way to approach old problems. This is one reason that the invention of Calculus was such an important advance.

Functions which require Calculus for their definition are (usually) called **analytic** functions[1].

The exponential and logarithmic functions which we take up next occupy a middle ground between the elementary and the analytic functions. They can be defined without Calculus, which is why you're probably already familiar with them. But in some ways it is better to use Calculus. The exponential functions give us our first, fairly easy-to-understand introduction to the construction of new functions using Calculus so we will start there.

Initial Value Problems (IVPs)

Let's step back for a moment. Recall that an IVP consists of two parts:

1. The differential equation (for example, $\frac{dy}{dx} = 2x$), and

2. The initial value[2] (for example, $y(0) = 0$).

A common way to create new functions using Calculus is by defining the new function to be the solution(s) of a specified IVP.

Example #37:

We've seen that when we differentiate the formula $y = x^2$ we get the **differential equation** $dy = 2x\,dx$, or

$$\frac{dy}{dx} = 2x. \tag{7.1}$$

If we did not already know that the function $y(x) = x^2$ satisfies Equation (7.1) we could give a name to the solution (sqr(x), perhaps?) and by fiat, define sqr(x) to be whatever function solves this equation. But there is a problem. The solution of Equation (7.1) is a multifunction, remember? To choose a single branch we need to impose an initial condition.

Drill #260:
Solve each of the following IVPs. Graph your solutions:

(a) $\frac{dy}{dx} = 2x$, $\quad y(0) = 0$

(b) $\frac{dy}{dx} = 2x$, $\quad y(0) = 1$

(c) $\frac{dy}{dx} = 2x$, $\quad y(0) = -10$

(d) $\frac{dy}{dx} = 2x$, $\quad y(1) = 2$

(e) $\frac{dy}{dx} = 2x$, $\quad y(-1) = 1$

(f) $\frac{dy}{dx} = x$, $\quad y(0) = 1$

(g) $\frac{dy}{dx} = 2x$, $\quad y(x_0) = y_0$ where x_0 and y_0 are fixed, but unspecified constants.

End Of Example #37

---

[1] The precise definition of **analytic** actually comes directly from the work we did in Section 6.4 on approximating functions with polynomials. But one way or another the definition of **analytic** is tied to Calculus.

[2] It's called an initial value because when time is the independent variable we usually know the value of our function initially, when $t = 0$.

Simply naming the function tells us nothing about it. However the IVP itself can give us a some insight into the nature of the solution. For example since $2x < 0$ when $x < 0$, the slope of the graph of $y(x)$ is clearly also negative when $x < 0$, Similarly, the slope of the graph of $y(x)$ is positive when $x > 0$.

Of course we already knew that since we have a formula for $y(x) = \text{sqr}(x) = x^2$. This won't be true in the next section.

7.1   The Natural Exponential

 See also the TRIUMPHS Primary Source Project in Appendix A.2.

In exactly the same way that we can define $\text{sqr}(x)$ via any of the Initial Value Problems in Drill #260 we can declare, by fiat, the following:

Definition 8: **The Natural Exponential Function**
The function which satisfies the IVP

$$\frac{dy}{dx} = y, \quad y(0) = 1. \tag{7.2}$$

is called the **natural exponential function**, denoted $\exp(x)$.

But of course as we said earlier, simply giving the function a name does not tell us anything about it.

In Section 6.3 we investigated this IVP in some detail and we were able to draw an approximate graph of the natural exponential (at least near the initial value, $\exp(0)$). We will explore this function further here.

Recall that the Taylor Polynomial of a function, as described in Section 6.4, Equation 6.8, given by[3]

$$T_n(x) = y(0) + \frac{y'(0)}{1!}x + \frac{y^{(2)}(0)}{2!}x^2 + \frac{y^{(3)}(0)}{3!}x^3 + \cdots + \frac{y^{(n)}(0)}{n!}x^n,$$

can approximate the function $y(x)$ well, near a given point. Since we know the value of the natural exponential at the initial value let's try to generate the Taylor Polynomial approximation of $\exp(x)$ near that point.

Notice that because $\exp(x)$ satisfies IVP (7.2) it also satisfies each of the following (why?):

$$\exp^{(2)}(x) = \exp'(x) = \exp(x)$$
$$\exp^{(3)}(x) = \exp^{(2)}(x) = \exp'(x) = \exp(x)$$
$$\vdots$$
$$\exp^{(n)}(x) = \cdots = \exp^{(2)}(x) = \exp'(x) = \exp(x) \tag{7.3}$$

---

[3]Recall that the parenthetical superscript, (n), indicates the nth derivative. Thus $y^{(2)}(x)$ represents the second derivative of $y(x)$, $y^{(3)}$ represents the third derivative, and so on.

Problem #261:

Let $T_n(x)$ be the nth degree Taylor polynomial approximation of $\exp(x)$ and use Equation (7.3) and the initial value, $\exp(0) = 1$ to show that

$$T_n(x) = 1 + x + \frac{x^2}{2!} + \frac{x^3}{3!} + \cdots + \frac{x^n}{n!}.$$

It is now time to solve IVP (7.2) by finding an explicit formula for $\exp(x)$.

But how? Nothing really presents itself as a potential solution so what should we do? Since we don't seem to have any better options, let's see if we can guess a solution.

Digression #13: The Art of Guessing Effectively

No, really. Guessing can be surprisingly effective.

You know this of course. You've been doing it all of your life, but in the past – especially in math classes – guessing was probably discouraged so you tend to deny doing it, possibly even to yourself. It's OK. Guess anyway. We won't tell anyone.

The fact is that guessing is a tried and true solution technique and we encourage you to use it regularly. Guessing is nothing more, or less, than relying on your native intuition.

However, effective guessing is a skill. You need practice to do it well and, unfortunately, you have probably not had much chance to practice that skill in the context of mathematics. So we encourage you to guess often from now on. But be aware that making a guess is a process, not an event. If you guess wrong, which is most likely, then you have a new, related problem to think about: All of your intuition said this was a good guess. Why didn't it work? The answer to that question almost always gives some insight into the original problem. Even a bad guess can be useful.

However a bad guess, indeed any guess, in isolation is a waste of time. You must also take the time to figure out why your bad guess doesn't work.

But the real danger in guessing – the reason it is usually discouraged – is that when you do guess correctly, or nearly so, it is very tempting to just move on from there. Don't do that.

Guessing correctly means that your intuition was very good. But intuition is unconscious. It is at least as important to understand where a good guess came from, and why it worked as it is to understand why a bad guess didn't work. But when you guess well it is extremely tempting to just take your good guess and run with it. This will invariably lead to confusion later. So, when you guess correctly take a few moments to think about the intuition that led you to that guess. Bring that intuition out of your unconscious mind and into your conscious mind. If you don't do that your guesses are a waste of your time.

════════════ End Of Digression #13 ════════════

So let's take a guess. There is no need to get really crazy about it though. We already know that the Taylor polynomial of $\exp(x)$ approximates $\exp(x)$. Maybe we can find an n large enough that the approximation becomes exact.

Problem #262: Find the pattern

Show that none of the following[4] is a solution of IVP (8).
(**Hint:** Observe that if $y(x)$ is a solution then $y - \frac{dy}{dx} = 0$.)

(**a**) $y = 1 + x + \frac{x^2}{2!} + \frac{x^3}{3!}$

(**c**) $y = 1 + x + \frac{x^2}{2!} + \frac{x^3}{3!} + \ldots + \frac{x^{10}}{10!}$

(**b**) $y = 1 + x + \frac{x^2}{2!} + \frac{x^3}{3!} + \frac{x^4}{4!}$

(**d**) $y = 1 + x + \frac{x^2}{2!} + \frac{x^3}{3!} + \ldots + \frac{x^{999999}}{999999!} + \frac{x^{1000000}}{1000000!}$

Notice that if

$$y = 1 + x + \frac{x^2}{2!} + \frac{x^3}{3!} + \ldots + \frac{x^{999999}}{999999!} + \frac{x^{1000000}}{1000000!}$$

then

$$\frac{dy}{dx} = 1 + x + \frac{x^2}{2!} + \frac{x^3}{3!} + \ldots + \frac{x^{999999}}{999999!},$$

so that the difference between y and $\frac{dy}{dx}$ is

$$y - \frac{dy}{dx} = \frac{x^{1000000}}{1000000!}.$$

Since the difference between y and $\frac{dy}{dx}$ is that stupid one-millionth term – which is very small – it is clear that we've almost got something here. Surely we can handle that last term somehow!

Sadly no, we can't. In fact no polynomial will solve IVP (7.2).

Problem #263:

Show that the previous paragraph is true. That is, show that there is no (non-zero) polynomial that solves the differential equation: $\frac{dy}{dx} = y$.
(**Hint:** Consider the degree of the polynomial and the degree of its derivative.)

Since no polynomial will work a fair question is: Why have we taken you on this wild goose chase?

In fact, we almost have a solution here. One million is a very large number, so one million factorial (1000000!) is inconceivably large. Thus for any value of x we're likely to encounter that one millionth term, $\frac{x^{1000000}}{1000000!}$, is so incredibly close to zero that it almost isn't really there. And if it isn't really there then

$$y = 1 + x + \frac{x^2}{2!} + \frac{x^3}{3!} + \ldots + \frac{x^{999999}}{999999!} \underbrace{+ \frac{x^{1000000}}{1000000!}}_{\text{Not really here. Shhh!}}$$

----

[4]The notation 3! is read "three factorial" and means $3 \cdot 2 \cdot 1$. Similarly $4! = 4 \cdot 3 \cdot 2 \cdot 1$ and in general $n! = n(n-1)(n-2)\ldots 3 \cdot 2 \cdot 1$

and its derivative

$$\frac{dy}{dx} = 1 + x + \frac{x^2}{2!} + \frac{x^3}{3!} + \ldots + \frac{x^{999999}}{999999!}$$

are pretty much the same thing.

So we're . . . done, . . . right?

No, of course not. Although that last term really is practically zero it is not actually zero, no matter how small it is. As Newton said, "In mathematics the smallest of errors must be dealt with[5]."

So we haven't solved our problem in the sense of having an explicit formula for $\exp(x)$. But we do know a great deal about it at this point. In particular we know that the Taylor polynomial $1 + x + \frac{x^2}{2!} + \frac{x^3}{3!} + \ldots + \frac{x^{999999}}{999999!} + \frac{x^{1000000}}{1000000!}$ will be a very good approximation of $\exp(x)$, at least for values of x near zero.

But if there is no polynomial that solves equation (7.2) does that mean there is no solution at all? Certainly not. In fact, since that last term of the polynomial seems to be the stumbling block the solution is clear: All we need to do is not have a last term.

This is a startling idea but before we dismiss it, let's take our own advice from Digression #13. We'll trust our intuition, but also examine it closely. What we're saying is that the solution of Equation (7.2) is:

$$y = 1 + x + \frac{x^2}{2!} + \frac{x^3}{3!} + \cdots \tag{7.4}$$

where the dots at the end mean that the summation goes on forever. There is no last term.

You would expect a polynomial that doesn't end to be called an infinite polynomial but it is not. Such an expression is called an **infinite series.** Usually we just call it a series. A series is not a polynomial. That is, a polynomial is defined to have only finitely many terms and a series is defined to have infinitely many terms. We distinguish them from each other specifically so that we don't confuse a series with a polynomial.

An obvious question to ask is, "Does this infinite series even mean anything?" Or, equivalently, "What does it mean to add up infinitely many numbers?" These are excellent questions which will have to be addressed eventually. But for now we won't let them trouble us. We'll just assume that $y = 1 + x + \frac{x^2}{2!} + \frac{x^3}{3!} + \ldots$ makes sense, in the same way we assumed that differentials make sense and defer those questions until later.

Problem #264:

Having set aside those deeper questions (for now) we can show that we have found the solution of our IVP.

(a) Differentiate the series $y = 1 + x + \frac{x^2}{2!} + \frac{x^3}{3!} + \ldots$ term-by-term to show that $\frac{dy}{dx} = y$.

(b) Show that $y(0) = 1$.

  (**Hint:** Yes, this really is as easy as it looks.)

---

[5]Newton wrote his scientific works in Latin. This is a very loose translation of the phrase "*In rebus mathematicis erores quam minimi non sunt contemnendi.*" from his book *Quadraturam Curvarum* (On the Quadrature of Curves).

We would be remiss if we did not mention that we have lead you up to the edge of an abyss here. It is not at all clear that the Sum Rule for differentiation can be extended to infinite sums in any meaningful manner. In fact, this is a very delicate question. Sometimes the extension is valid and sometimes it is not. This is another of the foundational questions (like "What is a differential?") that took mathematicians nearly 200 years to resolve and understanding that resolution requires the use of considerably more subtle tools than we have at this point. You will learn more about this in the next course. For now we will assert the prerogative of the teacher and simply tell you that in this case term-by-term differentiation still works.

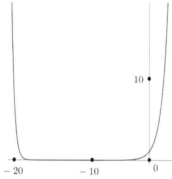

Problem #264 shows that we appear to have the exact solution of IVP (7.2) in the form of the infinite series,

$$\exp(x) = 1 + x + \frac{x^2}{2!} + \frac{x^3}{3!} + \frac{x^4}{4!} + \dots \qquad (7.5)$$

This actually is a correct solution of IVP (7.2), and eventually you will learn to work with infinite series solutions of IVPs directly. But, unfortunately, we don't yet have the tools that allow us to do that. So we will have to find another way. What now?

At the left is the graph of the polynomial $y = 1 + x + \frac{x^2}{2!} + \frac{x^3}{3!} + \dots + \frac{x^{50}}{50!}$ which we believe, from our work in Section 6.4, should be a good approximation to $\exp(x)$, at least when x is near zero. When we zoom in on the part of the graph which is near $x = 0$ we see that the following graph should be a reasonable approximation to the solution of IVP 7.2 in the interval shown.

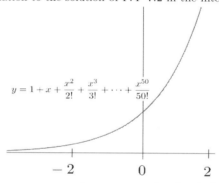

In your earlier math courses you may have seen graphs that looked like this before. If not, then consider the following graphs of the **exponential functions**, $y = 2^x$ and $y = 3^x$

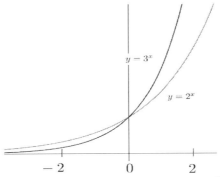

and notice that they are very similar to the graph of $y = 1 + x + \frac{x^2}{2!} + \frac{x^3}{3!} + \cdots + \frac{x^{50}}{50!}$. This is much clearer when we graph all three functions on the same axes as seen here:

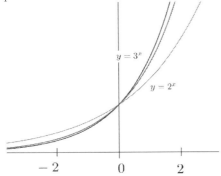

As you can plainly see near $x = 0$ they are indeed very similar.

Since the polynomial $y = 1 + x + \frac{x^2}{2!} + \frac{x^3}{3!} + \cdots + \frac{x^{50}}{50!}$ is an approximation to the solution of IVP 7.2 it appears that either of $y(x) = 2^x$ or $y(x) = 3^x$ might be a viable candidate for the solution of our IVP. Is it possible we've had the solution in our hands all along? Let's differentiate $y(x) = 2^x$ to see if solves IVP (7.2).

If $y(x) = 2^x$ then $y(0) = 2^0 = 1$ so the initial condition is satisfied.

To check the differential equation it is tempting to assume that we can apply the Power Rule, giving us $\frac{d(2^x)}{dx} = x2^{x-1}$. But this can't possibly be correct because when x is negative then $x2^{x-1}$ is also negative. But the slope of $y(x) = 2^x$ is positive everywhere as you can see from its graph.

In fact, none of our differentiation rules will give us the derivative of $y = 2^x$. So we will have to go back to basics and find $\frac{dy}{dx}$ from first principles, without using any of our Differentiation Rules.

Let $y(x) = 2^x$ and observe that dy is the (infinitesimal) difference between $y(x + dx)$ and[6] $y(x)$, or

$$dy = y(x + dx) - y(x)$$

---

[6]Our notation fails us a bit here. Recall that $y(x)$ is a function so $y(x + dx)$ means "y evaluated at $x + dx$." This is not multiplication.

Since $y(x + \mathrm{d}x)$ is equal to $2^{x+\mathrm{d}x}$ and $y(x) = 2^x$ we have,

$$\mathrm{d}y = 2^{x+\mathrm{d}x} - 2^x.$$

Thus

$$\mathrm{d}y = 2^x(2^{\mathrm{d}x} - 1). \tag{7.6}$$

We want to form $\frac{\mathrm{d}y}{\mathrm{d}x}$ so we divide Equation (7.6) by $\mathrm{d}x$, giving

$$\frac{\mathrm{d}y}{\mathrm{d}x} = \frac{2^x(2^{\mathrm{d}x} - 1)}{\mathrm{d}x}. \tag{7.7}$$

The differential in the exponent is a bit concerning. We will have to be clever.

We have become comfortable thinking of $\mathrm{d}x$ as infinitely small, but it should be clear that if we take $\mathrm{d}x$ to be a very small, but finite number, say $\mathrm{d}x = 0.0000001$, we can use Equation (7.7) to approximate $\frac{\mathrm{d}y}{\mathrm{d}x}$ as accurately as we wish.

Replacing $\mathrm{d}x$ with 0.0000001 on the right side of Equation (7.7) we get

$$\frac{\mathrm{d}y}{\mathrm{d}x} = \frac{\mathrm{d}(2^x)}{\mathrm{d}x} \approx 2^x \left[\frac{(2^{\mathrm{d}x} - 1)}{\mathrm{d}x} \right]_{\mathrm{d}x=0.0000001} \approx 2^x(0.7). \tag{7.8}$$

Drill #265: Confirm Equation 7.8.

This isn't bad for a first try! Do you see that we have almost satisfied the differential equation? We have $\frac{\mathrm{d}(2^x)}{\mathrm{d}x} \approx (0.7)2^x$ when what we need is $\frac{\mathrm{d}(2^x)}{\mathrm{d}x} = 2^x$. The constant factor is a bit too small. If it were 1 instead of 0.7 we'd have the solution of IVP (7.2). This is hopeful.

Performing the same calculation using $y(x) = 3^x$ we see that once again we almost have a solution:

$$\frac{\mathrm{d}y}{\mathrm{d}x} = \frac{\mathrm{d}(3^x)}{\mathrm{d}x} \approx 3^x \left[\frac{(3^{\mathrm{d}x} - 1)}{\mathrm{d}x} \right]_{\mathrm{d}x=0.0000001} \approx 3^x(1.1). \tag{7.9}$$

The initial condition is still satisfied and once again the differential equation in (7.2) is *almost* satisfied. But this time the coefficient, 1.1 is a bit too big.

It stands to reason that there must be some number between 2 and 3 with the property that $y = (\text{number})^x$ satisfies IVP (7.2). For historical reasons this number, whatever it is, has been named e. So the solution of IVP (7.2) is

$$\exp(x) = e^x.$$

The function $y(x) = e^x$ is called the **natural exponential** function[7] and e is its base just as 2 is the base of the exponential function $y(x) = 2^x$ and 3 is the base of the exponential function $y(x) = 3^x$.

Of course, we only know that $2 < e < 3$ so far. How might we find a better approximation to e?

---

[7]You can decide for yourself how natural this really is. Opinions vary. But whether you decide you like this name or not it is the name everyone uses so we're stuck with it.

Drill #266:

Since we know that $\exp(x) = 1 + x + \frac{x^2}{2!} + \frac{x^3}{3!} + \cdots$ solves IVP 7.2, it should be clear that we can approximate $e = e^1$ by computing the sum of, say fifty, terms of the series.

$$e \approx 1 + 1 + \frac{1^2}{2!} + \frac{1^3}{3!} + \cdots + \frac{1^{50}}{50!}.$$

Compute this approximation using your favorite computing technology to confirm that $e \approx 2.718$.

(**Comment:** If you don't have any computing technology available just compute the sum of the first six terms.)

The upshot of Drill #266 is that if we replace 2 with $e \approx 2.718$ in Equation 7.8, or if we replace 3 in Equation 7.9 the constant we get should be closer to 1 than either 0.7 or 1.1.

Checking this gives

$$\frac{dy}{dx} = e^x \left[\frac{2.718^{dx} - 1}{dx} \right]_{dx=0.0000001} \approx e^x (1.00000004943).$$

We did not get exactly 1 because

1. We used an approximation of e, not e itself, and

2. 0.0000001 is a very small, finite number, not a differential.

But the evidence is compelling that $\exp(x) = e^x$ is the solution of the IVP (7.2). Henceforth then, we will reserve the letter e to designate the base of the natural exponential function.

You might ask, "Why not just figure out what e actually is, and use that? Why use the letter e?" The answer is that e is an irrational number much like π. Among other things this means that its decimal expansion never ends, so we use e for the same reason we use π.

Digression #14: Exponential Notation

We originally named this function $\exp(x)$, and this is still a valid name for it, just as $\text{sqr}(x)$ is a valid name for the function $\text{sqr}(x) = x^2$. However, just as the formula $y(x) = x^2$ better represents the way we usually think about the squaring function ("square the input variable"), the notation $y(x) = e^x$ better represents the way we usually think about the natural exponential function.

You should think of the natural exponential as "this funny number e raised to the power of the input variable."

However, it is a curious fact that the modern definition of the natural exponential is not e^x. The modern definition is actually the infinite series we derived earlier:

$$e^x = \exp(x) = 1 + x + \frac{x^2}{2!} + \frac{x^3}{3!} + \cdots.$$

To see why this is, ask yourself what the expression $e^{1/2}$ means.

That's easy enough. Since $x^{1/2} = \sqrt{x}$ clearly $e^{1/2} = \sqrt{e}$. It would not necessarily be easy to compute the square root of e but we're only asking about the meaning of our symbols here.

Since e is a positive number we can take its square root and that is what $\sqrt{e}$ means, even if we can't compute it. In precisely the same way $e^{5/7} = \sqrt[7]{e^5}$, $e^{2/3} = \sqrt[3]{e^2}$ and in general if a and b are positive integers, $e^{a/b} = \sqrt[b]{e^a}$.

But what could the expression 2^e possibly mean? Since e is not an integer it doesn't mean "e copies of 2 multiplied together." Since e can't be represented as ratio of integers (because it is irrational after all) it doesn't mean some root of 2 raised to a power the way that say, $2^{5/7}$ means $\sqrt[7]{2^5}$. This difficulty is compounded if we ask for the meaning of e^π or π^e since both e and π are irrational.

And this is not just a matter of not knowing the value of e. The difficulty is built into the real numbers. Recall that we saw the same issue come up in Section 3.2 when we tried to extend the Power Rule to irrational exponents. This is weird.

Even if we can't compute it we need to find a way to give meaning^a to the expression e^x that works when x is irrational. Ideally, we'd like our interpretation to be consistent with our understanding that $e^3 = e \cdot e \cdot e$.

This is precisely why we define natural exponential as an infinite series. It can be shown that if m, and n are integers ($n > 0$) then

$$\exp(m/n) = \left(\sqrt[n]{e}\right)^m = 1 + (m/n) + \frac{(m/n)^n}{n!} + \frac{(m/n)^3}{3!} + \frac{(m/n)^4}{4!} + \dots,$$

If there is only one solution to the IVP (there is) then $y(x) = e^x$ and $y(x) = 1 + x + \frac{x^2}{2!} + \frac{x^3}{3!} + \dots$ must be the same solution. Defining $\exp(x)$ as

$$\exp(x) = 1 + x + \frac{x^2}{2!} + \frac{x^3}{3!} + \frac{x^4}{4!} + \dots, \tag{7.10}$$

rather than $\exp(x) = e^x$ addresses all of these issues. For example e^π means

$$e^\pi = 1 + \pi + \frac{\pi^2}{2!} + \frac{\pi^3}{3!} + \frac{\pi^4}{4!} + \dots.$$

Of course we are still free to think of the natural exponential as e^x, regardless of the definition and we encourage you to do that. It can be very helpful.

Problem #267:

For this problem use the approximation

$$e^x \approx 1 + x + \frac{x^2}{2!} + \frac{x^3}{3!} + \frac{x^4}{4!} + \frac{x^5}{5!} + \frac{x^6}{6!} + \frac{x^7}{7!} + \frac{x^8}{8!} \tag{7.11}$$

a) Use Equation (7.11) to show that $e^{-1} \approx 0.36788$. Compare this with the numerical value of $\frac{1}{e} \approx \frac{1}{2.71828}$ you get from a calculator.
(**Hint:** In equation (7.11) take $x = -1$.)

b) Use Equation (7.11) to show that $\sqrt{e} \approx 1.64872$. Compare this with the numerical value of $\sqrt{e} \approx \sqrt{2.71828}$ you get from a calculator.

[a]Many people are repelled when they encounter this situation. Especially in mathematics. After all, mathematics is about having the answers to mathematical problems isn't it?
Well, no. Actually it isn't. You're thinking of engineering.
Mathematics is about finding the answers to mathematical problems, not having them.

━━━━━━━ **End Of Digression #14** ━━━━━━━

We now have a new differentiation rule to remember. This one is particularly easy to remember: The natural exponential function is its own derivative,

$$\frac{d(e^x)}{dx} = e^x.$$

But just because we have a new rule, does not mean that our old differentiation rules are ignored. As always, all of the rules work together.

Example #38:

Find the derivative of $y = e^x \sin(3x)$.

Using the product rule, we have

$$d\left(e^x \sin(3x)\right) = e^x \, d(\sin(3x)) + \sin(3x) \, d(e^x)$$
$$= e^x \cos(3x) \, d(3x) + \sin(3x)e^x \, dx$$
$$= e^x \cos(3x)3 \, dx + \sin(3x)e^x \, dx$$
$$\frac{d\left(e^x \sin(3x)\right)}{dx} = e^x \left[3\cos(3x) + \sin(3x)\right]$$

End Of Example #38

Drill #268:

Compute dy for each of the following, and use this to find the IVP that each one solves.
(**Hint:** Use a substitution to make each one easier on your eyes.)

(a) $y = e^{2x}$

(b) $y = e^{\pi x}$

(c) $y = e^{\sqrt{2}x}$

(d) $y = e^{rx}$ where r is an unknown constant.

Drill #269:

For each of the following find $\frac{dy}{dx}$:

(a) $y = \sin(e^x)$

(b) $y = e^{\sin(x)}$

(c) $y = \cos(e^x)$

(d) $y = e^{\cos(x)}$

(e) $y = e^{5x}\sin(\pi x)$

(f) $y = e^x\cos(3x)$

(g) $y = \dfrac{x}{e^x}$

(h) $y = \frac{e^x - 1}{e^x + 1}$

(i) $y = \dfrac{e^x}{4x^2 + 3x - 5}$

(j) $y = e^{x^2 + \sin(x)}$

(k) $y = \frac{3\sqrt{x}+1}{e^x}$

(l) $y = \tan(e^x)$

Drill #270:

Find an equation of the line tangent to each function below at the given point.

(a) $y = \dfrac{x}{e^x}$, $(0,0)$

(b) $y = \dfrac{x}{e^x}$, $(1, 1/e)$

(c) $y = \dfrac{e^x}{4x^2 + 3x - 5}$, $(0, -1/5)$,

(d) $y = \dfrac{e^x}{4x^2 + 3x - 5}$, $(1, e/2)$

Problem #271:

(a) Show that when we use Newton's Method to approximate the coordinates of the intersection point of the curves $y = -x$ and $y = e^x$, we get the iteration formula

$$r_{n+1} = \frac{r_n - 1}{1 + e^{-r_n}}$$

(b) Starting with $r_0 = 0$ compute r_1, r_2, and r_3. Compare your approximation with a solution obtained from whatever computing technology you prefer.

Problem #272: (Find the Pattern)

(a) Compute $\frac{dy}{dt}$ for each of the following:

(i) $y = te^t$

(ii) $y = (t + 1)e^t$

(iii) $y = (t^2 + t + 1)e^t$

(iv) $y = (t^3 + t^2 + t + 1)e^t$

(b) From your work in part (a) what do you expect $\frac{dy}{dt}$ to be if

$$y = \left(t^n + t^{n-1} + \cdots + t + 1\right)e^t.$$

Show that your guess is correct or find the correct solution if you guessed wrong.

Problem #273:

For each of the following, assume that $x = x(t)$, $y = y(t)$, and $z = z(t)$. Find an equation relating $\frac{dx}{dt}$, $\frac{dy}{dt}$, and $\frac{dz}{dt}$.

(a) $e^y = x^2 + 3z - 2$

(b) $\sin(xy) = (e^z)^y$

(c) $\tan(x + z) = e^y e^x$

(d) $e^{xyz} = 3$

(e) $x^2 + y^2 + z^2 = 2$

(f) $e^{x^2 + y^2 + z^2} = 2$

Problem #274:

(a) Show that $y = e^{t+a}$ satisfies $\frac{dy}{dt} = y$ for any constant a.
(**Comment:** This problem is not the same as IVP (7.2). How does it differ?)

(b) Show that $y = Ae^t$ also satisfies $\frac{dy}{dt} = y$ for any constant A.

(c) Parts (a) and (b) imply that $e^{t+a} = Ae^t$. Use this knowledge to to show that

$$e^{t+a} = e^t \cdot e^a.$$

You might recognize this property of exponents from your Algebra class.

Problem #275:

(a) For $y = e^x$, $y = \sin(x)$, and $y = \cos(x)$ compute

(i) $\dfrac{dy}{dx}$ **(ii)** $\dfrac{d^2 y}{dx^2}$ **(iii)** $\dfrac{d^3 y}{dx^3}$ **(iv)** $\dfrac{d^4 y}{dx^4}$

(b) Does it seem significant that $\frac{d^4 y}{dx^4} = y$ for all three functions? What does your intuition say?

Hyperbolic Trigonometry: The Hanging Chain

We commented in Section 4.9 that Galileo believed erroneously that a chain hanging from two pegs falls naturally into the shape of a parabola. In Problem #134 we showed that Galileo was wrong but we have not yet addressed the question: What is the shape of a hanging chain?

Recall that the hanging chain must satisfy the differential equation

$$\frac{d^2y}{dx^2} = \frac{w}{H}\sqrt{1 + \left(\frac{dy}{dx}\right)^2}$$

where w is the weight density of the chain and H is the (constant) magnitude of the horizontal tension. In Problem 276 we will see that although the natural exponential function $y = e^x$ is not the solution itself, it is the key to the solution.

Problem #276: The Shape of a Hanging Chain

The Calculus in this problem is pretty straightforward but the Algebra gets a bit messy. To avoid some of this mess in parts (a), (b), and (c) we will solve the special case where $\frac{w}{H} = 1$. In part (d) we'll use our solution of this special case to solve the original problem.

So assume that $\frac{w}{H} = 1$. For this special case we will call our variables X and Y, rather than x and y. The reasons for this will become clear in part (d).

(a) Show that $1 + \left(\frac{e^X - e^{-X}}{2}\right)^2 = \left(\frac{e^X + e^{-X}}{2}\right)^2$.

(**Hint:** It might help to make the substitution $e^X = a$ just to make things "easier on the eyes." That makes $e^{-X} = \frac{1}{a}$.)

(b) Show that $\frac{d\left(\frac{1}{2}(e^X + e^{-X})\right)}{dX} = \frac{1}{2}(e^X - e^{-X})$ and that $\frac{d\left(\frac{1}{2}(e^X - e^{-X})\right)}{dX} = \frac{1}{2}(e^X + e^{-X})$

(c) Show that the curve $Y = \frac{1}{2}\left(e^X + e^{-X}\right)$ satisfies differential Equation (4.14):

$$\frac{d^2Y}{dX^2} = \sqrt{1 + \left(\frac{dY}{dX}\right)^2}$$

Now let's tackle the original problem.

(d) Show that

$$y = \frac{H}{w}\left(\frac{e^{\frac{wx}{H}} + e^{-\frac{wx}{H}}}{2}\right) \tag{7.12}$$

satisfies the equation

$$\frac{d^2y}{dx^2} = \frac{w}{H}\sqrt{1 + \left(\frac{dy}{dx}\right)^2}$$

where w is the weight density of the chain, and H is the constant (magnitude of the) horizontal tension.

(**Hint:** This is essentially the same computation you did for the special case, but the Algebra is messier. Consider making it "easier on the eyes" with the substitutions

$$X = \frac{wx}{H} \text{ and } Y(X) = \frac{1}{2}\left(e^X + e^{-X}\right).$$

We already know from part (c) that $\frac{d^2Y}{dX^2} = \sqrt{1 + \left(\frac{dY}{dX}\right)^2}$. Notice that $y = \frac{H}{w}Y(X)$ and use this to show that $\frac{dy}{dx} = \frac{dY}{dX}$ and that $\frac{d^2y}{dx^2} = \frac{w}{H}\frac{d^2Y}{dX^2}$.)

(e) Assume $w = 1$, and $H = 1$ and graph the curve given by Equation (7.12). Does it look like a hanging chain? What happens to the graph if we use $w = 1, H = 2$ or $w = 2, H = 1$. Does this make sense physically? Why or why not?

The expressions $\frac{1}{2}\left(e^x + e^{-x}\right)$ and $\frac{1}{2}\left(e^x - e^{-x}\right)$ arise frequently in many scientific and engineering problems and have been named the **hyberbolic cosine** and **hyberbolic sine** and are denoted $\cosh(x)$ and[8] $\sinh(x)$, respectively. As you see these names break with the long-standing mathematical tradition of giving important functions three letter names. Why do you suppose we would do that?

Recall that the unit circle, $x^2 + y^2 = 1$, is parameterized by

$$P(t) = \left\{ \begin{array}{c} \cos(t) \\ \sin(t) \\ 0 \le t < 2\pi \end{array} \right\}$$

since

$$x^2 + y^2 = \cos^2(t) + \sin^2(t) = 1.$$

Problem #277:

Analogously, show that the **unit hyperbola**, $x^2 - y^2 = 1$ is parameterized by

$$P(t) = \left\{ \begin{array}{c} \cosh(t) \\ \sinh(t) \\ -\infty < t < \infty \end{array} \right\}.$$

That is, show that $x^2 - y^2 = \cosh^2(t) - \sinh^2(t) = 1$.

The obvious similarity between the formulas

$$\cos^2(x) + \sin^2(x) = 1 \text{ and } \cosh^2(x) - \sinh^2(x) = 1$$

is not a coincidence. It also explains why they are called **Hyperbolic Trigonometric Functions**.

The many scientific and engineering problems that involve the hyperbolic functions are slightly outside the scope of this text. So we will only examine some of their more elementary properties in the next problem.

---

[8]Traditionally, sinh is read as "cinch".

Problem #278:

In addition to $\cosh(x)$ and $\sinh(x)$ we make the following definitions which are clearly modeled on the definitions of the trigonometric functions:

$$\tanh(x) = \frac{\sinh(x)}{\cosh(x)}, \quad \coth(x) = \frac{\cosh(x)}{\sinh(x)}, \quad \text{sech}(x) = \frac{1}{\cosh(x)}, \quad \text{csch}(x) = \frac{1}{\sinh(x)}.$$

(a) Show that

$$\textbf{(i)} \quad \frac{d(\cosh(x))}{dx} = \sinh(x)$$

$$\textbf{(ii)} \quad \frac{d(\sinh(x))}{dx} = \cosh(x).$$

$$\textbf{(iii)} \quad \frac{d(\tanh(x))}{dx} = \text{sech}^2(x).$$

$$\textbf{(iv)} \quad \frac{d(\coth(x))}{dx} = -\text{csch}^2(x).$$

$$\textbf{(v)} \quad \frac{d(\text{sech}(x))}{dx} = -\text{sech}(x)\tanh(x).$$

$$\textbf{(vi)} \quad \frac{d(\text{csch}(x))}{dx} = -\text{csch}(x)\coth(x).$$

(b) Show that: $\sinh(-x) = -\sinh(x)$

(c) Show that: $\cosh(-x) = \cosh(x)$

(d) Show that: $\sinh(x \pm y) = \sinh(x)\cosh(y) \pm \cosh(x)\sinh(y)$.

(e) Show that: $\cosh(x \pm y) = \cosh(x)\cosh(y) \pm \sinh(x)\sinh(y)$.

(f) Compare each of the identities above with the corresponding trigonometric identity.

Problem #279:

Show that $y = \cosh(x)$ and $y = \sinh(x)$ both satisfy the differential equation:

$$\frac{d^2y}{dx^2} = y$$

and compare this with Problem #164.

The Gateway Arch

When he designed the Gateway Arch[9] in St. Louis, Missouri, architect Eero Saarinen wanted to build it in the shape of an inverted catenary. The arch would have a height of 630 feet and a width of 630 feet. Its cross sections would be equilateral triangles with sides 54 feet at ground level shrinking to 17 feet at the top. To obtain the shape of the arch, Saarinen decided that the centers of the triangular cross sections should follow the curve

$$y = 693.8597 - 68.7672 \cosh(.0100333x), \tag{7.13}$$

The Gateway Arch in St. Louis

where $-299.226 \le x \le 299.226$.

Problem #280:

A true catenary is the graph of any function of the form

$$y = \frac{1}{a}\cosh(ax).$$

(a) Show that $y = 68.7672\cosh(0.0100333x)$ is not a true catenary.

(b) Plot the graph of Equation (7.13), and determine the x and y intercepts.

(c) Notice that the answers in part (b) do not determine an arch whose height and width are exactly 630 feet. This is because this curve represents the centers[10] of the triangular cross sections.

    (i) The sketch below represents the cross-section of the the arch, which is an equilateral triangle. In the sketch each side is equal to s, and the point P is equidistant from A, B, and C. Show that the perpendicular distance from P to one side is $\frac{s}{2\sqrt{3}}$.

    (ii) Use the result in part (i) to determine the height and width of the arch.

(d) The curve Saarinen used is called a **weighted catenary**. It is the shape of a hanging chain whose density is not uniform. Saarinen decided to go with this since the size of the

---

[9]For more information on the history and mathematics of the Gateway Arch, see the article by Robert Osserman *How the Gateway Arch Got its Shape*

[10]Actually the centroids. You will learn about centroids when you take Integral Calculus.

triangles was decreasing as they approached the apex of the arch. A true catenary arch would be something of the form

$$y = \left(625.0925 + \frac{1}{0.00842976}\right) - \frac{1}{0.00842976}\cosh(0.00842976x) \qquad (7.14)$$

Graph equations (7.13) and (7.14) on the same set of axes and use this to show that they both have the same requisite height and width.

7.2 Exponential Growth

Example #39: Population Growth

Suppose we start with a colony of 10 grams of bacteria in a Petri dish and we wish to model the growth of the population as a function of time. In order to keep our initial discussion simple we begin by assuming that 30% of our bacteria divide once per day at the same time. Such a population is growing at a rate of 30% per day. If we start with 10 grams of bacteria on day zero, then on day one we'll have 30% more, or 13 grams. On day two we'll have 30% more than on day one, or 16.9 grams. It should be clear that the rate of growth from day n to day $n+1$ is proportional to how many bacteria we have on day n. Thus from any one day to the next we see that the change in P (ΔP) is given by

$$\Delta P = 0.3P\Delta t \qquad (7.15)$$

where $\Delta t = 1$ day, and ΔP is the change in population on that day.

But we assumed that 30% of the bacteria were dividing in sync once per day, which is unrealistic. To get closer to reality suppose next that enough of them divide during any one hour so that at the end of one day the population has still grown by 30%. Then from any one hour to the next we again have Equation (7.15) but this time Δt is equal to one hour, or $\frac{1}{24}$ day. However, we don't have to measure time in days. If we measure it in hours instead we again have $\Delta t = 1$ hour $= \frac{1}{24}$ day. The constant factor is still 0.3 because we assumed that the population was growing at 30% per day, and this is still true. That factor is called the **nominal**[11] growth rate.

If we measure time in seconds the same reasoning will give us Equation (7.15), with $\Delta t = 1$ second $= 1.15741 \times 10^{-5}$ day. If we measure in nanoseconds we get Equation (7.15), with $\Delta t = 1$ nanosecond $= 1.15741 \times 10^{-14}$ day. If we measure time in infinitesimal increments we get

$$\mathrm{d}P = 0.3P\,\mathrm{d}t.$$

Notice that we are using the Principle of Local Linearity here. In this infinitesimal time interval the **nominal** growth rate, $0.3P$, is virtually constant and so we are treating it as linear growth.

---

[11]The word nominal means "in name or thought" so this is the named growth rate. It is not always the actual growth rate as we will see soon.

Since we started with 10 grams of bacteria we have the initial condition $P(0) = 10$. This says that the amount of bacteria at time t must satisfy the IVP

$$\frac{dP}{dt} = 0.3P, \ P(0) = 10. \tag{7.16}$$

Take specific notice that the differential equation in IVP (7.16) expresses the idea that the rate of change of the population, $\frac{dP}{dt}$, is proportional to the size of the population, P. The constant of proportionality is 0.3, or 30%.

Clearly there is nothing particularly special about the number 0.3. If our colony had been increasing at a **nominal** rate of 15% we'd have arrived at the IVP:

$$\frac{dP}{dt} = 0.15P, \quad P(0) = 10.$$

Drill #281: To begin solving IVP (7.16 show that one solution of the **differential equation** $\frac{dP}{dt} = 0.3P$, from IVP (7.16) is:

$$\rho(t) = e^{0.3t}.$$

There are other solutions. Find one of them.

From Drill #281 we see that a solution of the differential equation in our bacterial growth problem, IVP (7.16), is $\rho(t) = e^{0.3t}$. But $\rho(t)$ does not satisfy the initial condition since

$$\rho(0) = e^{(0.3)0}$$
$$= e^{0}$$
$$= 1 \neq 10,$$

so $\rho(t)$ can't be the solution of our bacterial growth problem, IVP (7.16).

We've found that $P(t) = e^{0.3t}$ satisfies the differential equation but not the initial condition. Can we tweak this so that it satisfies the initial condition?

Problem #282: Find the Pattern

(a) Show that $P(t) = 5e^{0.3t}$ solves the differential equation: $\frac{dP}{dt} = 0.3P$. What is $P(0)$?

(b) Show that $P(t) = 20e^{0.3t}$ solves the differential equation: $\frac{dP}{dt} = 0.3P$. What is $P(0)$?

(c) Show that if α is any constant then $P(t) = \alpha e^{0.3t}$ solves the differential equation $\frac{dP}{dt} = 0.3P$. What is $P(0)$?

(d) Did your answer in part (c) account for the possibility that $\alpha = 0$? If not, redo it assuming that $\alpha = 0$. What is $P(t)$ in this case?

Problem #283:

(a) Use the results of parts (a) and (b) of Problem (282) to show that

$$P(t) = 10e^{0.3t}$$

is the solution of IVP (7.16).

(b) According to the model in part (a), how much did the colony grow over the first day and how does this compare to the growth rate of 30%?

(c) Use the model to predict the size of the colony in 30 days. Is this reasonable? What does it say about our assumptions in this problem?

(d) Suppose our growth rate was 15% per day. Would the bacteria have grown half as much in the first day as it did when the growth rate was 30% per day?

    (i) Make your best guess.   **(ii)** Use Calculus to test your guess.

End Of Example #39

In general, if we start with a population of, say P_0, and the rate of change of $P(t)$ is proportional to P itself then it will satisfy an IVP of the form:

$$\frac{dP}{dt} = rP, \ P(0) = P_0. \tag{7.17}$$

The constant r is called the **nominal** growth rate as we've seen. Because $r = \frac{\frac{dP}{dt}}{P}$ it is also called the **relative** growth rate of the population and is often given as a percentage, as we have done here.

The IVP (7.17) should look familiar to you. Notice that when $r = 1$ and $P_0 = 1$ it is the same as IVP (7.2)

$$\frac{dy}{dx} = y, \ \ y(0) = 1,$$

which we used to define the the natural exponential. Except, of course, for the names of the variables. To put it another way IVP (7.2) is the special case of IVP (7.17) when $r = 1$. Since these are so similar it is not surprising that the solution of IVP (7.17) involves the natural exponential.

Problems #282 and #283 suggest, rather convincingly, that the general solution of IVP (7.17) is

$$P(t) = P_0 e^{rt}. \tag{7.18}$$

Drill #284: Show that $P(t) = P_0 e^{rt}$ is a solution of IVP (7.17).

Part (c) in Problem #283 indicates that there are limitations to the usefulness of IVP (7.16) and its solution, $P(t) = 10e^{0.3t}$. If we use it to predict how much bacteria there would be after one year we get $P(365) = 10e^{0.3 \times 365} \approx 3.59 \times 10^{48}$ grams. Since current estimates of the mass of the entire universe are around 6×10^{27} grams, it is pretty clear that our model doesn't work in the long term.

Clearly the bacteria can not sustain a growth rate of 30% indefinitely. If nothing else, they will eventually run out of food. Our point here is that this model, like all models, is limited. To use a mathematical model effectively we need to stay within its limitations.

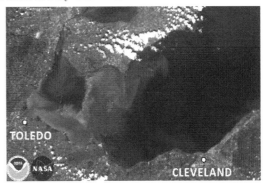

But in the short term this is actually a very good model. The picture at the right shows the surface of Lake Erie during what is called an algal bloom. The green discoloration on the western side of the lake is from an explosive (exponential) growth of algae. When the conditions for algae growth are nearly optimum – if there is abundant food, there is room for the population to expand into, and the water temperature is exactly right – the population of algae in Lake Erie tracks with our model nearly perfectly[12]. The quantity of algae grows exponentially until the conditions become sub-optimal. Then the population of algae drops again to normal levels.

An algal bloom can happen in any body of water where algae grow. They are common in alpine lakes in the early spring when nutrients are released by the melting snow, but the fish and insects that feed on the algae have not yet emerged in large numbers. We will return to this problem in Section 10.1 where we will tweak this model to extend its usefulness to longer periods of time. But for now we will continue to use this exponential growth model with the understanding that for large values of t it is unreliable.

Problem #285:

Suppose our bacteria population is increasing at a nominal rate of 10% per day. If we started with 100 grams, how much would there be after one, two, and three days?

Speaking loosely, the observation that lead us to IVP 7.17 is that the number of baby bacteria in a given generation is proportional to how many parental bacteria were present in the previous generation. Speaking very loosely, more mamas and poppas now, means proportionally more babies later. This is all that is required for exponential growth to occur.

Exponential Functions and Compound Interest

The natural exponential function also arises naturally in financial mathematics. If we invest money in a bond which pays a **nominal interest** rate of 5% annually, and the interest is **compounded** quarterly then the **effective yield** will be 5.09%.

---

[12]Except that the nominal growth rate and the initial condition would need to be adjusted to fit the situation.

There is a lot of financial jargon in the previous paragraph which makes it hard to understand if we don't speak financial-ese. So we will take a few pages to learn the vocabulary. After that things will clear up pretty quickly.

To start, the effective yield represents the actual amount of money earned at the end of one year – how much money the investment actually pays out. For example, if the investment was not compounded at all, then at the end of one year, every dollar invested would yield $1.05 in return, so the effective yield is the same as the **nominal yield**: 5% annually.

If the investment is compounded semiannually (twice per year), then half of interest earned is paid out midway through the year. This money is then re-invested for the next half year. This is summarized in the table below.

5% nominal interest compounded semiannually

Time t in years	Amount investment is worth in dollars
0	$1
1/2	$1 + \$1 \left(\frac{0.05}{2} \right) = \$1 \left(1 + \frac{0.05}{2} \right) = \$1.025$
1	$\$1 \left(1 + \frac{0.05}{2} \right) + \$1 \left(1 + \frac{0.05}{2} \right) \left(\frac{0.05}{2} \right)$ $= \$1 \left(1 + \frac{0.05}{2} \right)^2 = \$1.050625$

The effective yield in this case is approximately 5.06%.

The table below shows, in abbreviated form, the computations needed if the investment is compounded three times in a year.

5% nominal interest, compounded three times annually

Time in years	Amount investment is worth in dollars
0	$1
1/3	$\$1 \left(1 + \frac{0.05}{3} \right)^1$
2/3	$\$1 \left(1 + \frac{0.05}{3} \right)^2$
1	$\$1 \left(1 + \frac{0.05}{3} \right)^3 \approx 1.0508$

Quarterly compounding means that the interest is re-invested four times and is shown in the next table.

5% nominal interest, compounded $1 quarterly

Time in years	Amount investment is worth in dollars
0	$1
1/4	$\$1 \left(1 + \frac{0.05}{4} \right)^1$
1/2	$\$1 \left(1 + \frac{0.05}{4} \right)^2$
3/4	$\$1 \left(1 + \frac{0.05}{4} \right)^3$
1	$\$1 \left(1 + \frac{0.05}{4} \right)^4 \approx 1.0509$

Notice how these three tables differ from and are similar to each other. The effective yield comes from the last entry in each table. It is the difference between the amount the investment is worth at the end of the year and what it is worth at the beginning of the year. So if we compound quarterly the effective yield is $1.0509 - 1 = 0.0509 = 5.09\%$.

Similarly, if the investment is compounded daily, then the effective yield is $\left(1 + \frac{0.05}{365}\right)^{365} - 1 \approx 0.0513 = 5.13\%$. If we compound 5% nominal interest, n times in a year, then the return on an investment of one dollar at the end of one year would be $\left(1 + \frac{0.05}{n}\right)^{n}$ dollars, after 2 years $\left(1 + \frac{0.05}{n}\right)^{2n}$ dollars, after 3 years $\left(1 + \frac{0.05}{n}\right)^{3n}$ dollars.

In general,, if we let $A(t)$ denote the value of the investment of one dollar earning 5% annually, compounded n times per year, after t years, we have

$$A(t) = \$1 \cdot \left(1 + \frac{0.05}{n}\right)^{nt}, \ t = 0, 1, 2, \ldots$$

What if the investment was compounded continuously? That is, suppose the interest is being continuously paid out and simultaneously reinvested? Obviously, this can't actually be done, but it comes to the same thing if at the end of the year we get an effective yield that is equal to the effective yield that would come from continuous compounding. All we have to do is figure out what this is.

To do this, it will be convenient to write $A(t)$ as

$$A(t) = \$1 \cdot \left(1 + \frac{0.05}{n}\right)^{nt}$$

$$= \$1 \cdot \left(\left(1 + \frac{0.05}{n}\right)^{\frac{n}{0.05}}\right)^{0.05t}$$

$$= \$1 \cdot \left(\left(1 + \frac{1}{\frac{n}{0.05}}\right)^{\frac{n}{0.05}}\right)^{0.05t}$$

Setting $m = \frac{n}{0.05}$ we see that

$$A(t) = \$1 \cdot \left(\left(1 + \frac{1}{m}\right)^{m}\right)^{0.05t}.$$

We are particularly interested in the quantity $\left(1 + \frac{1}{m}\right)^{m}$ as we compound the interest more frequently (as m becomes very large). The following table shows some values of $\left(1 + \frac{1}{m}\right)^{m}$, for large values of m. Does the numbers in the right colum look familiar to you?

m	$\left(1 + \frac{1}{m}\right)^{m}$
100	2.70481382942
1000	2.71692393224
10000	2.71814592683
100000	2.71826823717
1000000	2.71828046932
10000000	2.71828169255

In Section 7.1 we saw that $e \approx 2.7182$. From this table it would appear that $\left(1 + \frac{1}{m}\right)^{m}$ approaches the number e as m grows larger – that is, as we compound the interest more frequently. We will show that this is in fact the case in Section 11.4.

If this is true (it is) then if we compound the interest continuously we have

$$A(t) = \$1 \cdot (e)^{0.05t}. \tag{7.19}$$

This equation was derived under the assumption that our initial investment was only \$1. In general if the initial investment is A_0 we have

$$A(t) = A_0 e^{0.05t}. \tag{7.20}$$

Does this look familiar?

Drill #286:
The function $A(t)$ has the same form as our solution of IVP #7.16 so it must satisfy the differential equation: $\frac{dA}{dt} = 0.05A$. Confirm that it does.

This is interesting. It appears that IVP #7.17 models continuously compounded investments as well as population growth. Does this make sense to you?

Think about it for a moment. When money invested the rate of return (rate of growth) is always proportional to the initial investment, in the same way that the rate of growth of a population (the rate of return) is. Speaking very loosely, the amount of baby dollars in the next generation will be proportional to the amount of mama dollars and papa dollars in the current generation in the same way that the number of baby bacteria in the next generation is proportional to the number of parent bacteria now. So it makes sense that these two very different real world phenomena are modeled by the same IVP.

From the point of view of a banker or a biologist, these are very different problems so we assign different meanings to the variables and parameters. But since relationship between the variables and parameters is the same whatever we call them, to a mathematician these are the same problem.

This sort of abstraction is one of the strengths of mathematics. It is not at all obvious that population growth, investment income, or nuclear decay (which we will study shortly) are all essentially the same problem. It is only when we have abstracted out the critical features of each that we can see this.

Problem #287:

(a) What would the effective yield be for a bond nominally rated at 5% annually, compounded continuously? How does this compare to the effective yield of an investment compounded daily?

(b) Suppose we had two investments growing continuously with nominal rates of 5% and 10% annually? After one year would the effective yield of the second investment be twice that of the first? Justify your answer.

A natural question to ask is, "How long will it take for my money to double?" Would an investment compounding continuously at a nominal rate of 10% double in half the time as one growing at a nominal rate of 5%. Take a guess and write it down for later reference.

To answer this question we'd need solve $e^{0.05t} = 2$, for t and compare this to the solution of $e^{0.1t} = 2$. To solve either equation we need a way to "undo" the natural exponential function. That is, we need the inverse of the natural exponential function. This leads us to a discussion of the **natural logarithm** function in the next section.

7.3   The Natural Logarithm

John Napier Logs In

In the 16th and 17th centuries the computational needs of science, engineering, finance and navigation were growing increasingly complex, time-consuming, and error prone. The problem of navigating at sea using only the stars as a guide was particularly vexing. It became increasingly important to find very accurate methods of computation that were also as simple as they could possibly be; that could be broken down into simple steps that anyone could do without necessarily understanding the underlying concepts. The Scottish mathematician John Napier (1550 − 1617) invented logarithms specifically to address this problem.

Napier described logarithms in *Mirifici logarithmorum canonis descriptio*, published in 1614, well before Newton or Leibniz were born so logarithms actually predate the invention of Calculus by several decades. He coined the term "logarithm" from the Greek words logos meaning "reasoning," or " reckoning" and arithmos meaning "number." To Napier logarithms were "reckoning numbers" which seems an apt description, given their original purpose.

To see how logarithms work we start with the observation that

$$10^8 = (10 \cdot 10 \cdot 10) \cdot (10 \cdot 10 \cdot 10 \cdot 10 \cdot 10) = 10^{3+5}.$$

More generally, if a is any positive number and m and n are any real numbers then

$$a^{n+m} = a^n \cdot a^m,$$

John Napier
1555-1617

The crucial observation here is that exponentiation (raising to a power) takes the addition of the exponents n and m and turns it into the multiplication of a^n and a^m. Of course, multiplying instead of adding makes computations more complex, not less. This is exactly the reverse of what is needed. What Napier wanted was a way to turn the complexity of multiplication into the simplicity of addition. This would make complex computations – especially computations done by hand with paper and pencil (the only kind there was in those days) much simpler.

To turn multiplication into addition all we have to do is read the equation $a^{n+m} = a^n \cdot a^m$ in the other direction:

$$a^n \cdot a^m = a^{n+m}.$$

Now the multiplication of a^n and a^m has become the addition (in the exponent) of n and m. Of course there is much more to be done to make this a usable computational scheme. But this is the essential idea. For example if we wanted to use this scheme to multiply 123.2387×43.8378 we would first need to know that $123.2387 \approx 10^{2.0907}$ and that $43.8378 \approx 10^{1.6418}$. Adding the exponents gives 3.7325 so the result of the multiplication is $10^{3.7325} \approx 5401$. The way to make this a workable scheme is to compile a large table of numbers and their associated exponents. This is, essentially, what Napier did[13]

Today we call 2.0907 and 1.6418 the **base 10**, or **common logarithms**, of 123.2387, and 43.8378, respectively. Notationally we have

$$\log_{10}(123.2387) = 2.0907$$
$$\log_{10}(43.8378) = 1.6418$$

which is simply a way to say $10^{2.0907} = 123.2387$ and $10^{1.6418} = 43.8378$ backwards.

In general, $\log_{10}(10^n) = n$, and we see that the function $\log_{10}()$ simply undoes the function $f(x) = 10^x$, which makes $\log_{10}()$ the functional inverse of $f(x) = 10^x$, in exactly the same way that $\tan^{-1}(x)$ is the functional inverse of $\tan(x)$ as you recall from Section (5.5).

To use a table of base 10 logarithms to find the product of two numbers we would first look up the logarithm of each number, then add the logarithms. The resulting sum is the base 10 logarithm of the product, so we'd look up in our table what this sum is the logarithm of. The result is the product of the two original numbers. Since the invention of modern computing technology the original purpose of base 10 logarithms – simplifying numerical computations – is completely obsolete. So tables of base 10 logarithms are rarely seen in the wild anymore. On the other hand the **natural exponential** function $\exp(x) = e^x$ and its functional inverse, the **natural logarithm** are both still quite useful in a variety of contexts, both scientific and mathematical.

The graph of the natural exponential is very similar to the graph of $y = 3^x$. As we saw in Section 5.5 if we have the graph of some function we can find the graph of its inverse by interchanging the horizontal and vertical axes. As a practical matter, this is the same as reflecting the graph across the line, $y = x$. The graph of the natural exponential and its inverse the natural logarithm are shown in the diagram at the right.

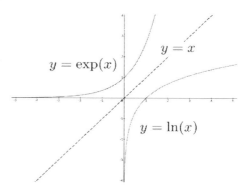

In the same way that $\log_{10}(x)$ is the functional inverse of the base ten exponential, 10^x, the **natural logarithm** - usually denoted $\ln(x)$ – is the functional inverse of the natural exponential, e^x. This inverse relationship allows us to immediately observe two important properties of the natural logarithm.

---

[13]We're taking liberties with the history here. Napier's original scheme was not based on 10^x. We explain how Napier actually defined his logarithms in Digression 17. For now it is useful to pretend that he used 10^x. Also, although Napier started compiling a table of logarithms, sadly he died before finishing. It fell to his friend and colleague Henry Briggs to complete the task.

Two Immediate Properties of the Natural Logarithm

1. $\ln(e^x) = x$.

2. $e^{\ln(x)} = x$.

The properties that make the natural logarithm useful as a theoretical tool are the same properties that made $\log_{10}(x)$ useful as a computational[14] tool:

Four More Properties of the Natural Logarithm

3. $\ln(e) = 1$.

   Notice that this is a special case of Property #1.

4. $\ln(ab) = \ln(a) + \ln(b)$.

5. $\ln\left(\frac{a}{b}\right) = \ln(a) - \ln(b)$.

6. $\ln\left(a^b\right) = b \ln(a)$.

Digression #15: Exponential and Logarithmic Notation

Consider reviewing Digression #9 before reading this one. It will probably help.

As we've observed the **natural logarithm** function is, by definition, the inverse of the **natural exponential** in precisely the same way that $\tan^{-1}(x)$ is, by definition, the inverse of $\tan(x)$. Unfortunately the notation that is used for the **natural exponential** and the **natural logarithm** is not helpful.

It has become standard practice to notate a function using the first three letters of its name. That is why the trigonometric functions are denoted sin, cos, tan, cot, sec, and csc. By that standard we should properly denote the natural exponential with $\exp(x)$. We have used this notation in the past and will continue to use it when we want to emphasize the functional nature of the natural exponential, but most of the time it is more helpful to think of it as the number "e raised to a power" and to denote it with e^x which, unfortunately, doesn't look like the name of a function at all.

As we saw in Digression #9 before it is also fairly standard practice to denote the inverse of a given function with the exponent -1. By that standard we should properly denote the natural logarithm by $\exp^{-1}$, but this is extremely rare.

By the "three letter name" standard the next best name for the natural logarithm should be "$\log(x)$" but that has been used for over 400 years to denote the base 10 logarithm. As a result for historical reasons we are stuck with symbol "$\ln(x)$" to denote the natural logarithm. This notation comes from the initials of the Latin name of the function: *logarithms naturali*. This is unfortunate for the student because it adheres to no standard naming scheme whatsoever. But once you get used to it, it isn't so bad.

Sometimes there are reasons to use logarithms with bases other than 10 or e. For example, computer scientists frequently use logarithms with a base of 2 which they denote $\mathrm{lb}(x)$ (binary logarithm). Even worse, when we talk among ourselves mathematicians tend to use the natural logarithm (because for us it is the most important), but we often denote it as "$\log(x)$." When we are talking to scientists and engineers we use whatever is appropriate to their discipline.

---

[14]In fact if we replace the base 10 with the base e and "ln" with "$\log_{10}$" all of the properties in this list remain true.

None of this affects what the natural logarithm is, how we use it, or how we think about it. Only how we write it. We only bring this up to warn you that because of this wide variation in usage logarithmic notation can be hard to get comfortable with. Be careful. The generic notation is $\log_b(x)$ where b indicates the base. In this scheme the natural logarithm is $\log_e(x)$, the common logarithm is $\log_{10}(x)$, and the binary logarithm is $\log_2(x)$. If you find yourself getting confused it can help to revert to this generic notation.

It is, after all, just notation. Do not confuse the name of a concept with the the concept itself. Conceptually the natural logarithm $(\ln(x))$ is the inverse of the natural exponential (e^x) and you should think of it as such.

It is often helpful to think of $\ln(x)$ as the function that peels the exponent off of e^x as in Property #1: $\ln(e^x) = x$.

—————————————————— End Of Digression #15 ——————————————————

Drill #288:
Evaluate each of the following:

(a) $\ln(e^2)$ **(b)** $\ln(e^{\sin(t)})$ **(c)** $e^{\ln(2)}$ **(d)** $e^{\ln(x+y)}$

Take the time to become very comfortable using all of the properties of logarithms, for exactly the same reason you took time to become very comfortable with the differentiation rules: Exponential and logarithmic functions are basic tools in science.

Problem #289:
Like Property #3, Property #5 is really just a convenience. Show that it is really an immediate consequence of Property #4 and Property #6.
(**Hint:** Find a way to express a/b as a product.)

The simplest use to which we can put a **natural logarithm** is to aid in solving an equation like:
$$3^x = 17.$$

The difficulty here is that the variable x is in the exponent so to isolate it we have to "undo" an exponential. This is exactly what logarithms do! By Property #6, $\ln(3^x) = x\ln(3)$, so we can solve our equation like this:

$$3^x = 17$$
$$\ln(3^x) = \ln(17)$$
$$x\ln(3) = \ln(17)$$
$$x = \frac{\ln(17)}{\ln(3)}.$$

At this point we can use technology to find that $\ln(17) \approx 2.8332$ and $\ln(3) \approx 1.0986$ so that $x = \frac{\ln(17)}{\ln(3)} \approx 2.5789$.

Drill #290: Use your favorite computational tool to confirm that $3^{2.5789} \approx 17$.

Drill #291:

Find approximate solutions for each of the following equations:

(a) $e^x = 5$

(b) $e^x = \frac{1}{\sqrt{e}}$

(c) $e^{3x} = 7$

(d) $e^{x/3} = 12$

(e) $2^x = 3^x$

(f) $e^{x-5} = e^5$

(g) $7^{x^2-x} = e$

(h) $7e^{x+3} = 2$

(i) $e^{2x} - 3e^x + 2 = 0$

(j) $e^{2x} - e^x - 2 = 0$

(k) $\sin(e^x) = \frac{1}{\sqrt{2}}$

Similarly if we needed to solve the equation $\ln(2x - 4) = 0$ we would take advantage of Property #2. Taking the exponential of both side we see that:

$$e^{\ln(2x-4)} = e^0$$
$$2x - 4 = 1$$
$$x = 5/2.$$

Drill #292:

Solve each of the following equations exactly, without the use of technology.

(a) $\ln(2x) - \ln(x + 1) = 4$

(b) $2\ln(x) = \ln(3x - 2)$

(c) $-\ln(2x) = 8$

(d) $-\ln\left(\frac{1}{2x}\right) = 8$

(e) $\ln(2x) + \ln(2) = 8$

(f) $\ln(5x) = \ln(x) + x$

(g) $[\ln(x)]^2 + 3\ln(x) + 2 = 0$

(h) $[\ln(2x)]^2 - \ln(x) - 2 = 0$

(i) $\ln(x) \cdot \ln(2x) = 1$

(j) $\ln(2x) \cdot \ln(x) = \ln(3x)$

Problem #293:

(a) A particle is moving on the x-axis so that its position at time $t \geq 0$ is given by

$$x(t) = \sin(e^t).$$

(i) When is the first time the particle stops moving forward and starts moving backward?

(ii) When does the particle start moving forward again?

(b) A particle is moving on the x-axis so that its position at time $t \geq 0$ is given by $y(t) = e^t - \cos(e^t)$. Show that this particle either moves forward or stops momentarily and then continues moving forward, but never moves backward. At which times does it stop?

Let's return to the question that motivated our look into the logarithm function in the first place: "How long will it take for my money to double?"

Problem #294: Find the pattern

(a) Suppose that P_0 dollars are invested in two separate accounts, A and B, where the interest in compounded continuously at the nominal rates of 5% and 10%, respectively. Let t_A be the time it takes for the initial investment in account A to double, and let t_B be the time it takes for the initial investment in account B to double. Is $t_B = \frac{1}{2}t_A$?

(b) At the end of the last section we asked you to guess the answers to part (a). Did you guess correctly? What was the intuition that lead you to your correct, or incorrect, guess?

(c) Suppose that P_0 dollars are invested in two separate accounts, A and B, where the interest in compounded continuously at the rates r_A and r_B, respectively. Let t_A be the time it takes for the initial investment in account A to reach nP_0, and let t_B be the time it takes for the initial investment in account B to reach nP_0, were n is some positive number. How are t_A and t_B related?

When we were modeling exponential population growth, we always stated the relative growth rate for you, but in real applications this rate will rarely be known *a priori*. Usually we will have to compute the relative growth rate based on other information from the problem. For this, logarithms are needed. An example will help to clarify what we mean.

Example #40:

Suppose we have a bacteria culture which grows at a rate proportional to the amount of bacteria present. Suppose further that it has been observed that we have 2 grams of the bacteria initially, then 24 hours later we have 3 grams. Can we predict how much would we have in 48 hours?

Let $B(t)$ represent the amount of bacteria present. This time our model is

$$\frac{dB}{dt} = rB, \text{ (The growth rate is proportional to the amount of bacteria present.)}$$

$B(0) = 2$, (Initially we have 2 grams of bacteria.)

$B(24) = 3$. (There are 3 grams of bacteria present after 24 hours.)

Drill #295:
Before we proceed, try to guess how much bacteria we will have after 48 hours. Will it be 4 grams? 6 grams? More? Less? Write down your best guess. We will revisit this in Drill #296, as soon as we have a formula for $B(t)$.

Note that our model is an IVP plus the extra datum: $B(24) = 3$. The first two pieces of our model, $\frac{dB}{dt} = rB$, and $B(0) = 2$, define an IVP very similar to IVP (7.16) which we repeat here for convenience:

$$\frac{dy}{dt} = 0.3y, \ y(0) = 10.$$

In fact the only difference is that where we had 0.3 before, we now have the unknown parameter, r. In Problem #283 we saw that $y(t) = 10e^{0.3t}$, so it appears that the solution of the problem in this example must be

$$y(t) = 2e^{rt}$$

but we don't know the value of r.

To determine r, we use the second datum. Since $B(24) = 3$ we have $\frac{3}{2} = e^{24r}$. Had we not taken the trouble to invent the natural logarithm it would be very difficult to proceed from this point. Since we did take the trouble, the next step is straightforward. Taking the natural logarithm of both sides, we see that $\ln\left(\frac{3}{2}\right) = 24r$ or

$$\frac{1}{24} \ln\left(\frac{3}{2}\right) = r.$$

Thus our growth model for this bacterial growth culture is

$$B(t) = 2e^{\left(\frac{1}{24} \ln \frac{3}{2}\right)t}.$$

Expressing it in this form is cumbersome. It is not wrong, just awkward. We can use the properties of exponents to clean it up at bit. This is not strictly necessary, but in general the simpler we keep our notation the better. Using the properties of exponents and the mutually inverse nature of the natural exponential and the natural logarithm, we have

$$B(t) = 2e^{\left(\frac{1}{24} \ln(3/2)t\right)} = 2\left(e^{\ln\left(\frac{3}{2}\right)}\right)^{\frac{t}{24}} = 2\left(\frac{3}{2}\right)^{\frac{t}{24}}.$$

So after 48 hours we have

$$B(48) = 2\left(\frac{3}{2}\right)^{48/24} = 2\left(\frac{3}{2}\right)^2 = 2\left(\frac{9}{4}\right) = \frac{9}{2} = 4.5 \text{ grams.}$$

Drill #296:
How good was your guess in Drill #295? Whether it was good or bad isn't really the point. Either way take a moment to hone your guessing skills by considering why you guessed the way you did. What was your intuition telling you about the problem?

A natural question to ask is, "How long will it take for the culture to reach 4 grams?" Translating this into a mathematical question, we want to find t when $B(t) = 4$, That is, we need to solve

$$4 = 2\left(\frac{3}{2}\right)^{\frac{t}{24}}$$

for t.

Drill #297: Show that $t = \frac{24\ln(2)}{\ln\left(\frac{3}{2}\right)} \approx 41.03$ hours.

End Of Example #40

Problem #298:

At a certain time a Petri dish contains 3 grams of bacteria. Three hours earlier it contained 0.5 grams of bacteria.

(a) Find a formula for the function, $A(t)$, which gives the amount of bacteria at any time, $t > 0$.

(b) How long does it take for the dish to contain 8 grams of bacteria?

Problem #299:

Starting with an unknown number of bacteria a culture is growing at a nominal (relative) rate of $0.25\frac{\text{grams}}{\text{hour}}$.

(a) How long does it take for the culture to double in size?

(b) How long does it take for the culture to triple in size?

Radioactive Dating

Radioactive isotopes have the curious property that in time they break down into other, more stable, substances. This process is known as **radioactive decay**. While there is no way to predict when an individual radioactive atom will decay, the decay of a large collection of radioactive isotopes is very regular and can be predicted.

For example, if we have two pounds of the radioactive isotope Cesium-137 (Cs_{137}) it is known that after the passage of 30 years and 70 days we will have only one pound. The rest will have decayed into barium. Even more curious though, is this: If we wait another 30 years and 70 days only one-half pound of the remaining one pound will have decayed. The numbers change depending on the isotope but the general principle is that a fixed percentage of a radioactive isotope will decay during a fixed interval of time.

Do you see the implications of this? Since a fixed percentage decays in a fixed time interval the rate of change of $A(t)$ will be proportional to A itself. Since this is exactly what we said about both population growth and return on investment, IVP (7.17) should model this phenomenon as well. There is, of course, the difference that the quantity is now shrinking rather than growing. How do you think that will manifest in our model? Take a guess.

Example #41:

For the sake of being definite suppose that our isotope is decaying (shrinking) at a **relative** (**nominal**) rate of 25%. Then if we start with 20Kg, the IVP to be solved is

$$\frac{\mathrm{d}A}{\mathrm{d}t} = 0.25A, \ A(0) = 20. \tag{7.21}$$

which we recognize as a special case of IVP (7.17), so the solution will be

$$A(t) = 20e^{0.25t}$$

Wait a minute. This can't be right. It says that the number of isotopes is increasing, not decreasing. Graph it and see.

So what did we do wrong?

The derivative of $A(t)$ is its rate of change. If $A(t)$ is increasing then its rate of change is going to be positive. If it is decreasing then its rate of change will be negative. We seem to have committed one of the classic blunders of mathematics. We got the sign wrong. We should have been solving the IVP

$$\frac{\mathrm{d}A}{\mathrm{d}t} = -0.25A, \ A(0) = 20. \tag{7.22}$$

instead of IVP #7.21. Since IVP #7.22 also has the same form as IVP #7.17), the correct solution is

$$A(t) = 20e^{-0.25t} \tag{7.23}$$

Drill #300:

Graph $A(t) = 20e^{-0.25t}$ to confirm that it is decreasing.

Did you guess correctly that the sign of the exponent would be negative in this model?

End Of Example #41

Example #42:

Suppose we have 6 pounds of a very unstable isotope which is known to lose half of its mass to radioactive decay in 2 hours. If we let $y(t)$ be the mass of our isotope sample at any time t, then the IVP we need to solve is[15]

$$\frac{\mathrm{d}y}{\mathrm{d}t} = ry, \ y(0) = 6.$$

---

[15]In view of our discussion above about positive versus negative rates of change it is tempting to write the differential equation as $\frac{\mathrm{d}y}{\mathrm{d}t} = -ry$. While this is not necessarily wrong, it is not helpful. The variable r can be any number, positive or negative. If we do our analysis correctly the correct value will emerge.

As always the solution of a differential equation of this form is

$$y(t) = 6e^{rt}$$

where and r is an unknown constant. To find r we must use the additional information given. Half of our isotope's mass is lost in 2 hours, so $y(2) = 3$. Thus

$$y(2) = 3 = 6e^{r(2)}$$
$$\frac{1}{2} = e^{r(2)}$$
$$\ln\left(\frac{1}{2}\right) = \ln\left(e^{2r}\right)$$
$$= 2r$$

or

$$r = \frac{1}{2}\ln\left(\frac{1}{2}\right).$$

Thus

$$y(t) = 6e^{\frac{t}{2}\ln\left(\frac{1}{2}\right)}.$$

This is correct but again it is cumbersome. Also the lack of an obvious negative in the exponent is a little troubling.

Drill #301:

(a) Use the properties of logarithms and exponentials to show that $6e^{\frac{t}{2}\ln\left(\frac{1}{2}\right)} = 6e^{-\frac{t}{2}\ln(2)}$.

(b) Use the properties of logarithms and exponentials to show that $6e^{\frac{t}{2}\ln\left(\frac{1}{2}\right)} = \dfrac{6}{\left(\sqrt{2}\right)^t}$

End Of Example #42

The length of time that it takes for a quantity of a radioactive isotope to decay by one-half is called the **half-life** of the isotope. Each substance has its own half-life[16]. The half-life for Carbon-14 is roughly $5,730$ years; for Fluorine-18, it is 110 minutes; for Potassium-40, it is 1.25 billion years.

Problem #302:

A certain isotope has a half-life of h, and is decaying exponentially:

$$A(h) = \frac{1}{2}A_0 = A_0 e^{rh}.$$

(a) Find the value of r in terms of h.

---

[16]In fact, all substances have a half-life. But some are more useful than others.

(b) Use the result of part (a) to show that the amount of our radioactive material at time t is given by $A(t) = A_0 e^{\frac{1}{h}\ln\left(\frac{1}{2}\right)t}$.

(c) The formula in part (a) is correct but it is a little awkward to use, as written.

Use the properties of exponents and logarithms to show that this can be rewritten as $A(t) = A_0 \left(\frac{1}{2}\right)^{\frac{t}{h}}$.

What are $A(0)$, $A(h)$, $A(2h)$, and $A(3h)$? Is this consistent with calling h the half-life? Explain.

Radiocarbon (C_{14}) is a radioactive isotope of carbon which is constantly being created in the atmosphere by the interaction of cosmic rays with atmospheric nitrogen. The resulting radiocarbon combines with atmospheric oxygen to form radioactive carbon dioxide, which is incorporated into plants by photosynthesis. Animals then acquire C_{14} by eating the plants. When the animal or plant dies, it stops absorbing carbon from the environment. From that point onward the amount of C_{14} it contains begins to decrease as the C_{14} undergoes radioactive decay. During life the ratio of C_{14} to other, stable, isotopes remains stable. However after an organism dies this ratio begins to decrease due to the decay of C_{14}

By measuring the amount of C_{14} in a sample from a dead plant or animal such as a piece of wood or a fragment of bone we can calculate, approximately when the plant or animal died. This is called **radiocarbon dating**, and it was developed by Willard Libby (1908 – 1980) in 1949. Radiocarbon dating revolutionized the field of archaeology. Libby was awarded the Nobel Prize in Chemistry in 1960 for this development.

Problem #303:

The Shroud of Turin is a Christian religious relic which bears an image of a man. Some people believe it is the burial cloth of Jesus and that the image is that of Jesus himself. In 1987 the Vatican agreed to subject pieces of the shroud to radiocarbon dating. In this problem we will recreate the computations done to determine the age of the Shroud.

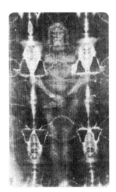

Let $A = A(t)$ be the amount of C_{14} (in mg) at time t years, where $t = 0$ represents when the shroud was used. Let $A(0) = A_0$ be the initial amount of C_{14} present in the sample.

(a) How much C_{14} would be present if the shroud was 2000 years old?

(b) If one of the samples of the Shroud contained 88.9% of the original C_{14}. How old would this sample be[17]?

---

[17]This does not settle the question of the age of the Shroud. The technique of carbon dating is not in dispute, but there are other issues including questions about the quality of the samples. If you are interested you can read more here: https://www.usatoday.com/story/news/world/2013/03/30/shroud-turin-display/2038295/.

Problem #304:

In medicine, Positron Emission Tomography (PET) scans use radioactive tracers to image body functions. One of the most commonly used radioactive tracers is Fluorine-18 (F_{18}) which has a half life of 110 minutes. Typically F_{18} is injected into the body and the imaging is done about one hour after the tracer is injected. Suppose that s units of F_{18} must remain in the body for the PET scan results to be useful. How much F_{18} must be injected into the patient 60 minutes prior?

Problem #305:

The half-life of C_{14} limits it to dating artifacts that are no older than $50,000$ years. What percentage of the original amount of C_{14} would remain in a $50,000$-year-old artifact? How does this explain the limitation on radiocarbon dating?

Problem #306:

The radioactive isotope Potassium-40 (K_{40}) has a half life of 1.25 billion years. Radiometric dating using K_{40} is especially effective for dating very old volcanic rock as the quickly cooling lava traps the Argon formed by the decaying of K_{40}.

This has been used by scientists to study the frequency of geomagnetic reversals. A geomagnetic reversal is a change in the earth's magnetic polarity where the magnetic north and south poles (not to be confused with the geographic north and south poles) are switched. Basically, the magnetic polarity of the planet is "recorded" in cooled lava flows. By dating the age of the lava flows, scientists can date these reversals.

(a) A rock sample which appears to have a reversed magnetic field is determined to contain between 99.9541% and 99.9593% of the K_{40} that it originally contained. Approximately how old is the rock? (This is the latest geomagnetic reversal called the Brunhes-Matuyama reversal.)

(b) Approximately what is the age of the youngest rock that can be dated using this technique?

Chillin' with Newton: The Law of Cooling

Example #43:

Suppose a container of water at a temperature of $40°F$ is placed into a freezer maintained at a constant temperature of $5°F$. We'd like to have a model that will allow us to compute how long it will take for the water to cool down to a temperature of, for example, $32°F$ where it will start to freeze.

In the late 17th century Isaac Newton showed experimentally that the rate at which the water cools will be proportional to the difference between its current temperature and the ambient (surrounding) temperature. This is known as Newton's Law of Cooling and it holds generally, not just for water.

For this problem we see that the ambient temperature is $5°F$ and the initial temperature of the water is $40°F$. We let $T(t)$ represent the temperature of the water at any given time. Then the difference between the current temperature and the ambient temperature is $T - 5$, and (as always) the rate of change of the temperature of the water with respect to time is $\frac{dT}{dt}$, (or $\dot{T}$ if you are Newton). Letting r be the (unknown) constant of proportionality we have the IVP

$$\frac{dT}{dt} = r(T - 5), \quad T(0) = 40.$$

This differential equation looks like it will be tougher to solve than the IVPs we dealt with earlier. But in fact we can make this problem "easier on the eyes" with the substitution $D = T - 5$. Notice that $\frac{dD}{dt} = \frac{d(T-5)}{dt} = \frac{dT}{dt}$ so we have the IVP

$$\frac{dD}{dt} = rD \quad D(0) = 40 - 5 = 35. \tag{7.24}$$

Do you recognize this equation? This has the same form as IVP 7.16 so the solution is

$$D(t) = D(0)e^{rt} = 35e^{rt}.$$

Reversing the substitution we see that

$$T(t) - 5 = (T(0) - 5)\, e^{rt}$$
$$T(t) = 5 + 35e^{rt}.$$

To complete our model we need to determine r. We can find r if we know the temperature of the water at a second time during the cooling. Assume that we measured the temperature of the water after 10 minutes and it was $35°F$. Thus we have

$$35 = T(10) = 5 + 35e^{10r}$$

so that

$$\frac{30}{35} = e^{10r}$$
$$r = \frac{\ln(6/7)}{10}$$

and our complete model is

$$T(t) = 5 + 35e^{\frac{\ln(6/7)}{10}t}$$
$$= 5 + 35\left(\frac{6}{7}\right)^{\frac{t}{10}}.$$

Newton's Law of Cooling accurately models the cooling of any object placed in cooler surroundings. We used water in our example just to be definite.

Drill #307: Since the temperature of the water is decreasing we would expect r to be less than zero. Show that it is.

End Of Example #43

Problem #308:

(a) Answer the original question: How long does it take for the water to cool from $40°F$ to $32°F$

(b) Take a guess: Would it take the same amount of time to cool another $8°F$ from $32°F$ to $24°F$? Check to see if your guess was correct.

(c) What would the initial temperature of the water need to be to take twice as long to cool to $32°F$ as it did for the $40°F$ water?

Problem #309:

The forensic rule of thumb for determining the time of death of a person is to start with a body temperature of $37°C$ and[18] subtract $1.5°C$ for each hour the person is dead. Of course, this simple linear model isn't as accurate as Newton's Law of Cooling since it does not take into account the surrounding temperature, size of the body, etc. and can only be applied until the temperature of the body reaches the surrounding temperature.

(a) Suppose the ambient temperature is $20°C$. Using the forensic rule of thumb, how long would it take for the body to reach the ambient temperature? Using the forensic rule of thumb, what would the body temperature be halfway through the cooling process.

(b) Use the temperature predicted by the rule of thumb at the halfway point to give a complete model of the body's cooling as predicted by Newton's Law of Cooling.

(c) Of course, in Newton's Law of Cooling, the body temperature will never quite reach the ambient temperature, but just for comparison, substitute the time when the rule of thumb predicts that the body temperature is $20°C$ and see how close it is to the ambient temperature.

(d) Using the answer you obtained in part (c), find the rate of change of the body temperature at the beginning of the time interval and the rate of change of the body temperature at the end of the time interval. How do these compare with the rule of thumb rate of change?

---

[18]Notice that we've switched to measuring temperature in degrees Celsius.

Of course, Newton's Law of Cooling can be used just as well to model an object heating. Consider the following:

Problem #310:

A whole turkey is considered to be safely cooked when the internal temperature is $165°F$. Suppose a turkey is taken out of a refrigerator set at $35°F$ and is put directly into an oven set at $325°F$. You check it 2 hours later and the internal temperature is $100°F$. How much longer does the turkey need to cook?

7.4 The Derivative of the Natural Logarithm

Since the **natural logarithm** is the inverse of the **natural exponential** we can find its derivative using the same trick that we used to find the derivatives of the inverse trig functions. Start with the identity

$$e^{\ln(x)} = x \quad \text{(Property 1)} \tag{7.25}$$

and make this easier on our eyes with the substitution $y = \ln(x)$. Differentiating Equation (7.25) we see that

$$e^y \, dy = dx.$$

Thus

$$dy = \frac{1}{e^y} \, dx.$$

Once more making the substitution $y = \ln(x)$ we have

$$dy = \frac{1}{e^{\ln(x)}} \, dx,$$

and since $e^{\ln(x)} = x$ we have

$$dy = \frac{1}{x} \, dx.$$
$$dy = \frac{1}{x} \, dx$$
$$d(\ln(x)) = x^{-1} \, dx. \tag{7.26}$$

Equation (7.26 is the last differentiation rule you need to memorize. Memorize it.

As always the difficulty here is not remembering what the differentiation rule is, the difficulty is in learning to use it in tandem with all of the other rules. So practice is required. Lots of practice.

Drill #311:

For each of the following find dy, and $\frac{dy}{dx}$.

(a) $y = \ln\left(\frac{7-x}{5+x}\right)$

(b) $y = \dfrac{\ln(x)}{e^x}$

(c) $y = \tan(\ln(x))$

(d) $y = \ln(\tan(x))$

(e) $y = \tan^{-1}(\ln(x))$

(f) $y = x\ln(x) - x$

(g) $y = \ln(\ln(\sec(x)))$

(h) $y = \ln(\sin(x^2 + 1))$

(i) $y = \sqrt{x} \cdot \ln\left(\sqrt{x}\right)$

(j) $y = \ln(2x + 2)$

(k) $\ln(y) = \sin(e^x)$

(l) $\ln(x + y) = x\tan^{-1}(y)$

(m) $\ln(x + y) = e^{x+y}$

Problem #312:

For each of the following find dy, and $\frac{dy}{dx}$.
(**Hint:** Use the properties of logarithms to make these drills easier on the eyes.)

(a) $y = \ln\left(\frac{x-1}{x+1}\right)$

(b) $y = \ln(\sec(x)\tan(x))$

(c) $y = \ln\left(\frac{(2x+1)^2(3x-2)}{x^2+1}\right)$

(d) $y = \ln\left(\frac{e^{x^2}\sin(x)}{\sqrt{x^3-7x+4}}\right)$

(e) $y = \ln\left(\left[\frac{(2x+3)(4x+5)^{20}}{x^{\frac{1}{2}}-\ln(x)}\right]^{\frac{4}{3}}\right)$

Problem #313:

Recall that in Section 5.9 (Problem 5.15) we showed the curvature of the graph of a function $y = y(x)$ is given by

$$\kappa = \frac{\left|\frac{d^2y}{dx^2}\right|}{\left(1 + \left(\frac{dy}{dx}\right)^2\right)^{\frac{3}{2}}}.$$

(a) Show that the curvature of the graph of $y = e^x$ is given by

$$\kappa = \frac{e^x}{\left(1 + e^{2x}\right)^{\frac{3}{2}}}.$$

Graph both of these functions and use this to approximate the point (x, y), where the curvature of the graph of the natural exponential function is the greatest.

(b) Show that the curvature of the graph of the $y = \ln(x)$ is given by

$$\kappa = \frac{x}{\left(1 + x^2\right)^{\frac{3}{2}}}.$$

Graph both of these functions and use this to approximate the point (x, y), where the curvature of the graph of the natural logarithm is the greatest.

(c) What do you notice about the points where the curvature is greatest in parts (a) and (b)? Does this surprise you? Explain.

Digression #16: A Curious Fact

Observe that if $y = x^\alpha$, then $\frac{dy}{dx} = \alpha x^{\alpha-1}$. This is, of course, just the Power Rule but we take particular notice of the fact that the Power Rule guarantees that the derivative of any monomial (x^α) is another monomial. But what happens if we try to go the other direction?

If $\frac{dy}{dx} = x^2$ then clearly[a] $y = \frac{x^3}{3}$. In general if

$$\frac{dy}{dx} = x^\alpha$$

then

$$y = \frac{x^{\alpha+1}}{\alpha + 1} \text{ for } \alpha \neq -1.$$

But if $\alpha = -1$ running the Power Rule backwards would give us $y = \frac{x^{-1+1}}{-1+1}$ which is meaningless since the denominator is $-1 + 1 = 0$. When $\alpha = -1$ we get is $y = \ln(x)$.

It seems very strange that there would be this one, single exception doesn't it? Or, to come at the question a little differently, maybe this says that the logarithm function is somehow related to polynomials? What do you think?

[a] Actually, this should be $y = \frac{x^3}{3}$ plus an arbitrary constant. Do you see why? Since the constant is of no importance to our current point, we ignore it.

======= End Of Digression #16 =======

7.5 General Logarithms and Exponentials

"You have no idea how much poetry there is in the calculation of a table of logarithms!"

– Carl Friederich Gauss (1777-1855)

So far we've focused on the **natural** exponential and logarithm functions even though we started our discussion of logarithms by defining $\log_{10}(x)$ as the inverse of the base-10 exponential: 10^x.

But we've seen that 2^x is also an exponential, and it's inverse is $\log_2(x)$. In fact, we've seen that for any $a > 0$, $a \neq 1$, a^x is the "base a" exponential and the corresponding inverse function is called the "base a" logarithm, and is denoted $\log_a(x)$.

Drill #314: Why do we impose the conditions, $a > 0$ and $a \neq 1$?

Calculus is not needed for the next problem which establishes that all logarithm functions change multiplication into addition (Property 4) and exponentiation into multiplication (Property 6) as we stated (but didn't prove) earlier.

Problem #315:

Let $a > 0$, $a \neq 1$, $x > 0$, $y > 0$ and let c be any real number.

(a) Show that $\log_a(xy) = \log_a(x) + \log_a(y)$.
(**Hint:** Consider $a^{\log_a(x) + \log_a(y)}$ and use the properties of exponents to show that this equals xy.)

(b) Show that $\log_a(x^c) = c \log_a(x)$.
(**Hint:** Consider $a^{c \log_a(x)}$ and use the properties of exponents to show that this equals x^c.)

But if there are so many different exponential and logarithm functions, don't we need differentiation rules for all of them? If so, what are the derivatives of the other exponentials and logarithms?

General Exponentials

It is not as hard to differentiate $y = a^x$ as you might think. Since we already know how to differentiate the natural exponential all we have to do is re-express $y = a^x$ in terms of e^x.

Here's how to do that. Recall that from the inverse relationship between the natural exponential and the natural logarithm (Properties 1 and 2) $a = e^{\ln(a)}$. So we make that substitution[19] to get

$$y = a^x = \left(e^{\ln(a)}\right)^x = e^{x \ln(a)}$$

Now differentiate:

$$a^x = e^{x \ln(a)}$$

$$\mathrm{d}(a^x) = \mathrm{d}\left(e^{x \ln(a)}\right) = e^{x \ln(a)} \, \mathrm{d}(x \ln(a)).$$

Since a is a constant, $\ln(a)$ is also a constant so

$$\mathrm{d}(a^x) = e^{x \ln(a)} \ln(a) \, \mathrm{d}x,$$

---

[19]Some may see this step as making a^x "harder on the eyes." But often it is often necessary to temporarily make things more complicated so that we can recognize a pattern or to reduce the situation to a previously solved problem.

and since $a^x = e^{x\ln(a)}$ we have

$$d(a^x) = a^x \ln(a)\, dx.$$

Many people simply memorize this formula and you are welcome to do that if you like. However we (the authors) prefer to emulate nature and be lazy. We find it much simpler to find the derivative of a^x by rewriting it as $e^{x\ln(a)}$ first.

The following problem shows an alternative (and equivalent) method if you can't remember how to rewrite a^x.

Problem #316:

Starting with $y = a^x$, take the natural logarithm of both sides and solve for dy to obtain the same formula as above.

Taking a logarithm of complicated formulas sometimes allows us to simplify things considerably via the properties of logarithms. It is a nice trick. Keep it in mind. We'll be using it later.

Drill #317:

Find dy and $\frac{dy}{dx}$ for each of the following:

(a) $y = 2^x$

(b) $y = 3^x \cdot 3^x$

(c) $y = x3^x$

(d) $y = 3 \cdot 7^x + 7 \cdot 3^x$

(e) $y = e^{5^x}$

(f) $y = \ln(2^x)$

(g) $y = 2^x \cdot 3^x$

(h) $y = \frac{2^x}{3^x}$

(i) $y = 2^x \cdot 4^x \cdot 8^{x^2}$

General Logarithms

Just as we computed the derivative of the general exponential, a^x by re-expressing it as a natural exponential, we will compute the derivative of the general logarithm, $\log_a(x)$, by re-expressing it as a natural logarithm. This is a bit more difficult, but only a bit.

We begin with the exponential. If $y = \log_a(x)$ then $a^y = x$. Taking the natural logarithm of both sides of $a^y = x$ and using Property 6 we have, $y\ln(a) = \ln(x)$, or $y = \frac{\ln(x)}{\ln(a)}$. Since $y = \log_a(x)$ we have successfully re-expressed the base-a logarithm as a natural logarithm:

$$\log_a(x) = \frac{\ln(x)}{\ln(a)}. \tag{7.27}$$

This is why many scientific calculators don't bother including a $\log_a(x)$ button.

An easy mnemonic for remembering this formula is to simply notice that on both sides of the equation the a appears lower than the x.

Since $\ln(a)$ is a constant (why?) we have

$$d(\log_a(x)) = \frac{1}{\ln(a)} \cdot d(\ln(x)) = \frac{1}{\ln(a)} \cdot \frac{1}{x}\, dx.$$

So we have the differentiation formula:

$$\frac{d(\log_a(x))}{dx} = \frac{1}{x \ln(a)}.$$

As with the differentiation formula for general exponential functions we (the authors) find it easier to remember this conversion than the differentiation formula. But you are welcome to memorize it if you prefer.

Drill #318:
Compute dy and $\frac{dy}{dx}$ for each of the following.

(a) $y = \log_2(7x)$ **(b)** $y = \log_{10}(x^2 + 1)$

Problem #319: Assume $x \neq 1, x > 0$ and let $y = \log_x(2)$. Show that

$$\frac{dy}{dx} = -\frac{\ln(2)}{x(\ln(x))^2}.$$

Problem #320:
For a given sound, the sound power level L, in decibels, is given by

$$L = 10 \log_{10}\left(\frac{P}{P_0}\right)$$

where P is the sound power of the source measured in watts and P_0 is the sound reference level taken to be 1 picowatt or 10^{-12} watts.

(a) Suppose the sound power of a speaker is 0.0001 watts. How many decibels does this correspond to?

(b) Suppose that the sound power of the speaker is being raised at a rate of 0.0001 watts per second. How fast is the sound power level rising?

Digression #17: Common and Napierian Logarithms

It is a well worn truism among research mathematicians that the first solution of a substantial problem is frequently both very hard to understand and very hard to convey to others, even to other mathematicians. We publish our solutions, in part, so that others can look at the problem, consider the approach used, and find simplifications that the original investigator missed.

This is what happened to Napier. Although his original scheme allowed him to convert multiplication to addition it was more complicated than necessary. Shortly after Napier published his work in 1614, Henry Briggs (1561 – 1630), Professor of Geometry at Gresham College in London, visited Napier and suggested that a few simple changes to his logarithm table would make it more practical. In particular it was Briggs who suggested that since our number system is in base-10, creating a table of base-10 logarithms might be more useful.

Napier had had the same idea himself, but was unable to pursue it "on account of ill-health." As a result, Briggs took on the task of computing tables of base-10 logarithms, collaborating with Napier until the latter's death two years later. The results of their collaboration are known as the Briggsian or **Common Logarithms**. Common Logarithms are the base 10 logarithms we discussed earlier and were an important computational aid for nearly 400 years until the invention of modern computational technologies.

As the mathematical historian Howard Eves put it, the invention of (common) logarithms literally "doubled the life of the astronomer," because they so drastically reduced the time spent doing arithmetic.

Most modern scientific calculators have both the natural and the common logarithms built in. The "**ln**" button on a calculator computes natural logarithms while the "**log**" computes common logarithms.

Drill #321:

(a) Use whatever technology you prefer to compute the natural logarithms of the numbers 21.2343 and 5689.121343 and their product. Confirm that $\ln(21.2343) + \ln(5689.121343) = \ln(21.2343 \times 5689.121343)$.

(**Comment:** If you don't like these numbers use others. We just picked these at random.)

(b) Do the same using common logarithms.

(c) Do the same using $\log_5(x)$.

(**Comment:** Or any other base. Again we just picked 5 at random.)

Example #44:

A calculator is a useful tool, but only if the human operating it understands what to calculate, and why. Blind computation is pointless and wasteful. As powerful and convenient as our modern technology is, there is still no substitution for a deep understanding of basic principles.

For example, how many base-10 digits long do you suppose the number $2^{1234567890}$ is? You cannot solve this by punching $2^{1234567890}$ into a calculator and counting the digits. Try it and see. If you can solve this by punching $2^{1234567890}$ into a calculator, that just means that technology has outpaced this particular problem. In that case use a bigger exponent, say 12345678901234567890.

This feels like the sort of problem a math professor might make up just for fun (though it often feels like we do it just to torment our students), but it is not. Computer programmers routinely have to allocate space in memory to hold information. If the information being held happens to be the number $2^{1234567890}$ the programmer will need to know how much space to allocate to hold the number.

Drill #322:

Show that if n is a positive integer and $10^n \leq \alpha < 10^{n+1}$ then α will have $n+1$ digits to the left of the decimal point.

(**Hint:** This is true because our number system is based on "powers of ten." That is, it is based on the base 10 exponential.)

Suppose we let $\alpha = 2^{1234567890}$ and take the base 10 logarithm (common logarithm) of both sides. This gives:

$$\log_{10}(\alpha) = \log_{10}(2^{1234567890}) = 1234567890 \cdot \log_{10}(2) \approx 371641966.574.$$

Thus

$$2^{1234567890} = \alpha \approx 10^{371641966.574}$$
$$\approx 10^{0.574} \times 10^{371641966}$$
$$\approx 3.75 \times 10^{371641966}.$$

Since $10^{371641966} \leq 2^{1234567890} \leq 10^{371641967}$ our number, α, is 371641967 base-10 digits long. But since computer arithmetic is binary (base-2) what we really need to know how many binary digits (bits) are needed to store a given number.

Drill #323:

How many bits are needed to allocate to store these numbers?

(**a**) $2^{1234567890}$?

(**c**) $5^{1234567890}$?

(**b**) $10^{1234567890}$?

(**d**) $12^{1234567890}$?

End Of Example #44

Problem #324:

For each of the following numbers:

(**i**) $3^{1234567890}$ (**ii**) $9^{1234567890}$ (**iii**) $\left(\frac{1}{3}\right)^{1234567890}$ (**iv**) $\left(\frac{1}{9}\right)^{1234567890}$

(**a**) Find the number of binary digits needed to store the number.

(**b**) Find the number of base-8 digits needed to store the number.

(**c**) Find the number of base-10 digits needed to store the number.

(d) Find the number of base-100 digits needed to store the number.

(e) Find the number of base-9 digits needed to store the number.

The discussion above suggests the question: What base did Napier use when he first invented logarithms, before Briggs suggested using base-10?

Napier defined his original logarithms as follows. Consider a point C moving along line segment AB and a point F moving along an infinite ray DE as seen below.

At the beginnning both C and F are moving at the same speed, and F continues to move at that initial speed. But the speed of C is always equal to the distance from C to B. If we let $CB = x$ and $DF = y$, then we define the **Naperian Logarithm** as

$$y = \text{Nap}\log(x).$$

Since Calculus hadn't been invented yet, Napier used Trigonometry to develop his table of logarithms. The details of those computations are not relevant for us, except that he took the length of AB to be 10^7, because the best sine tables at the time were to accurate to seven decimal places.

It is not altogether clear from the description above that the Napierian logarithm actually is a logarithm, let alone what its base is. The next problem explores both of these questions.

Problem #325:

In this problem we have suppressed the variable t.

(a) Show that $\frac{dy}{dt} = 10^7$, and $y(0) = 0$.

(b) Solve the IVP: $\frac{dx}{dt} = -x$, $x(0) = 10^7$,

(c) Use the information in parts (a) and (b) to show that

$$\text{Nap}\log(x) = y(x) = 10^7 \log_{\frac{1}{e}}\left(\frac{x}{10^7}\right).$$

Thus the base of Napier's original logarithm was $\frac{1}{e}$.

================ End Of Digression #17 ================

Logarithmic Differentiation

Recall that in Section 3.2 we observed that the Power Rule does not easily extend to $y = x^\alpha$, where α is an irrational number. The properties of the natural exponential and the natural logarithm functions will (finally) allow us to make this extension.

Suppose α is any real number[20]. Starting with $y = x^\alpha$ we take the logarithm of both sides, obtaining

$$\ln(y) = \alpha \ln(x).$$

Differentiating gives

$$\frac{1}{y}\, dy = \alpha \frac{1}{x}\, dx.$$

Solving for x we see that

$$\frac{dy}{dx} = \frac{\alpha y}{x} = \frac{\alpha x^\alpha}{x} = \alpha x^{\alpha-1} \tag{7.28}$$

which is the Power Rule. Since we did not constraint α except to say that it is a real number the different versions of the Power Rule that we saw in Section 3.2 are all special cases of Equation (7.28).

The same trick we just used can make some differentiations much easier to do.

Example #45:

For example, suppose we need to differentiate

$$y = \frac{\sqrt{x^3 + 2x} \cdot \tan(x)}{(x^5 - 7)^4}.$$

While we can do this using our Differentiation Rules, it will be very tedious. But nice things happen if we take the natural logarithm of both sides before we differentiate.

$$\ln(y) = \ln\left(\frac{\sqrt{x^3 + 2x} \cdot \tan(x)}{(x^5 - 7)^4}\right)$$

Since the natural logarithm changes division into subtraction (Property 5) we can rewrite the right side as:

$$= \ln\left[\sqrt{x^3 + 2x} \cdot \tan(x)\right] - \ln\left((x^5 - 7)^4\right).$$

And since the natural logarithm changes multiplication into addition (Property 4) we can re-express the right side again. This time as:

$$= \ln\left(\sqrt{x^3 + 2x}\right) + \ln\left(\tan(x)\right) - \ln\left((x^5 - 7)^4\right).$$

Re-expressing the square root as an exponent gives

$$= \ln\left(x^3 + 2x\right)^{1/2} + \ln\left(\tan(x)\right) - \ln\left((x^5 - 7)^4\right).$$

and we can now bring the exponents down in front (Property 6).

$$\ln(y) = \frac{1}{2}\ln(x^3 + 2x) + \ln(\tan(x)) - 4\ln(x^5 - 7).$$

---

[20]In particular we do not assume that α is rational.

Notice that we have not yet started differentiating. All we've done so far is re-express our function using the properties of logarithms.

But differentiating is now relatively easy.

$$d(\ln(y)) = \frac{1}{2(x^3 + 2x)} \, d(x^3 + 2x) + \frac{1}{\tan(x)} \, d(\tan x) - \frac{4}{x^5 - 7} \, d(x^5 - 7)$$

$$\frac{dy}{y} = \frac{1}{2(x^3 + 2x)}(3x^2 + 2) \, dx + \frac{1}{\tan(x)} \sec^2(x) \, dx - \frac{4}{x^5 - 7}(5x^4) \, dx$$

If we multiply by y we get

$$dy = y \left[\frac{(3x^2 + 2)}{2(x^3 + 2x)} \, dx + \frac{\sec^2(x)}{\tan(x)} \, dx - 4 \left(\frac{5x^4}{x^5 - 7} \right) \, dx \right]$$

$$= \left[\frac{\sqrt{x^3 + 2x} \cdot \tan(x)}{(x^5 - 7)^4} \right] \cdot \left[\frac{(3x^2 + 2)}{2(x^3 + 2x)} \, dx + \frac{\sec^2(x)}{\tan(x)} \, dx - 4 \left(\frac{5x^4}{x^5 - 7} \right) \, dx \right]$$

End Of Example #45

This looks like a lot of work when it's laid out on the page but it really isn't. With practice you can differentiate an expression like $\frac{\sqrt{x^3 + 2x} \cdot \tan(x)}{(x^5 - 7)^4}$ in your head as fast as you can write it down. Really. Even if this is not true, would you rather compute this derivative using the Quotient Rule and Product Rule?

Drill #326: Try it and see.

Recall that in Problem #46 you used the Product Rule to compute $d\left[(x + 1)(x + 2)(x + 3) \cdots (x + n)\right]$. You should redo this problem before attempting Problem #327.

Problem #327:

Let $y = (x + 1)(x + 2)(x + 3) \cdots (x + n)$.

(a) Take the logarithm of both sides of this formula and use the properties of logarithms to show that for $x \neq -1, -2, -3, \cdots, -n$

$$dy = (x + 1)(x + 2)(x + 3) \cdots (x + n) \left[\frac{1}{x + 1} + \frac{1}{x + 2} + \frac{1}{x + 3} + \frac{1}{x + n} \right] \, dx.$$

(b) Show that the result of part (a) is equivalent to the solution of Problem #46.

The technique of taking the logarithm of both sides of an expression like $y = y(x)$ and then differentiating is called **Logarithmic Differentiation**. It can reduce the amount of tedious computation needed considerably, so it is worth knowing how to use it.

Problem #328:

Show that if $y = \sqrt{e^{x^2+x}\sin(x)}$, then $dy = \frac{1}{2}\sqrt{e^{x^2+x}\sin(x)}\,(2x + 1\cot(x))\,dx$ by

(a) Using Logarithmic Differentiation.

(b) Not using Logarithmic Differentiation.

(c) Does either method seem preferable to you? Explain.

Problem #329:

Compute the derivative of each of the following functions.

(a) $y = [x(x + 1)]^7$ (b) $y = \sqrt{x(x + 1)}$ (c) $y = \frac{1}{x(x-1)(x-2)}$ (d) $y = \ln\left(\frac{x\sqrt{x^2+1}}{(x+1)^{2/3}}\right)$

There are some situations where logarithmic differentiation is your only option. Consider something like $y = x^x$. Unfortunately, this is not a monomial like x^2 nor is it an exponential like 2^x. This is some strange combination of both and our existing rules don't directly apply. But Logarithmic Differentiation will work.

Problem #330:

For each of the following find dy, and $\frac{dy}{dx}$.

(a) $y = x^x$ (b) $y = x^{\ln(x)}$ (c) $y = x^{\frac{1}{\ln(x)}}$ (d) $y = (x^2 + 1)^{\sin(x)}$

Finally, because we've given it a name it is easy to get the impression that Logarithmic Differentiation is a new differentiation rule, but it isn't. It is really just a trick as the next problem shows. A handy trick, to be sure, but still a trick.

Problem #331:

Suppose we want to differentiate $y = [\alpha(x)]^{\beta(x)}$ where $\alpha(x)$ and $\beta(x)$ are two differentiable functions.

(a) Compute $\frac{dy}{dx}$ using Logarithmic Differentiation.

(b) Now express $\alpha(x)$ as $\alpha(x) = e^{\ln(\alpha(x))}$ and compute $\frac{dy}{dx}$ again using the ordinary rules of differentiation and show that you get the same thing as in part (a).

Problem #332: Suppose $x^y = y^x$ and show that $\frac{dy}{dx} = \frac{y - x\ln(y)}{x - y\ln(x)}$.

7.6 Leonhard Euler, Harmonic Oscillators, and Complex Numbers

"After exponential quantities the circular functions, sine and cosine, should be considered because they arise when imaginary quantities are involved in the exponential."

– Leonhard Euler (1707 − 1783)

Recall that in Section 5.3 we saw that the differential equation that models the motion of an object having mass m, bouncing on a spring without resistance is the simple harmonic oscillator equation:

$$m\frac{\mathrm{d}^2 y}{\mathrm{d}t^2} = -ky, \tag{7.29}$$

where k is the spring constant. The solution of Equation (7.29) is

$$y(t) = A\sin\sqrt{\frac{k}{m}}t + B\cos\sqrt{\frac{k}{m}}t \tag{7.30}$$

where A and B are arbitrary constants.

Equation (7.30) is unrealisitic because the oscillations described never vary. In the real world, as a result of friction, the spring's oscillations will get shorter and shorter, eventually stopping altogether. How could we modify this model in order to capture the effects of, say, air resistance?

A relatively simple way to model this resistance is to assume that the resistive force is proportional to the speed of the object. This sounds imposing but you are quite familiar with this sort of resistance. If you put your hand out the window of a moving car you'll notice that as the car moves faster there is more force (wind) pushing back on your hand. This simple model breaks down at high speeds where factors such as turbulence will also affect the resistance, but it can be shown experimentally that the assumption that the resistive force is proportional to velocity works well for our spring.

Putting the words "resistance is proportional to velocity" into symbols means we need to add the term $-b\frac{\mathrm{d}y}{\mathrm{d}t}$ to Equation (7.29) where $b > 0$ is a constant which depends on the viscosity of the ambient medium (air, in this case). (Why must this proportionality be negative?)

Thus our model for harmonic oscillation with resistance becomes

$$m\frac{\mathrm{d}^2 y}{\mathrm{d}t^2} = -b\frac{\mathrm{d}y}{\mathrm{d}t} - ky$$

or

$$\frac{\mathrm{d}^2 y}{\mathrm{d}t^2} + \frac{b}{m}\frac{\mathrm{d}y}{\mathrm{d}t} + \frac{k}{m}y = 0. \tag{7.31}$$

Equation (7.31) is a little scary to look at, let alone try to solve. We'll begin with a simplified version where $b = k = m$:

$$\frac{\mathrm{d}^2 y}{\mathrm{d}t^2} + \frac{\mathrm{d}y}{\mathrm{d}t} + y = 0. \tag{7.32}$$

Problem #333:

(a) Show that:

$$y(t) = e^{-\frac{t}{2}} \left[A \cos \left(\frac{\sqrt{3}}{2} t \right) + B \sin \left(\frac{\sqrt{3}}{2} t \right) \right]$$

satisfies Equation (7.32) for any constants A and B.

(b) Let $A = 1, B = 0$ and plot this solution for $0 \leq t \leq 15$ and $-0.5 \leq y \leq 0.5$. Does this seem to model a damped oscillation?

It is one thing to confirm a given solution as in Problem #333, but quite another to find the solution in the first place. A natural question to ask is "How was this problem solved the first time?"

How Euler Did It[21]

Leonhard Euler[22] $(1707 - 1783)$ solved the differential Equation (7.32) by guessing that for some carefully chosen value of c

$$y(t) = e^{ct}$$

would be a solution. In view of the results of Problem #333 this guess looks completely crazy. Where is the sine? Where is the cosine? Nothing seems to be oscillating!

It is difficult to imagine what might have led him to make such a guess. But Euler knew that if his guess didn't pan out he didn't have to tell anyone about it. He could just toss all of his notes into his fireplace and pretend that he'd never made his crazy-seeming guess.

The really crazy thing though, is that Euler's guess worked. Here's how.

The key is the constant c. By leaving it unspecified Euler[23] gave himself a little "wiggle room." All he had to do now was find a value of c that would work.

Leonhard Euler
$(1707 - 1783)$

---

[21]This heading was borrowed from the series of articles of the same name, written by the late Prof. Ed Sandifer, of Western Connecticut State University

[22]Euler was one of the all-time great mathematicians. In any list of stellar mathematicians, he would stand out among the best. Indeed, Pierre-Simon Laplace $(1749 - 1827)$, an outstanding mathematician in his own right, was once asked by a novice how best to learn Calculus. Laplace told him "Read Euler, read Euler, he is the master of us all."

[23]By the way, his name is pronounced "oiler," not "you-ler."

Problem #334:

Show that if $y = e^{ct}$ satisfies the differential equation $\dfrac{d^2 y}{dt^2} + \dfrac{dy}{dt} + y = 0$ then c must satisfy the quadratic equation

$$c^2 + c + 1 = 0. \tag{7.33}$$

(**Hint:** Put the first two derivatives of y into the differential equation.)

Solving Equation (7.33 we see that $c = \frac{-1}{2} \pm \frac{\sqrt{-3}}{2}$, so we conclude that if $c = -\frac{1}{2} + \frac{\sqrt{-3}}{2}$ or $c = -\frac{1}{2} - \frac{\sqrt{-3}}{2}$ then $y = e^{ct}$ satisfies Equation (7.32).

The appearance of $\sqrt{-3}$ is troubling since there is no real number which is the square root of a negative number. But Euler knew that such "imaginary" numbers had been effectively used in the previous century, although no one could yet explain what they really were[24]. Knowing that if nothing useful came of his efforts he could discard them and try something else, Euler decided to treat the square roots of negative numbers, like differentials, as "convenient fictions"

Since he had assumed that c was a constant Euler wanted to see where that assumption would lead. In particular he decided to treat $\sqrt{-3}$ as the constant it is. To make things "easier on the eyes," Euler wrote $\sqrt{-3} = \sqrt{3} \cdot \sqrt{-1}$ and set $\sqrt{-1} = i$.

Euler now had two solutions of Equation (7.32), one for each possible value of c:

$$y_1(t) = e^{\left(-\frac{1}{2} + \frac{\sqrt{3}}{2} i\right) t} = e^{-\frac{t}{2}} \cdot e^{\frac{\sqrt{3}}{2} it}$$

and

$$y_2(t) = e^{\left(-\frac{1}{2} - \frac{\sqrt{3}}{2} i\right) t} = e^{-\frac{t}{2}} \cdot e^{-\frac{\sqrt{3}}{2} it},$$

but the presence of $i = \sqrt{-1}$ makes it hard to understand what these solutions could mean.

Problem #335:

Assume that $i = \sqrt{-1}$ is a constant.

(a) Show that $y_1(t)$ is a solution of Equation (7.32).

(b) Show that $y_2(t)$ is also a solution of Equation (7.32).

(c) Show that if a and b are constants then $w(t) = ay_1(t) + by_2(t)$ is also a solution of Equation (7.32).

To find meaning in his solutions he returned to the simpler Equation (7.29),

$$m\frac{d^2 y}{dt^2} = -ky,$$

---

[24]Descartes had dubbed them as "imaginary" in his book *La Geometrie* in 1637: ". . . whereas we can always imagine as many roots for each equation as I have predicted, there is still not always a quantity which corresponds to each root so imagined."

which he already knew how to solve. To make things simpler still he assumed that $m = k = 1$ and tried his crazy guess, $y = e^{ct}$ again on

$$\frac{\mathrm{d}^2 y}{\mathrm{d}t^2} = -y. \tag{7.34}$$

Problem #336:

Show that $y = e^{ct}$ is a solution of the differential Equation (7.34) when $c = i$ or $c = -i$.

Problem #336 shows that $y = e^{it}$ and $y = e^{-it}$ are both solutions of Equation (7.34), but Euler knew (as we do[25]) that the solution of Equation (7.34) is $y(t) = a\cos(t) + b\sin(t)$ where a and b are constants.

He now had very different looking solutions of Equation (7.34). Euler guessed that somehow these must be the same, so he set

$$e^{it} = a\cos(t) + b\sin(t)$$

and tried to find a and b.

Problem #337:

(**a**) Show that if $e^{it} = a\cos(t) + b\sin(t)$, then $a = 1$ and $b = i$.
   (**Hint:** To get a, substitute $t = 0$. To get b, differentiate first.)

(**b**) Show that if $e^{-it} = a\cos(t) + b\sin(t)$, then $a = 1$ and $b = -i$.

From part (a) of Problem #337 we get the formula,

$$e^{it} = \cos(t) + i\sin(t). \tag{7.35}$$

Equation (7.35 is known as **Euler's Identity** and it is foundational to electrical engineering, and physics (especially Quantum Mechanics). For mathematicians it is the key to understanding the geometry of the **Complex Numbers** (numbers of the form $a + bi$, where a and b are real numbers and $i^2 = -1$).

For Euler, it was a way to translate trigonometric functions to exponential (and hyperbolic trigonometric) functions and back. For us, it is the key to our dampened oscillation problem.

Before we get to that, notice the following curious[26] consequences of Euler's Identity.

Drill #338:

Show that $e^{i\pi} + 1 = 0$.

---

[25]See Section (6.4).
[26]We call this curious because it relates the numbers $0, 1, i, e$, and π all in one simple formula. To find out what it actually means you'll need to become a mathematics major and take a course in Complex Analysis. It's fun. You should do that.

Another curious consequence is that the trigonometric functions and the hyperbolic trigonometric functions are related via the constant $i = \sqrt{-1}$.

Problem #339:

(a) Show that $\cosh(it) = \frac{e^{it} + e^{-it}}{2} = \cos(t)$ **(b)** Show that $\frac{1}{i}\sinh(it) = \frac{e^{it} - e^{-it}}{2i} = \sin(t)$.

Finally, we return to Equation (7.32). In Problem #333 we saw that

$$z(t) = e^{-\frac{t}{2}}\left[A\cos\left(\frac{\sqrt{3}}{2}t\right) + B\sin\left(\frac{\sqrt{3}}{2}t\right)\right]$$

and in part (c) of Drill #335 we saw that

$$y = e^{-\frac{t}{2}}\left[ae^{\frac{\sqrt{3}}{2}it} + be^{-\frac{\sqrt{3}}{2}it}\right]$$

is another. If these are the same solution we can find a relation between the constants a, b, A, and B.

Problem #340:

(a) Assuming that

$$z(t) = e^{-\frac{t}{2}}\left[A\cos\left(\frac{\sqrt{3}}{2}t\right) + B\sin\left(\frac{\sqrt{3}}{2}t\right)\right],$$

that

$$w(t) = e^{-\frac{t}{2}}\left[ae^{\frac{\sqrt{3}}{2}it} + be^{-\frac{\sqrt{3}}{2}it}\right],$$

and that $z(t) = w(t)$, use Euler's Identity to show that $A = a + b$ and that $B = i(a - b)$.

(b) Show that if $w(t)$ satisfies the initial conditions

$$w(0) = 0$$
$$w'(0) = 1.$$

then $a = -\frac{i}{\sqrt{3}}$ and $b = \frac{i}{\sqrt{3}}$.
(**Hint:** If $i^2 = -1$ what is $\frac{-1}{i}$ equal to?)

(c) Use a and b from part (b) to show that A and B are real numbers.

Chapter 8

Optimization: Going to Extremes

8.1   Introduction

While it would not be correct to say that Calculus was invented solely to solve optimization problems, it's pretty close[1]. Recall that one of the fundamental tenets of modern science is that nature is lazy. Light follows the fastest (minimal) path between two points. Soap bubbles are spherical because that is the shape that encloses the most (maximal) volume for a given surface area. Alternatively, a soap bubble uses the least (minimal) surface area to enclose a particular volume[2]. Nature optimizes.

Mathematically speaking all optimization starts in the same place: We have some quantity (revenue, tax liability, temperature, resource consumption, travel time, potential energy, volume, surface area, whatever), which depends on one or more variables. The variables are (usually) constrained in some way, and we need to find conditions that make the quantity as large, or as small as possible within those constraints. The "thing to be optimized" is called the **objective function** and the constraints on the variables are called . . . well, they're called the **constraints**.

When we looked at Fermat's Method of Adequality in Section 2.4 we observed that if $f(x)$ is a (continuous) function then near an optimal point $f(x + h) \approx f(x)$ as long as h is not too big. Loosely speaking, this says that near an extremum the graph of the function is practically horizontal. More formally we have:

Theorem 1: [Fermat's Theorem]

If a function, $f(x)$, is differentiable at $x = a$ and $f(a)$ is either a maximum or a minimum then $\left.\frac{\mathrm{d}f}{\mathrm{d}x}\right|_{x=a} = 0$.

---

[1]Once it was invented, of course, Calculus turned out to be a very useful tool for lots of other problems as well.

[2]Actually, a physicist would say that soap bubbles are spherical because that is the shape the minimizes the potential energy contained in the soap film. It all comes to the same end. Something must be optimized.

In view of Fermat's Theorem it appears that a likely strategy for attacking optimization problems is to find an expression, say $f(x)$, for the objective function and then solve the equation $\frac{df}{dx} = 0$. In fact, this is precisely the strategy we used in Section 4.4 to find the maximal height attained by a tossed ball. If we toss a ball upward we know that it will reach a maximal height. At the top of its flight, when the ball transitions from upward movement to downward movement, there is a moment when its velocity is zero. Thus we saw that if $p(t)$ is a formula that gives the height of the ball at any time, setting $\frac{dp}{dt} = 0$ and solving for t will yield the time when the ball is at the top of its flight.

Drill #341:

Suppose a ball is tossed vertically from the surface of the earth with an initial velocity of $20 \frac{\text{meters}}{\text{sec}}$. Show that the ball reaches its maximum height when $t = \frac{20}{9.8} \approx 2$ seconds.
(**Hint:** You may want to review Problem #95)

At their simplest, optimization problems really are just that straightforward. But "straightforward" does not necessarily mean easy. There are several nuances that, if not clearly understood, can cause much confusion and difficulty. We will proceed carefully.

To begin, take careful note of what Fermat's Theorem says and, just as important, what it does not say: It says that if $(a, f(a))$ is a point on the graph of a differentiable function $f(x)$, and if $f(a)$ is known to be an extremum (either a maximum or a minimum) then $\left.\frac{df}{dx}\right|_{x=a} = 0$.

Fermat's Theorem does not say that if $\left.\frac{df}{dx}\right|_{x=a} = 0$ then $f(a)$ must be an extremum. In fact, that is not necessarily true. For example, if $f(x) = x^3$ then $\left.\frac{df}{dx}\right|_{x=0} = 0$ but the graph has neither a maximum or a minimum at $(0, f(0))$. Confirm this by graphing it.

We have a lifetime of experience with tossed balls telling us that a tossed ball will reach a maximum height. Fermat's Theorem tells us that whenever that maximum height is attained, $\frac{dp}{dt}$ will be zero. So all we had to do for this problem is find the one and only time when $\frac{dp}{dt} = 0$. This is the time when the maximum height is reached. But suppose after the ball is released there are forces other than gravity involved. Suppose, for example, that our tossed ball is being buffeted by the wind on a blustery day is such a way that the height of the ball is given by

$$p(t) = (t-1)^4 + (t-1)^3 + 5.$$

We have no experience, hence no intuition, with a ball moving in this fashion so we have no way to decide if there even is a maximum, let alone what it might be. We also have no tools to help us find the maximum height of the ball if it does exist. Fermat's Theorem doesn't help because it tells us what happens at an extremum $\left(\frac{dp}{dt} = 0\right)$, not how to find it. In this chapter we will build up some tools to help us find extrema.

Drill #342:

Let $p(t) = (t-1)^4 + (t-1)^3 + 5$.

(**a**) Show that $\frac{dp}{dt} = 0$ when $t = 1$ and when $t = \frac{1}{4}$.

(**b**) Graph $p(t)$. Does it have a maximum? Explain.

8.2   Preliminaries: Some Simple Optimizations

To begin we will consider problems that will allow us to use our intuition. Our goal is to build a set of tools. By the end of this chapter we will be able to rely more on the tools of Calculus and less on intuition to solve a wide variety of optimization problems. This does not mean that you should stop using your intuition, only that you will have a set of tools that will allow you to either confirm your instincts, or refute them.

Many of the examples in this section can be solved by more elementary methods than Calculus. If you can see a more fundamental way to solve these problems and examples, that's great! Do that. But keep the goal in mind. We're interested in these examples as a means to elucidate the subtleties inherent in optimization problems. These problems are a means to that end, not an end in themselves.

Example #46: **Constructing A Square on a Line**

What is the area of the smallest possible square having one corner at the point $(2, 3)$ and an adjacent corner on the line

$$5x + 3y = 2. \tag{8.1}$$

The diagram at the right is a visualization of this problem. We can imagine the blue square growing and shrinking as we move the point (a, b) along the line. It seems clear that the square having the least area is the one pictured in black (when (a, b) is at (x, y). It is worth taking a moment to notice this explicitly because not all optimization problems are solvable. If we had asked for the largest possible square there would be no solution because the blue square in our diagram can always be make larger by moving the point (a, b) further to the left on the graph of Equation (8.1).

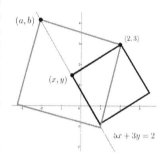

But a convincing picture is not a solution. To complete the solution we'll need to compute the coordinates of the point (x, y) in our sketch and compute the minimal area.

In any optimization problem the first question to ask is, "What do we need to optimize?" In other words, "What is our objective function?" For this problem the length of the line segment between the point $(2, 3)$ and any point (x, y) is given by the Distance Formula: $\sqrt{(x - 2)^2 + (y - 3)^2}$. Therefore the area of the square constructed from this line segment is given by the function:

$$A(x) = \left(\sqrt{(x - 2)^2 + (y - 3)^2} \right)^2 = (x - 2)^2 + (y - 3)^2.$$

So our objective function is $A(x)$. Since the point (x, y) is constrained to lie on the line $5x + 3y = 2$, Equation (8.1), is our constraint.

Notice that we've abused our notation a bit. Although the notation $A(x)$ indicates that A depends on x alone, we've given A in terms of both x and y. But solving Equation (8.1) gives[3] $y = \frac{1}{3}(2 - 5x)$ so it should be clear that A really depends only on x.

---

[3]If we make this substitution immediately we can get the objective function solely in terms of x: $A(x) = (x - 2)^2 + \left(\frac{1}{3}(2 - 5x) - 3 \right)^2$, But does that really help? Either way we're going to have to differentiate $A(x)$. Which form of $A(x)$ would you rather use? We think using two variables makes this objective function a bit "easier on the eyes."

We've seen visually that this problem has a solution and Fermat's Theorem tells us that the derivative of our objective function will be zero at that solution. So we differentiate both sides of

$$A = (x - 2)^2 + (y - 3)^2$$

which gives

$$dA = 2(x - 2)\,dx + 2(y - 3)\,dy.$$

But recall that x and y are constrained by the Equation (8.1) from which we see that $dy = -\frac{5}{3}\,dx$. Therefore

$$dA = 2(x - 2)\,dx + 2(y - 3)\left(-\frac{5}{3}\,dx\right)$$
$$= \left[2(x - 2) + 2(y - 3)\left(-\frac{5}{3}\right)\right]\,dx$$

or

$$\frac{dA}{dx} = 2(x - 2) + 2(y - 3)\left(-\frac{5}{3}\right).$$

Setting $\frac{dA}{dx}$ equal to zero we have

$$2(x - 2) + 2(y - 3)\left(-\frac{5}{3}\right) = 0.$$
$$(x - 2) + (y - 3)\left(-\frac{5}{3}\right) = 0.$$
$$x - 2 - \frac{5}{3}y + 5 = 0.$$
$$x + 3 - \frac{5}{3}y = 0. \tag{8.2}$$

From our constraint we have $y = \frac{1}{3}(2 - 5x)$. Inserting this into Equation (8.2) we see that

$$x + 3 - \frac{5}{3}\left(\frac{1}{3}(2 - 5x)\right) = 0.$$

Solving for x gives

$$x + 3 - \frac{5}{3}\left(\frac{2}{3} - \frac{5}{3}x\right) = 0,$$

$$x + 3 - \frac{10}{9} + \frac{25}{9}x = 0,$$

$$\frac{9x + 27 - 10 + 25x}{9} = 0,$$

$$\frac{34x + 17}{9} = 0,$$

$$34x = -17$$

$$x = -\frac{1}{2}. \tag{8.3}$$

To find y we use our constraint and the value of x from Equation (8.3,

$$y\Big|_{x=-1/2} = \frac{1}{3}(2 - 5x)\Big|_{x=-1/2} = \frac{3}{2}.$$

So we have found that the minimal square occurs when $x = -\frac{1}{2}$, and $y = \frac{3}{2}$ and it feels like we're done, doesn't it? We're not. The question asked was "What is the area of the smallest possible square?" To find the area we need to put $(x, y) = (-1/2, 3/2)$ into our area formula which yields

$$A(x, y)\Big|_{(x,y)=\left(-\frac{1}{2}, \frac{3}{2}\right)} = (x - 2)^2 + (y - 3)^2\Big|_{(x,y)=\left(-\frac{1}{2}, \frac{3}{2}\right)}$$

$$= \left(-\frac{1}{2} - 2\right)^2 + \left(\frac{1}{2} - 3\right)^2 = \frac{17}{2} \text{ square units.}$$

Always remember to check that you have actually answered the question asked before you stop.

Problem #343:

(a) Do you see that the point (x, y) which minimizes the area of our square also minimizes the length of the line segment from $(2, 3)$ to (x, y)? What objective function would we get if we tried to minimize the length of the segment instead of the area of the square. Does this change the problem? If so, how?

(b) This example specified that $(2, 3)$ and (x, y) were adjacent corners of the square. What would the objective function look like if those points were diagonally opposite each other. Does this change the problem? If so, how?

Problem #344:

It seems fairly intuitively clear that the minimal square occurs when the line through $(2, 3)$ is orthogonal[4] to the graph of the line $5x + 3y = 2$.

(a) Verify that our intuition is correct.

(b) Does this remain true if the point on the line and $(2, 3)$ are not adjacent corners of the square?

End Of Example #46

A Few General Comments on Example 46

1. The first step in any optimization problem is to identify the objective function. Sometimes more than one will work. In that case use the simplest one, but without an objective function we can't even get started.

2. We need to identify constraint(s) as well, if any exist. (Not all optimization problems will have constraints. Some will have more than one.) We may not need these immediately, but we will need them sooner or later.

3. It was intuitively clear from our sketch that there actually is a minimal square in this example; that a solution exists. This will be true often enough that it will be easy to start believing that you can rely on your intuition alone to solve optimization problems. This is a mistake.

   Intuition is important and we encourage you to use it, especially when you first start thinking about a new problem. But intuition is based on past experience. It is a way of saying that you expect today to go pretty much the same way yesterday did. Most of the time this is true, but you never know when things will go awry so you must always verify that your intuition is correct by some other means[5].

4. Most of the heavy lifting in this problem was done in the Algebra, not the Calculus. This will be true of many of the mathematics problems you will encounter from now on. There is a strong tendency to think of algebraic manipulations as "just algebra" and to be careless with them. This is also a mistake. Every step toward solving a problem is just as important as every other step, whether it is Algebra, Calculus, Geometry, Arithmetic, or just "thinking about the problem." Every step must be successfully completed. Strive to be skillful, and careful, with all of your tools.

5. We were very careful to write out, in detail, every algebraic and arithmetic step in this problem but if we were to do this for every problem this text would become too long to be useful. We don't want that to happen so we will regularly do several elementary algebraic steps at once.

---

[4] "Orthogonal" is the word mathematicians use when everyone else would say "perpendicular." The reasons for this are abstruse.

[5] Calculus, in this case.

But "elementary" does not mean "easy." You may not be able to follow all of the steps in your head, especially at first. When you do not see how to get from one line of computation to the next you may be tempted to just skip it. Don't. Do. That. Keep a writing pad handy at all times. If there is any question of understanding a given computation take out that pad and do the computation yourself. If you are unable to do the computation yourself, ask for help. Ask a classmate, a friend, your instructor, whomever. Ask for help when you need it. If you do this habitually you will find that following the steps gets easier over time. If you do not it will remain difficult forever. We're serious. Do all elementary computations yourself! It is your responsibility to make sure you understand the computations we show you.

Example #47: **Constructing A Square on a Circle**

We want to find the area of the largest and the smallest squares that can be constructed with one corner at the point $(2, 3)$ and an adjacent corner on the unit circle: $x^2 + y^2 = 1$.

The solution of this problem is very clear once it has been sketched. The purpose of Drill #345 is for you to see the solution intuitively. We will solve it again analytically below.

Drill #345:

(a) Sketch the unit circle, plot the point $(2, 3)$, and draw the smallest and largest squares you can which have one corner at the point $(2, 3)$ and an adjacent corner on the unit circle: $x^2 + y^2 = 1$, Explain how you can tell from your sketch that that there is both a maximal (largest area) and a minimal (smallest area) square.

(b) Explain how you can tell from your sketch, that the second corner of the maximal and minimal squares are at the intersection points of the line $y = \frac{3}{2}x$ and the unit circle.

(c) Show that the areas of the maximal square is $A \approx 21.2$ units and that the area of the minimal square is $A \approx 6.8$ units.

The solution in Drill #345 relies heavily on the intuition gained from sketching the problem. As we have said many times you should use your intuition but not rely on it. To confirm our solution in Drill #345 using Calculus tools we will start at the beginning and solve this problem again, relying as much as possible on our computations. Eventually, we would like to rely exclusively on our computations, but this is not quite possible yet.

We have the same objective function as in Example #46: $A(x) = (x - 2)^2 + (y - 3)^2$. So

$$dA = 2(x - 2)\,dx + 2(y - 3)\,dy \tag{8.4}$$

as before. But this time our constraint is

$$x^2 + y^2 = 1 \tag{8.5}$$

so $dy = -\frac{x}{y}\,dx$. Plugging this into Equation (8.4) we have

$$dA = 2(x - 2)\,dx + 2(y - 3)\left(-\frac{x}{y}\right)dx$$

$$\frac{dA}{dx} = 2\left(-2 + \frac{3x}{y}\right) \tag{8.6}$$

In order to use Fermat's Theorem we must first know that one maximum and one minimum exists. No computation we've done guarantees the existence of an extremum, let alone its location. However, as a result of the work you did to solve Drill #345 we do know, intuitively, that there are two optimal solutions: one maximal and one minimal. Therefore Fermat's Theorem does guarantee that at each of these (wherever they are) $\frac{dA}{dx} = 0$.

We proceed as just discussed. Since we know (from Drill #345) that both a maximal and a minimal solution exist we set $\frac{dA}{dx} = 2\left(-2 + \frac{3x}{y}\right) = 0$. Solving this yields

$$3x = 2y, \tag{8.7}$$

and since (from our constraint, Equation (8.5)) $y = \pm\sqrt{1 - x^2}$ we have

$$3x = \pm 2\sqrt{1 - x^2}. \tag{8.8}$$

The square root symbol, and the plus-or-minus ($\pm$) make Equation (8.8) seem a little scary at first but it is really just a quadratic equation in disguise. Squaring both sides of Equation (8.8) gives $9x^2 = 4(1 - x^2)$ or

$$13x^2 = 4. \tag{8.9}$$

So we have two solutions: $x = \frac{2}{\sqrt{13}}$ and $x = -\frac{2}{\sqrt{13}}$. From Drill #345 we know that these must correspond to the maximal and minimal solutions. Fermat's Theorem doesn't tell us which is which but now all we need to do is distinguish between them by evaluating $A(x)$ for each.

Drill #346:

(a) Show that the area of the maximal square is approximately 21.2 units. Which value of x does this correspond to?

(b) Show that the area of the minimal square is approximately 6.8 units. Which value of x does this correspond to?

End Of Example #47

Since a circle is a special case of an ellipse the following problem is a slight generalization of Drill #345. But the algebra is a bit trickier.

Problem #347: Extremal Squares on an Ellipse

There are two extremal squares with one corner at $(2, 3)$ and an adjacent corner on the ellipse:

$$x^2 + \frac{1}{4}y^2 = 2.$$

Find the area of each one of them.

Steps (a) through (g) will guide you through the process.

(**Hint:** Not all of the problems in these steps are easily solved algebraically. Use Newton's Method or computational software as needed to find approximations.)

(a) Draw a sketch of this problem. Explain how you can tell from the sketch that there is one maximal, and one minimal square.

(b) The objective function for this problem is, once again: $A(x) = (x-2)^2 + (y-3)^2$.

What is the constraint?

(c) Use the constraint to show that $dy = -\frac{4x}{y}\,dx$ and that $y = \pm 2\sqrt{2-x^2}$.

(d) Show that $\frac{dA}{dx} = -6x - 4 + \frac{24x}{y}$.

(e) Show that if we choose $y = 2\sqrt{2-x^2}$ then the only root of $\frac{dA}{dx} = 0$ is $x \approx 0.86$.

(f) Show that if we choose $y = -2\sqrt{2-x^2}$ then the only root of $\frac{dA}{dx} = 0$ is $x \approx -0.28$.

(g) Find (approximately) the area of the square associated with both of these points. Which one is the maximal and which is the minimal square?

Problem #348:
Here is a sketch of the optimal squares in Problem #347:

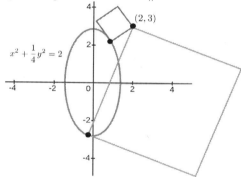

Notice that for both the maximal and the minimal square one of the sides appears to be orthogonal to (the line tangent to) the ellipse.

(a) Show that they actually are orthogonal.

(b) It is generally true that the shortest (or longest) line segment from a point (a, b) to a curve, C, will be orthogonal to the line tangent to the curve at their point of intersection. The figure below shows an arbitrary, differentiable curve, C, and an arbitrary point (a, b).

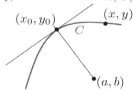

Suppose that the area of a square with one corner at (a, b) and an adjacent corner on the curve at (x, y) is optimal (minimal or maximal) at (x_0, y_0). Show that the line joining (a, b) and (x_0, y_0) is orthogonal to the tangent line of C at (x_0, y_0) .

Try to solve this problem completely on your own, but if you get stuck here is an outline you can follow:

(i) Find the objective function, $A(x)$. (This will be the area of the square on the line from (a, b) to (x, y).)

(ii) Use the fact that $\left.\frac{dA}{dx}\right|_{(x_0, y_0)} = 0$ to find the slope of C at (x_0, y_0).

(iii) Find the slope of the line from (a, b) to (x_0, y_0).

(iv) Compare the two slopes.

(v) What happens if the tangent line is horizontal? If it is vertical?

Example #48: **Differentials vs. Derivatives**

But take a moment to consider this. Is it clear to you that there must be such a maximal rectangle? If so then, as before, setting the derivative of the objective function equal to zero and solving for the variable will provide all of the values of the variable where the maximal rectangle might occur. If we're lucky there will only be a few such and we can check them one at a time.

Finding the objective function is easy. The area, A, of any rectangle is its length, l, times its width, w, so

$$A = lw \tag{8.10}$$

is the objective function.

The perimeter, P is

$$P = 2l + 2w \tag{8.11}$$

and is constrained to be a constant (fixed) value so Equation (8.11) is the constraint. Throughout this example keep in mind that P is a fixed constant, not a function of l and w.

At this point we can complete the problem using Calculus in either of two equivalent ways.

Using Differentials: In our opinion this is how Leibniz intended for his Calculus to be used so we tend to favor it.

1. Compute $dA = l\,dw + w\,dl$, from the objective function.

2. Differentiate the constraint, giving the differential form of the constraint: $2\,dl + 2\,dw = 0$.

3. Set $dA = 0$ and solve this equation using the constraint and its differential form as needed. In this problem we have $dl = -\,dw$ so

$$l\,dw + w\,dl = 0$$
$$l\,dw - w\,dw = 0$$
$$(l - w)\,dw = 0.$$

Since $dw \neq 0$ we have $l = w$ and thus the square encloses the most area.

Using Derivatives: The modern approach emphasizes the use of functions and derivatives rather than curves and differentials.

1. Solve the constraint for either w or l in terms of the other. For example, $l = \frac{1}{2}(P - 2w)$.

2. Substitute this into the objective function to rewrite it in terms of a single variable:

$$A(w) = \frac{1}{2}(P - 2w) \cdot w = \frac{1}{2}(Pw - w^2).$$

3. Now think of the objective function, $A(w)$, as an abstract function and find its maximum point by setting $\frac{dA}{dw} = 0$ and solving for w.

Proceeding, we have

$$\frac{dA}{dw} = \frac{d}{dw}\left(\frac{1}{2}(Pw - 2w^2)\right) = \frac{1}{2}(P - 4w) = 0$$

so $w = \frac{P}{4}$. Putting this back into our constraint gives $P = 2 \cdot \frac{P}{4} + 2l$ we see that l is also equal to $\frac{P}{4}$. Since $l = w = \frac{P}{4}$ the square encloses the most area.

As we said, the two approaches are completely equivalent. Use whichever feels most comfortable to you.

End Of Example #48

In Chapter 2 we used Fermat's Method of Adequality to solve the following problem which is closely related to Example #48.

Problem #349:

Find the dimensions of the rectangle having the smallest perimeter, given that the area is fixed.

Since we are still relying on Fermat's Theorem, the first step is to convince yourself that this problem has a solution. Once you have done that, use both of the approaches outlined in Example #48 to complete the solution. Which method do you prefer?

Problem #350:

Consider all lines connecting the point $(-4, -3)$ to an arbitrary point (x, y), on the unit circle as pictured. There is clearly one point where the slope of the associated line is maximum and another point where the slope of the associated line is minimum. These are the outermost lines depicted in the figure.

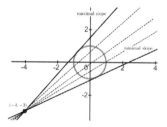

Find an equation for each of these lines. If you aren't sure how to begin use the following steps.

(a) Find an appropriate objective function for this problem.

(b) Find the constraint for this problem.

(c) Differentiate both your objective function and your constraint to show that the points where the maximum and minimum slope occur must satisfy

$$x^2 + y^2 = -4x - 3y. \tag{8.12}$$

(**Comment:** There is usually more than one way to solve a given problem so it is possible that you came up with a different equation than we did. That's OK. Solve the problem using yours and use ours to check your solution.)

(d) Solve Equation (8.12) and the constraint simultaneously to find the equations of the lines with maximal and minimal slope. Verify your answer by graphing both lines and the unit circle.

Drill #351:
Sketch the graphs of $y = e^x$ and $y = \ln(x)$ and convince yourself that there is a point on each graph which is closest to the origin.

(a) Find the approximate coordinates of the point on the curve $y = e^x$ that is closest to the origin.

(b) Find the approximate coordinates of the point on the curve $y = \ln(x)$ that is closest to the origin.

(c) Are the solutions of parts (a) and (b) related? Explain.

Drill #352:
Suppose a point is moving in a plane so that its (x, y) coordinates are given by:

$$P(t) = \left\{ \begin{array}{c} t - 1 \\ e^t \\ -\infty < t < \infty \end{array} \right\}$$

(a) Find the value of t where the point, $P(t)$, is closest to the origin. Is it clear that there is such a point?

(b) Find the (x, y) coordinates of the point's location when it is closest to the origin.

Problem #353:

(a) Of all the rectangles that can be inscribed in the unit circle show that the one with the maximum area is a square.

(b) Of all the rectangles that can be inscribed in the ellipse $x^2 + \frac{y^2}{9} = 1$ show that the one with the maximum area is three times taller than it is wide.

(c) Of all the rectangles that can be inscribed in the ellipse $\frac{x^2}{16} + y^2 = 1$ show that the one with the maximum area is four times wider than it is tall.

(d) Of all the rectangles that can be inscribed in the ellipse $\frac{x^2}{a^2} + \frac{y^2}{b^2} = 1$ show that the one with the maximum area has a height to width ratio of $\frac{b}{a}$.

Digression #18: Triangles with Fixed Perimeters

In Examples 4 and 48 we saw that of all rectangles with fixed perimeter, the square (an equilateral rectangle) has the largest area. Is this also true of triangles? More precisely, does an equilateral triangle have the largest area out of all triangles with a fixed perimeter? This may sound like a simpler problem but it is actually a bit harder.

Here's why. With a rectangle each set of parallel sides varied together so we only had two independent parameters to deal with. For triangles all three sides vary independently, giving us three independently varying parameters, which is inherently more complex than two.

How might we address this question?

A standard ploy for solving difficult problems is to first try a simpler "adjacent" problem. To create such a problem in this case we hold one side fixed and only allow two sides of our triangle to vary. We'll show that when the area of the triangle is maximal the two varying sides must be the same length. We want to use this adjacent problem to gain some insight into how to solve our actual problem.

So our adjacent problem is this: Given all triangles with a fixed base and a fixed perimeter, does an isosceles triangle have the largest area? The sketch below has all of the pertinent parameters labeled.

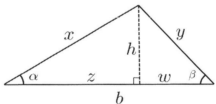

If we hold b fixed minimizing the area, $A = \frac{1}{2}bh$, is equivalent to maximizing h. So the length of h is the natural objective function for this problem. Also if h is at its maximum then by Fermat's Theorem (Theorem #1), $dh = 0$. Notice that there are two right triangles in our sketch and h is the height of both of them.

Problem #354: The Adjacent Problem

(a) Use the sketch above to express h as a function of x and z and show that when h is maximal $x\,dx - z\,dz = 0$.

(b) Express h as a function of y and w and show that when h is maximal $y\,dy - w\,dw = 0$.

(c) Use the fact that b is constant to find an equation relating dz and dw.

(d) Use the fact that the perimeter P is constant to find an equation relating $\mathrm{d}x$ and $\mathrm{d}y$.

(e) Use the results from parts (a), (b), (c), and (d) to show that h is maximized when

$$\frac{z}{x} = \frac{\mathrm{d}x}{\mathrm{d}z} = \frac{w}{y}.$$

(**Hint:** Use an appropriate trigonometric function.)

(f) Use part (e) to conclude that the base angles, α and β, must be congruent and thus $x = y$.

To show that the maximal area of an arbitrary triangle with a fixed perimeter must be equilateral we do not need Calculus, only reasoning. An example of the kind of reasoning we need appears in the Sherlock Holmes short story *The Adventure of the Beryl Coronet*. Early in the story Holmes says to Watson, "It is an old maxim of mine that when you have excluded the impossible, whatever remains, however improbable, must be the truth." Our solution will follow Holmes' lead: We will eliminate what is impossible leaving only the truth behind[a].

Problem #355: The Largest Triangle with a Fixed Perimeter is Equilateral
Observe that every triangle is either equilateral, or it is not equilateral.

(a) Suppose we have a triangle with sides a, b, and c which is not equilateral. Then at least two sides, say a and c, are not equal. Explain how Problem #354 implies that there must be another triangle with the same perimeter and a larger area.

(b) Use Holmes' maxim to explain why a triangle with a fixed perimeter enclosing maximal area must be equilateral.

---

[a]Holmes is using a tried and true mathematical proof technique, known colloquially as "the process of elimination." In mathematics it goes by its Latin name *Reduction Ad Absurdum* (RAA). If only one of two statements can be true – for example a triangle is either equilateral or it is not – we show logically that one of them is impossible under the constraints of the problem. We then conclude that the other statement must be true. In this way we "eliminate the impossible" so what is left "must be the truth."
If more than two statements are possible and we can eliminate all but one, that one "must be the truth." If only two statements are possible, as in this problem, the method is also called **Proof by Contradiction**.

═══ End Of Digression #18 ═══

8.3 Reflections, Refractions, and Rainbows

Because they are called "Optimization Problems" it is natural to assume that such problems are always about finding the maximum or minimum value of something. Certainly many of them are, but not all. Optimization problems come in two flavors:

1. Find the extreme values of some objective function, if there are any. Examples of this

kind of problem are Examples #46, and #47, Drill #346, and Problem #347.

2. Show that some property holds when the objective function is optimized. Examples of this kind of problem are Problems #344, #348, and #353, and Example #48.

Reflection

Another example of this second type is the problem of reflecting light we looked at in Chapter 2. Recall that we showed that light bounces off of a mirror in such a manner that the angle of incidence equals the angle of reflection. We did this by reasoning geometrically from the figure at the right to show that the minimal path must satisfy the condition $\alpha = \gamma$.

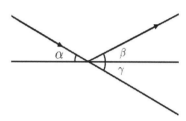

The geometric argument was actually pretty easy to understand once we found the right trick. But that's the difficulty. The geometric argument required the very counter-intuitive trick of pretending that the light passed through the mirror instead of reflecting off of it! Calculus provides a more systematic approach, one that does not require a stroke-of-genius level of insight to solve each new problem. Let's re-solve this problem, this time using the Calculus tools we've learned.

We will need an objective function so we modify the sketch above to suit the needs of Calculus. In particular, the relevant quantities need names as shown below.

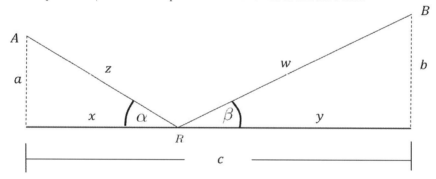

We assume that a (the height of the light source), b (the height of the observer's eye), and c (the distance between the light source and the observer) are constants while x, y, z, and w are variables.

We wish to show that when the path of the light from A to R to B is shortest, then $\alpha = \beta$. Since the length of that path is $z + w$ a natural objective function is:

$$L = z + w. \tag{8.13}$$

We also have the following constraints

$$a^2 + x^2 = z^2, \text{ and} \tag{8.14}$$

$$b^2 + y^2 = w^2. \tag{8.15}$$

$$x + y = c. \tag{8.16}$$

Differentiating Equation (8.13) gives $dL = dz + dw$.

Differentiating Equation (8.14) gives $dz = \frac{x}{z} dx$ so, combining these two results, we have

$$dL = \frac{x}{z} dx + dw.$$

Differentiating Equation 8.15 gives $dw = \frac{y}{w} dy$, so

$$dL = \frac{x}{z} dx + \frac{y}{w} dy.$$

And finally differentiating Equation (8.16) gives $dy = - dx$, so that

$$dL = \frac{x}{z} dx - \frac{y}{w} dx,$$

or

$$\frac{dL}{dx} = \frac{x}{z} - \frac{y}{w}.$$

Now suppose that the path from A to R to B is the shortest possible path, i.e., suppose that L is minimal. Then by Fermat's Theorem we know that $\frac{dL}{dx} = 0$, and therefore

$$\frac{x}{z} = \frac{y}{w}.$$

Since $\frac{x}{z} = \cos(\alpha)$ and $\frac{y}{w} = \cos(\beta)$ we see that $\alpha = \beta$.

This Calculus based argument is not as elegant as the geometric argument we used in Chapter 2. In the geometric argument we could easily visualize what was happening. Our Calculus based argument wasn't at all visual and it involved a lot of computation. But, believe it or not, this is a strength not a weakness. None of the computations are particularly hard, just tedious and detailed. But – and this is the point – we also had a clearly defined procedure to follow. We needed to: (1) Compute $\frac{dL}{dx}$, and (2) set $\frac{dL}{dx}$ equal to zero. The rest was Algebra which is straightforward though not necessarily easy.

Problem #356:

In the figure above suppose that $a = 5$, $b = 3$, and $c = 10$.

(a) Show that $\frac{dL}{dx} = \frac{x}{\sqrt{25+x^2}} - \frac{10-x}{\sqrt{9+(10-x)^2}}$.

(b) Show that the solution of $\frac{dL}{dx} = 0$ is $x = \frac{25}{4}$.

(c) Use the result of part (b) to show that $\alpha = \beta$.

Refraction: Snell's Law

We began the derivation of Snell's Law in Section 2.7, using the following sketch

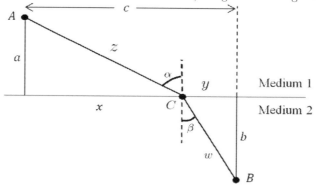

and assuming that the velocity of light in Medium 1 is v_1, and the velocity of light in Medium 2 is v_2. In Problem #38 in you found that the time for a ray of light to travel from point A to point B is given by

$$T(x) = \frac{\sqrt{a^2 + x^2}}{v_1} + \frac{\sqrt{b^2 + (c - x)^2}}{v_2}.$$

But we stopped there with the comment that, although Fermat successfully proved Snell's Law by minimizing $T(x)$ using his Method of Adequality, it is very very difficult to do. We said we would return to the problem when we could use the rules of Calculus. The time to do that has arrived.

Notice that we have an optimization problem. The objective function we need to minimize is $T(x)$. There are several constraints. For example, $x + y = c$ is one. Another is $a^2 + x^2 = z^2$. There is at least one more.

It is tempting to compute $\frac{\mathrm{d}T}{\mathrm{d}x}$ and proceed to solve $\frac{\mathrm{d}T}{\mathrm{d}x} = 0$ as we've done before. Computing $\frac{\mathrm{d}T}{\mathrm{d}x}$ is a bit challenging but it can be done if you proceed carefully.

The real issue is solving $\frac{\mathrm{d}T}{\mathrm{d}x} = 0$ for x. Unfortunately, this is still rather difficult to accomplish. But fortunately we we are not really interested in the value of x when $T(x)$ is minimal. We want to show that the tie traveled along the path from A to C to B is minimal when $\frac{\sin(\alpha)}{v_1} = \frac{\sin(\beta)}{v_2}$. We'll proceed carefully.

Problem #357:

(a) We know that the total time traveled from point A to C to B is given by
$$T(x) = \frac{z}{v_1} + \frac{w}{v_2}.$$
Write down all of the constraints involving the variables x, y, z, and w, and the constants a, b, and c. (We'll ignore α and β for now.)

(b) Show that when T is minimum (that is, when $\frac{\mathrm{d}T}{\mathrm{d}x} = 0$) we have

$$\frac{1}{v_1} \frac{x}{z} = \frac{1}{v_2} \frac{y}{w}. \tag{8.17}$$

(c) Use Equation 8.17 to derive Snell's Law of refraction: $\frac{\sin(\alpha)}{v_1} = \frac{\sin(\beta)}{v_2}$.

(d) Assuming that the speed of light in water is about $3/4$ of the speed of light in air, use Snell's Law to determine the range of possible angles for β as α ranges from 0 to $\pi/2$.

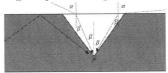

Physically, what part (d) of Problem #357 says is that when you are beneath the surface of a pond and look upward the entire view of the world above the surface is compressed into a circle at the top of a cone with central angle β. Attempts to look beyond that angle will result in you seeing a (probably dark) reflection from the bottom of the pond as no light that enters from above and outside this circle will reach your eye at point P. This phenomenon is called Snell's Window and is illustrated in the image at the right.

The solution to the following problem will rely on a derivation similar to the one we used to prove Snell's Law.

Snell's Window
courtesy of Eric Cheng

Problem #358:

Suppose that the cost to run a fiber optic cable underwater is k ($k \geq 1$) times the cost to run it on land. We wish to run a fiber optic cable from point A 1 km from the river, to point B on the other side 10 km downstream. The river is 1 km wide.

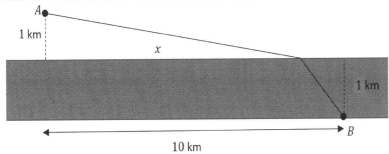

(a) Show that the value of x necessary to minimize the cost of running the cable must satisfy the equation

$$(k^2 - 1)x^4 - 20(k^2 - 1)x^3 + 101(k^2 - 1)x^2 - 20k^2x + 100k^2 = 0.$$

(b) When the formulas we're working with get this complicated it is a good idea to check them against our intuition in simple cases. Does this formula make sense to you when $k = 1$?

(c) Use any appropriate technology, or Newton's Method, to provide approximate values for x in the following table

k	x
1.1	
1.2	
1.3	
1.4	
1.5	

Do these values surprise you? Explain.

Rainbows

Look carefully at the double rainbow in the pictures below and notice that the order of the colors is reversed from the primary (brighter) to the secondary rainbow? Why do you think this happens?

Niagara Falls
photo by Mary Savage

Tsfat/Safed, Israel
photo by Elizabeth Enari

A few other questions come readily to mind. What conditions are required for a rainbow to form? Why is red on the top of the primary rainbow? Why is the primary rainbow below the secondary one? Why is the primary rainbow brighter and why are double rainbows so rare?

To tackle these questions the first thing we'll need to do is build a mathematical model of the problem. As you will see developing the model is probably the most challenging part.

When a ray of light enters a raindrop it gets both refracted and reflected, so we will need to use all that we have learned about how light refracts and reflects. Clearly Snell's Law will play a prominent role. To keep things simple we assume the drop is spherical.

By the Principle of Local Linearity when light strikes a point on a curved surface it will refract (if the surface is transparent) or reflect (if the surface is reflective) as if the surface is actually the line tangent to the surface. Since we're assuming for simplicity that our raindrops are spherical this means that the light will reflect or refract as if it is striking the tangent line of the circle in the diagram at the point where the light enters the droplet, A, exits the droplet, C, or reflects inside of the droplet, B. All of the angles in the

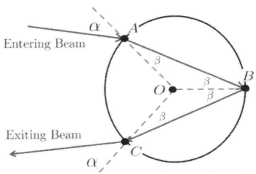

diagram at the right are measured between the light beam (in red) and the extended radii (blue, dashed lines) at points A, B, and C.

As displayed in the diagram above, the light ray traveling at velocity v_1, entering the raindrop at A and making an angle of α radians with the radial line OA is refracted to an angle of radian measure β according to Snell's Law:

$$\frac{\sin(\alpha)}{v_1} = \frac{\sin(\beta)}{v_2},$$

where v_2 is the velocity of light inside the raindrop. It is helpful to think of this refraction as a rotation about the point A. This is "Rotation 1" in the diagram below. The reflection at point B and the refraction at point C can similarly be thought of as rotations about their respective points.

Actually, only a portion of the light is refracted. The rest is reflected off the exterior of the raindrop, and is no longer of concern to us. Once inside the raindrop, it reflects off of the back of the raindrop (again only a portion is reflected) so that the angle of incidence equals the angle of reflection. A portion of the light then exits the raindrop, and once again the angles are governed by Snell's Law.

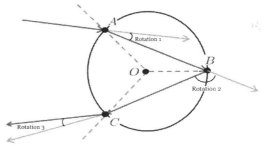

The total amount of (clockwise) rotation in this process is called the **deviation angle**, denoted $D(\alpha)$. This is shown in the sketch above. Notice that the total rotation is a sum of three separate rotations.

<u>Problem #359:</u> Show that $D(\alpha) = \pi - 4\beta + 2\alpha$.

Remember that the angles α and β are not independent. They are related by Snell's Law which we will rewrite as

$$\sin(\alpha) = \frac{v_1}{v_2}\sin(\beta) = k\sin(\beta), \qquad (8.18)$$

where $k = \frac{v_1}{v_2}$ is called **index of refraction** (for water). In the case of white light, this index of refraction is about[6] $\frac{4}{3}$. Graphing $D(\alpha)$ for $k = \frac{4}{3}$ and $0 \le \alpha \le \frac{\pi}{2}$ gives the graph at the left.

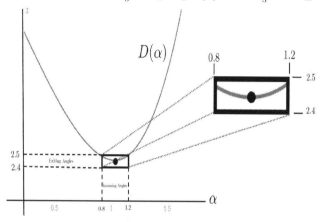

From this graph it appears that the minimum of the curve is approximately at the point $(1.03, 2.41)$. So the minimum value of $D(\alpha)$ is about 2.41 radians $\approx 138°$ and it occurs when the angle at which the light enters the raindrop is $\alpha \approx 1.03$ radians $\approx 59.4°$. Notice (from the enlargement of the graph near that minimum) that because the graph of $D(\alpha)$ is nearly horizontal[7] for values of α near 1.03 the amount of deviation is roughly the same for those values of α.

This is pertinent because it means that the lower the deviation angle the more concentrated that light rays exiting the raindrop. So the light rays entering the raindrop at approximately 59° have the highest concentration when exiting the raindrop. At other values of α the light is more diffused. It is these concentrated light rays that we see as a rainbow.

The angle supplementary to $D(\alpha)$ is called the **rainbow angle**, denoted $R(\alpha)$. Thus

$$R(\alpha) = \pi - D(\alpha) = \pi - (\pi - 4\beta + 2\alpha) = 4\beta - 2\alpha \text{ radians.}$$

The rainbow angle is also the angle that the rainbow makes with the eye of an observer, relative to the angle of the sun. For white light we have a rainbow angle of

$$R(1.03) = \pi - 2.41 \approx 0.732 \text{ radians} \approx 42°$$

as seen at the right.

So you will see a rainbow when the air is filled with water droplets, for example immediately after a rain, and the sun is behind you. Relative to the sun's rays the angle from your eye to the top of the rainbow will be about 42°. Every droplet reflects and refracts each ray of light entering it. The aggregation of all of those rays is the rainbow.

Of course, rainbows will manifest under other circumstances too, but we have not analyzed those.

---

[6]This is an average. k actually varies with the frequency (color) of the light.

[7]This is Fermat's Theorem coming into play again.

The Colors of the Rainbow

The Dark Side of the Moon,
Pink Floyd

The color spread in a rainbow occurs because the index of refraction k, changes with the frequency (color) of the light. This can be seen by shining a beam of light through a triangular prism or, by listening to rock music from the 1970s.

Of course we can only do so much by reasoning from graphs and pictures. If we want to nail things down very precisely (we do), we will eventually need to look at the problem analytically by minimizing an objective function. Fortunately, we already have our objective function. It is $D(\alpha)$. Our constraint comes from Snell's Law, $\sin(\alpha) = k\sin(\beta)$. We said that the general parameter k would depend on the frequency of the light[8] and we've observed that for water and air $k = \frac{4}{3}$. Rather than graphing the function for different values of k we'll just leave it as an arbitrary constant while we calculate. Afterward we can substitute specific values as needed.

Problem #360:
Differentiate the objective function, $D(\alpha)$, and the constraint, Equation (8.18), and use Fermat's Theorem (Theorem 1) to show that when D is a minimum

$$\cos(\alpha) = \frac{k}{2}\cos(\beta). \tag{8.19}$$

Combining Equation (8.19) with our constraint, we see that we need to solve the following system of two equations in two unknowns,

$$\cos(\alpha) = \frac{k}{2}\cos(\beta)$$
$$\sin(\alpha) = k\sin(\beta).$$

Normally to solve such a system, we would use one of the equations to eliminate one of the variables in the other equation. We could do that here but it would require some very messy expressions involving inverse trigonometric functions. Instead there is a trick that will be cleaner.

Suppose we square the quantities in each equation and then add the resulting equations together. This gives

$$1 = \sin^2(\alpha) + \cos^2(\alpha) = \frac{k^2}{4}\cos^2(\beta) + k^2\sin^2(\beta). \tag{8.20}$$

You might want to file this trick away in your memory. When Trigonometry is involved it is a good idea to look for, or to create, sums of the squares of sines and cosines.

---

[8]And the physical properties of the media the light is passing through, but we'll only consider water and air.

Problem #361:

(a) Use Equation (8.20) to show that for a given index of refraction k, $D(\alpha)$ is minimized when $\sin(\beta) = \sqrt{\frac{4-k^2}{3k^2}}$ and $\sin(\alpha) = \sqrt{\frac{4-k^2}{3}}$.

(b) Use this to complete the following table:

Color	k	β in degrees	α in degrees	$D(\alpha)$ in degrees	$R(\alpha)$ in degrees
Red	1.331				
Orange	1.332				
Yellow	1.333				
Green	1.335				
Blue	1.337				
Indigo	1.340				
Violet	1.344				

(c) How does this explain the order of the colors in the primary rainbow?

The values of $R(\alpha)$ you obtained in the table account for the various color bands that appear in the rainbow as sunlight hits droplets at various angles.

Double Rainbows

In a double rainbow the primary rainbow is created from light entering the upper portion of the droplet and exiting from the bottom. If light is bright enough then a secondary rainbow is created from light entering the lower portion and exiting the upper portion of the droplet as in the diagram below.

For the secondary rainbow the deviation angle $D(\alpha)$ is the total amount of counterclockwise rotation and the rainbow angle would be $R(\alpha) = D(\alpha) - \pi$. Note that the extra reflection explains why the secondary rainbow is not as bright as the primary.

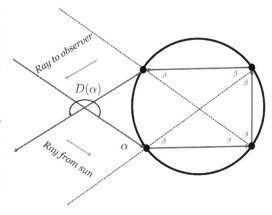

Problem #362:

(a) Show that in the case of the secondary rainbow, $D(\alpha) = 2\pi + 2\alpha - 6\beta$. This is our objective function for the secondary rainbow.

(b) Show that $D(\alpha)$ is minimized when $\sin(\beta) = \sqrt{\frac{9-k^2}{8k^2}}$ and $\sin(\alpha) = \sqrt{\frac{9-k^2}{8}}$.

(c) Use this to complete the following table:

Color	k	β in degrees	α in degrees	$D(\alpha)$ in degrees	$R(\alpha)$ in degrees
Red	1.331				
Orange	1.332				
Yellow	1.333				
Green	1.335				
Blue	1.337				
Indigo	1.340				
Violet	1.344				

(d) Use the table in part (c) of this problem and the table in the previous problem to explain why the secondary rainbow is above the primary rainbow and its colors are reversed.

8.4   Global vs. Local Extrema

So far in this chapter we've relied heavily on our intuition. For instance, in Example 46 it was very clear that a minimal square exists. Moreover, when we differentiated the objective function we found that $x = -\frac{1}{2}$ was the only solution of $\frac{dA}{dx} = 0$. So it was reasonable to conclude that the minimum occurs when $x = -\frac{1}{2}$.

Similarly in Problem 347 it was intuitively clear that there was both a maximal and a minimal square, so when we found two solutions of $\frac{dA}{dx} = 0$ it made sense to conclude that they correspond to the maximal and minimal squares, respectively.

Unfortunately things are rarely this straightforward. Consider the following example.

Example #49: Constructing a Square on a Parabola

We would like to find the area of the smallest square which can be constructed with one corner at the point $(2, 3)$ and an adjacent corner on the graph of $y = x^2$. This example is very similar to Problem 344 or Problem 347 so we will proceed in much the same way. The objective function is the same

$$A = (x - 2)^2 + (y - 3)^2 \tag{8.21}$$

but this time the constraint is

$$y = x^2. \tag{8.22}$$

In our previous examples we began by differentiating both the objective function and the constraint. This time substitute the constraint $y = x^2$ into $A(x)$ to obtain the objective function

$$A(x) = (x - 2)^2 + (x^2 - 3)^2$$

in terms of a single variable. We make this change of strategy simply to demonstrate that the two procedures are equivalent. In fact, for this particular problem they are almost identical. For more complex problems you may find that you prefer one strategy or the other.

Drill #363:

Show that $\frac{dA}{dx} = 0$ when $x \approx 1.75$, $x \approx -1.32$ and $x \approx -0.43$. Getting three distinct solutions of $\frac{dA}{dx} = 0$ is quite unexpected in light of our previous work. Can you explain this?

To find the minimal square in Drill #363 we need only substitute the x-values into $A(x)$. We get

$$A(1.75) \approx 0.07,$$
$$A(-1.32) \approx 12.6,$$
$$A(-0.43) \approx 13.83.$$

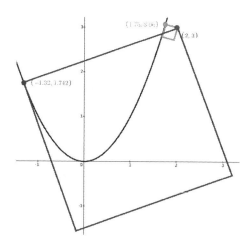

From these numbers, and from the sketch at the right, we can see that the minimal square seems to be the one whose second corner lies on the parabola at the point (approximately) $(1.75, 3.06)$. But those other two solutions of $\frac{dA}{dx} = 0$ are troubling. Do we get a maximal square at $\left(-0.43, (-0.43)^2\right)$ since $A(-0.43) \approx 13.83$ is the largest value of $A(x)$ among the three we've identified. And what about the point $(-1.32, 1.32^2)$? We clearly get neither a minimum nor a maximum. Why did our solution procedure point to it? This is all very puzzling.

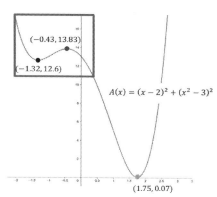

To begin addressing these questions let's look at the graph of our objective function, $A(x) = (x - 2)^2 + (x^2 - 3)^2$. The first coordinate of each point on the graph at the left corresponds to the x-coordinate of the corner of a square which lies on the constraint, $y = x^2$, and the second coordinate on the graph is the area of that square. Thus the minimal square will correspond to the lowest point on the graph at the left which is the square with a second corner at $x = 1.75$ as we have already concluded. But since the graph at the left continues to rise as we look farther to the right (or left) it should also be clear that there is no maximal square.

This graph also explains the why our procedure identified the squares with a second corner at both $x = -1.32$ and $x = -0.43$ as possible minimal squares as well. When we solve $\frac{dA}{dx} = 0$ we are locating the points on the graph of our objective function where its derivative is zero. That is, where the slope of the line tangent is horizontal. Fermat's Theorem only assures us that if $A(x)$ has an extremum at $x = a$ then $\frac{dA}{dx}\big|_{x=a} = 0$. In particular it does not tell us that there are no other values of x where $\frac{dA}{dx} = 0$.

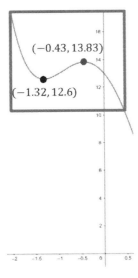

The problem here is that we have not been precise in our language. When we say "maximum" (or minimum) in ordinary speech we mean "the largest one," and it is clear that there can only be one "largest[9]."

However, if we confine our attention to the part of the graph inside the blue rectangle at the left we see that the point at $(-1.32, 12.6)$ is a minimum **locally** and the point at $(-0.43, 13.83)$ is a maximum **locally**. By "locally" we mean "if we restrict our attention to the graph near those two points" as seen at the right. We will need to distinguish between local and global optima in the future.

There are other issues as well.

Recall from Digression #10 that a function has two parts:

1. A rule to associate input with output, and

2. A domain.

Change either of these and you have a different function.

In this example our objective function is

$$A(x) = (x-2)^2 + (x^2 - 3)^2$$

and the constraint is

$$y = x^2, \text{ with domain } \mathbb{R}. \tag{8.23}$$

But suppose we change the constraint to

$$y = x^2, \text{ with domain } -2 \leq x \leq 0.5, \text{ (the part inside the blue rectangle).} \tag{8.24}$$

We now have a different problem because the only part of the graph we are interested in is the piece inside the blue rectangle. The global minimum no longer occurs at $x \approx 1.75$ because 1.75 is not in the problem domain, $x \approx 1.75$ simply doesn't exist in the domain of the function $y = x^2$, with domain; $-2 \leq x \leq 0.5$. However, since $x = -0.43$ and $x = -1.32$ are in the domain they still correspond to a local maximum and a local minimum, respectively. Are they also the global maximum and minimum? Give this question some thought and take your best guess. We will return to it in Problem #376.

Ḡnd Of Example #49

---

[9]Although it can occur more than once, at different places. Think about the graph of $y = \sin(x)$.

The existence of local extrema really complicates things for us because it means we have to find all of the **local** extrema and then figure out which of them, if any, are global. If we don't get organized we're likely to have a lot of trouble keeping this all straight.

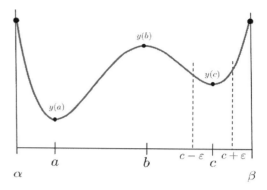

In the sketch at the right $y(a)$ is the **global** minimum of y since it is the lowest point on the graph of $y(x)$, whereas $y(c)$ is a local minimum because it is the lowest point on the graph when the domain of $y(x)$ is restricted to the interval $(c-\varepsilon, c+\varepsilon)$ (between the dashed lines). In this sketch the global maximum of $y(x)$ occurs at the endpoints of the interval, α and β. The fact that extrema can also occur at endpoints is a complicating detail we will come back to shortly.

Since the domain of the function affects the location of the extrema a definition of extrema will need to reference the function's domain. It is easy to get lost in the technicalities so keep Example #49 in mind as we proceed.

We have the following definitions.

Definition 9: Global Minimum

Suppose that g is a number in the domain of y such that[10] $y(g) \leq y(x)$ for every x in the domain of y. Then $y(g)$ is the **global minimum** of y.

Problem #364:

Provide a definition of Global Maximum modeled on Definition #9.

To define local extrema we need the concept of an open interval, so we digress briefly.

Digression #19: Interval Notation

An **interval** is a contiguous set of real numbers. For example, the set of numbers strictly between zero and one is an interval. Because the endpoints are not included it is called an **open interval** and is denoted by $(0, 1)$. Think of this notation as an abbreviation of the the two inequalities

$$0 < x \text{ and } x < 1 \text{ (also abbreviated sometimes as } 0 < x < 1)$$

Be careful. This notation can be ambiguous. Without some context it is not clear whether the notation (a, b) represents the open interval satisfying the inequalities $a < x < b$, or the point (a, b) in the x-y plane.

---

[10]The phrase "such that" is a term of art in mathematics. It means, "with the following property."

If we include the endpoints we have a **closed interval**, denoted by the ordered pair $[a, b]$. Think of this as an abbreviated form of the two inequalities

$$a \leq x \text{ and } x \leq b \text{ (also abbreviated sometimes as } a \leq x \leq b) .$$

Drill #365:
Re-express each of the following intervals using inequalities and state whether it is open, closed, or neither.

(a) $(-1, 1)$ **(b)** $[-1, 1]$ **(c)** $[-10, 25)$ **(d)** $(-32, 100]$

If we want to identify the interval of all numbers greater than, say $x = 1$ there is no right endpoint of the interval. Rather than writing this out in words every time we encounter it (which will be often) we force our notation to adapt to our need and denote this interval as: $(1, \infty)$. Similarly the interval of all numbers less than or equal to 7 is denoted: $(-\infty, 7]$. We've been using the symbol "$\mathbb{R}$" to denote all real numbers, but since the set of all real numbers is a (very large) interval we will sometimes use the interval notation, $(-\infty, \infty)$ as well.

Do not be fooled by this. "Infinity" (∞) is not a number and cannot be treated like one. This is just a notational shorthand that we use for our own convenience.

$$\text{End Of Digression \#19}$$

Now we can define local extrema.

Definition 10: **Local Minimum**

Suppose that l is a number in the domain of $y(x)$. Then $y(l)$ is a **local minimum** of y if there is an open interval, I, such that $y(l) \leq y(x)$ for every x in the interval I and in the domain of $y(x)$.

Problem #366:
Provide a definition of Local Maximum modeled on Definition #10.

Drill #367:
Explain why we can find a **global** maximum (minimum) by finding all of the **local** maxima (minima) and selecting the largest (smallest) among these.

8.5   Optimization, the Abstract Problem

As we saw in Example #49 once we've found the objective function, $O(x)$, our optimization problem becomes the more abstract problem of finding the extreme points of the graph of $O(x)$. An optimization problem ultimately comes down to finding all of the local extrema. The maximum among those will be the global maximum, and the minimum among those will be the global minimum. Assuming of course, that either exists.

Thus our first task is to identify all of the local extrema. But finding the local extreme points of the graph of an arbitrary objective function can be more complicated than we've seen in any of our examples so far. In this section we will address these complications. By the end of the section we will have a general procedure for solving this more abstract optimization problem.

Identifying and Distinguishing Maxima and Minima

Use your favorite graphing utility to graph the function $O(x) = x^3 - 3x$ and confirm visually that it has a local maximum at $(-1, 2)$, and a local minimum at $(1, -2)$. This seems to be easy to do when we have the graph in front of us. But in the absence of a graph how could we tell which is the maximum and which is the minimum?

Sometimes even having the graph isn't much help. For example, see if you can visually identify the global maximum and global minimum of the graph of

$$O(x) = (x^4 - 17x^3 + 239x)\sin(2x), \ 10 \le x \le 20.$$

We'll need an analytic method; one that doesn't rely on pictures. To that end, consider the following theorem from elementary Algebra.

Theorem 2:

1. If a line has positive slope then the y coordinate increases as the x coordinate increases.

2. If a line has negative slope then the y coordinate decreases as the x coordinate increases.

Lines are easy to think about of course, because the slope of a line is constant. If the slope of a line is 5 here, then it is also 5 over there, and way back there too. But we know that the slope of a curve can change from point to point so we will need to generalize Theorem 2 to a statement about curves. Theorem #2 generalizes to curves as follows.

Theorem 3: [The First Derivative Test]
Suppose f is a function of x. The following statements are true[11]:

1. If $f'(a) > 0$, on some interval then $f(x)$ is increasing on the interval.

2. If $f'(a) < 0$, on some interval then $f(x)$ is decreasing on the interval.

---

[11]This is a rather naive statement of this theorem, but it will suffice for our current purposes. We will revisit, restate, and prove the First Derivative Test in Section 14.3

The First Derivative test is precisely the tool we need to distinguish a maximum from a minimum. It will also turn out to be the tool that will allow us to determine via computation, rather than intuition, if a given objective function has a maximum or minimum. Take a moment to think about how this might be done before reading further.

Transition Points, and Possible Transition Points on Open Intervals

For the moment notice that we are confining our attention to functions whose domains are open intervals.

From Theorem 3 we see that if the derivative of $O(x)$ is positive then $O(x)$ is increasing and if the derivative of $O(x)$ is negative then $O(x)$ is decreasing. So, at a maximum $O(x)$ will transition from increasing to decreasing, and $O'(x) = \frac{\mathrm{d}O}{\mathrm{d}x}$ will transition from positive to negative. We conclude that to find a maximum we need to find those places where the derivative transitions from positive to negative.

Similarly, to find a local minimum, we need to find a place where the derivative transitions from negative to positive. We call such points **optimal transition points** because they are the places where (local) optima must occur.

The simplest way for $O'(x) = \frac{\mathrm{d}O}{\mathrm{d}x}$ to make either transition is for it to pass through zero. Thus the solutions of $O'(x) = \frac{\mathrm{d}O}{\mathrm{d}x} = 0$ are **possible optimal transition points (POTPs)** because these are points where and optimum might occur. This is not guaranteed.

In the simplest case all we have to do is find the solutions of $O'(x) = \frac{\mathrm{d}O}{\mathrm{d}x}$, then determine the sign of the derivative on either side of each such point. If it changes then we have a local extremum.

Drill #368: In the paragraph above we used the phrase "in the simplest case." We chose our words carefully. Can you think of another way for $O'(x) = \frac{\mathrm{d}O}{\mathrm{d}x}$ to transition from positive to negative, or from negative to positive? Give this some thought. We will come back to it.

The POTPs which are solutions of $\frac{\mathrm{d}O}{\mathrm{d}x} = 0$ are the easiest to think about and work with so we will focus on those for now. Unfortunately, extrema can sometimes occur at other points as well. We will address that possibility once we have thoroughly examined this simpler case.

Example #50:

Let $O(x) = x^3 - 3x$. The solutions of $\frac{\mathrm{d}O}{\mathrm{d}x} = 3x^2 - 3 = 0$ are $x = -1$ and $x = 1$ so these are the POTPs. Sketch the graph of $O(x)$ and follow along with our reasoning below, confirming our conclusions visually.

To determine if they actually are transition points we proceed as follows:

At $x = -1$: Pick a number less than -1, say $x = -2$. Since $\frac{\mathrm{d}O}{\mathrm{d}x}\big|_{x=-2} > 0$ we see that $O(x)$ is increasing to the left of $x = -1$. Next pick a number between -1 and the next POTP, $x = 1$. We'll take $x = 0$. Since $\frac{\mathrm{d}O}{\mathrm{d}x}\big|_{x=0} < 0$ we see that $O(x)$ is decreasing to the right of $x = -1$. Thus $O(-1) = 2$ is a local maximum value of $O(x)$.

At $x = 1$: As we saw above $O(x)$ is decreasing to the left of $x = 1$ since $\frac{\mathrm{d}O}{\mathrm{d}x}\big|_{x=0} < 0$. (Zero is between $x = -1$ and $x = 1$.) Next choose any number to the right of $x = 1$. We'll choose $x = 2$. Since $\frac{\mathrm{d}O}{\mathrm{d}x}\big|_{x=2} > 0$ we see that $O(x)$ is increasing to the right of $x = 1$. Thus $O(1) = -2$ is a local minimum of $O(x)$.

Drill #369: Does the graph of $O(x) = x^3 - 3x$ have a global maximum or minimum? Explain.

In this example we only tested one number between adjacent POTPs. Is that enough? Give this some thought before reading on.

Of course it is. Consider that the POTPs are precisely those places where $O'(x)$ might change sign. Therefore the sign of $O'(x)$ must either be always positive or always negative in between POTPs. Therefore, we only need to test at one value of x to find the sign of $O(x)$ on the entire interval between POTPs.

If a is the greatest POTP we need only test the sign of one number greater than a to determine the sign of $O'(x)$ for every value of x greater than a.

Similarly, if a is the least POTP we need only test the sign of one number less than a to determine the sign of $O'(x)$ for every value of x less than a.

We state all of this formally in Lemma #4 below.

End Of Example #50

Lemma 4:

Let $f(x)$ be a differentiable function.

(a) Suppose r_1 and r_2 are two POTPs of $f(x)$ such that there is not another POTP between them. If $f'(x) > 0$ for some x in the domain of f between r_1 and r_2, then $f'(x) > 0$ for every x in the domain of f between r_1 and r_2. Similarly, if $f'(x) < 0$ for some x between r_1 and r_2, then $f'(x) < 0$ for every x in the domain of f between r_1 and r_2.

(b) Suppose r_1 is the greatest POTP of $f(x)$. If $f'(x) > 0$ (< 0) for some $x > r_1$ then $f'(x) > 0$ (< 0) for all $x > r_1$, in the domain of f.

(c) Suppose r_2 is the least POTP of $f(x)$. If $f'(x) > 0$ (< 0) for some $x < r_2$ then $f'(x) > 0$ (< 0) for all $x < r_2$, in the domain of f.

In mathematics Theorems and Lemmas are always stated very formally, very concisely, and with as much generality as possible. There are good reasons for this but it does sometimes make them hard to read.

Drill #370:

Read Lemma 4 very carefully and convince yourself that it really does say the same thing as our conclusions at the end of Example #50.

Remember that POTPs are *possible* optimal transition points. The existence of a POTP does not imply the existence of an optimum, as the next example demonstrates.

Example #51:

Find all extrema of the graph of $O(x) = x^5$.

Solving $\frac{dO}{dx}\big|_{x=0} = 5x^4 = 0$ we see that $x = 0$ is the only POTP. But elsewhere $O'(x) > 0$ (confirm this) so $\frac{dO}{dx}$ is positive for every value of x except zero. In particular it is positive on the left and on the right of zero. Therefore $O(x) = x^5$ never transitions between increasing and decreasing, so we conclude that it does not have an extremum at $x = 0$, despite the fact that $\frac{dO}{dx}\big|_{x=0} = 0$. This may seem very curious until you graph the function.

Drill #371:

Sketch the graph of $O(x) = x^5$ and use it to explain how we can have $\frac{dO}{dx}\big|_{x=0} = 0$ yet not have either a maximum or a minimum at $x = 0$.

End Of Example #51

Example #52: Constructing a Parabola on a Square (Example #49), Revisited

Given our new understanding of the distinction between local and global extrema we will revisit Example #49. Recall the problem:

Find the area of the smallest square which can be constructed with one corner at the point $(2, 3)$ and an adjacent corner on the graph of $y = x^2$.

The objective function is still $A = (x-2)^2 + (y-3)^2$ so when we substitute the constraint, $y = x^2$, we get the abstract problem of finding the lowest points on the graph of

$$A(x) = (x-2)^2 + (x^2 - 3)^2$$

Solving $\frac{dA}{dx} = 0$ gives us three POTPs: $x \approx -1.32$, $x \approx -0.43$, and $x \approx 1.75$ as before, so the intervals we need are, $(-\infty, -1.32)$, $(-1.32, -0.43)$, $(-0.43, 1.75)$, and $(1.75, \infty)$. Because our POTPs are approximations these intervals are also approximate.

Now pretend that you don't already know the solution of this problem. Just as in Example #50 we can use the First Derivative Test to determine which of the POTPs we've identified corresponds to a local minimum or maximum.

Problem #372:

Choose a point in each interval and confirm that the following statements are true.

On the (approximate) interval $(-\infty, -1.32)$: $O'(x) < 0$

On the (approximate) interval $(-1.32, -0.43)$: $O'(x) > 0$

On the (approximate) interval $(-0.43, 1.75)$: $O'(x) < 0$

On the (approximate) interval $(1.75, \infty)$: $O'(x) > 0$

(a) Use the First Derivative Test and the data displayed above to show that there is a local minimum at $x \approx -1.32$ a local maximum at $x \approx -0.43$ and a local minimum at $x \approx 1.75$.

(b) Is the data above sufficient to support the conclusion that there is a global minimum at $x \approx 1.75$? Explain why not.

(c) What additional data do we need to conclude that there is a global minimum at $x \approx 1.75$?

End Of Example #52

Drill #373:
Identify all possible optimal transition points, and identify the intervals on which each function is increasing and decreasing. Label each possible optimal transition point as a local or global minimum, or a local or global maximum, or neither.

(a) $f(x) = 2x^3 + x^2 - 20x + 1$

(b) $f(x) = 4x^3 - 3x^4$

(c) $f(x) = 8x^5 - 5x^4 - 20x^3$

(d) $f(x) = x^3 - x^2 - 40x + 8$

(e) $f(x) = x^6 - 3x^5$

(f) $f(x) = x^6 - 3x^5 + x$

(g) $f(x) = x^2 \left(x^2 - 4\right)^{\frac{1}{3}}$

(h) $f(x) = \left(4x^3 - 3x^4\right)^{\frac{4}{3}}$

Undefined Derivatives

> *"Happy families are all alike; every unhappy family is unhappy in its own way."*
>
> – Leo Tolstoy, (1847-1910)

In Drill #368 we asked if you think of a "way for $O'(x) = \frac{dO}{dx}$ to transition from positive to negative, or from negative to positive" without passing through zero. Clearly this is possible, otherwise we would not have asked. But it's hard to see how this can be isn't it? After all, at a transition point the derivative of the objective function changes signs: It transitions from negative-to-positive or from positive-to-negative. Obviously, the only number that has positive numbers on one side and negative numbers on the other is zero. So won't the solutions of $\frac{dO}{dx} = 0$ give us all of the possible transition points?

Example #53:

No, they won't. We can also have a transition point wherever $\frac{dO}{dx}\big|_{x=a}$ is meaningless. That is, when $\frac{dO}{dx}\big|_{x=a}$ is **undefined**. Drill #374 below demonstrates one way in which a derivative might be undefined.

Drill #374: Suppose

$$y(x) = x^{\frac{1}{3}}$$

The graph of $y(x)$ looks like this:

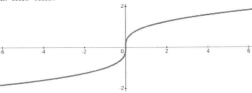

(a) Show that $\left.\frac{dy}{dx}\right|_{x=0}$ is undefined.
(**Hint:** Recall Digression #5.)

(b) Graph $\frac{dy}{dx}$ to verify that $\frac{dy}{dx} > 0$ when $x \neq 0$.

End Of Example #53

Based on Drill #374 it would be easy to conclude that the derivative of $y(x)$ can only be undefined at a point x where the formula for $\frac{dy}{dx}$ requires that we divide by zero. But this conclusion is due to the poverty of our experience with non-differentiabilty. There are many ways that a function can fail to be differentiable at a point. Dividing by zero is only one of them. In many ways it is the simplest. The family of non-differentiable functions is a very unhappy family, indeed. We might even call it dysfunctional.

The functions whose graphs are shown below is a representative sample of functions which are non-differentiable at $x = 0$. Can you see what they all have in common?

$$(a) \ \ y(x) = |x| \qquad (b) \ \ y(x) = \left(\sqrt{1 - x^{\frac{2}{3}}}\right)^3 \qquad (c) \ \ y(x) = \begin{cases} 1, & \text{if } x > 0 \\ -1, & \text{if } x < 0 \\ 0, & \text{if } x = 0 \end{cases} \qquad (d) \ \ y(x) = \begin{cases} \frac{1}{x}, & \text{if } x \neq 0 \\ 0, & \text{if } x = 0 \end{cases}$$

In our comments just before Definition #3 we stated that the Principle of Local Linearity is exactly what makes Calculus useful and we have relied on that truth in all of our subsequent investigations. But there is more to it than that. The Principle of Local Linearity is not only what makes Differential Calculus useful, its what makes Differential Calculus possible.

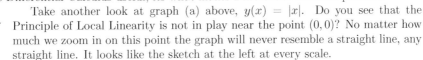

Take another look at graph (a) above, $y(x) = |x|$. Do you see that the Principle of Local Linearity is not in play near the point $(0,0)$? No matter how much we zoom in on this point the graph will never resemble a straight line, any straight line. It looks like the sketch at the left at every scale.

$(0,0)$ The same is true of every function given above. They all violate the Principle of Local Linearity. Near $x = 0$ none of them looks like a straight line no matter what viewing scale we use.

The case of a vertical tangent line is slightly problematic because near $x = 0$ the graph of, for example, $y = x^{\frac{1}{3}}$ looks like a vertical straight line. But the derivative of $y = x^{\frac{1}{3}}$ is

$$\frac{dy}{dx} = \frac{1}{3x^{\frac{2}{3}}}$$

so it is not differentiable at zero, which is the point: Any point where a given function is not differentiable is a POTP.

We formalize this observation with the following definition.

Definition 11: Possible Optimal Transition Points (POTPs)

The **possible optimum transition points** of a function, $O(x)$, come in two categories:

1. Any point, $x = a$, where $\left. \frac{dO}{dx} \right|_{x=a} = 0$ is a possible optimal transition point.

2. Any point, $x = a$, where $\left. \frac{dO}{dx} \right|_{x=a}$ is not defined is a possible optimal transition point.

Drill #375:

For each function identify all POTPs, and identify the intervals on which the function is increasing and decreasing. Label each POTP as a local or global minimum, maximum, or neither.

(**Comment:** For some of these you will have to rely on their graphs to find the POTPs. In Chapter 15 you will learn how to find them by computing.)

(a) $f(x) = \frac{x}{x^2+9}$

(b) $f(x) = \frac{1}{x}$

(c) $f(x) = \frac{x^2}{x^2+5}$

(d) $f(x) = x^{\frac{1}{3}}$

(e) $f(x) = x^{\frac{2}{3}}$

(f) $f(x) = x - 3x^{\frac{1}{3}}$

(g) $f(x) = x^{\frac{1}{3}}(x + 4)$

(h) $f(x) = x^{\frac{2}{3}}(x^2 - 8)$

(i) $f(x) = 5x^{\frac{2}{3}} - 2x^{\frac{5}{3}}$

(j) $f(x) = \left| x^2 - 1 \right|$

(k) $f(x) = |x| - 3|x - 3|$

(l) $f(x) = |x| - |x - 3|$

Transition Points on a Closed Interval; the Problem of Endpoints

Real world optimization problems will have a natural domain on which the objective function is defined. It is pointless to consider values of x outside of that domain. We actually saw this in Example 47, although we didn't remark on it at the time. Recall that in Example 47 we needed to optimize the area of a square with one of its corners on the unit circle: $x^2 + y^2 = 1$. Obviously it makes no sense to consider any value of x greater than 1 or less than -1 (why not?), so the natural domain of this problem is $-1 \leq x \leq 1$.

When the natural domain of a problem is a closed interval (one that includes both endpoints) it is possible that an extremum might also occur at one of those endpoints.

Example #54:

For example, suppose we need to optimize the function,

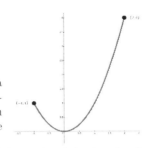

$$O(x) = x^2, \ -1 \le x \le 2.$$

From the graph at the right we can see that this function has a global minimum at $(0, 0)$. We can find this minimum by the methods we are already familiar with. But it also has a local maximum at $(-1, 1)$ and global maximum at $(2, 4)$, and nothing we've done so far would identify these two points as possible extrema.

It is clear from the graph what is happening, though. If we hadn't restricted the domain of our function then the graph would continue to rise on both sides and there would be no local or global maximum at all. The restriction on the domain forces the graph to stop rising at the endpoints of the interval which makes each of these endpoints a local maximum.

Thus we see that when the domain of our function is a closed interval there is also the possibility that a local or global extremum might occur at the endpoints of the interval as well. As a result, when searching for extrema we must always check the endpoints of the domain interval (if there are any).

To be clear, the end points of a closed interval are not transition points because there can be no transition between increasing and decreasing at an endpoint. It simply stops. However, since it is possible to have extrema at the endpoints they must also be checked whenever they are in play.

Be careful. When the domain of a function is artificially constrained like this it is easy to forget that the constraint is present. We tend to think of it as "not really there." This is a mistake. Recall from Digression #10 that the definition of the domain is a part of the definition of a function. Think of the function's domain as the "universe" for that particular problem. Nothing exists outside of the domain. Thus in this example nothing exists outside of the interval (universe) $[-1, 2]$.

End Of Example #54

It appears that to find global extrema for a function whose domain consists entirely of closed intervals all we need to do is

1. Find the POTPs.

2. Evaluate our objective function at the POTPs and at any end points of intervals in the domain of the objective function.

3. Determine which among those is greatest and which is least.

And that's it. When the domain of our function is a closed interval (or the union of closed intervals) optimization really is that straightforward[12].

We formalize all of this in Theorem 5 below.

---

[12]Remember that "straightforward" does not mean "easy."

Theorem 5: [**Extreme Value Theorem**]

If $f(x)$ is a continuous function whose domain consists entirely of closed, bounded intervals then:

(a) There is at least one point in the domain, say $x = c$ such that $f(c)$ is the global maximum value of $f(x)$. Moreover c will either be an end point of one of the domain intervals, or an optimal transition point.

(b) There is least one point in the domain, say $x = d$, and $f(d)$ is the global minimum of $f(x)$. Moreover d will either be an end point of one of the domain intervals, or optimal transition point.

Problem #376:

We ended Example #49 after posing the problem of finding the global extrema of

$$A(x) = (x - 2)^2 + (x^2 - 3)^2$$

with the constraint

$$y = x^2, \ -2 \le x \le 0.5.$$

Solve this problem now.

Problem #377:

(a) Notice that $y = x^2$ has no extrema on $(0, \infty)$. Explain why this does not violate the Extreme Value Theorem.

(b) Notice that $y = \frac{1}{x}$ has no extrema on $[-1, 1]$. Explain why this does not violate the Extreme Value Theorem.

Problem #378:

If we had known Theorem 5 when we first looked at Example #47 it would have saved us some time. Redo Example #47, using the knowledge that the domain of the problem is $-1 \le x \le 1$ because the constraint is $x^2 + y^2 = 1$.

Problem #379:

Find the global maximum and global minimum of each function with the domain restricted to the given intervals. Verify your solution by graphing the function.

(a) $O(x) = x^3 - 3x$

    (i) $[-1.5, 1.5]$ **(iii)** $[1, 2]$ **(v)** $[-1, 0]$

    (ii) $[-3, 3]$ **(iv)** $[0, 1]$ **(vi)** $[-2, -1]$

(b) $f(x) = x^3 - 12x$

    (a) $[0, 4]$ **(c)** $[-2, 2]$ **(e)** $[-2, 1]$

    (b) $[-4, 0]$ **(d)** $[-1, 3]$ **(f)** $[-5, 5]$

Problem #380:

Find the global maximum and global minimum of each of the following functions with domains on the given intervals. Verify your solution with graphing software.

(a) $y = 4 - x^3$
on the interval $[-2, 1]$

(b) $y = (x^3 - 27)^{\frac{1}{3}}$
on the interval $[-5, 5]$

(c) $y = \sqrt[3]{x}$
on the interval $[-1, 8]$

(d) $y = -3x^{2/3}$
on the interval $[-1, 1]$

(e) $y = x\sqrt{1 - x^2}$
on the interval $[-1, 1]$

(f) $y = x(2 - x)^{1/3}$
on the interval $[1, 3]$

(g) $y = x^{1/2} - x^{3/2}$
on the interval $[0, 4]$

(h) $y = \dfrac{7}{x^2 + 5}$
on the interval $[-2, 2]$

(i) $y = \dfrac{x}{x^2 - x + 1}$
on the interval $[0, 3]$

(j) $y = \dfrac{1 - x}{x^2 + 3}$
on the interval $[-2, 5]$

(k) $y = -\dfrac{1}{x}$
on the interval $[1/2, 3]$

(l) $y = xe^x$
on the interval $[-3, 4]$

(m) $y = x^2 e^x$
on the interval $[-3, 1/2]$

(n) $y = e^{-x^2}$
on the interval $[2, 10]$

(o) $y = e^{-x^2}$,
on the interval $[-2, 1]$

(p) $y = e^{-x^2}$
on the interval $[-1, 2]$

(q) $y = e^{-\frac{1}{x^2}}$
on the interval $[2, 10]$

(r) $y = x \ln(x)$
on the interval $[1/5, 1]$

(s) $y = x^2 \sin(x^2)$,
on the interval $[0, 2]$

(t) $y = \dfrac{\ln(x)}{x}$,
on the interval $[2, 10]$

Problem #381:

For each of the following functions defined on closed, bounded intervals, find the maximum and minimum of the function on that interval.

(a) $f(x) = 2x^3 + 3x^2 - 12x + 1$
on $[-3, 2]$

(b) $f(x) = 2x^3 + 3x^2 - 12x + 1$
on $[-3, 3]$

(c) $g(x) = 4x^{\frac{3}{2}} - 3x^2 - 2$
on $[0, 2]$

(d) $h(z) = 3z^{2/3} + 2z - 4$
on $[-2, 1]$

(e) $L(x) = \ln((x-2)^6) - x^2$
on $[-1.5, 4]$

(f) $f(\theta) = \frac{\theta}{2} - \sin\theta$
on $[0, 2\pi]$

8.6   Concavity and the Second Derivative Test

Theorem 5 explicitly assumed that the domain of our function consisted of closed (and bounded) intervals. This assumption was crucial. Without this assumption even simple functions that you would expect to have extrema do not.

Example #55:

For example, suppose our objective function is $O(x) = x$, and that the domain is the open interval $(-1, 1)$. Do you see why the graph of this function has no extrema of any kind? If not here is one way to prove it.

Proof: Observe that $\frac{dO}{dx} = 1 > 0$. Therefore $O(x)$ is always increasing on $(-1, 1)$. If x is any number between -1 and 1 then $f(x)$ can't be a maximum (minimum) because any number just to the right (left) of x will give us an $f(x)$ that is higher (lower) than $f(x)$.

Can we always find a number "just to the right" of x without leaving the interval $(-1, 1)$? Sure. Just take the number halfway between x and 1. ∎

Drill #382:

Show that the function $O(x) = x$ also has no minimum on the open interval $(-1, 1)$.

End Of Example #55

This leaves us with a dilemma: If the domain is not closed and bounded we can't rely on the Extreme Value Theorem to guarantee the existence of extrema. In fact Example #55 shows that there might not be any extrema. But if there are we'd still like to be able to find them.

This is a problem but it is not an insurmountable problem. In fact we already have most of the tools we need. It is still true that local extrema, if they exist, can only occur at optimal transition points or at endpoints. So finding these is still the first step.

Example #56:

For this example we strongly suggest that you do not graph the objective functions first. Yes, we know this goes directly against our previous advice to always visualize your problem when you can, but one purpose of this section is for you to learn to analyze a problem using your Calculus tools. Much as an airline pilot must train to fly using only the cockpit instruments in case they have no other choice due to poor visibility, you should also practice "flying blind" so you can be successful even when you are not able to draw a useful graph. You will learn more, and you will learn better, that way.

Of course, once we've moved beyond this section you should visualize your problem if you possibly can. We weren't kidding about that. You don't want to fly blind, you just need to be able to when it is necessary.

Problem #383:

(a) Suppose that $O_1(x) = 3x^3 - 9x$.

    (i) Show that the POTPs are $x = -1$ and $x = 1$.

    (ii) Show that $O_1(x)$ is increasing on $(-\infty, -1)$, decreasing on $(-1, 1)$, and increasing again on $(1, \infty)$.

(b) Suppose that $O_2(x) = \frac{-x}{x^2+1}$.

    (a) Show that $O_2(x)$ is increasing on $(-\infty, -1)$, decreasing on $(-1, 1)$, and increasing again on $(1, \infty)$.

From the information gathered in Drill: 383 can we conclude that either $O_1(x)$ or $O_2(x)$ has a global maximum at $x = -1$ and a global minimum at $x = 1$?

No we can't. They both have a local maximum and minimum at those points since both functions increase on $(-\infty, -1)$, decrease on $(-1, 1)$, and then increase again on $(1, \infty)$. But from the information we have gathered so far we can't tell if the graph of either function rises above its value at $x = -1$ or drops below its value at $x = 1$.

When we analyze $O_1(x)$ and $O_2(x)$ using the First Derivative Test we get exactly the same information from both functions. But they are very different functions. In particular, $O_1(x)$ does not have any global extrema, while $O_2(x)$ has both a global maximum and a global minimum. Graph them now and see. To distinguish, analytically, between $O_1(x)$ and $O_2(x)$ we will need a new tool called the Second Derivative Test.

But before we leave this example we need to address a small issue with our language. The phrase "x gets farther from zero in the negative (or positive) direction so does $O_1(x)$" is awkward[13]. In future examples we will instead usually abbreviate these as: "as x goes to negative (or positive) infinity, $O_1(x)$ also goes to negative (or positive) infinity." Do not invest too much in these phrases. They cannot possibly mean what they pretend to mean. "Infinity" is neither a number nor a place so it is meaningless to say that x "goes to" infinity. Think of this as a kind of verbal shorthand, or notation.

End Of Example #56

---

[13]It is also a bit imprecise for our purposes.

The Second Derivative Test

Just as the First Derivative Test tells us whether the graph of a function is increasing or decreasing, the Second Derivative Test tells us whether the graph is **concave upward** or **concave downward**. We need to begin by explaining the meaning of the phrases **concave upward** and **concave downward**.

concave up   concave down

The graphs at the right are illuminative. Loosely speaking concave upward means "like a bowl that opens up," and concave downward means "like a bowl that opens down." However it is easy to get the wrong impression from these simple examples. The graphs of the natural exponential and the natural logarithm (seen below)

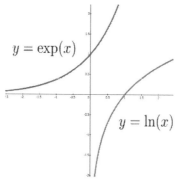

$y = \exp(x)$

$y = \ln(x)$

are also concave upward and concave downward, respectively. This is true despite the fact that the exponential never turns up on the left, and the logarithm never turns down on the right.

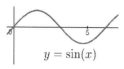

$y = \sin(x)$

Nor is every graph always concave up or concave down. We can see from its graph at the left that the sine function is both concave upward and concave downward. On the interval $(0, \pi)$ it is concave downward and on the interval $(\pi, 2\pi)$ it is concave upward. The concavity of a graph, like the property of increasing and decreasing, depends on the interval we are looking at.

Now what about these two functions?

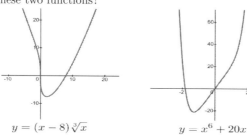

$y = (x - 8)\sqrt[3]{x}$ $y = x^6 + 20x$

The graph on the right appears to be concave up everywhere, but is it? Can you tell from the graph what the concavity of either function is near $x = 0$? If it is important for us to distinguish concave upward from concave downward (it is), then clearly we will need a more precise method than simply looking at graphs. We'll proceed carefully.

Since we're studying Calculus it seems likely that the derivative will play an instrumental role, so let's see what we can say about the derivative of a function whose graph is concave upward as shown at the right. In this example notice how the slope of the line tangent to the graph (the derivative) changes as x increases. At x the tangent line is horizontal (slope is zero), to the left of x the tangent line has negative slope and to the right it has positive slope. Speaking loosely, when the graph of a function is concave up its the derivative increases as x increases.

Drill #384:
Does that mean that the derivative of a concave downward function will decrease as x increases? Yes, of course it does. Look back at the graphs of the other "concave up" and "concave down" examples and convince yourself that this is true of them as well.

Apparently in order to distinguish where a function is concave upward from where it is concave downward we need to locate those intervals where the derivative is increasing and where it is decreasing. That is, we need a tool that tells when some function (the derivative function in this case) is increasing and when it is decreasing.

But we already have that tool! It's called the First Derivative Test.

To find out where the graph of $y(x)$ is concave upward or concave downward, we ask where its derivative, $\frac{dy}{dx}$, is increasing and where it is decreasing. To find out where $\frac{dy}{dx}$ is increasing and decreasing we ask where its derivative, $\frac{d^2y}{dx^2}$, is positive and where it is negative.

The function $\frac{dy}{dx}$ will be increasing (meaning that $y(x)$ is concave upward) wherever its derivative, $\frac{d^2y}{dx^2}$, is positive. It will be decreasing ($y(x)$ is concave downward) wherever its derivative, $\frac{d^2y}{dx^2}$, is negative.

So, to determine concavity of $y(x)$, we need to look at the sign of its second derivative, $\frac{d^2y}{dx^2}$. More formally we have the following theorem.

Theorem 6: [Concavity]
Suppose $y = y(x)$ is a differentiable function of x. The following statements are true:

1. If $\left.\frac{d^2y}{dx^2}\right|_{x=a} > 0$ on some open interval then $\frac{dy}{dx}$ is increasing, and therefore the graph of y is concave upward on the interval.

2. If $\left.\frac{d^2y}{dx^2}\right|_{x=a} < 0$, on some open interval then $\frac{dy}{dx}$ is decreasing, and therefore the graph of y is concave downward on the same interval.

Example #57:

Let $y = x^2$. Then $\frac{dy}{dx} = 2x$, and $\frac{d^2y}{dx^2} = 2$. Since the second derivative of y is always positive the graph must always be concave upward.

Drill #385:

Graph $y = x^2$ and verify that it is always concave upward.

End Of Example #57

Example #58:

Let $y = x^3$. Then $\frac{dy}{dx} = 6x^2$, and $\frac{d^2y}{dx^2} = 3x$. Since the second derivative of y is negative on the interval $(-\infty, 0)$ the graph must be concave downward on for $x < 0$. Since the second derivative of y is positive on the interval $(0, \infty)$ the graph must be concave upward for $x > 0$.

Drill #386:

Graph $y = x^3$ and verify that it is always concave downward on the interval $(-\infty, 0)$, and concave upward on the interval $(0, \infty)$.

End Of Example #58

Because we are applying the First Derivative Test to the first derivative of $y(x)$ our language necessarily gets a little complex here. The point to remember is that we are ultimately interested in what the first two derivatives, $\frac{dy}{dx}$ and $\frac{d^2y}{dx^2}$, tell us about the graph of $y(x)$. We will define some vocabulary to help us keep all of this clear.

We called the solutions of $\frac{dy}{dx} = 0$ possible optimal transition points (POTPs) because these are the places where the graph of $y(x)$ might transition between increasing and decreasing. So they are possible local optimal points.

We will call the solutions of $\frac{d^2y}{dx^2} = 0$ possible inflective transition points (PITPs) because they are those places where the **inflection** of the graph of $y(x)$ might transition between concave upward and concave downward.

Problem #387:

Suppose that $y(x) = x^4 - x^2$.

(a) Show that the PITPs of $y(x)$ are $x = -\frac{1}{\sqrt{6}}$, and $x = \frac{1}{\sqrt{6}}$.

(b) Show that the graph of y is concave upward on the intervals $\left(-\infty, \frac{-1}{\sqrt{6}}\right)$ and $\left(\frac{1}{\sqrt{6}}, \infty\right)$.

(c) Show that the graph of y is concave downward on the interval $\left(\frac{-1}{\sqrt{6}}, \frac{1}{\sqrt{6}}\right)$. In particular notice that y is concave downward at $x = 0$.

Part (c) of Problem #387 displays a very useful fact about the second derivative. At $x = 0$ the first derivative of $y(x) = x^4 - x^2$ is equal to zero, which means that the line tangent at zero is horizontal. Also at $x = 0$ the second derivative is negative, which means that at $x = 0$ the graph is concave downward. Taking these two facts together we can conclude that $y(x)$ must have a (local) maximum at $x = 0$.

That is, for any curve $y(x)$, if

$$\frac{dy}{dx}\bigg|_{x=a} = 0 \text{ and } \frac{d^2y}{dx^2}\bigg|_{x=a} < 0$$

then y must have a (local) maximum at $x = 0$. Similarly, for any curve $y(x)$, if

$$\frac{dy}{dx}\bigg|_{x=a} = 0 \text{ and } \frac{d^2y}{dx^2}\bigg|_{x=a} > 0$$

then y must have a (local) minimum at $x = a$.

Problem #388:

(a) Use the observation in the previous paragraph to show that the graph of

$$y(x) = x^4 - x^2$$

has local minima at $x = \frac{1}{\sqrt{2}}$, and at $x = -\frac{1}{\sqrt{2}}$.

(b) What is the value of the minima (the y value) of $y(x)$ at each $x = \frac{1}{\sqrt{2}}$, and $x = -\frac{1}{\sqrt{2}}$?

We formalize this idea in the Second Derivative Test, stated below.

Theorem 7: [The Second Derivative Test]

Suppose y is some differentiable function and that at some point a in its domain

$$\frac{dy}{dx}\bigg|_{x=a} = 0.$$

Then the following statements are true:

(a) If $\frac{d^2y}{dx^2}\bigg|_{x=a} > 0$ then y has a local minimum at $x = a$.

(b) If $\frac{d^2y}{dx^2}\bigg|_{x=a} < 0$ then y has a local maximum at $x = a$.

(c) If $\frac{d^2y}{dx^2}\bigg|_{x=a} = 0$ then we get no information about possible extrema of y at $x = a$.

Drill #389:

Use the Second Derivative Test to find the local maxima and minima of each function. Also identify any global maxima and minima.

(a) $y(x) = x^2 - 5x + 2$

(b) $y(x) = x^3 - 2x^2 - x$

(c) $y(x) = 3x^3 - 9x$

(d) $y(x) = x^4 - 5x^2 + 4$

(e) $y(x) = \sin(x)$
on $[0, 4\pi]$

(f) $y(x) = \sin(x) + \cos(x)$
on $[0, 2\pi]$

(g) $y(x) = \sec(x)$
on $[0, 2\pi]$

As you saw in Drill#389 when the Second Derivative Test works it can make quick work of many optimization problems. But unfortunately part (c) of Theorem 7 is its Achilles heel. It is surprisingly common for both the first and second derivative to be equal to zero at a POTP. When this happens the Second Derivative Test cannot tell us whether it is an optimal point or not, so we have to fall back on the First Derivative Test and analyze the intervals between the the POTPs.

Drill #390:

Analyze the concavity of the graphs of each of the following functions.

(a) $y(x) = x^4$

(b) $y(x) = x^3$

(c) $y(x) = x^4(x - 1)^3$

(d) $y(x) = \frac{1}{x^4 + 1}$

(e) $y(x) = x^4 + x^3$

(f) $y(x) = e^{-x^3}$

Drill #391:

Identify all intervals where the given curve is concave upward, concave downward, increasing, and decreasing. Identify all local optima, and all global optima, if any.

Graph the curve to check your work after you have solved each problem.

(a) $y = x^3 - 2x^2 + x + 1$

(b) $y = 3x^4 - 4x^3 + 6$

(c) $y = 2x^6 - 6x^4$

(d) $y = (x^2 - 1)^2$

(e) $y = \sqrt[5]{x} - 1$

(f) $y = x^2 - \frac{27}{x^2}$

(g) $y = \frac{x}{x^2 + 1}$

(h) $y = \sqrt[3]{x^2}(3x + 10)$

(i) $y = 8x^{\frac{1}{3}} + x^{\frac{4}{3}}$

(j) $y = \sqrt[3]{x}(x - 8)$

(k) $y = \sin^2(x)$

(l) $y = x + \sin(x)$

(m) $y = \cos(2x) + \sin(2x)$

(n) $y = xe^x$

(o) $y = x^3 e^{-x^2}$

(p) $y = x \ln(x)$

(q) $y = x^2 \ln(x)$

(r) $y = \ln(x)e^x$

Problem #392: Show that $y(x) = \frac{x(x-1)}{x^3-27}$ has

   (a) both a global and a local minimum if its domain is the interval $(-5, 0)$, and

   (b) only a local minimum if its domain is the interval $\left(-5, \frac{5}{2}\right)$.

   (c) Does the graph of this function have a global maximum for either of the domains given in parts (a) or (b)? Explain.

(Hint: Use Newton's Method, and the First Derivative Test.)

Problem #393: Does $f(x) = \sin(x)$ have a global extremum (minimum or maximum) on the interval $\left(0, \frac{\pi}{2}\right)$? How about on $(0, \pi)$? On $(0, 2\pi)$? Explain.
(Hint: Use the First Derivative Test.)

Problem #394:
Suppose that $O(x) = \frac{x^2}{1+x^2}$ and that the domain of the problem is all real numbers ($\mathbb{R}$).

   (a) Find all local extrema.

   (b) Find all global extrema.

(Hint: Use the First Derivative Test.)

Problem #395:
Consider the polynomial $y(x) = (x+1)^3(x-1)(x+3)$.

   (a) Show that $\left.\frac{dy}{dx}\right|_{x=-1} = 0$.

     (Hint: You can save yourself a lot of work on this problem by keeping your eye on the goal. The problem is to show that $\left.\frac{dy}{dx}\right|_{x=-1} = 0$, not to compute $\frac{dy}{dx}$ and then "simplify" it.)

   (b) Graph y near $x = -1$ to convince yourself that y has neither a maximum nor a minimum at $x = -1$.

    As we've said before, Calculus is merely one tool in your problem solving toolbox. Moreover it is almost never the first tool you should reach for. You will frequently need to use your skills with Algebra, Geometry, or Trigonometry to transform a problem into a form which allows you to bring Calculus to bear on it. You will need to take it slowly, think clearly, and be careful.

Frequently you will find that your first first few ideas aren't working. When that happens, find another idea and start again.

On the other hand you will often have a good deal of insight into real-world problems because they are, well, real-world problems, and you understand a lot about the real world.

8.7 Optimization Problems

So far in this chapter the examples and problems we've chosen we've chosen emphasized the different aspects of optimization. Our intention was to show you the subtleties involved one at a time so you could understand them separately.

Of course, this is entirely unrealistic. Real problems rarely tell you where the difficulties will lie, so in this final section we offer you a selection of problems. It is up to you to

1. Find an appropriate objective function.

2. Identify the constraints.

3. Decide whether the natural domain of the problem consists closed intervals or not.

4. Identify any POTPs.

   If the problem domain consists only of closed intervals use Theorem 8.7. Otherwise use the First or the Second Derivative Test.

5. Identify which, if any, of the POTPs are global optima.

6. Re-read the problem and confirm that you have solved it.

   In the process of finding an optimum it is easy to lose track of the question and stop too soon. Always make sure you have actually solved the problem as stated.

Recall that in Example #4 we observed that most people can see intuitively that of all rectangles with a fixed perimeter the one that encloses the greatest area will be a square. We gave an algebraic demonstration of this in Chapter 2 but now that we know how to use Calculus to optimize let's revisit this problem.

Example #59: **Example #4 revisited again**

We first solved this problem in Example #4 where we solved it algebraically. We revisited it the first time in Problem #349 where we solved it again analytically (using Calculus) twice. But to do this we relied on Fermat's Theorem and Fermat's Theorem only allows us to find a maximum that we already know exists. At that time we did not have the tools to show that we actually had a maximum. We do now so we will solve this problem one last time before we move on.

Show that of all rectangles with a fixed perimeter, P, the one with the greatest area is a square.

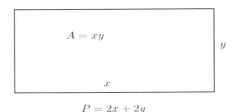

$$P = 2x + 2y$$

We will follow the outline above.

1. The objective function is
$$A = xy, \tag{8.25}$$

2. The only constraint is
$$P = 2x + 2y \tag{8.26}$$

where P is constant.

3. Since we are talking about a length it must be that $x \geq 0$. From Equation (8.26) we see that x must be less that or equal to $\frac{P}{2}$. Otherwise the perimeter will be greater than P. So the domain[14] of our problem is $0 \leq x \leq \frac{P}{2}$.

4. Since the problem domain is a closed interval we will use the Extreme Value Theorem (Theorem #5).

To find the POTPs we will need $\frac{\mathrm{d}A}{\mathrm{d}x}$. From Equation (8.25) we see that
$$\mathrm{d}A = x\,\mathrm{d}y + y\,\mathrm{d}x. \tag{8.27}$$

From Equation (8.26) we have
$$\mathrm{d}y = -\,\mathrm{d}x \tag{8.28}$$

and also
$$y = \frac{1}{2}\left(P - 2x\right) \tag{8.29}$$

Combining Equations (8.26), (8.27), and (8.29) we see that
$$\frac{\mathrm{d}A}{\mathrm{d}x} = \frac{P}{2} - 2x.$$

The only solution of $\frac{\mathrm{d}A}{\mathrm{d}x} = 0$ is $x = \frac{P}{4}$, so the POTPs for this problem are the end points, $x = 0$ and $x = \frac{P}{2}$, and $x = \frac{P}{4}$.

5. The area, $A = xy$, will be zero when $x = 0$ and when $x = \frac{P}{2}$ (why?) so by the Extreme Value Theorem the maximum occurs when $x = \frac{P}{4}$.

---

[14]Strictly speaking if $x = 0$ or $x = \frac{P}{2}$ we don't actually have a rectangle. But it is simpler to use the Extreme Value Theorem (Theorem #5) than to find the increasing and decreasing intervals using the First Derivative Test. Since the Extreme Value Theorem requires a closed domain we make things simpler by allowing "zero width" rectangles.

6. This problem asks us to show that the maximal rectangle must be a square, so we need to show that $x = y$. We know that the maximum occurs when $x = \frac{P}{4}$. Plugging this value into Equation #8.29 we see that y is also equal to $\frac{P}{4}$. Thus the maximal rectangle is a square as stated.

End Of Example #59

In Example #59 we were careful to follow the steps we listed at the beginning of this section in the sequence given. That list is helpful. That's why we wrote it out. However, it would be a mistake to think of it as a recipe to be followed blindly. Think of it as an outline. An outline is a guide, not a recipe and it is not necessary to follow it rigidly, step-by-step. If you find it simpler to do these steps in a different order for some problem there is no reason that you shouldn't. But before you declare the problem solved look back at this outline and make sure that you have done everything that needs to be done. This is what an outline is for.

In Example #6 in Chapter 2 we considered the related problem of minimizing the perimeter when the area is fixed. The following problem asks you to solve this problem using Calculus. Notice that just as above we have

$$A = xy$$

and

$$P = 2x + 2y$$

but this time A is constant, not P.

Problem #396:

Out of all rectangles with a fixed area, find the dimensions of the one with the smallest perimeter.

(a) Identify the objective function and the constraint for this problem.

(b) Find the natural domain of this problem and show that it is not a closed interval.

(c) Show that we have a POTP when $x = y$.

(d) Show that when $x = y$ we have a minimum by:

   (i) Using the first derivative test.   (ii) Using the second derivative test.

   Note that both tests will require you to use the constraint to reduce the number of variables in the objective to one.

   Which test was easier to use?

Problem #397:

Redo Problem #12 from Chapter 2 using Calculus. Verify that you get the same answer as before.

The following example demonstrates how different approaches to the same problem can lead to different challenges. In this case just changing the labels on the diagram makes a big difference.

<u>Example #60:</u>

The pages of a book are to have an area of 90 square centimeters. The side and bottom margins are to be 1 centimeter in width and the top margin is to be 1/2 centimeter in width.

Find the dimensions of the page that has the largest possible printed area, P_A.

First Solution:

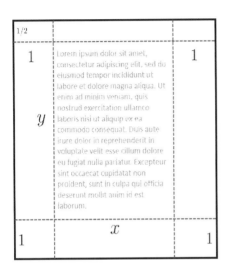

This problem can be visualized as in the diagram at the left. Since it is the printed area that is to be maximized it seems natural to label the width of the printed area, x, and the height, y, as shown. If we call the printed area P_A then our objective function is,

$$P_A = xy. \tag{8.30}$$

The width of the entire page will be $x + 2$, and the height will be $y + 3/2$. The area of each page is constrained to be 90 square centimeters so our constraint is,

$$(x + 2)(y + 3/2) = 90. \tag{8.31}$$

Differentiating Equation (8.30) we see that

$$\mathrm{d}(P_A) = x\,\mathrm{d}y + y\,\mathrm{d}x \tag{8.32}$$

Solving Equation (8.31) for y we have

$$y = \frac{90}{x + 2} - 3/2 \tag{8.33}$$

Differentiating Equation #8.31 and solving for $\mathrm{d}y$ gives

$$\mathrm{d}y = -\left(\frac{y + 3/2}{x + 2}\right)\mathrm{d}x.$$

Substituting these into Equation #8.32 we have

$$\mathrm{d}(P_A) = -x\left(\frac{\frac{90}{x+2} - 3/2 + 3/2}{x + 2}\right)\mathrm{d}x + \left(\frac{90}{x + 2} - 3/2\right)\mathrm{d}x.$$

Since we'll have to set this equal to zero and to find any POTPs it is clearly in our interest to reduce this algebraically to

$$\frac{\mathrm{d}(P_A)}{\mathrm{d}x} = \frac{-90x}{(x + 2)^2} + \frac{90}{x + 2} - 3/2. \tag{8.34}$$

Adding the fractions we see that we must solve

$$\frac{\mathrm{d}(P_A)}{\mathrm{d}x} = \frac{-90x + 90(x+2) - 3/2(x+2)^2}{(x+2)^2} = \frac{180 - 3/2(x+2)^2}{(x+2)^2} = 0.$$

At this point it is tempting to expand $(x+2)^2$, but recall that our goal is to solve for x. Multiplying through by $(x+2)^2$ gives

$$0 = 180 - \frac{3}{2}(x+2)^2$$

so that

$$(x+2)^2 = 120.$$

Solving this gives[15] $x = \pm\sqrt{120} - 2$. But the width of a page can't be negative so a negative solution is meaningless for this problem. Thus $x = \sqrt{120} - 2$ is our one and only POTP, and we conclude that we can maximize the printed area by taking $x = \sqrt{120} - 2 \approx 8.95$ centimeters.

That was a lot of work but we are not finished The problem asks us to find the dimensions (plural) of the page. To find y we use Equation (8.33) to compute

$$y \approx \frac{90}{\sqrt{120} - 2 + 2} - 3/2 = \frac{90}{\sqrt{120}} - 3/2 \approx 8.08.$$

But we're still not finished. The problem asks for the dimensions of the page, but we've only found the dimensions of the printed area. The dimensions of the page are

$$\text{Width of page} = \text{width of text} + \text{margins} = \sqrt{120} - 2 + 2 = \sqrt{120} \approx 10.95 \text{ cm}$$

$$\text{Height of page} = \text{height of text} + \text{margins} = \frac{90}{\sqrt{120}} - 3/2 + 3/2 = \frac{90}{\sqrt{120}} \approx 8.22 \text{ cm}.$$

Finally, the last item in our outline says to make sure we have done everything that needs to be done to solve the problem. Have we?

No, clearly not. We never did step #3: Identify the natural domain of the problem. As a result we don't know for certain that we have a maximum. It may be that the critical point we've identified is not in the problem domain. It may be that it is in the domain, but that we have a minimum instead of a maximum. Or that we have neither. The point is that we can't know until we have found the natural domain of the objective function, and verified that there is a global maximum at $x = \sqrt{120} - 2 \approx 8.95$ centimeters.

We mentioned earlier that the width of the page can't be negative so the smallest possible value of x, the left endpoint of our interval, is zero.

Problem #398:

(a) Show that the largest possible value of x is $x = 58$ and thus the natural domain for this problem is the closed interval $[0, 58]$.

(b) Show that the maximal printed area occurs when $x = 2\sqrt{30} - 2$.

---

[15]You can "simplify" $x = \pm\sqrt{120} - 2$ to $x = \pm2\sqrt{30} - 2$ if you like, but there is no real advantage to doing so. We prefer to leave it as $x = \pm\sqrt{120} - 2$.

Second Solution:

There is often more than one objective function that will work for any given problem. If your first attempt does not seem to be working — even if you are sure you have an objective that will work — you always have the option of going back to the beginning and trying to find another valid objective function.

For our second solution we will use the same diagram, but with different labeling. As you can see at the left, this time we've let x and y represent, respectively, the width and height of the page rather than of the printed area.

Our objective function is still the area of the printed portion of the page, but with the updated labeling this becomes

$$P_A = (x - 2)(y - 3/2). \qquad (8.35)$$

Differentiating this we have

$$d(P_A) = (x - 2)\, dy + (y - 3/2)\, dx. \qquad (8.36)$$

The constraint is still that the area of the page is 90 square centimeters, but this is now given by

$$90 = xy. \qquad (8.37)$$

Differentiating the constraint gives

$$x\, dy + y\, dx = 0,$$

from which we see that $dy = -\frac{y}{x}\, dx$. From Equation (8.37) we see that $y = \frac{90}{x}$. Substituting these into Equation (8.36) we get

$$d(P_A) = (x - 2)\left(-\frac{y}{x}\right) dx + \left(\frac{90}{x} - \frac{3}{2}\right) dx$$

$$= \left[-(x - 2)\left(\frac{90}{x^2}\right) + \frac{90}{x} - \frac{3}{2}\right] dx$$

$$\frac{d(P_A)}{dx} = -(x - 2)\left(\frac{90}{x^2}\right) + \frac{90}{x} - \frac{3}{2}$$

Setting this equal to zero and solving for x gives

$$-(x - 2)\left(\frac{90}{x^2}\right) + \frac{90}{x} - \frac{3}{2} = 0$$

$$-\frac{90}{x} - \frac{180}{x^2} + \frac{90}{x} - \frac{3}{2} = 0$$

$$\frac{180}{x^2} - \frac{3}{2} = 0$$

$$\frac{2}{3} \cdot 180 = x^2 \text{ or}$$

$$x = \pm\sqrt{120}.$$

As before, we know that the width of a page cannot be negative so the only POTP is $x = \sqrt{120}$.

This time x and y represent the width and height of the page, so the width of the printed text is will be $\sqrt{120} - 2$ as before. Similarly the height of the printed text will be $\frac{90}{\sqrt{120}} - \frac{3}{2}$.

Drill #399:
Determine the natural domain of $P_A(x)$ and show that $P_A(x)$ is a global maximum when $x = \sqrt{120}$. Do you get the same page dimensions as before?

End Of Example #60

You will find that, quite often, simplifying complex expressions as much as possible with Algebra, Geometry, or Trigonometry will lead to easier Calculus computations. Conversely less non-Calculus work often leads to more challenging differentiations. But this is not a hard-and-fast rule. Sometimes you will find that leaving the formulas you generate unsimplified gives better insight into the problem, making things a little simpler overall, even if it makes the differentiation quite onerous.

Which parts of a given problem you find easy or difficult will depend on your skill level with your tools. With experience comes the ability to balance the workload across your skills. When you realize that one approach will lead to a complication that you know you will find difficult to handle, it can be beneficial to stop and look for another approach. If you find one, stop and try again from the beginning.

Then identify where your skill is lacking and give yourself some practice with that particular skill to improve your skills overall. Review, practice, and improve your Algebra, Geometry, and Trigonometry skills as needed.

A common mistake when abandoning a first attempt is to try to preserve and reuse computations left over from your first try. But that attempt didn't work. You need to try something new.

Problem #400: Variations on a Theme

(a) (i) Find two positive numbers whose sum is 10, and whose product is a maximum. What is the maximum?

(ii) Find two positive numbers whose sum is 8, and whose product is a maximum. What is the maximum?

(iii) Find two positive numbers whose sum is K, and whose product is a maximum. What is the maximum?

(b) (i) Find two positive numbers such that the sum of one of them and twice the other is 10, and whose product is a maximum. What is the maximum?

(ii) Find two positive numbers such that the sum of one of them and three times the other is 10, and whose product is a maximum. What is the maximum?

(iii) Find two positive numbers such that the sum of one of them and five times the other is 10, and whose product is a maximum. What is the maximum?

(iv) Find two positive numbers such that the sum of one of them and n times the other is K, and whose product is a maximum. What is the maximum?

(c) **(i)** Find two positive numbers whose product is 10, and whose sum is a minimum. What is the minimum?

(ii) Find two positive numbers whose product is M, and whose sum is a minimum. What is the minimum?

(iii) Find two positive numbers whose product is M, and the sum one number and three times the other is a minimum. What is the minimum?

(iv) Find two positive numbers whose product is M, and the sum one number and n times the other is a minimum. What is the minimum?

Problem #401: Variations on a Theme

You have 500 meters of fencing with which to build an animal pen.

(a) **(i)** What is the largest area you can enclose with a freestanding rectangular pen?

(ii) You want to build a pen with a fence across the center to divide the large pen into two equally sized internal pens. What is the largest area you can enclose?

(iii) You want to build a pen with two parallel fences across the center to divide the large pen into three equally sized internal pens. What is the largest area you can enclose?

(iv) You want to build a pen with parallel fences across the center which divide the large pen into n equally sized internal pens. What is the largest area you can enclose? If w is the width and l is the length of the external pen what is $\frac{w}{l}$.

(b) **(i)** You want to use one side of a building as one full side of your pen as shown in the sketch below. What is the largest area you can enclose? What are the dimensions of the pen?

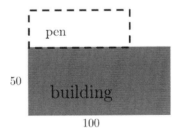

(ii) You want to use one side of a building as one partial side of your pen as shown in the sketch below. What is the largest area you can enclose? What are the dimensions of the pen?

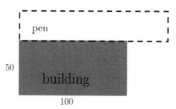

(iii) You want to build your pen as shown in the sketch below. What is the largest area you can enclose? What are the dimensions of the pen?

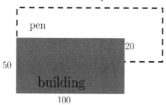

(iv) You want to build your pen as shown in the sketch below. What is the largest area you can enclose? What are the dimensions of the pen?

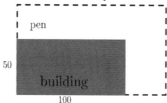

(v) You want to your pen to be subdivided into three parts as shown in the sketch below. What is the largest area you can enclose? What are the dimensions of the pen?

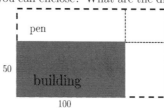

(vi) You want to build your pen as shown in the sketch below. What is the largest area you can enclose? What are the dimensions of the pen?

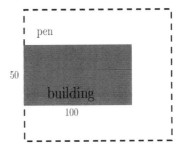

Problem #402: Variations on a Theme

You have a piece of wire 100 inches long.

(a) You cut the wire into pieces. Find the length of each piece of the wire that yields the least total area bounded by the pieces when:

  (i) You cut the wire into two pieces and bend each piece to form a square.

  (ii) You cut the wire into two pieces and bend each piece to form a circle.

  (iii) You cut the wire into two pieces and bend one piece to form a square and the second to form a circle.

  (iv) You cut the wire into two pieces and bend one piece to form a rectangle with one side three times as long as the other. Then bend the second piece to form a square.

  (v) You cut the wire into three pieces and two pieces are each bent to form squares and the third is bent to form a circle.

(b) Repeat each problem in part (a), but this time find the length of each piece of the wire that yields the most total area bounded by the pieces.

Problem #403:

Consider the side view of a person at point P looking at a 20 foot tall billboard sign that is 10 feet off of the ground as shown in the diagram below.

(a) Find a formula for the viewing angle θ in terms of x. Don't forget to put in the range for possible values for x.

(b) Find the value of x that will maximize the viewing angle θ.

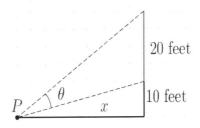

Problem #404:

Find the value of r that maximizes the blue shaded area, $A(r)$, in the following diagram:

Problem #405: (Variations on a theme)

(a) The **strength** of a rectangular wooden beam is proportional to its width times the square of its height. What is the ratio of the height to width of the strongest beam that can be cut from a cylindrical log?

(b) The **stiffness** of a rectangular wooden beam is proportional to its width times the cube of its height. What is the ratio of the height to width of the stiffest beam that can be cut from a cylindrical log? Compare this to the answer in the previous problem.

(c) Suppose we have an objective function which is proportional to the width times the nth power of the height? What would the optimal ratio be now?

Problem #406:

A box with a square base and an open top must have a volume of $32,000$ square centimeters.

Find the dimensions of the box that minimize the amount of material used to make the box.

Problem #407:

The diagram at the right depicts the view from above a pole of length L being maneuvered horizontally around the 90° corner of two hallways of widths a, and b. Find the longest pole which can be turned around the corner.

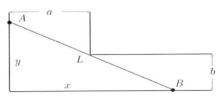

(a) Show that the maximum value of L is $\left(a^{\frac{2}{3}} + b^{\frac{2}{3}}\right)^{\frac{3}{2}}$.

(b) What would the maximum of L be in the special case where $a = b$? Does this answer make sense geometrically?

(c) In the problem statement we specified that the pole was being maneuvered horizontally, meaning that the pole is kept parallel to the ground at all times. Suppose we remove that constraint and that the height of the hallway is h. What is the longest pole we can get around the corner now?

Problem #408: (Variations on a theme)

(a) A Norman window has the shape of a rectangle surmounted by a semicircle.

Find the dimensions of the window that allow the most light to enter if the perimeter of the window is 30 feet,

(b) Find the dimensions of the window that allow the most light to enter if the window is surmounted by an equilateral triangle.

Problem #409: At which points on the curve $y = 1 + 40x^3 - 3x^5$ does the tangent line have the greatest slope?

Problem #410: Find the coordinates of the points on the graph of $4x^2 + y^2 = 4$ which are farthest from the point $(1, 0)$.

Problem #411: Find the area of the smallest triangle formed by the x and y axes and a line passing through the point $(2, 1)$.

Problem #412: Variations on a Theme

(a) We draw the right triangle whose hypotenuse starts at the origin, $(0, 0)$ and ends on the Witch of Agnesi, $W(x) = \frac{1}{1+x^2}$. The other legs are as shown in the figure below:

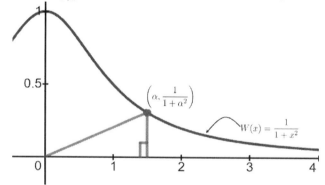

Of all possible such triangles for which α is in the interval $[0, \infty)$ which one has the largest area?

(b) Now suppose that for each function given below a triangle is constructed in the same manner used in part (a). Assume a, b, c, and k are constants. Of all possible such triangles for which α is in the interval $[0, \infty)$ which one has the largest area?

(i) $f(x) = \frac{k}{x^2+1}$ **(iii)** $f(x) = \frac{1}{5x^2+1}$

(ii) $f(x) = \frac{1}{x^2+3}$ **(iv)** $f(x) = \frac{a}{bx^2+c}$

Problem #413: Variations on a Theme

To prevent squirrels from eating her bird-seed a mathematician[16] wants to hang a bird feeder so that its top is 5 feet above the ground. To do this she attaches each end of a wire between two trees at a height of 8 feet above the ground, with the feeder hanging from a second wire, x, attached at the midpoint of the first as seen in the sketch at the right.

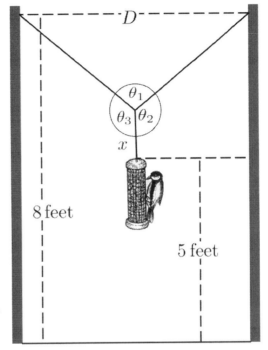

(a) Find the value of x that requires the least amount of wire if the trees are 10 feet apart.

   (i) What will the total length of the wire be?

   (ii) Show that $\theta_1 = \theta_2 = \theta_3$.

(b) Find the value of x that requires the least amount of wire if the trees are 12 feet apart.

   (i) What will the total length of the wire be?

   (ii) Show also that $\theta_1 = \theta_2 = \theta_3$.

Problem #414:

Suppose we have a light source whose intensity is I candela at a point H meters above a surface, as seen in the sketch at the right. Then the illuminance (how brightly the surface is illuminated) E (in lux) at the point P on the surface is given by the formula

$$E = \frac{I \cos(\theta)}{r^2}$$

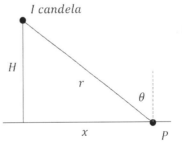

where r is the distance from the light source to P and θ is the angle the ray of light makes with the line normal to the surface[17].

(a) Find a formula for the illuminance at the point P

[16]This problem is adapted from *Hanging a Bird feeder: Food for Thought*, by John W. Dawson, Jr. *The College Mathematics Journal*, Mar., 1990, Vol. 21, No. 2, pp. 129-130

[17]The cosine allows for the fact that the illuminance diminishes if the surface is tilted at an angle, θ, to the

(i) in terms of I, H, and x, and   **(ii)** in terms of I, H, and r.

(b) Consider two streetlamps, each with an intensity of $I = 1300$ candela mounted on 5 meter poles at a distance of 15 meters apart.

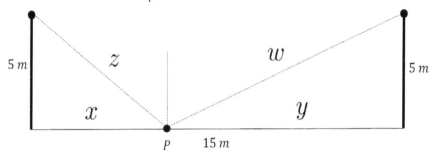

Find the approximate positions of the points between the light poles where the illuminance E is minimimal and where it is maximal.

(**Comment:** Recall from Example #48 that you have two choices here. (1) Use the constraints of the problem to find a formula for the illuminance in terms of a single variable and compute $\frac{dE}{d\xi}$ where ξ is whichever variable you chose to use. (2) Write down E and all of the constraints, differentiate them, and rearrange the results to form either $\frac{dE}{dx} = 0$ or $\frac{dE}{dy} = 0$ and solve for x or y.

We had you find two different formulas in part (a) because one of them is more helpful if you choose (1) and the other helps with choice (2).)

(c) You may have noticed in part (b) that the maximum illuminance was near but not at either endpoint. Show that, in general, if the intensity is I, the height is H and the distance between the poles is L, then $\frac{dE}{dx}\big|_{x=0} > 0$ and $\frac{dE}{dx}\big|_{x=L} < 0$ and use this to explain why the maximum illuminance will never occur directly under one of the streetlamps.

(d) Use your favorite graphing tool and Newton's Method to repeat this problem with three streetlamps 15 meters apart in a straight line, with $I = 1300$, and $H = 5$. Approximately where is the illuminance a maximum? Approximately where is it minimum?

---

light source, even if the distance remains fixed.
We (the authors) found the presence of $\cos(\theta)$ troubling when we first encountered it. But this is the correct formula. If you also find this troubling, think about the extreme case where $\theta = \frac{\pi}{2}$. In this case the illuminance must be zero ($= \cos(\pi/2)$) since the surface is then parallel to the light beam

Chapter 9

Graphing with Calculus

"Mankind invented a system to cope with the fact that we are so intrinsically lousy at manipulating numbers. it's called a graph."

$-$ Charlie Munger 1924-

In an age when everyone can open their cell phone and graph, for example, the function

$$y(x) = x^4 - 400.5x^3 + 40099.49x^2 + 4.005x - 400.995, \qquad (9.1)$$

literally in seconds it may not seem important to understand the nature of functions at any deeper level. After all, if you have a formula you know everything there is to know about a function, right?

Well, yes . . . , and no.

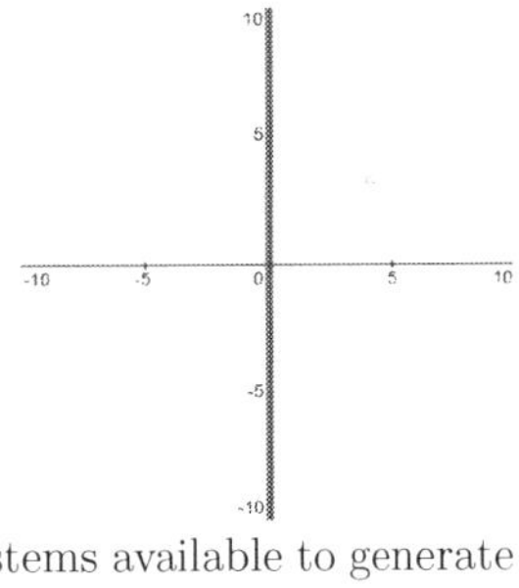

In a sense, obtaining a formula that describes whatever real-world phenomena you might be investigating is the Holy Grail, of science. And for exactly the reason you would expect. Formulas can tell us a great deal about the phenomenon. But they don't tell us everything.

For example, suppose Equation (9.1) describes some real world phenomenon. Does reading the formula give you any sense of the essential qualities of $y(x)$? No, of course not. Because pictures are easier to understand than formulas we usually look at the graph of a function to get a sense of it. We used one of the many graphing systems available to generate the graph of $y(x)$ seen at the right. Impressive, isn't it?

Because we simply used the default settings of our graphing tool this picture doesn't really help much either. We'll have to modify the viewing window to see anything useful. Take out your favorite graphing utility and adjust the settings until you find settings that give you a more useful display like the one below.

To be sure, this graph does tell us great deal about the qualitative behavior of $y(x)$. Visualizing the graph in this way is a good thing. But getting more detailed information can be tricky. For example, what are the exact values of the x coordinates of the two places where the graph appears to graze the x axis? One appears to be $x = 0$ and the other appears to be $x = 200$, but is that right? No-

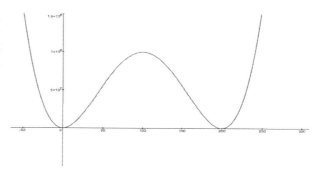

tice the horizontal and vertical scales. Can we be sure that at these scales all of the important bumps an wiggles on the graph are visible? When the top of the graph is at $y =$ ten million can we tell, just by looking, if $y(0) = y(200) = 0$?

You might well ask, "Obviously when $x = 0$ and $x = 200$ y is near zero. Is it really important to know whether or not it is exactly zero?"

Drill #415:
Compute $y(0)$ and $y(200)$ to see if they are really near zero.
(**Hint:** Use a calculator for $y(200)$, not for $y(0)$.)

The fact is that it is hard to get good quantitative information from anything but very simple graphs. But does that matter? From the graph above we can see very plainly what is happening over a very large interval. Isn't that enough?

Well, that depends.

Suppose you are a nuclear engineer and you've invented a simple process that requires an external source of energy. Suppose further that the graph above shows the rate of energy consumption, y, of your process as a function of the ambient temperature, x. Then any temperature at which $y < 0$ is a temperature where the process is producing energy, not consuming it. Depending on rate of production and how simple the process is, being able to identify the temperature range where $y(x) < 0$ could be the difference between winning the Nobel Prize, and becoming a laughing stock.

You would want to know.

In this chapter we will explore some techniques that will help you win your Nobel Prize[1]. Please mention us in your acceptance speech.

9.1 Graphing with a Formula for $y(x)$

In Chapter 8 we saw that the First and Second Derivative Tests are exactly the tools necessary to answer each of the following questions:

1. On what intervals is the function increasing and on what intervals is it decreasing?

2. Where are the local extrema located?

---

[1]All you have to do is invent the process. Good luck.

3. What are the values of the local extrema?

4. Where does the inflection of the graph transition between concave up and concave down?

Example #61:

For example consider the following function. $y = \frac{x}{1+x^2}$. Differentiating y we see that

$$\frac{dy}{dx} = \frac{(1+x^2) - 2x^2}{(1+x^2)^2} = \frac{1-x^2}{(1+x^2)^2}.$$

This tells us that $y(x)$ will have POTPs at $x = 1$, and $x = -1$. Testing a single point in each of the intervals between POTPs we see that

$$\left.\frac{dy}{dx}\right|_{x=-2} = \frac{-3}{25}, \quad \left.\frac{dy}{dx}\right|_{x=0} = 1, \text{ and } \left.\frac{dy}{dx}\right|_{x=2} = \frac{-3}{25},$$

and conclude that the graph is decreasing on the interval $(-\infty, -1)$, increasing on the interval $(-1, 1)$, and decreasing again on $(-2, -\infty)$.

Computing the second derivative gives:

$$\frac{d^2y}{dx^2} = \frac{-2x(3-x^2)}{(1+x^2)^3}.$$

This tells us that $y(x)$ will have PITPs at $x = -\sqrt{3}$, $x = 0$, and $x = \sqrt{3}$. Testing a single point in each of these intervals between PITPs we see that

$$\left.\frac{d^2y}{dx^2}\right|_{x=-2} < 0, \quad \left.\frac{d^2y}{dx^2}\right|_{x=-1} > 0, \quad \left.\frac{d^2y}{dx^2}\right|_{x=1} < 0, \text{ and } \left.\frac{d^2y}{dx^2}\right|_{x=2} > 0,$$

and conclude that the graph is concave downward on the interval $\left(-\infty, -\sqrt{3}\right)$, concave upward on the interval $\left(-\sqrt{3}, 0\right)$, concave downward on the interval $\left(0, -\sqrt{3}\right)$, and concave downward on the interval $\left(\sqrt{3}, \infty\right)$.

Drill #416:
Use your favorite graphing tool to graph $y = \frac{x}{1+x^2}$ and confirm our conclusions.

End Of Example #61

Example #62:

The previous example was fairly simple so it was easy to keep all of the important information in mind at the same time. This will not always be the case so we will need ways to organize the data we collect. This will ensure that it is not overwhelming. Below we demonstrate one way to do this. It is not the only way.

Let's sketch the graph of

$$y = \frac{2 + 2x^2 + 2x^4}{1 + x^4}$$

using Calculus. To use the First Derivative Test we'll need the derivative.

Drill #417: Confirm that the derivative is $\frac{dy}{dx} = y'(x) = \frac{4x(1-x^4)}{(1+x^4)^2}$.

Setting the first derivative equal to zero and solving we see that we have a POTP at $x = -1$, $x = 0$, and at $x = 1$. To make all of this easier to see we arrange this data in the following table. Notice that we have organized our POTPs (and hence the intervals that we are testing) from left to right, just as they would appear on a number line.

POTP		-1		0		1	
Interval	$(\infty, -1)$		$(-1, 0)$		$(0, 1)$		$(1, \infty)$
$y'(x)$	> 0		< 0		> 0		< 0
$y(t)$	↗	3 local max	↘	2 local min	↗	3 local max	↘

Based on the table above we could reasonably infer that the graph might might have the shape shown at the right. The next step is to locate this graph on the x-y plane. From our table above we see that the local minimum is at $y(0) = 2$, and the two local maxima are at $y(-1) = y(1) = 3$.

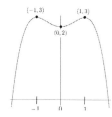

Thus we can, again reasonably, infer that the graph of $y(x)$ is located on the plane as shown at the left.

Unfortunately, we don't know that our graph is correct[2] because we've made assumptions regarding its concavity that we haven't justified. This is the same error we made in the discussion following Example #3, back in Chapter 1 when we drew a right triangle because it "seemed to be" correct. It is very easy to make this sort of mistake. Be careful.

We can analyze the concavity of the graph using the second derivative in a manner very similar to what we did earlier with first derivative.

Drill #418:

(a) Confirm that the second derivative of our function is: $\frac{d^2y}{dx^2} = \frac{4(1-12x^4+3x^8)}{(1+x^4)^3}$.

(b) Use an appropriate computational tool, or Newton's Method, to show that the PITPs of $y(x)$ are: $x \approx -1.41$, $x \approx -0.54$, $x \approx 0.54$, and $x \approx 1.41$.

(c) The approximations in part (b) can actually be computed exactly. Find the exact solutions and confirm the approximations.

---

[2]In fact, it is not.

Now set up a table to analyze concavity.

PITP		≈ -1.41		≈ -0.54		≈ 0.54		≈ 1.41	
Interval	$(-\infty, -1.41)$		$(-1.41, -0.54)$		$(-0.54, 0.54)$		$(0.54, 1.41)$		$(1.41, \infty)$
$y''(x)$	> 0		< 0		> 0		< 0		> 0
$y(x)$	$\cup$	≈ 2.80	$\cap$	≈ 2.54	$\cup$	≈ 2.80	$\cap$	≈ 2.54	$\cup$
		inflection point		inflection point		inflection point		inflection point	

Combining the data in this table with the data in our previous table it would seem reasonable to infer that the graph of our function looks like the one at the right. Does this graph above seem complete to you now? Obviously it is not, or we would not have asked, but do you see what is missing? What happens to $y(x)$ as x is very far from zero either the positive or the negative direction? Does $y(x)$ continue to drop? Or does it eventually level off?

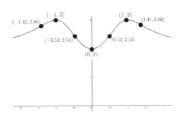

We're not quite ready to talk about this yet, so give it some thought and take you best guess. We'll come back and finish this example in Section 11.1 after we've developed some essential notation and definitions.

End Of Example #62

Problem #419:
Use the first and second derivatives to sketch the graph of each of the following functions.
(**Comment:** If you already know what some of these graphs look like use the tests to confirm what you already know.)

(**a**) $y = e^x$

(**b**) $y = \ln(x)$

(**c**) $y = \sin(x)$

(**d**) $y = \cos(x)$

(**e**) $y = \sin(x)\cos(x)$

(**f**) $y = xe^x$

(**g**) $y = \frac{e^x - e^{-x}}{2}$

(**h**) $y = \frac{e^x + e^{-x}}{2}$

(**i**) $y = x(x - 1)$

(**j**) $y = x^2(x - 1)$

(**k**) $y = x^2(x^2 - 1)$

(**l**) $y = x(x - 1)(x - 2)$

(**m**) $y = x\sqrt[3]{x - 8}$

(**n**) $y = \sqrt[3]{x}(x - 8)$

9.2   Graphing Without Formulas

At its most fundamental, a function is just a rule for associating a given input with its unique output. For example, we could specify a particular function by writing "take two copies of the input, multiply them together and return the result as output." This is a complete and valid description but it is cumbersome to use. This is why we've instead invented notation that allows us to write the description succinctly as the formula $f(x) = x^2$. It is easy to sketch an accurate graph of a function that is given as a formula, especially using modern technology, because the formula tells you the steps for finding the output for any given input.

As mentioned earlier, formulas are the Holy Grail of modern science and business. But, despite what you have seen in your mathematics education so far, very often we don't have such a formula. This is the usual situation. If you own a trout fishery business for example, you would love to have a formula that tells you how many trout your fishery will have on any given day of the year. With such a formula you could make plans for your business well into the future. We will talk about this in more detail in the next section.

Example #63:

For example, suppose we have the following information about a certain function. Can we sketch a reasonable graph of the function?

- $y(1) = 2$
- $\left.\dfrac{dy}{dx}\right|_{x=1} = 0$
- $\left.\dfrac{dy}{dx}\right|_{x=5} = 0$
- $\left.\dfrac{d^2y}{dx^2}\right|_{x=3} = 0$

- $\left.\dfrac{d^2y}{dx^2}\right|_{x=5} = 0$
- $\dfrac{dy}{dx} > 0$ for all $x < 1$
- $\dfrac{dy}{dx} < 0$ for $1 < x < 5$ and $x > 5$

- $\dfrac{d^2y}{dx^2} > 0$ for $3 < x < 5$
- $\dfrac{d^2y}{dx^2} < 0$ for $x < 3$ and $x > 5$

Actually, this is easier than the previous problems, since intervals of increase, decrease, concave up, and concave down have already been determined for us. For example, here are the tables for each.

POTP		1		5	
Interval	$(-\infty, 1)$		$(1, 5)$		$(5, \infty)$
$\dfrac{dy}{dx}$	$\dfrac{dy}{dx} > 0$		$\dfrac{dy}{dx} < 0$		$\dfrac{dy}{dx} < 0$
y	↗	2 (local max)	↘	$y(5)$ (neither)	↘

PITP		3		5	
Interval	$(-\infty, 3)$		$(3, 5)$		$(5, \infty)$
$\dfrac{d^2y}{dx^2}$	$\dfrac{d^2y}{dx^2} < 0$		$\dfrac{d^2y}{dx^2} > 0$		$\dfrac{d^2y}{dx^2} < 0$
y	∩	$y(3)$ (inflection point)	∪	$y(5)$ (inflection point)	∩

Problem #420:

In this example we have $\frac{dy}{dx}\big|_{x=5} = 0$ and $\frac{dy}{dx} < 0$ on the intervals $(1, 5)$ and $(5, \infty)$. Given that $\frac{dy}{dx}\big|_{x=5} = 0$ and $\frac{d^2y}{dx^2} < 0$ when $x > 5$, did we really need to specify that $\frac{dy}{dx} < 0$ on the interval $(5, \infty)$?

Based on the information given, the function $y = y(x)$ has a local maximum at $x = 1$ and inflection points at $x = 3$ and $x = 5$. A sketch of the graph might look something like this:

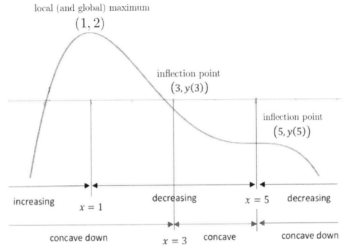

End Of Example #63

Problem #421: (Continued on the next page)
Sketch the graph of $y = y(x)$ which satisfies the given requirements.

(a) $y(-8) = 10$,
$\frac{dy}{dx} < 0$ for all x
$\frac{d^2y}{dx^2} > 0$ for all x.

(b) $y(0) = 0$,
$\frac{dy}{dx}\big|_{x=0} = 0$,
$\frac{dy}{dx}\big|_{x \neq 0} > 0$,
$\frac{d^2y}{dx^2} < 0$ for $x < 0$,
$\frac{d^2y}{dx^2} > 0$ for $x > 0$,

Problem #421: (Continued from the previous page)

(c) $-\frac{\pi}{2} < y < \frac{\pi}{2}$ for all x,

$y(0) = 0$,

$\frac{dy}{dx}\Big|_{x=0} = 1$,

$\frac{dy}{dx} > 0$ for all x,

$\frac{d^2y}{dx^2} > 0$, for $x < 0$,

$\frac{d^2y}{dx^2} < 0$, for $x > 0$,

(d) $y(0) = 0$,

$\frac{dy}{dx}\Big|_{x=0}$ does not exist,

$\frac{dy}{dx}\Big|_{x\neq 0} > 0$,

$\frac{d^2y}{dx^2} > 0$, for $x < 0$

$\frac{d^2y}{dx^2} < 0$, for $x > 0$

(e) $y > 0$ for all x,

$y(0) = 1$,

$\frac{dy}{dx} > 0$ for all x,

$\frac{d^2y}{dx^2} > 0$ for all x.

(f) $y(0) = 0$, $\frac{dy}{dx}\Big|_{x=0} = 0$, $\frac{dy}{dx}\Big|_{x=2} = 0$,

$\frac{dy}{dx} > 0$ for x in $(-\infty, 0)$,

$\frac{dy}{dx} > 0$ for x in $(0, 2)$,

$\frac{dy}{dx} < 0$ for $x > 2$,

$\frac{d^2y}{dx^2}\Big|_{x=0} = 0$, $\frac{d^2y}{dx^2}\Big|_{x=1} = 0$,

$\frac{d^2y}{dx^2} > 0$ for x in $(0, 1)$,

$\frac{d^2y}{dx^2} < 0$ for x in $(-\infty, 0)$,

$\frac{d^2y}{dx^2} < 0$ for x in $(1, \infty)$,

(g) $y(3) = 7$,

$\frac{dy}{dx} = 1$, for $x < 3$,

$\frac{dy}{dx} = -1$, for $x > 3$

(h) $y(-x) = y(x)$ for all x,

$y(0) = 1$,

$\frac{dy}{dx}\Big|_{x=0} = 0$,

$\frac{dy}{dx}\Big|_{x=2} = 0$,

$\frac{dy}{dx} > 0$, for $0 < x < 2$

$\frac{dy}{dx} < 0$, for $x > 2$

$\frac{d^2y}{dx^2}\Big|_{x=1} = 0$,

$\frac{d^2y}{dx^2} > 0$ for x in $(0, 1)$,

$\frac{d^2y}{dx^2} < 0$ for x in $(1, \infty)$

(i) $y(-x) = -y(x)$, for all x,

$\frac{dy}{dx}\Big|_{x=0} = 0$,

$\frac{dy}{dx}\Big|_{x=2} = 0$,

$\frac{dy}{dx} > 0$, for $0 < x < 2$,

$\frac{dy}{dx}\Big|_{x>2} < 0$,

$\frac{d^2y}{dx^2}\Big|_{x=1} = 0$,

$\frac{d^2y}{dx^2} > 0$, for $0 < x < 1$,

$\frac{d^2y}{dx^2} < 0$ for $x > 1$.

(j) For this problem we restrict the domain to the interval $[0, 2\pi]$.

$y(0) = y(2\pi) = -2$, $y(\pi) = 2$,

$\frac{dy}{dx}\Big|_{x=0} = \frac{dy}{dx}\Big|_{x=\pi} = \frac{dy}{dx}\Big|_{x=2\pi} = 0$,

$\frac{dy}{dx} > 0$, for $0 < x < \pi$,

$\frac{dy}{dx} < 0$, for $\pi < x < 2\pi$,

$\frac{d^2y}{dx^2}\Big|_{x=\frac{\pi}{2}} = \frac{d^2y}{dx^2}\Big|_{x=\frac{3\pi}{2}} = 0$,

$\frac{d^2y}{dx^2} > 0$ for $0 < x < \frac{\pi}{2}$,

$\frac{d^2y}{dx^2} > 0$ for $\frac{3\pi}{2} < x < 2\pi$,

$\frac{d^2y}{dx^2} < 0$ for $\frac{\pi}{2} < x < \frac{3\pi}{2}$

In Section (5.6) we found the graph of $\tan^{-1}(x)$ by examining the graph of its derivative, the Witch of Agnesi, The procedure we used in Section (5.6) is quite general. For example, suppose the graph of $\frac{dy}{dx}$ is given below.

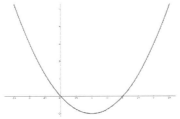

Recall that with a graph for $\frac{dy}{dx}$, finding where y is increasing or y is decreasing is just a matter of determining where the derivative is positive (above the x axis) or negative (below the x axis). Similarly the concavity of the graph of $y(x)$ can be determined by finding where $\frac{dy}{dx} = y'(x)$ is increasing (concave upward) and decreasing (concave downward). Given the graph of $\frac{dy}{dx}$ at the right, we can produce the following tables.

POTP		0		2	
Interval	$(-\infty, 0)$		$(0, 2)$		$(2, \infty)$
$\frac{dy}{dx}$	> 0		< 0		> 0
y	↗	local max	↘	local min	↗

PITP		1	
Interval	$(-\infty, 1)$		$(1, \infty)$
$\frac{d^2 y}{dx^2}(x)$	< 0		> 0
y	∩	inflection point	∪

From the data in our tables we see that the graph of y looks something like this.

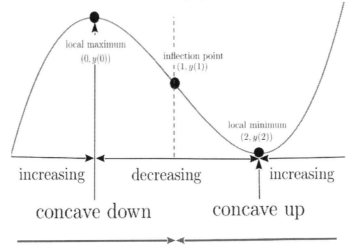

Problem #422:

Each of the following graphs is the derivative of some function. Find the shape of the graph of the function.

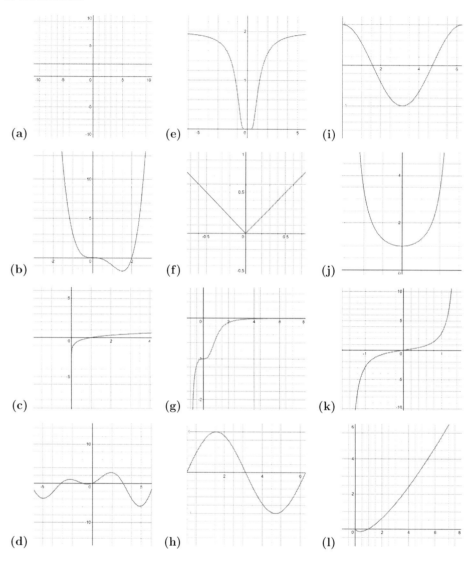

(a)

(b)

(c)

(d)

(e)

(f)

(g)

(h)

(i)

(j)

(k)

(l)

9.3 Graphing with a Formula for $\frac{dy}{dt}$: Initial Value Problems

When $\frac{dy}{dt}$ depends on t alone.

Example #64:

Consider the IVP,

$$\frac{dy}{dt} = t(4-t), \quad y(0) = 0.$$

In Integral Calculus (probably your next math course) you will learn how to find $y(t)$ explicitly. For now we will be satisfied with sketching an approximate graph of $y(t)$.

Setting $\frac{dy}{dt} = 0$ and solving we see that $t = 0$ and $t = 4$ are the POTPs for $y(t)$. Thus on each of the intervals $(-\infty, 0)$, $(0, 4)$, and $(4, \infty)$ the graph of $y(t)$ is either always increasing or always decreasing. We tabulate this information as follows:

POTP		0		4	
Interval	$(-\infty,0)$		$(0,4)$		$(4,\infty)$
$y'(t)$	< 0		> 0		< 0
$y(t)$	↘	0 / local min	↗	$y(4)=?$ / local max	↘

Based on this table, we can see that $y(0) = 0$ is a local minimum and $y(4)$ is a local maximum. Observe that we do not know the value of $y(4)$, only that it must be a local maximum. Nor do we have any way to determine the value of $y(4)$ in this problem.

We proceed in a similar fashion to determine concavity. The second derivative is

$$\frac{d^2 y}{dt^2} = \frac{d(t(4-t))}{dt} = 4 - 2t.$$

Setting $\frac{d^2 y}{dt^2} = 0$ and solving, we see that $t = 2$ is a PITP for $y(t)$. Making a table as before we have

PITP		2	
Interval	$(-\infty, 2)$		$(2, \infty)$
$y''(t)$	> 0		< 0
$y(t)$	$\cup$	0 / inflection point	$\cap$

Based on the table we see that the point $(2, y(2))$ is an inflection point.

We want to make a reasonable sketch of the graph of $y = y(t)$ based on this information. But there is a lot of information in the tables and our graph needs to be consistent with all of it. So we first organize all of our conclusions by plotting the transition points (both optimal and inflective) on the t axis and identifying the intervals where y is increasing, decreasing, concave up, or concave down.

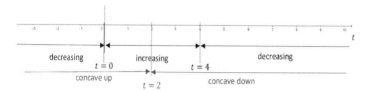

This information, along with the initial value, $y(0) = 0$ allows us to provide a reasonable graph of $y(t)$.

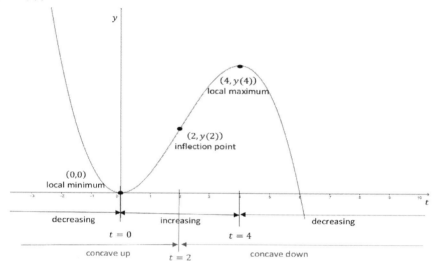

From the initial condition in the IVP we know that $y(0) = 0$ but we have no information about the vertical coordinate of any other point on the graph. Thus, from the information given the scale Of this graph is unknowable. But we know that the graph above is reasonable because it is consistent with the data given in the IVP. This sort of graphical, qualitative analysis is the best we can do with the information we have but, as you see, we can glean a great deal of information about the "shape" of the graph of a function from its derivative alone.

End Of Example #64

Problem #423:

For each of the following IVPs:

(i) Find the intervals on which the graph of the solution is increasing and decreasing. Identify the location all local extrema.

(ii) Find the intervals on which the graph of the solution is concave upward and concave downward. Identify the location of all inflection points.

(iii) Plot a reasonable sketch of the graph for $y = y(t)$. Approximate transition points using the appropriate technology or Newton's Method as necessary.

(a) $\frac{dy}{dt} = t^2(4 - t)$, $y(0) = 0$.

(b) $\frac{dy}{dt} = t^2(4 + t)$, $y(0) = 0$.

(c) $\frac{dy}{dt} = \sin(t)$, $y(0) = 0$.

(d) $\frac{dy}{dt} = \sin(t)$, $y(0) = 2$.

(e) $\frac{dy}{dt} = \cos(t)$, $y(0) = 0$.

(f) $\frac{dy}{dt} = \sin(t)\cos(t)$, $y(0) = \pi$.

(g) $\frac{dy}{dt} = t\sin(t)$, $y(0) = 0$.

(h) $\frac{dy}{dt} = 5e^t - t$, $y(1) = 1$.

(i) $\frac{dy}{dt} = -e^{-t} + \ln(t)$, $y(1) = e$.

(j) $\frac{dy}{dt} = e^t \sin(2t)$, $y(0) = 1$.

(k) $\frac{dy}{dt} = \tan(t)$, $y(0) = 1$.

(l) $\frac{dy}{dt} = \sqrt{t}$, $y(0) = 1$

(m) $\frac{dy}{dt} = t^3 - t$, $y(1) = 3$

(n) $\frac{dy}{dt} = t - t^3$, $y(1) = 3$
(**Hint:** Compare this to problem (m).)

When $\frac{dy}{dt}$ depends on y alone.

> *"To see a World in a Grain of Sand*
> *And a Heaven in a Wild Flower*
> *Hold Infinity in the palm of your hand*
> *And Eternity in an hour"*
>
> – William Blake 1757-1827

Consider the IVP

$$\frac{dy}{dt} = y, \ y(0) = 1. \tag{9.2}$$

This is the same IVP we approximated in Section 6.3. The analysis we will do here is related so you may find it useful to review that section before proceeding.

As we've seen every IVP has two parts: a differential equation (in this case, $\frac{dy}{dt} = y$, and an initial value (in this case, $y(0) = 1$ or equivalently, $(0, 1)$).

We will focus on the differential equation first. The differential equation $\frac{dy}{dt} = y$ says that at each point on the graph of $y(t)$ the slope of the graph is equal to the vertical coordinate at that point. For example if $(0,1)$ is a point on the graph of $y(t)$, then nearby the graph of $y(t)$ will look like the orange part of the sketch at the right. On the other hand, if $(1,1)$ is a point on the graph of $y(t)$ then near the point $(1,1)$, graph of $y(t)$ will look like the red graph in the sketch at the right.

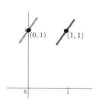

In fact, for any value of t, we know that if $(t,1)$ is a point on the graph of $y(t)$ then the slope of the graph which passes through that point will be parallel to the orange and red lines above (that is, if a solution of the differential equation passes through a point $(t,1)$ then its slope will be equal to 1 at $(t,1)$).

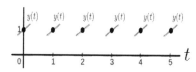

This is seen in the figure at the left where each black dot represents a point with vertical coordinate equal to 1 and each orange segment represents the graph of the curve that both satisfies the differential equation from IVP #9.2, and passes through that point.

Similarly, if we know that $(t,2)$ is a point on the graph of $y(t)$, where $y(t)$ both solves the differential equation from IVP #9.2 and passes through that point, then the slope at $(t,2)$ will be 2, as seen in the following sketch.

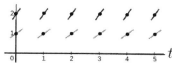

By tagging more points in the plane in the same way we get the image below.

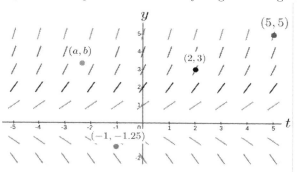

A sketch like this is called a **slope field**. The short line segment at each point, (a,b), is a short section of the graph of the function[3] which satisfies the differential equation $\frac{dy}{dt} = y$. If we know where to start (i.e., if we have an initial condition) the slope field allows us to determine the shape of the entire graph.

For example to sketch the graph of $y(t)$ if it passes through the point $(2,3)$, we simply follow the line segments in our slope field starting at that point. This is the black graph in the sketch below. The graph of the $y(t)$ that passes through the point $(5,5)$ is shown in red below,

---

[3]Actually the Principle of Local Linearity applies so it is a short section of the line tangent at (a,b).

and the graph that passes through the point $(-1, -1.25)$ is shown in blue.

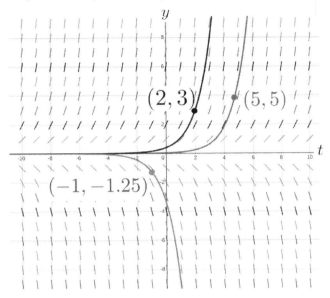

IVP #9.2 has the initial condition, $y(0) = 1$. Plot the point $(0, 1)$ and use this slope field to sketch the solution of IVP #9.2. Compare your solution with the approximation we obtained in Section (6.3). Do they look like the same solution?

Problem #425: Find the Pattern

(a) Confirm that $y(t) = 3e^{t-2}$ is the solution of the IVP $\frac{dy}{dt} = y$, $y(2) = 3$.
(This is the black graph above.)

(b) Confirm that $y(t) = 5e^{t-5}$ is the solution of the IVP $\frac{dy}{dt} = y$, $y(5) = 5$.
(This is the red graph above.)

(c) Based on parts (a) and (b) guess what the solution of the IVP $\frac{dy}{dt} = y$, $y(-1) = -2$ will be. Confirm that your guess is correct. If you guess wrong, guess again.

(d) Based on parts (a) and (b), and (c) make a conjecture what the solution of the IVP $\frac{dy}{dt} = y$, $y(a) = b$ will be. Confirm that your guess is correct.

To sketch the graph of the solution of a given IVP begin by drawing the **slope field** for the differential equation. Then plot the value and follow the slope field to sketch the graph.

Problem #426:

For each of the following IVPs sketch the **slope field** in the ranges given and use your slope field to sketch the solution of the IVP.

(**Comment:** It is easiest to begin by sketching slopes at integer coordinate points but that doesn't always give you a clear picture. Begin with the integer coordinate points and then fill in between them to get a clearer sense of the graphs.)

(a) $\frac{dy}{dt} = \sqrt{y}$,
   $y(0) = 1$,
   $-5 \le t$,
   $y \ge 0$

(c) $\frac{dy}{dt} = (y-1)^2$,
   $y(1) = 0$,
   $-5 \le t \le 5$,
   $-5 \le y \le 5$

(e) $\frac{dy}{dt} = y(2-y)$,
   $y(1) = 1$,
   $-1 \le t \le 1$,
   $-2 \le y \le 3$

(b) $\frac{dy}{dt} = y^2$,
   $y(-1) = -2$,
   $-5 \le t \le 5$,
   $-5 \le y \le 5$

(d) $\frac{dy}{dt} = y(y-2)$,
   $y(1) = 1$,
   $-1 \le x \le 1$,
   $-2 \le y \le 3$

(f) $\frac{dy}{dt} = (y^2 - 1)$,
   $y(0) = 1$,
   $-2 \le t \le 2$,
   $-2 \le y \le 2$

So far we've examined the situation when $\frac{dy}{dt}$ depends on t alone: $\frac{dy}{dt} = f(t)$ and when $\frac{dy}{dt}$ depends on y alone: $\frac{dy}{dt} = f(y)$. But, of course, it could happen at $\frac{dy}{dt}$ depends on both y and t: $\frac{dy}{dt} = f(t,y)$. Analytically, this is a more complex situation. However it is possible, and quite useful, to get a qualitative sketch of the solution of an IVP from the slope field.

Problem #427:

For each of the following IVPs draw The **slope field** in the ranges given and use your slope field to sketch the solution of the IVP.

(a) $\frac{dy}{dt} = yt$,
   $y(0) = 1$,
   $-3 \le t \le 3$,
   $y \ge 0$

(b) $\frac{dy}{dt} = \frac{y}{t^2+1}$,
   $y(1) = 0$,
   $-5 \le x \le 5$,
   $-5 \le y \le 5$

(c) $\frac{dy}{dt} = ye^x$,
   $y(-4) = 2$,
   $-5 \le t \le 5$,
   $-5 \le y \le 5$

(d) $\frac{dy}{dt} = ye^{-x}$,
   $y(0) = 2$,
   $0 \le t \le 5$,
   $-5 \le y \le 5$

Chapter 10

Modeling with Calculus

> *"The purpose of mathematical models is not to fit to data but to sharpen one's questions."*
>
> – Samuel Karlin (1924-2007)

In the introduction to Chapter 8 we mentioned that the original motivation for the invention of Calculus was optimization. But after it was invented scientists and mathematicians found that Calculus is useful for solving a wide variety of other kinds of problems. In this chapter we will explore how Calculus helps us solve various non-optimization problems. As you will see the ability to sketch the graph of a function, even if it is only qualitative, is extremely useful.

10.1 Population Dynamics

Modeling a Trout Farm

> *"A man may fish with the worm that hath eat of a king, and eat of the fish that hath fed of that worm."*
>
> – William Shakespeare, (1564-1616)

Suppose we are running an industrial trout fishery. There are a number of questions we'd really like to be able to answer at any given time. How large is the current stock? Do we have too few? Too many? Is our stock of trout in danger of dying off due to under or over population? How frequently can we harvest our stock without endangering it? Even if precise numbers aren't possible, it would still be useful to have a good, qualitative understanding of the life cycle of our stock of trout so we could make reliable estimates.

To gain such an understanding we will build a model of our trout population as a function of time. As a first approximation assume that we have complete control of the lake where we will hold the trout. We can supply all of the food and space that our trout need to continue reproducing.

Suppose that our lake is stocked with an initial purchase of 10 tons of trout. Let $P(t)$ represent the amount of fish we have, in tons, at time, t, in years, (so $P(0) = 10$ tons). We can estimate the rate of growth of our population by casting a net into the same point of the lake each year and weighing the catch[1]. Comparing the weight of the catch from year to year will give a reasonable estimate of the rate at which the trout population grows in one year.

For the sake of specificity, suppose that the population is growing continuously at a nominal growth rate of 10%. Then we have

$$\frac{dP}{dt} = 0.1P$$

just as we did in Section 7.2.

So the first model for our trout fishery lake is the following IVP:

$$\frac{dP}{dt} = .1P, \quad P(0) = 10. \tag{10.1}$$

This IVP should look familiar. When we were modeling the growth of a bacteria colony in Example #39 Section 7.2 we got IVP (7.16), which is almost the same equation, remember? The only difference between them is that in IVP (10.1) the coefficient of P is 0.1 and in IVP (7.16) the coefficient of y is 0.3.

Since the solution of Equation (7.16) was $y(t) = 10e^{0.3t}$ it seems reasonable to conclude that the solution of Equation (10.1) is:

$$P(t) = 10e^{0.1t}.$$

Drill #428: Confirm that $P(t) = 10e^{0.1t}$ solves IVP (10.1).

The graph of $P(t)$ is shown at the right. As you can see our trout population is growing exponentially, so it appears that we're going to get very rich as soon as we sell of all of those fish.

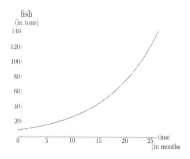

Of course, in practice this is not what happens. We made several simplifying assumptions when we began. We assumed that (1) we could supply all of the food our growing population needs, and (2) our trout would have all of the room they needed.

These assumptions are unrealistic in the long run. But in the short run they are not completely crazy.

Recall that in Chapter 7 we described a situation in Lake Erie near Toledo, Ohio when, for a few days, the algae population grew exponentially in much the same manner as that suggested by our trout model. Naturally such growth cannot be sustained. Eventually the algae will consume all of the available nutrients, or will simply run out of space. They will then begin to die off. But our model, simple as it is, gives pretty accurate predictions of the population for small values of t, be they a population of bacteria, algae, trout, or even humans.

In building a mathematical model of any physical phenomenon we start with the simplest model we can, find out where it goes bad, and then "tweak" it so that we:

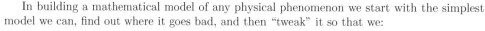

---

[1] Of course we'd want to always use the same sized net as well.

1. keep those properties of the model that make realistic predictions, and

2. eliminate those properties of the model that make unrealistic predictions.

Thus we need to tweak IVP (10.1) in such a way that $\frac{\mathrm{d}P}{\mathrm{d}t} = 0.1P$ when P is near zero (or, at least, $\frac{\mathrm{d}P}{\mathrm{d}t} \approx 0.1P$), but which also recognizes that exponential growth is unsustainable.

Since exponential growth can't be maintained indefinitely the population must eventually stop growing and drop to a lower level – or collapse entirely. Thus there must be a maximum population level, $P(t)$, where $\frac{\mathrm{d}P}{\mathrm{d}t} = 0$. Whatever that level is, we'll call it C.

One way to tweak IVP (10.1) to reflect this fact is to insert the factor $(C - P)$ as follows

$$\frac{\mathrm{d}P}{\mathrm{d}t} = 0.1P(C - P).$$

We see that if the trout population ever reaches C it must level off since in that case $\frac{\mathrm{d}P}{\mathrm{d}t} = 0$. Therefore this model avoids predicting that the trout population will grow exponentially.

However, notice that for values of P near zero, $C - P \approx C$. Thus this differential equation says that when P is near zero

$$\frac{\mathrm{d}P}{\mathrm{d}t} \approx (0.1C)\, P$$

but we needed $\frac{\mathrm{d}P}{\mathrm{d}t} \approx 0.1P$ so this particular tweak won't quite work because the difference between $\frac{\mathrm{d}P}{\mathrm{d}t} \approx 0.01P$ and $\frac{\mathrm{d}P}{\mathrm{d}t} \approx (0.01C)\, P$ could be substantial, depending on the value of C (which we don't know).

So we will try a slightly different tweak. Instead of $(C - P)$ we will insert the factor $\left(1 - \frac{P}{C}\right)$ as in IVP (10.2) below.

$$\frac{\mathrm{d}P}{\mathrm{d}t} = 0.1P\left(1 - \frac{P}{C}\right), \quad P(0) = 10. \tag{10.2}$$

Notice that we still have $\frac{\mathrm{d}P}{\mathrm{d}t} = 0$ when $P = C$. But now we also have $\frac{\mathrm{d}P}{\mathrm{d}t} \approx 0.1P$ when P is close to zero, so this change seems to meet the goal of our tweak. This type of IVP (10.2) is called the Logistic Equation (or the Logistic Model) and its solution is a better long-term predictor of population growth than is the solution of Equation (10.1) as we will see.

The parameter C would normally be determined experimentally (measured), but for purposes of this discussion we will arbitrarily assign it the value $C = 100$ just to keep the numbers easy to deal with. So, our IVP will be

$$\frac{\mathrm{d}P}{\mathrm{d}t} = 0.1P\left(1 - \frac{P}{100}\right), \quad P(0) = 10. \tag{10.3}$$

Drill #429:
Compute the growth rate of the trout population for $P =$

(a) 99   **(b)** 99.9   **(c)** 99.99   **(d)** 100.01   **(e)** 100.1   **(f)** 101

and use your results to explain why C in Equation (10.2) is sometimes called the "carrying capacity" of the environment (in this case the pond the trout are living in).

It would be nice if we could find a formula for $P(t)$ in terms of t but this will have to wait for a course in Integral Calculus. Still we would like to provide a reasonable sketch of the graph of $P = P(t)$. Aside from the initial condition, $P(0) = 10$, we don't know any specific values of $P(t)$ but we can at least capture the qualitative behavior of the population.

We will obtain a sketch of the graph of $P(t)$ in the same systematic way as before. We can use the first derivative test to determine when the trout population is increasing or decreasing. But keep in mind that we have $\frac{dP}{dt}$ in terms of P — not t — so we won't be able to say that the population is increasing or decreasing at a particular time. This will change how we interpret the results. For example we can say that when we have 25 tons of trout the population is increasing even though we do not know *when* this happens.

It should be straightforward to see that the POTPs are $P = 0, 100$. Since the context of our problem prohibits $P < 0$ (why?), we will look at intervals $[0, 100)$ and $(100, \infty)$ to determine for which values of P the population is increasing or decreasing. We summarize this analysis in the following table:

Interval	$(0, 100)$	$(100, \infty)$
$\frac{dP}{dt}$	> 0	< 0
P	$\nearrow$	$\searrow$

Drill #430:
Suppose we were to use the data in the table above to plot a graph of P versus t. Would there be a maximum when $P = 100$. Explain.

Problem #431:
In this problem we analyze the concavity of the graph of $P(t)$. In particular we'd like to find all values of P where PITPs occur.

(a) Show that $d\left(\frac{dP}{dt}\right) = 0.1\left(1 - \frac{P}{50}\right)dP$ and therefore $\frac{d^2P}{dt^2} = 0.1\left(1 - \frac{P}{50}\right)\frac{dP}{dt}$.

(b) Find all values of P where a PITP occurs.

(c) Create a table similar to the one above to determine the (vertical) intervals on which P is concave up or concave down.

We now have enough data on to plot a reasonable sketch of the graph of $P = P(t)$ but because all of our formulas are in terms of the dependent variable P, our transition points and intervals are will all be shown on the vertical axis, not the horizontal as seen below.

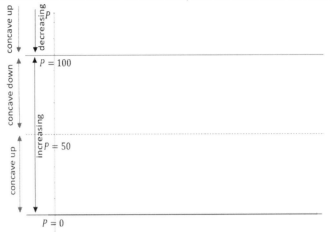

Notice that we drew solid horizontal lines at $P = 0$ and $P = 100$. At these population levels $\frac{dP}{dt} = 0$ so, theoretically at least, once the population has achieved either of these levels it will never change again. This is correct when $P(0) = 0$. Once all of our fish have died the only way we can get more is to buy them and start again. But for other values of P it is still not entirely clear what's happening to our fish population.

It is not possible to maintain a population of trout at a constant value of 100 tons. There will always be a little fluctuation above and below. All models are inaccurate in some way. This is one way in which this model is inaccurate.

The dashed line represents the population level where the graph of the population transitions from concave up to concave down. Physically this means that the rate of growth transitions from accelerating to decelerating.

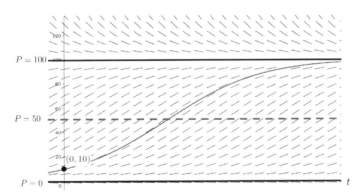

We can visualize this (at the left) using slope field technique we saw in Section 9.3. Starting with an initial value of $P(0) = 10$, we can plot the graph of the population and make a prediction of what will happened to the population in the long term. We just can't tell what "long term" means. That would have to be determined experimentally.

Notice that on the vertical interval $(0, 50)$ the population is accelerating until it reaches $P = 50$ tons. After that, it still grows, but is starting to decelerate. Over the long run it will approach (but never quite reach) a level of $P = 100$ tons.

Problem #432:

(a) On the same set of axes, plot reasonable graphs for $P(t)$ with the following initial values:

(i) $P(0) = 0$,   (iii) $P(0) = 75$,

(ii) $P(0) = 10$,   (iv) $P(0) = 100$.

(**Comment:** Is it clear to you that none of these curves can cross? Think about it a moment, if two of these curves crossed, it would force $\frac{dy}{dt}$ to take on two different values for some value of y. Do you see why this can't happen? This fact should help you in your graphing.)

(b) Sketch the graph you get if you start by purchasing 150 tons of trout, rather than 10 tons. Is this a good business decision?

Problem #433:

Suppose our fishery has another lake full of bass, that the intrinsic growth rate is

$$\frac{dB}{dt} = .25B\left(1 - \frac{B}{500}\right) \frac{\text{tons}}{\text{year}} \tag{10.4}$$

(a) Analyze this model in the same way we analyzed Equation (10.2). Draw several typical graphs.

(b) We can't make any money unless we sell some of our fish. Modify Equation (10.4) to account for harvesting at a uniform rate of $20\frac{\text{tons}}{\text{year}}$.

(c) Suppose $B(0) = 150$ tons. Sketch a graph of the population. What does the model predict about the amount of fish in the lake over a long period of time?

(d) Assume that $B(0)$ is still 150 tons as in part (b), but this time the amount of harvesting is increased from $20\frac{\text{tons}}{\text{year}}$ to $30\frac{\text{tons}}{\text{year}}$. Use a slope field to draw a graph of $B(t)$. What does the model predict now about the amount of fish over a long period of time?

The general logistic growth equation is

$$\frac{dP}{dt} = rP\left(1 - \frac{P}{C}\right) \tag{10.5}$$

where $P = P(t)$ is the population at time t and the positive constants r and C are the **intrinsic growth rate** and **carrying capacity**, respectively. Recall that we obtained Equation (10.5) by tweaking Equation (10.1) (the exponential model) to account for die-off due to overpopulation.

Problem #434:
Show that in this model P is increasing and concave up when $0 < P < \frac{C}{2}$, P is increasing and concave down when $\frac{C}{2} < P < C$, and P is decreasing and concave up when $P > C$.
(**Comment:** This is the same analysis we did above when we assumed that $C = 100$.)

Of course there is also a risk from underpopulation which our model does not account for. To catch this effect we tweak Equation (10.5) by inserting the factor $\left(1 - \frac{m}{P}\right)$ where $m < C$ is a small positive constant. We justify this tweak in problem #435 below.

Problem #435:
Our new model is then

$$\frac{\mathrm{d}P}{\mathrm{d}t} = rP\left(1 - \frac{m}{P}\right)\left(1 - \frac{P}{C}\right) = \frac{r}{C}(P - m)(C - P) \tag{10.6}$$

(a) Show that when P is very large Equation (10.6) reduces (approximately) to Equation (10.5).

(b) Show that when $P < m$ then $\frac{\mathrm{d}P}{\mathrm{d}t} < 0$. What does this say about the growth of the population when P is near zero?

(c) Find all values of P for which the graph of $P = P(t)$ is increasing and the values for which it is decreasing?

(d) Show that

$$\frac{\mathrm{d}^2 P}{\mathrm{d}t^2} = \frac{2r}{C}\left(\frac{C + m}{2} - P\right)\frac{\mathrm{d}P}{\mathrm{d}t}.$$

Use this to determine the values of P for which the graph of $P = P(t)$ is concave upward and the values for which the graph of $P(t)$ is concave downward.

(e) Use the information to plot a sketch of the graph of $P = P(t)$ where the initial value $P(0)$ satisfies each of the following:

  (i) $0 < P(0) < m$ (iii) $\frac{C+m}{2} < P(0) < C$
  (ii) $m < P(0) < \frac{C+m}{2}$ (iv) $C < P(0)$

(f) Explain why m is called the **minimum viable population** for the species.

The Competing Species Model

When we modeled the populations of trout and bass in an industrial farm we did not have to account for competition between species because we assumed that the two species of fish were kept in separate lakes. For fish living in the wild we cannot make that assumption, but we can tweak our original model to account for competition between species in a natural setting. To do this we'll have to use two equations, one for each species.

So let's introduce a competing species of fish into the same lake. Bass and walleye compete in the wild for the same food source, so each one's presence affects the other's growth rate. To model the walleye population take $C = 400$ for the carrying capacity, $r = 0.2$ as the intrinsic growth rate of the walleye, and let $W = W(t)$ denote the amount of walleye (in tons) at time t. Combining this with our model for the bass population from Problem #433 we have the following equations for each species separately:

$$\textbf{Bass:} \quad \frac{\mathrm{d}B}{\mathrm{d}t} = .25B\left(1 - \frac{B}{500}\right) \tag{10.7}$$

$$\textbf{Walleye:} \quad \frac{\mathrm{d}W}{\mathrm{d}t} = .2W\left(1 - \frac{W}{400}\right) \tag{10.8}$$

These equations have no terms modeling cross-species competition. That is, the value of $B(t)$ does not affect the value of $W(t)$ and *vice versa*, so we'll have to insert terms which do that.

Since they compete for food each species affects the others growth rate detrimentally. So we will model this interaction as follows[2]

$$\frac{\mathrm{d}B}{\mathrm{d}t} = .25B\left(1 - \frac{B}{500}\right) - 0.0001BW$$

$$\frac{\mathrm{d}W}{\mathrm{d}t} = .2W\left(1 - \frac{W}{400}\right) - 0.0001BW.$$

Notice that we took the growth rates from before and subtracted an identical term $0.0001BW$. This represents the detrimental effect of each species on the other's growth rate. For simplicity, we assumed that the effect of each on the other is the same. The fact that the new term, $-0.0001BW$, has the product BW in it reflects the idea that to have an appreciable effect on each other, both species must have a sufficient number to produce the required interactions. Again, this model is overly simplified, but let's see what long term effect this tweak has on both species.

To see that this is truly just a tweak of our previous model notice that if $W = 0$, then we would recover the previous model and over time B would approach its carrying capacity of 500 tons. Likewise, if $B = 0$, then, again we recover the previous model and over time W would approach its carrying capacity of 400 tons.

Given that $B, W \geq 0$, we want to determine what this model will predict happens to both species in the long term. Could they coexist or would one species drive the other to extinction? Take your best guess.

We'll start with B. We want to find all of the points where $\frac{\mathrm{d}B}{\mathrm{d}t} > 0$ (B is growing) and where $\frac{\mathrm{d}B}{\mathrm{d}t} < 0$ (B is shrinking). We will start by determining where $\frac{\mathrm{d}B}{\mathrm{d}t} = 0$.

$$0 = \frac{\mathrm{d}B}{\mathrm{d}t} = .25B\left(1 - \frac{B}{500}\right) - .0001BW = B\left[.25\left(1 - \frac{B}{500}\right) - .0001W\right].$$

---

[2]Just like the growth rates and carrying capacities we used earlier, these numbers are fabricated. We made them up. We (the authors) have inserted values for these parameters that we believe are reasonable but we do not pretend to know what might be realistic. If we were modeling a real population we would determine all of these parameters experimentally.

Thus we see that $\frac{dB}{dt} = 0$ when

$$B = 0 \qquad\qquad\qquad (10.9)$$

or when

$$.25\left(1 - \frac{B}{500}\right) - .0001W = 0$$

$$2500\left(1 - \frac{B}{500}\right) - W = 0$$

$$2500 - 5B - W = 0$$

$$5B + W = 2500. \qquad\qquad\qquad (10.10)$$

Next we form the (B)ass-(W)alleye plane, where each point (B, W) identifies a particular pair of possible populations. For example the point $(200, 500)$ represents the situation when there are 200 tons of bass and 500 tons of walleye in the lake.

In the sketch at the right we see from Equation (10.9) and Equation (10.10) that on each of the red lines we have $\frac{dB}{dt} = 0$.

Since the two red lines are the only locations where $\frac{dB}{dt} = 0$, it must be that $\frac{dB}{dt}$ is either greater than zero or less that zero in any region bounded by them. Choosing the point $(1, 1)$ in the shaded region we see that $\frac{dB}{dt}\big|_{(B,W)=(1,1)} > 0$. Choosing the point $(2000, 2000)$ outside the blue region we see that $\frac{dB}{dt}\big|_{(B,W)=(2000,2000)} < 0$. So for any bass/walleye pair, (B, W), the bass population is increasing when (B, W) lies below the diagonal line (in the blue region), and for any bass/walleye pair, (B, W), above the diagonal line, the amount of bass is decreasing.

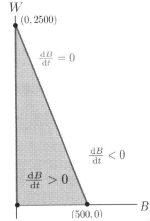

Finally, notice that when $W = 0$ the bass population will increase until it reaches the carrying capacity of the lake for bass alone (500), after which it will start to decrease. But if there are walleye in the lake the bass population will not reach the carrying capacity before it begins to decrease. This is consistent with the notion that the number of walleye adversely affect the growth rate of the bass.

Next we need to perform a similar analysis for the walleye population.

Problem #436:

Apply the same type of analysis to

$$\frac{dW}{dt} = .2W\left(1 - \frac{W}{400}\right) - .0001BW$$

to determine where W is increasing and where W is decreasing. Plot these regions in the first quadrant of the B-W plane just as we did above for the bass population.

If we superimpose the sketch you (should have) obtained from Problem #436 onto the graph we have above, we get the 4 regions seen in the sketch below.

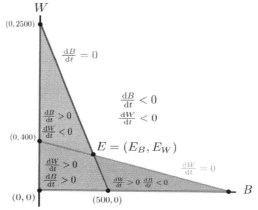

The points where the green and red lines intersect are called equilibrium points. Theoretically, if the two population levels are at an equilibrium point then neither population will ever change again because the growth rates are both zero.

Drill #437:

(a) Verify that the points $(0,0)$, $(500,0)$, and $(0,400)$, are equilibrium points for our bass/walleye populations.

(b) Compute the coordinates of the equilibrium point $E = (E_B, E_W)$ in the diagram.

But what happens if we don't start at an equilibrium point? Would the levels tend toward an equilibrium over time as the name suggests? Take your best guess.

We can figure this out by looking at the growth rates in each region. For example, suppose the initial populations of bass and walleye, (B, W) is in the blue region at the left. The bass population is increasing. Think of this as an arrow pointing to the right. In the same region the walleye population is decreasing which we can think of as an arrow pointing downward. Combining these arrows gives us an arrow pointing down and to the right.

Similarly, in the purple area the trajectory of the populations will be up and to the right since both populations are increasing. In the red area it will be up and to the left, while in the white area it will be down and to the left. All of this is displayed in the sketch at the left.

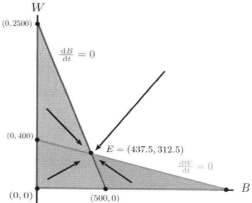

As rough as this qualitative drawing is, it gives us an idea of the population trajectories that the model predicts for the population levels of bass and walleye from various starting points.

Notice that these trajectories tend toward the equilibrium point, $E = (437.5, 312.5)$. This says that given these initial levels of bass and walleye, the levels will approach E_B tons of bass and E_w tons of walleye. This kind of problem is called a **dynamical system** and the path that the point (B, W) follows for any given set of initial conditions is called its **trajectory**.

Problem #438: Are there any initial conditions where the trajectory approaches the points $(0, 0)$, $(0, 400)$, or $(500, 0)$? Explain.

Problem #439:

(a) Suppose we adjust our differential equations slightly to

$$\frac{dB}{dt} = .25B \left(1 - \frac{B}{500}\right) - .0001BW$$

$$\frac{dW}{dt} = .2W \left(1 - \frac{W}{400}\right) - .001BW$$

Perform a similar graphical analysis to show that as long as $B \neq 0$, then any trajectory will approach the equilibrium point $(500, 0)$. That is, the walleye will become extinct, and the bass will approach their natural level of 500 tons. How is this consistent with the adjustments we made from the original differential equations? Explain.

(b) Now let's again adjust our differential equations to

$$\frac{dB}{dt} = .25B \left(1 - \frac{B}{500}\right) - .001BW$$

$$\frac{dW}{dt} = .2W \left(1 - \frac{W}{400}\right) - .001BW$$

   (i) Identify how this system of equations is different from the one in part (a), and interpret the difference in terms of the influence of each population on the other.

   (ii) Perform a similar graphical analysis to show that the equilibrium points are $(0, 0)$, $(500, 0)$, $(0, 400)$, and $(100, 200)$. While it is theoretically possible for a trajectory to approach $(100, 200)$, show that most trajectories will either approach $(500, 0)$ or $(0, 400)$. What does this mean for the fish populations, and is it consistent with the differential equations? Explain.

(c) Compare the results in parts (a) and (b) with the example that started this section (Equation 10.7 and Equation 10.8). How does the coefficient of the BW term affect the model?

10.2   Selected Modeling Problems

Epidemics, The SIR Model

> *"Life is an incurable disease."*
> – Abraham Cowley (1618-1667)

The SIR Model is a fairly simple model that is frequently used to understand the spread of an infectious disease through a population. As with any mathematical model, it is over-simplified but, just like IVP (10.1), it provides a foundation which can be tweaked as needed for better predictions.

We will assume that every member the population falls into one of three categories: (S)usceptible, (I)nfected, or (R)ecovered. We assume that any population member who has recovered from the disease is immune to it, and those that have not are susceptible to infection.

We let

$S = S(t) =$ The fraction of the population susceptible to infection.

$I = I(t) =$ The fraction of the population currently infected.

$R = R(t) =$ The fraction of the population no longer susceptible to infection.

Note that $R(t)$ includes those victims who have died[3]

Drill #440:

Assuming that no members are entering or leaving the population (by births, deaths from other diseases, or migration), explain why $S + I + R = 1$.

Since the disease spreads by contact between a susceptible and an infected individual, we will assume that the number of susceptible population members is decreasing (you cannot get the disease twice) and the rate of decrease is proportional to the number of susceptible and the number of infected currently present. This says that

$$\frac{dS}{dt} = -aSI$$

for some positive constant, a. The constant a is called the **transmission rate**. (Why?)

Drill #441:

Explain how we know that $\frac{dS}{dt}$ must be negative.

Since the only way to become immune is to recover from the disease, we also assume that the rate of change of R is proportional to the number of infected individuals present. This means that

$$\frac{dR}{dt} = bI$$

for some positive constant b. The constant b is called the **recovery rate**. (Why?)

---

[3]They have "recovered" in the sense that they can no longer be infected.

Problem #442:

(a) Explain how we know that $\frac{dR}{dt}$ must be positive.

(b) Show that
$$\frac{dI}{dt} = (aS - b)I.$$

(c) Use the information in part (b) to show that the number of infected is increasing when $S > \frac{b}{a}$ and decreasing when $S < \frac{b}{a}$.

(d) Show that
$$\frac{d^2 I}{dt^2} = a^2 I \left[S^2 - \left(\frac{2b}{a} + I \right) S + \left(\frac{b}{a} \right)^2 \right]$$

and use this to show that $\frac{d^2 I}{dt^2} < 0$ when

$$\frac{b}{a} + \left(\frac{I}{2} - \sqrt{\left(\frac{I}{2} \right)^2 + \frac{bI}{a}} \right) < S < \frac{b}{a} + \left(\frac{I}{2} + \sqrt{\left(\frac{I}{2} \right)^2 + \frac{bI}{a}} \right)$$

and is positive otherwise.

Putting this together we see that the number of infected is increasing and accelerating when

$$\frac{b}{a} + \left(\frac{I}{2} + \sqrt{\left(\frac{I}{2} \right)^2 + \frac{bI}{a}} \right) < S < 1$$

and increasing, but slowing down, when

$$\frac{b}{a} < S < \frac{b}{a} + \left(\frac{I}{2} + \sqrt{\left(\frac{I}{2} \right)^2 + \frac{bI}{a}} \right).$$

When $S < \frac{b}{a}$ it is decreasing.

The Tractrix

"Truckin', got my chips cashed in
Keep truckin', like the do-dah man
Together, more or less in line
Just keep truckin' on."

– The Grateful Dead (1967-1995)

Problem #443:

We first looked at the curve called the tractrix in Problem #252 of Section 6.3. Consider reviewing that problem before you proceed.

Recall that initially the center of the rear axle of the tractor is at the origin and the center of the rear axle of the trailer is at the point $(1,0)$ Also we assumed that the tractor pulls the front wheels vertically up the y-axis and that the rear wheels don't slip.

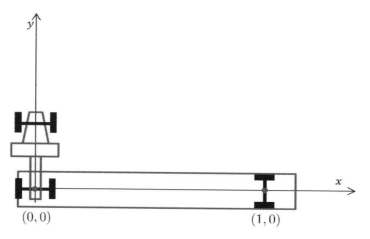

In Problem #252 we showed that the path followed by the center of the rear axle of the trailer follows, $y = y(t)$, must satisfy the IVP:

$$\frac{dy}{dx} = -\frac{\sqrt{1-x^2}}{x}, \quad y(1) = 0. \tag{10.11}$$

(a) Show that $y = \ln\left(\frac{1+\sqrt{1-x^2}}{x}\right) - \sqrt{1-x^2}$ satisfies the IVP in part (a). Graph this formula. Does it match your intuition about the shape of the curve? Does it match the graph you found using Euler's Method in Section 252?

You will learn how to derive this solution from IVP (10.11) when you take Integral Calculus.

(b) How far will the tractor have gone (in trailer lengths) before the trailer is within one degree of vertical?

The Pursuit Problem

"Our scientific power has outrun our spiritual power. We have guided missiles and misguided men."

— Martin Luther King, Jr. (1929-1968)

Like the the tractrix problem above, we first looked at this pursuit curve in Problem #253 of Section 6.3. Consider reviewing that problem before you proceed.

Problem #444:

In Problem #253 we assumed that rocket R starting is traveling vertically up the line $x = 1$ at a constant speed v. When the rocket reaches the point $(1, 0)$, a missile M is fired from the origin directly at the rocket.

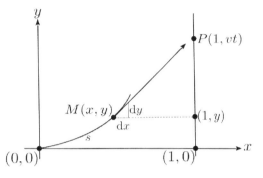

Assuming that the missile is always aimed directly at the rocket, and that it travels at a speed which is[4] k times the speed of the rocket ($k > 1$) we showed in Problem #253 that the curve described by the path the missile will satisfy the IVP:

$$\frac{\mathrm{d}y}{\mathrm{d}x} = \frac{\frac{s}{k} - y}{1 - x}, \quad y(0) = 0. \tag{10.12}$$

where s denotes the length of the the missile's path at time t.

(a) Use IVP (10.12) to show that the missile's path must satisfy the (second order) differential equation

$$(1 - x)\frac{\mathrm{d}^2 y}{\mathrm{d}x^2} = \frac{1}{k}\frac{\mathrm{d}s}{\mathrm{d}x} = \frac{1}{k}\sqrt{1 + \left(\frac{\mathrm{d}y}{\mathrm{d}x}\right)^2}$$

with the initial conditions: $y(0) = 0$ and $\left.\frac{\mathrm{d}y}{\mathrm{d}x}\right|_{x=0} = 0$.

(b) Show that

$$y = \frac{1}{2}\left(\frac{k}{k+1}(1 - x)^{\frac{k+1}{k}} - \frac{k}{k-1}(1 - x)^{\frac{k-1}{k}}\right) + \frac{k}{k^2 - 1}$$

satisfies the differential equation and initial conditions in part (a).

(c) Find how long it takes for the missile to catch the rocket for $k = 3$, $k = 2$, and $k = 1.1$. Does this make sense to you physically? Explain

---

[4]In Problem #253 we took $k = 1.5$. Here we look at the more general problem by letting $k > 1$ be arbitrar.

Chapter 11

Limits and L'Hôpital's Rule

 See also the TRIUMPHS Primary Source Project in Appendix A.3.

In our fishery model in the previous chapter we referred to the carrying capacity of the lake, $P = 100$, as an "asymptote." Loosely speaking, an asymptote is a line that the graph of a function "gets close to." Any line can be an asymptote but we will be primarily interested in horizontal asymptotes (lines like the graph of $y = 5$) and vertical asymptotes (lines like the graph of $x = 5$).

11.1 Horizontal Asymptotes as Limits "at Infinity"

Take another look at the graph of the Witch of Agnesi at the right. You can readily see that, as x moves to the right y gets "closer and closer" to zero. This is the essential idea but the phrase "closer and closer" is too vague for our purpose.

Here's why. In the sketch below, x is moving to the right. As you can see x gets "closer and closer" to a. But it also gets "closer and closer" to both b and c.

$$x \longrightarrow \quad a \quad b \qquad c$$

While x is getting "closer and closer" to all three of a, b, and c it is only getting "arbitrarily close" to a, and "arbitrarily close" is what we usually mean when we say "closer and closer." When x is getting "arbitrarily close[1]" to a we say that x approaches and we write $x \to a$.

It is clear that the graph of the Witch comes arbitrarily close to the line $y = 0$ so we write $y \to 0$ as $x \to \infty$. This is spoken aloud as "y approaches zero as x approaches infinity."

---

[1] The phrase "arbitrarily close" will be adequate for our present purposes but eventually even that will not be sufficiently precise. The need for precise language is real and very delicate. We will return to this matter Chapter 16.3. For now be aware that we are not quite done perfecting the meaning of "arbitrarily close."

Limit Notation

Of course, the notion of "approaching infinity" is troublesome as well. That we speak in this fashion has more to do with the construction of the English language than with the mathematics being represented. Since y is proceeding toward zero (an actual number) it makes sense to say "y approaches zero." The notation "$y \to 0$" captures this idea nicely. And since we usually pronounce the symbol ∞ as "infinity" it feels natural to write $x \to \infty$ and to speak this aloud as "x approaches infinity" as if ∞ is a place we could get to. But as we've observed, this is absurd. Properly speaking the symbols "$x \to \infty$" should be spoken aloud as "x increases without bound," but nearly everyone says "x approaches infinity" instead because it is a less cumbersome phrase. Like so much of mathematics this is perfectly clear once the underlying ideas have been internalized, but in the beginning it is can be quite confusing. Be patient with this.

An alternative, and more common notation is: $\lim_{x \to \infty} \frac{1}{1+x^2} = 0$ which we read aloud as "The limit as x approaches infinity of one over one plus x squared is equal to zero" but this also collides with the construction of the English language. From the discussion above we know that "$x \to \infty$" indicates that x increases without bound, but when we write $\lim_{x \to \infty} \frac{1}{1+x^2} = 0$ what exactly does "$= 0$" mean? What is equal to zero? Certainly the Witch is never equal to zero since its graph never crosses (or even touches) the x axis.

The expression $\lim_{x \to \infty} \frac{1}{1+x^2} = 0$ is making a very specific statement, one that is difficult to capture in a natural language like English. It says that the expression $\frac{1}{1+x^2}$ is approaching a particular value (zero) as x approaches ∞. The equals sign doesn't indicate that the function, $\frac{1}{1+x^2}$ actually equals that value. Instead it is the **limit** of $\frac{1}{1+x^2}$ which is equal to zero. Whether the function itself is ever equal to the limit, or not, is irrelevant. We're interested in what it gets arbitrarily close to.

We are treading at the edge of some very deep waters here so we will not attempt to address all of the nuances yet. Instead we will simply interpret the formula $\lim_{x \to \infty} \frac{1}{1+x^2} = 0$ to mean that as x approaches infinity ($x \to \infty$) the expression $\frac{1}{1+x^2}$ approaches zero $\left(\frac{1}{1+x^2} \to 0 \right)$.

In Chapter 16 we will replace "arbitrarily close" with something much more precise. Indeed, finding a better way to say "arbitrarily close" will be the culmination of our efforts. This is what will allow us to finally replace differentials with a solid theoretical foundation.

But for now, we have enough to give our first definition of the limit concept.

Definition 12: **An Intuitive Definition of a Limit at $\pm\infty$**

1. If, as $x \to \infty$, $f(x)$ gets arbitrarily close to some number A, we write
$$\lim_{x \to \infty} f(x) = A.$$

2. If, as $x \to -\infty$, $f(x)$ gets arbitrarily close to some number A, we write
$$\lim_{x \to -\infty} f(x) = A.$$

Example #65:

As we've observed, for very large positive values of x, the function $W(x) = \frac{1}{1+x^2}$ will be close to zero (the larger the x value, the closer $\frac{1}{1+x^2}$ is to zero).

Likewise, for very large, negative values of x, $W(x)$ will also get close to zero so:

$$\lim_{x \to -\infty} \frac{1}{1+x^2} = \lim_{x \to \infty} \frac{1}{1+x^2} = 0.$$

End Of Example #65

We used the Witch for our first example because we are quite familiar with its properties from our earlier investigations. However we needn't have started with so complex a function.

Drill #445: Use the graph of $f(x) = \frac{1}{x}$ to argue that $\lim_{x \to \infty} \frac{1}{x} = 0$ and $\lim_{x \to -\infty} \frac{1}{x} = 0$.

The limit concept is deeply abstract. We are introducing it here because, (1) the limit idea gives us a handy way to define asymptotes, and (2) when we return to in in Chapter 16 it will be helpful if you are comfortable with the notation and the essential underlying idea.

We have the following definition.

Definition 13: Horizontal Asymptotes

(a) If $\lim_{x \to \infty} f(x) = A$ then the graph of the function $f(x)$ has the horizontal asymptote, $y = A$.

(b) If $\lim_{x \to -\infty} f(x) = B$ then the graph of the function $f(x)$ has the horizontal asymptote, $y = B$.

as in the next three theorems.

In Definition #13 it will frequently be true that A and B are the same number. In that case we express both limits in the more compact form: $\lim_{x \to \pm\infty} f(x) = A$.

Problem #446:

(a) Justify the following assertion as clearly and as carefully as you can: $\lim_{x \to \infty} 5 = 5$.

(b) Generalize the statement in part (a).

From Problem #446 we know $\lim\limits_{x \to \infty} 5 = 5$ and from Drill #445 we know that $\lim\limits_{x \to \infty} \dfrac{1}{x} = 0$. Does it follow that

$$\lim_{x \to \infty} \left(5 + \frac{1}{x} \right) = \left(\lim_{x \to \infty} 5 \right) + \left(\lim_{x \to \infty} \frac{1}{x} \right) = 5 + 0 = 5?$$

Yes, of course it does. In fact the following theorem is true.

Theorem 8: [The Limit of a Sum]
If $\lim\limits_{x \to \pm\infty} f(x) = L$ and $\lim\limits_{x \to \pm\infty} g(x) = M$, then

$$\lim_{x \to \pm\infty} [f(x) + g(x)] = L + M = \lim_{x \to \pm\infty} f(x) + \lim_{x \to \pm\infty} g(x).$$

This can be expressed in words with the phrase, "The limit of a sum is the sum of the limits." The following two theorems are not quite as intuitive as Theorem 8, but they are also true.

Theorem 9: [The Limit of a Product]
If $\lim\limits_{x \to \pm\infty} f(x) = L$ and $\lim\limits_{x \to \pm\infty} g(x) = M$ then

$$\lim_{x \to \pm\infty} (f(x) \cdot g(x)) = \left(\lim_{x \to \pm\infty} f(x) \right) \cdot \left(\lim_{x \to \pm\infty} g(x) \right) = L \cdot M.$$

This can be expressed in words with the phrase "The limit of a product is the product of the limits."

Theorem 10: [The Limit of a Quotient]
If $\lim\limits_{x \to \pm\infty} f(x) = L$ and $\lim\limits_{x \to \pm\infty} g(x) = M \neq 0$ then

$$\lim_{x \to \pm\infty} \frac{f(x)}{g(x)} = \frac{\lim\limits_{x \to \pm\infty} f(x)}{\lim\limits_{x \to \pm\infty} g(x)} = \frac{L}{M}.$$

This can be expressed in words with the phrase "The limit of a quotient is the quotient of the limits."

Example #66:
Notice that in Theorem 10 we specifically required that $\lim\limits_{x \to \infty} g(x) = M \neq 0$. This is necessary because, as we stated quite emphatically in Digression #5, division by zero is an undefined concept. Thus if $\lim\limits_{x \to \infty} f(x)$ is equal to, say 1, and $\lim\limits_{x \to \infty} g(x) = 0$ then

$$\frac{\lim\limits_{x \to \infty} f(x)}{\lim\limits_{x \to \infty} g(x)} \quad \text{appears to be equal to} \quad \frac{1}{0}.$$

But this is meaningless, so we say that $\lim\limits_{x\to\infty} \dfrac{f(x)}{g(x)}$ does not exist, or equivalently that it is undefined.

End Of Example #66

Like the differentiation rules, when these limit theorems are used together they allow us to break a large problem into smaller, more tractable, pieces. Here are some examples.

Example #67:

We'd like to find the horizontal asymptotes of $y = \frac{2}{x} - \frac{3}{x^2}$ if any exist.

In this example we will write down all of the details of our computation. As you get more comfortable, you will probably abbreviate the process by doing much of this in your head. That's good, but also be sure you can fill in all of the details when needed. You will need to be able to do this when the problems get more complex.

From Definition #13 we see that if horizontal asymptotes exist they will be the lines $y = \lim\limits_{x\to\infty} \left(\dfrac{2}{x} - \dfrac{3}{x^2} \right)$ and $y = \lim\limits_{x\to-\infty} \left(\dfrac{2}{x} - \dfrac{3}{x^2} \right)$ so we need to evaluate these limits. For the first limit we see from Theorem 8 that

$$\lim_{x\to\infty} \left(\frac{2}{x} - \frac{3}{x^2} \right) = \lim_{x\to\infty} \frac{2}{x} - \lim_{x\to\infty} \frac{3}{x^2}.$$

Applying Theorem 9 (several times) we have

$$\lim_{x\to\infty} \left(\frac{2}{x} - \frac{3}{x^2} \right) = \underbrace{\left(\lim_{x\to\infty} 2 \right)}_{=2} \cdot \underbrace{\left(\lim_{x\to\infty} \frac{1}{x} \right)}_{=0} - \underbrace{\left(\lim_{x\to\infty} 3 \right)}_{=3} \cdot \underbrace{\left(\lim_{x\to\infty} \frac{1}{x} \right)}_{=0} \cdot \underbrace{\left(\lim_{x\to\infty} \frac{1}{x} \right)}_{=0} = 0. \qquad (11.1)$$

So the horizontal asymptote will be $y = 0$.

Drill #447: Evaluate $\lim\limits_{x\to-\infty} \left(\frac{2}{x} - \frac{3}{x^2} \right)$. Justify each step by citing the appropriate theorem or fact.

End Of Example #67

Example #68:

To find one horizontal asymptote of $y = \frac{x-1}{x}$ we evaluate:

$$\lim_{x\to-\infty} \frac{x-1}{x} = \lim_{x\to-\infty} \left(1 - \frac{1}{x} \right) = 1.$$

Drill #448: Evaluate $\lim\limits_{x\to\infty} \frac{x-1}{x}$ to find the other asymptote, if it exists.

End Of Example #68

Problem #449:
Find the horizontal asymptotes of the graphs of the following functions.

(a) $y = 5$ **(b)** $y = \frac{1}{x-2} + 3$ **(c)** $y = \frac{3x-5}{x-2}$ **(d)** $y = \frac{|x|}{x-1}$

Of course, not every curve has a horizontal asymptote so not every function has a limit as x approaches $\pm\infty$. For example, consider the curves $y = x^2$ and $y = x^3$. Clearly these curves have no horizontal asymptotes because as[2] $x \to \pm\infty$ they don't get close to a real number. In fact they either continue to rise or continue to drop as $x \to \pm\infty$.

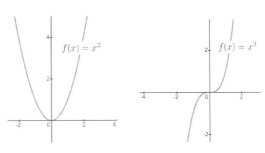

We represent this with the notation:

$$\lim_{x\to\infty} x^2 = \infty, \quad \lim_{x\to-\infty} x^2 = \infty, \quad \lim_{x\to\infty} x^3 = \infty, \quad \lim_{x\to-\infty} x^3 = -\infty.$$

But once again we need to keep in mind that the symbol "∞" does not represent a number so saying that something is "equal" to ∞ is meaningless[3]. What we mean when we write

$$\lim_{x\to\infty} x^2 = \infty$$

is that "as x increases without bound x squared increases without bound."

Drill #450: Similarly $\lim\limits_{x\to-\infty} x^3 = -\infty$ means that as $x \to -\infty$ $x^3 \to -\infty$. How would we say this in words?

It is especially important to keep in mind that ∞ is not a number when evaluating a limit like: $\lim\limits_{x\to\infty} (x^3 - 21x^2)$.

It is very tempting to attack this problem by noticing that each term is increasing without bound and write $\infty - \infty = 0$, but in fact this limit is not zero. Can you see what the limit is? Give it some thought and take your best guess. We'll come back to it shortly.

It is very clear that the limit: $\lim\limits_{x\to\infty} (x - x)$ is zero. After all, $x - x$ is constantly equal to zero so we have $\lim\limits_{x\to\infty} (x - x) = \lim\limits_{x\to\infty} 0 = 0$. So it seems to be clear that $\lim\limits_{x\to\infty} (x - x) = \infty - \infty = 0$. Anything minus itself has to be zero doesn't it? Even grandmother - grandmother must be zero, right?

But now consider this limit: $\lim\limits_{x\to\infty} [(x + 7) - (x - 5)]$. Both $(x+7) \to \infty$ and $(x-5) \to \infty$ so $\lim\limits_{x\to\infty} [(x + 7) - (x - 5)]$ also has the form $\infty - \infty$ doesn't it? But $(x+7) - (x - 5)$ is constantly

---

[2] Note that we have used the plus-or-minus ($\pm$) symbol to combine two limits into a single expression.
[3] Unless we define its meaning ourselves. How would you define the phrase "x equals infinity?"

equal to 12 so, we have

$$\lim_{x \to \infty} [(x + 7) - (x - 5)] = \lim_{x \to \infty} 12 = 12.$$

Thus it appears that $\infty - \infty$ can be zero, **and** that $\infty - \infty$ can be 12. But $0 \neq 12$ so that can't be! Moreover there is nothing special about 12. We could have chosen any number to make our point. So we conclude that $\infty - \infty$ is meaningless. Equivalently, we say it is undefined.

The source of the difficulty here is that only numbers can be subtracted[4]. But neither ∞ nor grandmother is a number so the expressions $\infty - \infty$ and grandmother - grandmother are utter nonsense.

Drill #451:
Find two functions, $f(x)$ and $g(x)$ such that as $x \to \infty$ both $f(x) \to \infty$ and $g(x) \to \infty$ but $\lim_{x \to \infty} [f(x) - g(x)]$ is equal to each of the following.

(a) 10 **(c)** 83, 744 **(e)** $\sqrt{2}$

(b) -21 **(d)** π **(f)** Any real number

Limits can be deceptive so be careful. It can be helpful to have built in notational cues to remind ourselves that these are subtle problems. When we are working with limits we will use the notation $(\to \infty)$ to remind ourselves that ∞ is not a number[5].

Returning to the limit $\lim_{x \to \infty} (x^3 - 21x^2)$ and using this notational cue we have

$$\lim_{x \to \infty} (x^3 - 21x^2) = (\to \infty) - (\to \infty).$$

This says that this limit consists of something which is approaching ∞ (increasing without bound) minus something else which is approaching ∞ (again, increasing without bound). When we say it like this – more importantly when we think about it like this – we can see that the value of the limit will depend upon precisely how the two parts increase without bound.

We now know that this limit is not necessarily equal to zero, but how can we discover what it actually is equal to? As in much of Calculus we need to re-express our formulas algebraically to see what is going on.

Rewriting $x^3 - 21x^2$ as $x^3 \left(1 - \frac{21}{x}\right)$ we have

$$\lim_{x \to \infty} (x^3 - 21x^2) = \lim_{x \to \infty} \left(x^3(1 - 21/x)\right)$$

$$= \lim_{x \to \infty} x^3 \cdot \left(1 - 21/x\right)^{0}$$

$$= (\to \infty) \cdot (\to 1).$$

[4]Your teacher will tell you, if you ask, that we aren't being entirely honest here. Mathematicians routinely add, subtract, multiply, and divide lots of things that you probably would not recognize as numbers. But grandmothers, and infinities are not among them.

[5]This is not a standard notation so you probably won't see it anywhere except in this textbook.

This says that we have an expression which is increasing without bound multiplied by an expression which approaches the number one. Obviously the product will also increase without bound so we write $\lim_{x \to \infty} (x^3 - 21x^2) = \infty$.

Similarly[6] evaluating $\lim_{x \to -\infty} (x^3 + 21x^2)$ gives

$$\lim_{x \to -\infty} (x^3 + 21x^2) = \lim_{x \to -\infty} \left(x^3(1 + 21/x) \right)$$

$$= \left[\lim_{x \to -\infty} x^3 \cdot \left(1 + \underset{}{21/x} \right) \right]$$

$$= (\to -\infty) \cdot (\to 1)$$

$$= -\infty.$$

This makes sense intuitively. We would expect that for large values of x (either positive or negative), x^3 will continually outgrow ("approach infinity" faster than) $21x^2$.

We have established that, because ∞ is not a number, the expression $\infty - \infty$ does not make sense. What about $\frac{\infty}{\infty}$? Is it true that $\frac{\infty}{\infty} = 1$?

No, of course not. The expression $\frac{\infty}{\infty}$ is meaningless for the same reason that ∞ - ∞ is meaningless.

Example #69:

Consider $\lim_{x \to \infty} \frac{x^4 + x^2}{5x^4 - 100x}$. It is tempting to write $\frac{\infty}{\infty} = 1$, but as we have observed, ∞ is not a number so this makes no more sense than $\infty - \infty = 0$.

Once again, the key is to re-express the function algebraically. Factoring out the highest power of the variable from both the numerator and the denominator[7] we see that

$$\lim_{x \to \infty} \frac{x^4 + x^2}{5x^4 - 100x} = \lim_{x \to \infty} \frac{x^4(1 + 1/x^2)}{x^4(5 - 100/x^3)} = \lim_{x \to \infty} \left[\frac{x^4}{x^4} \cdot \frac{1 + 1/x^2}{5 - 100/x^4} \right]$$

$$= 1 \cdot \left(\to \frac{1}{5} \right)$$

$$= \frac{1}{5}.$$

End Of Example #69

Example #62: (Continued from Section 9.1)

Recall that we did not complete Example 62 because we did not previously have any way to determine what happens to the graph of $y(x) = \frac{2 + 2x^2 + 2x^4}{1 + x^4}$ as $x \to \infty$ or as $x \to -\infty$. We

---

[6]This is not the same limit. Look closely.

[7]You may well ask, "How did we know to do that?" The answer is very unsatisfying. We were taught this technique by our teachers, just as you are being taught now. We'd have been hard pressed to come up with it on our own.

do now. Finding what happens to the graph of $y(x) = \frac{2+2x^2+2x^4}{1+x^4}$ as $x \to \infty$ or as $x \to -\infty$ is equivalent to evaluating the following limits:

$$\lim_{x \to \infty} \frac{2 + 2x^2 + 2x^4}{1 + x^4} \quad \text{and} \quad \lim_{x \to -\infty} \frac{2 + 2x^2 + 2x^4}{1 + x^4}.$$

We will evaluate the first one and leave the second as a drill.

Proceeding as in Example #69 we see that

$$\lim_{x \to \infty} \frac{2 + 2x^2 + 2x^4}{1 + x^4} = \lim_{x \to \infty} \frac{x^4(2/x^4 + 2/x^2 + 2)}{x^4(1/x^4 + 1)}$$

$$= \lim_{x \to \infty} \frac{x^4}{x^4} \cdot \frac{2/x^4 + 2/x^2 + 2}{1/x^4 + 1}$$

$$= 2.$$

Drill #452: Show that $\lim\limits_{x \to -\infty} \frac{2+2x^2+2x^4}{1+x^4}$ is also equal to two.

We can now see that $y(x) = \frac{2+2x^2+2x^4}{1+x^4}$ has a **horizontal asymptote** at $y = 2$. If you haven't already done so consider graphing this function to confirm.

End Of Example #62

Drill #453:
Show that each of the following statements is true.

(a) $\lim\limits_{x \to \infty} \dfrac{x^5 + x^3}{5x^5 - 100x} = \frac{1}{5}$ **(d)** $\lim\limits_{x \to -\infty} \dfrac{x^5 + x^3}{5x^4 - 10x} = -\infty$ **(g)** $\lim\limits_{x \to \infty} \dfrac{x^5 + 2x^3}{5x^6 - x} = 0$

(b) $\lim\limits_{x \to -\infty} \dfrac{2x^5 + x^3}{5x^5 - x} = \frac{2}{5}$ **(e)** $\lim\limits_{x \to \infty} \dfrac{x - \frac{1}{x^3}}{5x - \frac{-8}{x^2}} = \frac{1}{5}$ **(h)** $\lim\limits_{x \to -\infty} \dfrac{x^5 + 2x^3}{5x^6 - x} = 0$

(c) $\lim\limits_{x \to \infty} \dfrac{x^5 + x^3}{5x^4 - 10x} = \infty$ **(f)** $\lim\limits_{x \to -\infty} \dfrac{x + \frac{1}{x^3}}{5x + \frac{-8}{x^2}} = \frac{1}{5}$

Example #70:

Do you think the function $y(x) = \sqrt{x^2 + 2} - \sqrt{x^2 + x}$ has any horizontal asymptotes? Take your best guess before we begin this example.

To find any horizontal asymptotes we have to evaluate the limits $\lim\limits_{x \to \pm\infty} \left(\sqrt{x^2 + 2} - \sqrt{x^2 + x} \right)$. First we'll find the limit as $x \to \infty$ and leave the limit as $x \to -\infty$ as a drill for you.

As always the trick is to rearrange this expression inside the limit algebraically – without changing its value – until we can see clearly what happens as $x \to \infty$.

The square roots seem to be the difficulty here. So we'd like to find a way to make them go away. The standard trick for this is to multiply by the conjugate[8] of $\sqrt{x^2 + 2} - \sqrt{x^2 + x}$, namely $\sqrt{x^2 + 2} + \sqrt{x^2 + x}$. Of course, if we do that then we need to divide by the conjugate as well. That way we've multiplied by 1 and have not changed the value of the expression. This won't actually eliminate the square roots as we will still have them in the denominator. But let's see what happens.

$$\lim_{x \to \infty} \left(\sqrt{x^2 + 2} - \sqrt{x^2 + x} \right) = \lim_{x \to \infty} \left(\sqrt{x^2 + 2} - \sqrt{x^2 + x} \right) \underbrace{\left(\frac{\sqrt{x^2 + 2} + \sqrt{x^2 + x}}{\sqrt{x^2 + 2} + \sqrt{x^2 + x}} \right)}_{=1}$$

$$= \lim_{x \to \infty} \left(\frac{(x^2 + 2) - (x^2 + x)}{\sqrt{x^2 + 2} + \sqrt{x^2 + x}} \right) = \lim_{x \to \infty} \left(\frac{2 - x}{\sqrt{x^2 + 2} + \sqrt{x^2 + x}} \right).$$

Factoring the highest power of x out of the numerator and denominator gives

$$\lim_{x \to \infty} \left(\sqrt{x^2 + 2} - \sqrt{x^2 + x} \right) = \lim_{x \to \infty} \frac{x \left(2/x - 1 \right)}{\sqrt{x^2} \left(\sqrt{1 + 2/x^2} + \sqrt{1 + 1/x} \right)}$$

and since $\sqrt{x^2} = |x|$ we have

$$= \lim_{x \to \infty} \frac{x \left(2/x - 1 \right)}{|x| \left(\sqrt{1 + 2/x^2} + \sqrt{1 + 1/x} \right)}.$$

But we're evaluating a limit as $x \to \infty$. So, we're really only interested in large, positive values of x. In this case $|x| = x$ so

$$= \lim_{x \to \infty} \overset{=1}{\frac{x}{x}} \cdot \left[\frac{\overset{0}{2/x} - 1}{\sqrt{1 + \underset{0}{2/x^2}} + \sqrt{1 + \underset{0}{1/x}}} \right]$$

$$= -\frac{1}{2}.$$

Did you guess right? If you did, either you have a very strong intuition for these kinds of problems or you just had a moment of blind luck. So don't just pat yourself on the back and walk away. Be sure to take a moment to figure out whether it was intuition or luck. You don't want to confuse them.

If you guessed wrong, or (most likely) were unable to come up with a guess don't fret about it. You're normal. But be sure you review and understand the steps to this solution so you can begin to build some intuition about such problems.

This problem looked pretty intimidating, but once we got going in the right direction, it was all Algebra from there. Notice how the absolute value came into play. In this problem it

---

[8]We are using the identity $(A - B)(A + B) = A^2 - B^2$ to square both terms and get rid of the square roots. The factors $A + B$ and $A - B$ are mutually conjugate.

wasn't an issue since we were considering only positive values of x. But consider what would happen if x was negative, if $x \to -\infty$. In this case[9], $|x| = -x$.

Digression #20: $\sqrt{x^2} = |x|$

It is not true that $\sqrt{x^2} = x$, although this is an easy mistake to make. It is not true because the square root function, $\sqrt{x}$, is the functional inverse of the function

$$f(x) = x^2, \text{ with domain } x \geq 0.$$

Note that the domain restriction means that $\sqrt{x}$ always returns a positive number. Thus $\sqrt{2^2} = 2$, but $\sqrt{(-2)^2} = 2$, also. Similarly,

$$\sqrt{3^2} = \sqrt{(-3)^2} = 3, \ \sqrt{10^2} = \sqrt{(-10)^2} = 10, \text{ and in general } \sqrt{x^2} = |x|.$$

When x is negative $\sqrt{x^2} = -x$ because when x negative $-x$ is positive.

—————————— End Of Digression #20 ——————————

Drill #454:

Try to guess the value of $\lim\limits_{x \to -\infty} \left(\sqrt{x^2 + 2} - \sqrt{x^2 + x} \right)$ and then evaluate the limit to see if you guessed correctly.

End Of Example #70

Drill #455:
Determine the following limits.

(a) $\lim\limits_{x \to \infty} \sqrt{x^2 + x} - x$

(b) $\lim\limits_{x \to -\infty} \sqrt{x^2 + x} - x$

(c) $\lim\limits_{x \to \infty} \dfrac{1}{\sqrt{x + 1} - \sqrt{4x + 1}}$

(d) $\lim\limits_{x \to \infty} \dfrac{\sqrt{x^2 + 2} - \sqrt{x^2 + x}}{\sqrt{x^2 + 2} - \sqrt{x^2 - x}}$

(e) $\lim\limits_{x \to -\infty} \dfrac{\sqrt{x^2 + 2} - \sqrt{x^2 + x}}{\sqrt{x^2 + 2} - \sqrt{x^2 - x}}$

11.2 The Squeeze Theorem

It is clear from the graph at the right that $\lim\limits_{x \to \infty} \sin(x)$ does not exist since the $\sin(x)$ has no horizontal asymptotes. To say that this limit does not exist means that $y = \sin(x)$ is not approaching any particular value as $x \to \infty$. It's not even "approaching" $+\infty$ or $-\infty$ since it is bounded both above and below.

---

[9]This is important. If you don't see why $|x| = -x$ when $x < 0$ ask your teacher about it.

Now how about this limit: $\lim\limits_{x\to\infty}\frac{\sin(x)}{x}$? Since $\lim\limits_{x\to\infty}\sin(x)$ does not exist we can't apply Theorem 10. Neither is it of the form $\frac{(\to\infty)}{(\to\infty)}$, so none of the techniques we've used before will help us.

We need a new idea.

Look at the graph of $f(x)=\frac{\sin(x)}{x}$ below.

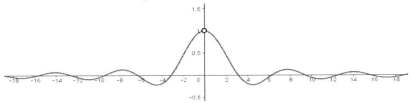

Can you see that the horizontal asymptote is $y=0$?

It certainly looks like $y=0$ is an asymptote in both directions which seems to suggest that

$$\lim_{x\to\infty}\frac{\sin(x)}{x}=\lim_{x\to-\infty}\frac{\sin(x)}{x}=0.$$

This is correct, but is there a way to see this algebraically? After all, this graph could just as easily support the conclusion that $y=0.00000001$ (or $y=$ any other number which is extremely close to zero) is the asymptote. We don't want to draw conclusions from a picture, but it is difficult to see what we can do, isn't it?

We will analyze what happens when $x\to\infty$ and leave the case $x\to-\infty$ as a drill for you.

Let's "disassemble" our function in order to understand it better. The function $f(x)=\frac{\sin(x)}{x}$ clearly comes in two parts: $\sin(x)$ and $\frac{1}{x}$. Because $-1\le\sin(x)\le 1$ we know that $-\frac{1}{x}\le\frac{\sin(x)}{x}\le\frac{1}{x}$. If we graph $y=\frac{\sin(x)}{x}$, $y=\frac{1}{x}$, and $y=-\frac{1}{x}$ together as in the sketch at the right we see that for positive values of x the graph of $y=\frac{\sin(x)}{x}$ is always caught between the graph of $y=\frac{1}{x}$ and $y=-\frac{1}{x}$.

We know that both $\pm\frac{1}{x}\to 0$ as $x\to\infty$. Since $\frac{\sin(x)}{x}$ is caught between $\frac{1}{x}$ and $-\frac{1}{x}$ it follows that, for positive values of x, the highest points on the graph of $\frac{\sin(x)}{x}$ must also approach zero as $x\to\infty$. Therefore $\lim\limits_{x\to\infty}\frac{\sin(x)}{x}=0$.

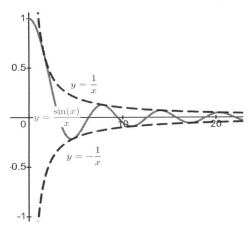

Drill #456:

Show that for negative values of x, $-\frac{1}{x}\le\frac{\sin(x)}{x}\le\frac{1}{x}$ also, so that $\lim\limits_{x\to-\infty}\frac{\sin(x)}{x}=0$ as well.

This idea is often called the Squeeze Theorem or the Sandwich Theorem.

Theorem 11: [The Squeeze Theorem, (when $x \to \pm\infty$)]
There are two cases:

1. If $\alpha(x) \leq f(x) \leq \beta(x)$ on some interval, (c, ∞) and

$$\lim_{x \to \infty} \alpha(x) = \lim_{x \to \infty} \beta(x) = L$$

then $\lim_{x \to \infty} f(x) = L$ also.

2. If $\alpha(x) \leq f(x) \leq \beta(x)$ on some interval, $(-\infty, c)$ and

$$\lim_{x \to \infty} \alpha(x) = \lim_{x \to -\infty} \beta(x) = L$$

then $\lim_{x \to \infty} f(x) = L$ also.

In the previous example, notice that we had $\frac{-1}{x} \leq \frac{\sin(x)}{x} \leq \frac{1}{x}$ for all $x \neq 0$, but this is more than is actually required. We only need for the inequality to be satisfied when x sufficiently large, in either the positive or negative direction. That's why we only require that $\alpha(x) \leq f(x) \leq \beta(x)$ on the interval (c, ∞) (positive case) or $(-\infty, c)$ (negative case) rather than for all values of x.

Problem #457:

Use the Squeeze Theorem to determine each of the following limits:

(a) $\lim_{x \to \infty} \dfrac{x \cos(x)}{x^2 + 1}$

(b) $\lim_{x \to -\infty} \dfrac{x \cos(x)}{x^2 + 1}$

(c) $\lim_{x \to \infty} \dfrac{\lfloor x \rfloor}{x^2}$, where $\lfloor x \rfloor$ represents the greatest integer[10] less than or equal to x.

Back in Section 7.6 you showed that $y(t) = e^{-\frac{t}{2}} \left[\cos\left(\frac{\sqrt{3}}{2} t\right) + \sin\left(\frac{\sqrt{3}}{2} t\right) \right]$ satisfies the differential equation of damped oscillation (oscillation with resistance):

$$\frac{d^2 y}{dt^2} + \frac{dy}{dt} + y = 0.$$

Since $y(t)$ is called a damped oscillator what do you expect $\lim_{t \to \infty} y(t)$ to be equal to? Guess, if you aren't sure.

---

[10]This is called the "greatest integer" function in mathematics, and the "floor" function in computer science. It rounds down to the greatest integer. For example $\lfloor 5.7 \rfloor = 5, \lfloor 2 \rfloor = 2, \lfloor \pi \rfloor = 3$, etc.

Problem #458:
Use the squeeze theorem to compute

$$\lim_{t \to \infty} e^{-\frac{t}{2}} \left[\cos\left(\frac{\sqrt{3}}{2} t \right) + \sin\left(\frac{\sqrt{3}}{2} t \right) \right].$$

Is this consistent with your guess? Explain.

11.3   Vertical Asymptotes

It should be clear from the sketch at the right that in addition to the horizontal asymptote $y = 0$, the graph of $y = \frac{1}{x}$ also has a vertical asymptote of $x = 0$.

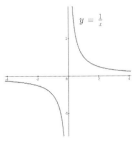

We can extend the ideas and the notation we've developed for horizontal asymptotes to handle vertical asymptotes as well. First note that since the expression $\frac{1}{x}$ is not defined for $x = 0$ we can't talk about the behavior of the function at zero. But we can talk about its behavior near zero. But the graph is very different depending on whether $x < 0$ or $x > 0$. We will focus first on positive values of x .

For x near zero, and positive, it is very clear what is happening. As $x \to 0$ the function continues to increase without bound. We capture this notationally[11] with

$$\lim_{\substack{x \to 0 \\ x > 0}} \frac{1}{x} = \infty. \tag{11.2}$$

The limit in Equation (11.2) is called a **right-hand limit** and is read aloud as "the limit as x approaches zero from the right, of one over x equals infinity."

The expression $x \to 0$ means that x is approaching the number zero. The qualification $x > 0$ specifies that it is approaching from the right. So writing $\lim_{\substack{x \to 0 \\ x > 0}} \frac{1}{x} = \infty$ means that as $x \to 0$ from the right, the function $\frac{1}{x}$ increases without bound[12].

If we restrict x to negative values then we see that[13]

$$\lim_{\substack{x \to 0 \\ x < 0}} \frac{1}{x} = -\infty. \tag{11.3}$$

---

[11]This notation is not universal. The standard notation is $\lim_{x \to 0^+} \frac{1}{x}$.

[12]This should probably be written as $\lim_{\substack{x \to 0 \\ x > 0}} \frac{1}{x} \to \infty$ but sadly, it has become standard to say, and to write, that this limit "equals infinity," which is absurd.

[13]Note that the sense of the inequality has changed from Equation (11.2). It is now "less than."

The limit in Equation (11.3) is called a **left-hand limit** and is read aloud as "the limit as x approaches zero from the left, of one over x equals negative infinity." Right- and left-hand limits are generically called **one-sided limits**. One-sided limits are important theoretical tools but their theoretical value is not important to us right now. We will discuss them in more depth in Section 15.1.

A function $f(x)$, will have a vertical asymptote as $x \to a$ if either of the one-sided limits is ∞ or $-\infty$ ($f(x)$ is increasing or decreasing without bound). We formalize this statement in the following definition.

Definition 14: **Vertical Asymptotes**

If
$$\lim_{\substack{x \to a \\ x > a}} f(x) = \pm\infty \text{ or } \lim_{\substack{x \to a \\ x < a}} f(x) = \pm\infty$$

then the line $x = a$ is a vertical asymptote of the graph of $y = f(x)$.

Drill #459:
Compute each of the following limits. Read the notation carefully.

(a) $\lim\limits_{\substack{x \to 3 \\ x > 3}} \frac{1}{(x-1)(x-3)}$

(b) $\lim\limits_{\substack{x \to 1 \\ x > 1}} \frac{1}{(x-1)(x-3)}$

(c) $\lim\limits_{\substack{x \to \frac{\pi}{2} \\ x > \frac{\pi}{2}}} \tan(x)$

Problem #460:
Find all vertical asymptotes of the graphs of each of the following functions.

(a) $f(x) = \frac{1}{x^2 - 1}$

(b) $f(x) = \frac{1}{(x^2 - 1)^2}$

(c) $f(x) = \frac{x-1}{x^2 - 4}$

(d) $f(x) = \frac{x-7}{x^2 - 5}$

(e) $f(x) = \tan(x)$

(f) $f(x) = \sec(x)$

11.4   Indeterminate Forms and L'Hôpital's Rule

Based on our experience so far it is tempting to conclude that we can locate vertical asymptotes by simply setting the denominator equal to zero and solving. But this is a naive conclusion as we will see next.

Example #71:

Consider $y = \frac{x-2}{x^2 - 4}$. Setting the denominator equal to zero yields $x = -2$ and $x = 2$, but only one of these is a vertical asymptote. Do you see which one?

Let's take a careful look at this example. By Definition #14 we will have a vertical asymptote when either one-sided limit of a function increases or decreases without bound, so we must evaluate each one-sided limit.

For $x = -2$, we have

$$\lim_{\substack{x \to -2 \\ x > -2}} \frac{x-2}{x^2-4} = \lim_{\substack{x \to -2 \\ x > -2}} \frac{x-2}{(x-2)(x+2)} = \lim_{\substack{x \to -2 \\ x > -2}} \overbrace{\left(\frac{x-2}{x-2}\right)}^{=1} \cdot \lim_{\substack{x \to -2 \\ x > -2}} \frac{1}{x+2} = 1 \cdot \frac{1}{(\to 0)} = \infty$$

So the line $x = -2$ is indeed a vertical asymptote.

Drill #461: Explain how you know the limit above is not $-\infty$.

Similarly

$$\lim_{\substack{x \to -2 \\ x < -2}} \frac{x-2}{x^2-4} = \lim_{\substack{x \to -2 \\ x < -2}} \frac{x-2}{(x-2)(x+2)} = \lim_{\substack{x \to -2 \\ x < -2}} \overbrace{\left(\frac{x-2}{x-2}\right)}^{=1} \cdot \lim_{\substack{x \to -2 \\ x < -2}} \frac{1}{x+2} = 1 \cdot \frac{1}{(\to 0)} = -\infty.$$

Drill #462: Explain how you know the limit above is not ∞.

We were careful to use one-sided limits to find the vertical asymptote at $x = -2$ because this is what Definition #14 calls for. Strictly speaking we only needed one of them, but since these limits were not equal we evaluated them both.

However, for $x = 2$, both one-sided limits are the same so we have

$$\lim_{x \to 2} \frac{x-2}{x^2-4} = \lim_{x \to 2} \frac{x-2}{(x-2)(x+2)} = \overbrace{\left(\lim_{x \to 2} \frac{x-2}{x-2}\right)}^{=1} \cdot \left(\lim_{x \to 2} \frac{1}{x+2}\right) = (\to 1) \cdot \left(\to \frac{1}{4}\right) = \frac{1}{4}.$$

Drill #463:
Confirm $\lim_{\substack{x \to 2 \\ x > 2}} \frac{x-2}{x^2-4} = \frac{1}{4}$ and $\lim_{\substack{x \to 2 \\ x < 2}} \frac{x-2}{x^2-4} = \frac{1}{4}$.

Observe that this limit has the form $\lim_{x \to 2} \frac{x-2}{x^2-4} = \frac{(\to 0)}{(\to 0)}$. A limit of this form is called an **Indeterminate Form**[14].

---

[14]There are other kinds of Indeterminate Forms. We will encounter them later in this chapter.

Problem #464:
Find all vertical asymptotes of the graphs of each of the following functions.

(a) $f(x) = \frac{x+2}{x^2-4}$ **(c)** $f(x) = \frac{x-2}{x^2-5x+6}$ **(e)** $f(x) = \frac{x}{x^3-1}$

(b) $f(x) = \frac{x-2}{x^2-4}$ **(d)** $f(x) = \frac{x-3}{x^2-5x+6}$ **(f)** $f(x) = \frac{x^2-x}{x^4-1}$

This example demonstrates that there is a difference between a function which does not exist at a point and a function with a vertical asymptote at a point. Notice that $g(x) = \frac{x-2}{x^2-4}$ is undefined at both $x = 2$ and $x = -2$, but it only has an asymptote at $x = -2$.

It also displays something subtle about limits. One would be tempted to say that

$$\frac{x-2}{x^2-4} = \frac{x-2}{(x-2)(x+2)} = \frac{1}{x+2},$$

and this is true when $x \neq 2$. However, if we graph the two functions, $g(x) = \frac{x-2}{x^2-4}$ and $f(x) = \frac{1}{x+2}$ we see that there is a small difference between them[15]:

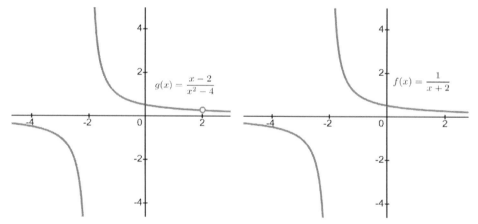

Do you see the difference? The value of $g(2)$ is not defined because $g(2) = \frac{2-2}{4-4}$ and we get a zero denominator. But no such difficulty occurs with f because $f(2) = \frac{1}{2+2} = \frac{1}{4}$.

So, when $x \neq 2$, $g(x)$ and $f(x)$ are the exactly the same. But they disagree when $x = 2$. More precisely $x = 2$ is not in the domain of $g(x)$ but it is in the domain of $f(x)$. Since the domains differ they must be different functions and it is incorrect to write $\frac{x-2}{x^2-4} = \frac{1}{x+2}$ even though it is true for all but one value of x.

End Of Example #71

---

[15]This discussion is also a cautionary tale about the use of graphing technology. These two graphs will appear to be identical if you use technology to graph them.

Problem #465:

Suppose $a \neq 0$ is a real number.

(a) Find all vertical asymptotes of $f(x) = \frac{x-a}{x^2-a^2}$.

(b) Does your solution of part (a) still work when $a = 0$?

Problem #466: The Folium of Descartes and Limits

Recall that in Problem #125 in Section 4.5 looked at the Folium of Descartes from Newton's dynamic point of view.

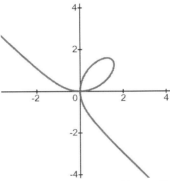

In that problem you showed that the fluents, $x(t) = \frac{3t}{1+t^3}$ and $y(t) = \frac{3t^2}{1+t^3}$ satisfy the equation of the Folium:

$$x^3 + y^3 = 3xy$$

and that $t = 0$ is the only value of t where $(x(t), y(t)) = (0,0)$. How then, can it be that the Folium crosses itself at the origin?

(a) In Problem #125 you determined that $y \geq 0$ when $t > -1$. Determine the values of t for which $x \geq 0$ and the which $x < 0$.

(b) Show that $\lim\limits_{t \to \pm\infty} x(t) = \lim\limits_{t \to \pm\infty} y(t) = 0$.

(c) Compute $\frac{dy}{dx} = \frac{\dot{y}}{\dot{x}}$ in terms of t and compute $\lim\limits_{t \to \pm\infty} \frac{\dot{y}}{\dot{x}}$. Is this consistent with what you see on the graph?

(d) Show that for $t \neq 0$, $t = \frac{y}{x}$ so that geometrically, t represents the slope of the line joining the origin to the point (x, y) on the graph of the Folium. Is this consistent with what you obtained in part a? Explain.

(e) Compute each of the following:

i. $\displaystyle\lim_{\substack{t\to-1\\t>-1}} x(t)$ **iii.** $\displaystyle\lim_{\substack{t\to-1\\t>-1}} y(t)$ **v.** $\displaystyle\lim_{\substack{t\to-1\\t>-1}} \frac{dy}{dx}$

ii. $\displaystyle\lim_{\substack{t\to-1\\t<-1}} x(t)$ **iv.** $\displaystyle\lim_{\substack{t\to-1\\t<-1}} y(t)$ **vi.** $\displaystyle\lim_{\substack{t\to-1\\t<-1}} \frac{dy}{dx}$

Is this consistent with the graph and the fact that t represents the slope from the origin to the point (x, y)? Explain.

L'Hôpital's Rule

We found earlier that $\displaystyle\lim_{x\to\infty} \frac{\sin(x)}{x} = 0$, so the function $y = \frac{\sin(x)}{x}$ has a horizontal asymptote at $y = 0$.

Does the graph of $y = \frac{\sin(x)}{x}$ have a vertical asymptote at $x = 0$? To answer this question we need to evaluate the limit $\displaystyle\lim_{x\to0} \frac{\sin(x)}{x}$. But how can we do that?

If we try the obvious ploy of just "plugging in" zero for x we get the indeterminate form $\frac{(\to 0)}{(\to 0)}$, and we know we need to proceed cautiously with an indeterminate form.

From the graph of $\frac{\sin(x)}{x}$ in the sketch at the right it would appear that $\frac{\sin(x)}{x} \to 1$ as $x \to 0$. This is correct, but we've learned to be wary of relying on graphs. It would be best to evaluate the limit by another technique if possible.

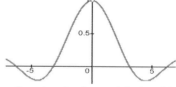

Can we apply some algebraic trick?

It is hard to see what it would be. There isn't much algebra we can do here. If there were other trigonometric functions involved we might be able to employ some trigonometric identity in the numerator, but there just isn't much we can do with $\sin(x)$. This problem poses a bit more of a challenge than the indeterminate forms we have dealt with so far. We need a new idea.

Since the $\sin(x)$ isn't helping maybe we can replace it with something simpler. Seriously. Give some thought to what might be a valid replacement before reading on[16].

The Principle of Local Linearity says that the graph of a function and its tangent line are locally indistinguishable. We're only interested in values of x near zero – locally around zero – so let's try replacing $\sin(x)$ with its tangent line.

Drill #467: Show that the line tangent to $y = \sin(x)$ at $x = 0$ is $y = x$.

Replacing $\sin(x)$ with x, we have[17]

$$\lim_{x\to0} \frac{\sin(x)}{x} \overset{?}{=} \lim_{x\to0} \frac{x}{x} = 1$$

---

[16]Remember that we're really only interested in values of x that are very close (infinitely close?) to zero.

[17]We've placed the question mark over the equals sign because we don't (yet) actually know that this is a valid approach. We're just trying out ideas at the moment.

which is consistent with what we see in the graph above. Our idea is showing some promise.

Example #72:

Let's try it again with $\lim\limits_{x \to 2} \frac{x^3 - 8}{x^2 - 4}$ which also has the indeterminate form $\frac{(\to 0)}{(\to 0)}$.

Drill #468:

(a) Show that the equation of the line tangent to $f(x) = x^3 - 8$ at $(2, 0)$ is: $y = 12(x - 2)$.

(b) Show that the equation of the line tangent to $g(x) = x^2 - 4$ at $(2, 0)$ is: $y = 4(x - 2)$.

Since we are evaluating the limit at $x = 2$ we will replace the numerator and denominator with their tangent lines at $x = 2$:

$$\lim_{x \to 2} \frac{x^3 - 8}{x^2 - 4} \overset{?}{=} \lim_{x \to 2} \frac{12(x - 2)}{4(x - 2)} = \lim_{x \to 2} \frac{12}{4} = 3.$$

For comparison we evaluate this one by methods we've used before. Specifically if we factor the numerator and denominator we get:

$$\lim_{x \to 2} \frac{x^3 - 8}{x^2 - 4} = \lim_{x \to 2} \frac{(x - 2)(x^2 + 2x + 4)}{(x - 2)(x + 2)} = \lim_{x \to 2} \frac{x^2 + 2x + 4}{x + 2} = \frac{2^2 + 2 \cdot 2 + 4}{2 + 2} = \frac{12}{4} = 3.$$

which is consistent with what we found previously. Our idea seems to be holding up.

End Of Example #72

Example #73:

Let's try one more. The limit $\lim\limits_{x \to 0} \frac{\tan(3x)}{\sin(2x)}$ is also the indeterminate form $\frac{(\to 0)}{(\to 0)}$ so we'll need the tangent lines of the numerator and denominator at $x = 0$ again.

Drill #469:

(a) Show that $y = 3x$ is the equation of the line tangent to $\tan(3x)$ at $x = 0$.

(b) Show that $y = 2x$ is the equation of the line tangent to $\sin(2x)$ at $x = 0$.

Replacing the numerator and denominator by their tangent lines at $x = 0$, we get

$$\lim_{x \to 0} \frac{\tan(3x)}{\sin(2x)} \overset{?}{=} \lim_{x \to 0} \frac{3x}{2x} = \frac{3}{2}.$$

Drill #470: Graph the equation $y = \frac{\tan(3x)}{\sin(2x)}$. Does it look like we've found the correct limit?

End Of Example #73

The idea of replacing the numerator and denominator of indeterminate forms with their tangent lines has worked in all of our examples so let's look at this problem in a more general context. If $f(x)$ and $g(x)$ are differentiable functions such that $f(a) = g(a) = 0$ then $\displaystyle\lim_{x \to a} \frac{f(x)}{g(x)}$ is an indeterminate form.

Drill #471:
Show that the equations of the lines tangent to $f(x)$ and $g(x)$ at $x = a$ are $y = f(a) + f'(a)(x-a)$ and $y = g(a) + g'(a)(x-a)$.

If we replace $f(x)$ and $g(x)$ with their tangent lines at $x = a$ we have[18]

$$\lim_{x \to a} \frac{f(x)}{g(x)} = \lim_{x \to a} \frac{f(a) + f'(a)(x-a)}{g(a) + g'(a)(x-a)}$$

$$= \lim_{x \to a} \frac{0 + f'(a)(x-a)}{0 + g'(a)(x-a)}$$

$$\lim_{x \to a} \frac{f(x)}{g(x)} = \frac{f'(a)}{g'(a)}$$

Johann Bernoulli
1667-1748

This is consistent with all of our examples above so it appears that the Principle of Local Linearity has led us in the right direction. All of the evidence we've gathered so far suggests rather strongly that when we are faced with the indeterminate form $\frac{(\to 0)}{(\to 0)}$ simply replacing the numerator and denominator with their tangent lines will work.

The Marquis de L'Hôpital
1661-1704

This idea is due to the Swiss mathematician Johann Bernoulli $(1667 - 1748)$. Johann and his brother Jacob Bernoulli $(1667 - 1748)$ were taught Calculus by Leibniz himself, but soon showed themselves to be his equal, or nearly so.

The Marquis de L'Hôpital, Guillaume François Antoine de L'Hôpital $(1661 - 1704)$. was keenly interested in the new Calculus so he struck a deal with Johann. The Marquis agreed to pay Bernoulli to tutor him and to keep L'Hôpital abreast of new mathematical developments. This was done with the understanding that L'Hôpital would include some of Bernoulli's research results in the Calculus textbook L'Hôpital was writing at the time. This turned out to be the very first Calculus textbook: *Analyse des Infiniment Petits pour l'Intelligence des Lignes Courbes (Analysis of the Infinitely Small for the Understanding of Curved Lines)*. It was published in 1696.

Even though L'Hôpital[19] acknowledged his indebtedness to Johann Bernoulli for this procedure it has always been known as **L'Hôpital's Rule**.

---

[18]We need to assume that $g'(a) \neq 0$. Do you see why?

[19]Pronounced LOW-Pea-Tall, not le-HOS-pital.

As a mathematician L'Hôpital was not in the same league as Leibniz, Newton, or the Bernoullis – few are – but he was a very competent mathematician and his work helped to disseminate the ideas of Calculus just as Maria Gaëtana Agnesi's text would do in the following century.

Now look back at the examples in this section and notice the following fact: In each case when the limit was finally evaluated it turned out to be the slope of the line tangent to the graph of the numerator divided by the slope of the line tangent to the graph of the denominator. But the slope of the line tangent to $f(x)$ at $x = a$ is simply[20] $f'(a)$. So we don't need to go to the trouble of finding the tangent lines. We can evaluate these indeterminate forms as follows:

Theorem 12: [L'Hôpital's Rule, (First Special Case)]

Suppose $f(x)$ and $g(x)$ are differentiable on an open interval containing a and that $f(a) = g(a) = 0$. Suppose also that

$$\lim_{x \to a} f'(x) = L \text{ and } \lim_{x \to a} g'(x) = M \neq 0$$

Then[21]

$$\lim_{x \to a} \frac{f(x)}{g(x)} \overset{\mathcal{L'H}}{=} \frac{L}{M}.$$

Because L'Hôpital's Rule applies directly to the indeterminate form $\frac{(\to 0)}{(\to 0)}$ we will refer to this as a **L'Hôpital Indeterminate**. Not all indeterminate forms can be handled so easily.

Example #74:

Consider $\lim_{x \to 0} \dfrac{\tan x}{x}$. This is a L'Hôpital indeterminate so

$$\lim_{x \to 0} \frac{\tan(x)}{x} \overset{\mathcal{L'H}}{=} \frac{\sec^2(0)}{1} = 1.$$

End Of Example #74

Example #75:

Consider $\lim_{x \to 0} \frac{\cos(x) - 1}{x}$. This is a L'Hôpital indeterminate so

$$\lim_{x \to 0} \frac{\cos(x) - 1}{x} \overset{\mathcal{L'H}}{=} \frac{\sin(0)}{1} = 0.$$

End Of Example #75

We want to emphasize very strongly that L'Hôpital's Rule requires a L'Hôpital indeterminate.

---

[20]Recall that in Section 4.5 we introduced Lagrange's prime notation: If $y = f(x)$ then

$$\frac{dy}{dx} = f'(x).$$

We said at the time that we would avoid using Lagrange's notation to avoid the confusion of multiple overlapping notations, but that there would be times when Lagrange's notation is much more convenient. This is such a time. In this section we will be using Lagrange's notation exclusively to indicate derivatives.

[21]We will use the notation "$A \overset{\mathcal{L'H}}{=} B$" to indicate that A is equal to B because of L'Hôpital's Rule.

If we don't have a L'Hôpital indeterminate we can not use L'Hôpital's Rule. If you try to use L'Hôpital's Rule when it does not apply, you will probably not get the correct answer. The difficulty here is that nothing in the computations will alert you that anything has gone wrong. You have to be watchful for this potential pitfall.

Example #76:

For example, if we mistakenly try to use L'Hôpital's Rule, on $\lim\limits_{x\to 1}\dfrac{x+1}{x+2}$ we will obtain $\lim\limits_{x\to 1} 1/1 = 1$, but this is obviously incorrect.

Drill #472:

Show that $\lim\limits_{x\to 1}\dfrac{x+1}{x+2} = \dfrac{2}{3}$.

End Of Example #76

Problem #473:

Compute each of the following limits:

(a) $\lim\limits_{x\to\frac{1}{2}}\dfrac{6x^2+5x-4}{4x^2+16x-9}$

(b) $\lim\limits_{x\to 1}\dfrac{x(x-1)}{x^2-1}$

(c) $\lim\limits_{x\to 2}\dfrac{x(x-1)}{x^2-1}$

(d) $\lim\limits_{x\to 0}\dfrac{\cos(x)-1}{x}$

(e) $\lim\limits_{x\to 1}\dfrac{\ln(x)}{x-1}$

(f) $\lim\limits_{x\to e}\dfrac{\ln(x^2)}{x+e}$

(g) $\lim\limits_{x\to 1}\dfrac{t^3-1}{t^4-1}$

(h) $\lim\limits_{x\to 0}\dfrac{\sin(3x)}{\sin(7x)}$

(i) $\lim\limits_{x\to 0}\dfrac{\cos(3x)}{\cos(7x)}$

(j) $\lim\limits_{x\to 0}\dfrac{\sin(4x)}{\tan(5x)}$

(k) $\lim\limits_{x\to 0}\dfrac{\tan^{-1}(x)}{x}$

(l) $\lim\limits_{x\to 0}\dfrac{\cot^{-1}(x)}{x}$

Example #77:

Theorem 12 is useful but it is much too limited, so to speak. For example, it does not help us with this limit: $\lim\limits_{x\to 0}\dfrac{\cos(3x)-1}{\cos(5x)-1}$. Even though it is a L'Hôpital indeterminate, when we apply Theorem 12 we have

$$\lim_{x\to 0}\frac{\cos(3x)-1}{\cos(5x)-1} \overset{\mathcal{L'H}}{=} \frac{-3\sin(3\cdot 0)}{-5\sin(5\cdot 0)} = \frac{0}{0}$$

This is useless because $\frac{0}{0}$ is still not defined.

We need to think about this again. It is true that $\frac{0}{0}$ is not defined, but if

$$f'(a) = \lim_{x\to a} f'(x) = 0$$

and

$$g'(a) = \lim_{x\to a} g'(x) = 0.$$

then $\lim\limits_{x\to a}\dfrac{f'(x)}{g'(x)}$ is a L'Hôpital Indeterminate so we extend Theorem #12 as follows:

End Of Example #77

Theorem 13: [L'Hôpital's Rule, (Second Special Case)]
Suppose $\lim\limits_{x \to a} \dfrac{f(x)}{g(x)}$ is the L'Hôpital Indeterminate form $\frac{(\to 0)}{(\to 0)}$. Then

$$\lim_{x \to a} \frac{f(x)}{g(x)} = \lim_{x \to a} \frac{f'(x)}{g'(x)}.$$

Our derivation of Theorem #13 is not entirely rigorous. We will not be providing a fully rigorous derivation of L'Hôpital's Rule because doing so is both difficult to produce and to understand. There are deep foundational issues involved and investigating these would take us too far from our primary purpose, gaining proficiency with its use.

Returning to our example and using Theorem #13 this time we have

$$\lim_{x \to 0} \frac{\cos(3x) - 1}{\cos(5x) - 1} \overset{\mathcal{L}'\mathcal{H}}{=} \lim_{x \to 0} \frac{-3\sin(3x)}{-5\sin(5x)}.$$

The limit on the right is yet another L'Hôpital Indeterminate so we apply L'Hôpital's Rule again.

$$\lim_{x \to 0} \frac{\cos(3x) - 1}{\cos(5x) - 1} \overset{\mathcal{L}'\mathcal{H}}{=} \lim_{x \to 0} \frac{-3\sin(3x)}{-5\sin(5x)} \overset{\mathcal{L}'\mathcal{H}}{=} \frac{3}{5}\lim_{x \to 0} \frac{3\cos(3x)}{5\cos(5x)} = \frac{3}{5} \cdot \frac{3\cos(0)}{5\cos(0)} = \frac{9}{25}.$$

Problem #474:
Use Theorem 13 to compute each of the following limits. If this limit given is not a L'Hôpital Indeterminate rearrange it algebraically, without changing its value, until it is a L'Hôpital Indeterminate.

(a) $\lim\limits_{x \to 0} \dfrac{e^x - 1 - x}{x^2}$

(b) $\lim\limits_{x \to 0} \dfrac{\cos(mx) - \cos(nx)}{x^2}$
Assume that $m \neq n$.)

(c) $\lim\limits_{x \to 1} \dfrac{x^a - ax + a - 1}{(x - 1)^2}$
Assume that $a \neq 1$.

(d) $\lim\limits_{x \to 0} \dfrac{1 - e^{-2x}}{\sin(x)}$

(e) $\lim\limits_{x \to 0} (1 - e^{-2x}) \csc(x)$

(f) $\lim\limits_{x \to 0} \dfrac{\ln(x)}{\frac{1}{x}}$

(g) $\lim\limits_{\substack{x \to 0 \\ x > 0}} x \ln(x)$

(h) $\lim\limits_{x \to 0} \cot(2x) \sin(6x)$

(i) $\lim\limits_{\substack{x \to 0 \\ x > 0}} \sin(x) \ln(x)$

L'Hôpital's Rule and Horizontal Asymptotes

Our discovery of L'Hôpital's Rule grew from our investigation of vertical asymptotes. Is there any way that we can extend L'Hôpital's Rule to help us with horizontal asymptotes? For example, consider

$$\lim_{x \to \infty} \frac{\sin\left(\frac{2}{x}\right)}{\sin\left(\frac{3}{x}\right)}.$$

This limit is indeterminate of the form $\frac{(\to 0)}{(\to 0)}$, so it seems like L'Hôpital's Rule would apply. But both versions of L'Hôpital's Rule (so far) require that $x \to a$, where a is a real number. And of course, infinity still insists on not being a number, real or otherwise. If we want to use L'Hôpital's Rule we'll have to find a way to modify this limit so that L'Hôpital's Rule does apply.

If we make the substitution $z = \frac{1}{x}$ then as $x \to \infty$, $\underset{z > 0}{z \to 0}$. After substituting we have[22]

$$\lim_{x \to \infty} \frac{\sin\left(\frac{2}{x}\right)}{\sin\left(\frac{3}{x}\right)} = \lim_{\substack{z \to 0 \\ z > 0}} \frac{\sin(2z)}{\sin(3z)}.$$

Now we apply L'Hôpital's Rule and we see that

$$\lim_{x \to \infty} \frac{\sin\left(\frac{2}{x}\right)}{\sin\left(\frac{3}{x}\right)} \overset{\mathcal{L'H}}{=} \lim_{\substack{z \to 0 \\ z > 0}} \frac{2\cos(2z)}{3\cos(3z)} = \frac{2}{3}.$$

Far more important than the answer in this example is the realization that we can use the same trick to extend L'Hôpital's Rule to the case where x approaches both ∞, and $-\infty$.

To see this in the general situation suppose that $\lim_{x \to \infty} f(x) = 0$ and $\lim_{x \to \infty} g(x) = 0$. Make the substitution $z = 1/x$, so that when $x \to \infty$ we would have the one-sided limit as z approaches zero from the right side. Now we can use L'Hôpital's Rule with z as the variable.

$$\lim_{x \to \infty} \frac{f(x)}{g(x)} = \lim_{\substack{z \to 0 \\ z > 0}} \frac{f\left(\frac{1}{z}\right)^{\nearrow 0}}{g\left(\frac{1}{z}\right)^{\nearrow 0}} \overset{\mathcal{L'H}}{=} \lim_{\substack{z \to 0 \\ z > 0}} \left(\frac{f'\left(\frac{1}{z}\right)^{\nearrow 0}}{g'\left(\frac{1}{z}\right)^{\nearrow 0}} \cdot \frac{-z^{-2}}{-z^{-2}}^{\nearrow = 1} \right)$$

$$= \lim_{\substack{z \to 0 \\ z > 0}} \frac{f'\left(\frac{1}{z}\right)}{g'\left(\frac{1}{z}\right)}$$

$$= \lim_{z \to \infty} \frac{f'(x)}{g'(x)}.$$

A similar development would work for $x \to -\infty$.

Although we have not discussed it, it is also true that L'Hôpital Rule applies directly to the indeterminate form $\frac{(\to \pm\infty)}{(\to \pm\infty)}$, so in addition to $\frac{(\to 0)}{(\to 0)}$, we will call these **L'Hôpital Indeterminates** as well.

Putting this all together gives us the general statement of L'Hôpital's Rule:

---

[22]Since $x \to \infty$ through positive values we need to constrain z to do the same.

Theorem 14: [L'Hôpital's Rule]

Suppose $\lim\limits_{x \to a} \dfrac{f(x)}{g(x)}$ is any L'Hôpital Indeterminate. Then

$$\lim_{x \to a} \frac{f(x)}{g(x)} = \lim_{x \to a} \frac{f'(x)}{g'(x)}.$$

We allow the possibility that $a = \pm\infty$ which we understand to mean that x increases or decreases without bound.

Problem #475:

Compute each of the following limits. Use Theorem 14 where appropriate.

(a) $\lim\limits_{x \to 0} \dfrac{5x}{\tan(x)}$ **(d)** $\lim\limits_{x \to 0} \dfrac{x+1-e^x}{x^2}$ **(g)** $\lim\limits_{x \to \infty} \dfrac{\ln(\ln(x))}{\ln(x^2)}$ **(j)** $\lim\limits_{x \to \infty} \dfrac{e^{x-2}}{1+e^{x+3}}$

(b) $\lim\limits_{x \to 2} \dfrac{2x^2-5x+2}{5x^2-7x-6}$ **(e)** $\lim\limits_{x \to \infty} \dfrac{e^{nx}}{\ln(x)}, \; n > 0$ **(h)** $\lim\limits_{x \to 0} \dfrac{\sin^{-1}(x)}{x-\sin(x)}$ **(k)** $\lim\limits_{x \to 0} \dfrac{e^{x-2}}{1+e^{-x+3}}$

(c) $\lim\limits_{x \to -3} \dfrac{x^2+2x-3}{2x^2+3x-9}$ **(f)** $\lim\limits_{x \to \infty} \dfrac{5-5^x}{7-7^x}$ **(i)** $\lim\limits_{x \to \infty} \dfrac{e^{x-2}}{1+e^{x+3}}$ **(l)** $\lim\limits_{x \to \infty} \dfrac{x}{\ln(1+2e^x)}$

Example #78:

As $x \to \infty$ both $f(x) = \ln(x)$ and $g(x) = \sqrt[3]{x}$ increase without bound, but which one increases faster? Take a quick look at the graphs below.

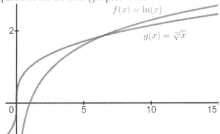

As $x \to \infty$ both graphs are flattening out, but it would appear that the natural logarithm function is outgrowing the cube root function. Is it?

We can answer this question by looking at the limit,

$$\lim_{x \to \infty} \frac{\ln(x)}{\sqrt[3]{x}}.$$

If the limit is ∞ then $f(x) = \ln(x)$ is growing faster. If it is zero then $g(x) = \sqrt[3]{x}$ is increasing faster than $f(x) = \ln(x)$. (Do you see why?)

Drill #476:

(a) Which of $f(x) = \ln(x)$ and $g(x) = \sqrt[3]{x}$ grows faster?

(b) Can we draw any conclusions about the rate of increase if the limit is something other than 0 or ∞?

End Of Example #78

Problem #477: Find the Pattern
Use L'Hôpital's Rule to determine which of the following pairs of functions are growing faster as $x \to \infty$.

(a) $f(x) = \ln(x)$
   $g(x) = x$

(c) $f(x) = \ln(x)$
   $g(x) = x^{1/3}$

(e) $f(x) = \ln(x)$
   $g(x) = x^{1/4}$

(g) $f(x) = \ln(x)$
   $g(x) = x^{1/5}$

(b) $f(x) = \ln(x)$
   $g(x) = x^{1/2}$

(d) $f(x) = \ln(x)$
   $g(x) = x^{2/3}$

(f) $f(x) = \ln(x)$
   $g(x) = x^{3/4}$

(h) $f(x) = \ln(x)$
   $g(x) = x^{4/5}$

(i) Based on the limits above write down a general conclusion about the rate of change of the natural logarithm as compared to roots.

(j) Prove that your statement is correct.

To most people this phrase "exponential growth" just means that something is growing very fast, but it actually means the growth rate is described by an exponential function. For example neither $f(x) = x^2$ nor $f(x) = x^{200}$ grows exponentially. but $f(x) = e^x$, $f(x) = 2^x$, and even $f(x) = 1.0001^x$ all do grow exponentially[23]. The next problem explores how "exponential growth" compares "polynomial growth."

Problem #478: Exponential vs. Polynomial Growth

(a) Show that each of the following limits is zero.

(i) $\lim\limits_{x \to \infty} \dfrac{x^2}{e^x} = 0$

(ii) $\lim\limits_{x \to \infty} \dfrac{x^{20}}{e^x} = 0$

(iii) $\lim\limits_{x \to \infty} \dfrac{x^{200}}{e^x} = 0$

Do you see that this means that e^x grows faster than x^2, x^{20}, or even x^{200}?

(b) Would $\lim\limits_{x \to \infty} \dfrac{x^p}{e^x} = 0$ for any positive integer p? Explain.

---

[23]As we saw in Section (7.2 $f(x) = \left(\frac{1}{2}\right)^x$ is said to "decay exponentially."

(c) Suppose that $P(x)$ any polynomial and show that $\lim\limits_{x \to \infty} \dfrac{P(x)}{e^x} = 0$. Do you see that this means that the natural exponential grows faster than any polynomial?

(d) Suppose that $P(x)$ any polynomial. Show that each of the following limits is also zero. What do you conclude from this?

(i) $\lim\limits_{x \to \infty} \dfrac{P(x)}{10^x}$ **(ii)** $\lim\limits_{x \to \infty} \dfrac{P(x)}{2^x}$ **(iii)** $\lim\limits_{x \to \infty} \dfrac{P(x)}{1.1^x}$ **(iv)** $\lim\limits_{x \to \infty} \dfrac{P(x)}{1.00001^x}$

Example #79: **More on L'Hôpital's Rule**

Consider the limit

$$\lim_{x \to \infty} \left[x \tan \left(\frac{1}{x} \right) \right].$$

If we want to evaluate this limit (we do) we seem to have few options. This is not a L'Hôpital Indeterminate, nor is it obvious what the limit might be.

Simply letting $x \to \infty$ we see that $x \to \infty$ and $\tan \left(\frac{1}{x} \right) \to 0$ so our limit has the Indeterminate form $(\to \infty) \cdot (\to 0)$. There is a real temptation to say that this must be zero since anything multiplied by zero is zero. But is it? Remember that the purpose of the arrow notation, $(\to 0)$, is to remind us that the expression $\tan \left(\frac{1}{x} \right)$ is never actually equal to zero. It merely approaches zero. At the same time x is increasing without bound ($x \to \infty$) so it seems that the value of the limit might depend on the relative speeds with which $x \to \infty$ and $\tan \left(\frac{1}{x} \right) \to 0$. But this reasoning feels very uncertain doesn't it? And, in any case, nothing we've said will help us evaluate the limit.

We'll have to find a way to re-express this limit as a L'Hôpital Indeterminate so that L'Hôpital's Rule does apply. In the meantime, take your best guess as to the value of this limit and write it down for later reference.

Suppose we rewrite this limit as $\lim\limits_{x \to \infty} \left[x \tan \left(\frac{1}{x} \right) \right] = \lim\limits_{x \to \infty} \dfrac{\tan \left(\frac{1}{x} \right)}{\frac{1}{x}}$. This is a little scary to look at so we'll make it easier on our eyes with the substitution $z = \frac{1}{x}$. As $x \to \infty$ we see that $z > 0$ and $z \to 0$. Since $\tan(0) = 0$ our limit is now $\lim\limits_{\substack{z \to 0 \\ z > 0}} \dfrac{\tan(z)}{z}$ which is the L'Hôpital Indeterminate $\frac{(\to 0)}{(\to 0)}$.

Thus by Theorem 14 we have

$$\lim_{x \to \infty} x \tan \left(\frac{1}{x} \right) = \lim_{\substack{z \to 0 \\ z > 0}} \frac{\tan(z)}{z} \overset{\mathcal{L}'\mathcal{H}}{=} \lim_{\substack{z \to 0 \\ z > 0}} \frac{\sec^2(z)}{1} = \frac{\sec^2(0)}{1} = 1$$

since $\sec(0) = 1$.

End Of Example #79

Did you guess correctly?

Notice that the trick we used was a simple substitution much like the ones we have used in the past to make things "easier on the eyes." The difference here is that we're not making anything "easier on the eyes." If anything we're making things harder to look at since rewriting x as $\frac{1}{\frac{1}{x}}$ certainly doesn't seem like it's going to help much. Until we try it. Always try your ideas out no matter how crazy they seem to be. Only after you try an idea can you tell if it will work or not.

Recall that in Section 7.1 where we defined the effective yield of an investment which is compounded continuously. We were led to examine the expression $\left(1 + \frac{1}{m}\right)^m$ for very large values of m.

As a result of that investigation we accumulated considerable numerical evidence that in one year an investment of \$1 growing at a nominal rate of 5%, compounded continuously would grow to \$$e^{0.05} \approx \$1.0513$, but we were unable to do more than gather evidence. It was pretty convincing evidence but it was not proof since we didn't yet have the mathematical technique necessary to evaluate the expression $\left(1 + \frac{1}{m}\right)^m$ as $m \to \infty$. Now we do.

Example #80:

We need to evaluate the limit:

$$\lim_{m \to \infty} \left(1 + \frac{1}{m}\right)^m.$$

It is tempting to reason as follows. We see that $1 + \frac{1}{m} \to 1$ as $m \to \infty$. That is, we have the indeterminate form $(\to 1)^{(\to \infty)}$ and since one raised to any power is equal to one this limit must equal 1, right? Surely you know better than to jump to that conclusion by now. Not only does all of the evidence of this chapter warn you that limits are more subtle than that, but in our investigations in Section 7.1 we saw overwhelming evidence that this limit is not equal to one.

Also, notice that we wrote $(\to 1)^{(\to \infty)}$, not $1^{(\to \infty)}$. Why do you think we did that?

The source of our difficulty here is that the variable m is in the exponent where we can't get at it. We'd like to find a way to bring it out of the exponent. The natural logarithm seems perfect for this task since it has the property that $\ln\left(a^b\right) = b \ln(a)$.

Begin by setting $y = \left(1 + \frac{1}{m}\right)^m$. Then

$$\ln(y) = \ln\left(1 + \frac{1}{m}\right)^m = m \ln\left(1 + \frac{1}{m}\right).$$

Rather than evaluating $\lim_{t \to \infty} y$ directly we evaluate the limit of the logarithm of y. Thus

$$\lim_{m \to \infty} \ln(y) = \lim_{m \to \infty} m \ln\left(1 + \frac{1}{m}\right).$$

The limit on the right is an indeterminate form but unfortunately it is not a L'Hôpital Indeterminate. So, as before, we'll have to do some algebraic manipulations first. Set $\frac{1}{m} = z$ so that

$$\lim_{t \to \infty} \ln(y) = \lim_{\substack{z \to 0 \\ z > 0}} \frac{\ln(1 + z)}{z} \overset{\mathcal{L'H}}{=} \lim_{\substack{z \to 0 \\ z > 0}} \frac{\frac{1}{1+z}}{1} = 1.$$

Since $\lim_{m \to \infty} \ln(y) = 1$ it seems intuitively clear that $\lim_{m \to \infty} y = \lim_{m \to \infty} \left(1 + \frac{1}{m}\right)^m = e^1$, doesn't it?

In fact it is not true generally that $\lim_{x \to a} f(g(x))$ is equal to $f\left(\lim_{x \to a} g(x)\right)$. (We have not yet discussed values of a that are not either 0 or ∞.) However this is true whenever f is continuous at $g(a)$. Since $f(x) = \ln(x)$ is continuous, for $x > 0$ this is a detail that needn't trouble us for now so we will ignore it. We will return to it in Section 16.3.

End Of Example #80

Problem #479:

(a) Show that $\lim_{m \to \infty} \left(1 + \dfrac{r}{m}\right)^{m} = e^{r}$

(b) Show that $\lim_{m \to \infty} \left(1 + \dfrac{r}{m}\right)^{mt} = e^{rt}$ for $t \geq 0$.
(**Hint:** Let $n = mt$ and manipulate this limit until it looks like the limit in part (a) (with different letters, of course.).)

(c) Suppose we have an investment of $\$10,000$ compounded continuously with a relative annual rate of 5%. How much would the investment be worth in 20 years? How would this compare to an investment which is compounded quarterly?
(**Hint:** You may want to review similar problems in Section 7.1 before starting this problem.)

Example #81:

Consider $\lim_{\substack{t \to 0 \\ t > 0}} t^t$. Notice we are only considering positive values of t. (Why?) Proceeding in the same manner as before, let $y = t^t$, so that $\ln(y) = \ln(t^t) = t\ln(t)$. Thus

$$\lim_{\substack{t \to 0 \\ t > 0}} \ln(y) = \lim_{\substack{t \to 0 \\ t > 0}} t\ln(t) = \lim_{\substack{t \to 0 \\ t > 0}} \frac{\ln(t)}{\frac{1}{t}}.$$

This is a L'Hôpital Indeterminate so we apply L'Hôpital's Rule:

$$\lim_{\substack{t \to 0 \\ t > 0}} \ln(y) = \lim_{\substack{t \to 0 \\ t > 0}} \frac{\ln(t)}{t^{-1}} \overset{\mathcal{L'H}}{=} \lim_{\substack{t \to 0 \\ t > 0}} \frac{t^{-1}}{-t^{-2}} = \lim_{\substack{t \to 0 \\ t > 0}} (-t) = 0.$$

Thus

$$\lim_{\substack{t \to 0 \\ t > 0}} t^t = e^0 = 1.$$

End Of Example #81

We have seen the following indeterminate forms:

1. $(\to \infty) - (\to \infty)$ 3. $(\to 0)^{(\to 0)}$ 5. $\frac{(\to 0)}{(\to 0)}$

2. $(\to 0)(\to \infty)$ 4. $(\to 1)^{(\to \infty)}$ 6. $\frac{(\to \infty)}{(\to \infty)}$.

Of these, only the last two are L'Hôpital Indeterminate forms. The others must be evaluated by some method other than directly applying L'Hôpital's Rule. Often this simply means algebraically rearranging them into a L'Hôpital Indeterminate.

The following are not indeterminate forms. Don't try to use L'Hôpital's Rule on them[24].

1. $(\to \infty) + (\to \infty)$ 2. $(\to 1)^{(\to 0)}$ 3. $(\to 0)^{(\to \infty)}$.

Problem #480:

Evaluate each of the following limits.

(a) $\lim\limits_{t \to \infty} \left(1 + \dfrac{a}{t}\right)^{bt}$

(b) $\lim\limits_{t \to 0} (1 + t)^{\frac{1}{t}}$

(c) $\lim\limits_{t \to 0} (1 - 2t)^{1/t}$

(d) $\lim\limits_{t \to 0} (1 + at)^{\frac{b}{t}}$

(e) $\lim\limits_{\substack{t \to 0 \\ t > 0}} (\sin(t) + t)$

(f) $\lim\limits_{t \to \infty} t^{\frac{1}{\ln(t)}}$
(**Hint:** Not every indeterminant form requires L'Hôpital's Rule?)

(g) $\lim\limits_{t \to 1} \left(\dfrac{1}{\ln(t)} - \dfrac{1}{t - 1}\right)$

(h) $\lim\limits_{t \to 0} (\csc(t) - \cot(t))$

(i) $\lim\limits_{t \to \infty} (t - \ln(t))$
(**Hint:** Set $y = t - \ln(t)$ and consider $\lim(e^y)$.)

---

[24]In fact, you can evaluate each of these without just by knowing the form. Try it.

Finalized – Fri Jul 21 11:17:34 2023 –

Part II

. . . To Theory

Chapter 12

What's Wrong With Differentials?

"In the pursuit of truth we must beware of being misled by terms which we do not rightly understand. That is the chief point."

– George Berkeley (1685–1753)

Recall that in Digression #11 we saw that if $y = y(x)$ Newton would have had no difficulty interpreting the expression d^2x. But Leibniz would have a good deal of trouble understanding what d^2x might mean. As we commented in Digression #11 trying to make sense of "an infinitely small increment of an infinitely small increment" will drive you to madness.

But we also observed that this was not an issue that we could avoid forever. The time has come for us to wrestle with this problem.

A simple way to see what's wrong with differentials is to consider the circle and the differential triangle in the diagram at the right.

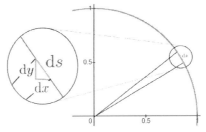

Suppose that ds is one of the differentials that makes up the circle. Since ds is a non-zero increment it has two distinct endpoints so we can draw the two radii shown. The two (distinct) endpoints are *infinitely* close together and lie on the circle. Therefore they must have the same slope. But all radii of a circle pass through the center of the circle. So these two in particular must also intersect at the center, and we are forced to conclude that these radii are two parallel lines that somehow intersect.

The only way that can happen is if they are actually the same line. If they are the same line then the points on the circle are not really distinct as we've drawn them. But if they are not distinct then dx, dy, and ds are all actually *equal* to zero. Finally, $dx = 0$ so, as a fraction, $\frac{dy}{dx}$ is meaningless (why?).

This simple argument appears to completely destroy the differential foundation upon which we've based everything we've done up until now. Unfortunately, overcoming the apparent contradictions in the notion of infinitely small numbers is very hard to do.

12.1 Calculus and Bishop Berkeley

"In my opinion, a mathematician, in so far as he is a mathematician, need not preoccupy himself with philosophy-an opinion, moreover, which has been expressed by many philosophers."

– Henri Lebesgue, (1875–1941)

Bishop George Berkeley
1685-1753

In 1734 an even more devastating repudiation of differentials was published by George Berkeley[1] (1685 − 1753), the Anglican Bishop of the Diocese of Cloyne, Ireland in a treatise ponderously entitled, *The Analyst; or, a Discourse Addressed to an Infidel* MATHEMATICIAN, WHEREIN *it is examined whether the Object, Principles, and Inferences of the modern Analysis are more distinctly conceived, or more evidently deduced, than Religious Mysteries and Points of Faith*[2].

You may well wonder why a Bishop in the Church of England and a philosopher would concern himself with the methods of scientific analysis and investigation. The fact is that Berkeley didn't really have any quarrel with the results obtained from Calculus at all. He was, in fact, a great admirer of Newton and he understood very well that the techniques Newton and Leibniz had introduced actually worked, at least most of the time. He says as much himself in *The Analyst*[3]:

> *"I have no Controversy about your Conclusions, but only about your Logic and Method. . . . It must be remembered that I am not concerned about the truth of your Theorems, but only about the way of coming at them; . . . it may perhaps seem an unaccountable Paradox, that Mathematicians should deduce true Propositions from false Principles, be right in the Conclusion, and yet err in the Premises . . . "*
> *(Section XX)*

Berkeley might not have bothered publishing his criticisms of Calculus but during the seventeenth and eighteenth centuries a religious movement known as Deism (called "Free-Thinking" in England) was very strong throughout Europe. The Free-Thinkers in England

---

[1] His name is properly pronounced "bark lee," not "burk lee."

[2] Usually it is just called *The Analyst*.

[3] In the eighteenth century English nouns were frequently capitalized, and spelling was not as standardized as it is today, so Berkeley's work looks a little odd to modern eyes.

explicitly espoused questioning and criticizing religious tenets and attitudes. Christianity was attacked by some Deists on the grounds that it was not logical and contained many mysteries.

As a member of the clergy Berkeley felt compelled to answer these challenges. Speaking directly to the English scientific community in *The Analyst* he said,

> *"Whereas then it is supposed, that you apprehend more distinctly, consider more closely, infer more justly, conclude more accurately than other Men, and that you are therefore less religious because more judicious, I shall claim the privilege of a Free-Thinker; and take the Liberty to inquire into the Object, Principles, and Method of Demonstration admitted by the Mathematicians of the present Age, with the same freedom that you presume to treat the Principles and Mysteries of Religion; to the end, that all Men may see what right you have to lead, or what Encouragement others have to follow you." (Section II)*

He made his purpose clear from the outset by including a biblical verse (Mathew, 7:5) on the title page of *The Analyst*:

> *"First cast out the beam out of thine own Eye; and then shalt thou see clearly to cast out the mote out of thy brother's eye."*

So Berkeley's purpose in writing *The Analyst* was to defend his religion rather than to attack mathematics. But he was well acquainted with the adage, "The best defense is a good offense" and he mounted a very good defense.

Berkeley's critique was both fierce and correct. Fortunately, in its time it was also (mostly) ignored. The early development of Calculus proceeded despite his challenge because mathematicians of the time were too busy *using* Calculus to concern themselves much with the underlying foundational issues. Similarly, we have pushed these foundational issues aside so that we could get to the business of using Calculus, even if our justifications would not bear close examination. In the beginning it was more important that you learn to use Calculus than that you understand all of the logical subtleties that have been used to justify it rigorously.

But the issues that Berkeley's objections bring to light are real and the time has come for us to address[4] the profound logical difficulties inherent in the notion of an infinitely small quantity.

Some of Berkeley's specific criticisms are illuminating[5].

> *". . . they consider the Increments or Decrements themselves, which they call Differences, and which are supposed to be infinitely small . . .. Now to conceive a Quantity infinitely small, that is, infinitely less than any sensible or imaginable Quantity, or than any the least finite Magnitude, is, I confess, above my Capacity. . . . But to conceive a Part of such infinitely small Quantity, that shall be still infinitely less than it, and consequently though multipliy'd infinitely shall never equal the minutest finite Quantity is, I suspect, an infinite Difficulty to any Man whatsoever . . ." (Section V)*

Do you see what he's complaining about? Berkeley is questioning the very existence of the differentials we have been relying on since we began. And he has a point. As we've seen our

---

[4]Actually, we won't address these problems as much find a way around them.

[5]The language of Calculus wasn't entirely established yet so when Berkeley says "Differences" he means what we've been calling differentials.

differentials have to satisfy two mutually exclusive properties. They can't be zero but they must be smaller than "the least finite Magnitude." On its face this seems to be impossible.

Recall that in Digression #11 we explicitly side-stepped the issue of a higher order differentials, commenting that Newton's and Leibniz' approaches were inconsistent on that point. We chose to proceed with Newton's approach, observing as we did that we would eventually need a more general theory.

Berkeley understood this very well. He says that:

> *". . . our modern Analysts are not content to consider only the Differences of finite Quantities: they also consider the Differences of those Differences, and the Differences of the Differences of the first Differences. And so on ad infinitum. That is, they consider Quantities infinitely less than the least discernible Quantity; and others infinitely less than those infinitely small ones; and still others infinitely less than the preceding Infinitesimals, and so on without end or limit . . . And (which is most strange) although you should take a Million of Millions of these Infinitesimals, each whereof is supposed infinitely greater than some other real Magnitude, and add them to the least given Quantity, it shall be never the bigger. For this is one of the modest postulata of our modern Mathematicians, and it is a Corner-stone or Ground-work of their Speculations." (Section VI)*

But wait a second. We know Calculus works. We've been successfully solving abstruse and difficult problems with it for some time. Throughout the first part of this text we've seen ample, even overwhelming, evidence of this fact. Isn't that sufficient? Can't we conclude from the fact that Calculus does seem to work that the notion of the differential is tenable after all?

Sadly, no. Berkeley thought of that too:

> *"But this inverted way of demonstrating your Principles by your Conclusions . . . is contrary to the Rules of Logic. The truth of a Conclusion will not prove either the Form or the Matter . . . to be true . . . I say that in every other Science Men prove their Conclusions by their Principles, and not their Principles by their Conclusions." (Section XX)*

In order to have confidence in our knowledge, we must begin with simple, clear ideas and build on them logically. Nothing else will do.

However, the path to simple, clear ideas is neither simple nor clear. As we've mentioned before, it took about two hundred years for the mathematical community to find and fully understand how to make Calculus rigorous[6]. We introduced the essential idea, the limit, intuitively in Section #11.1.

It would be possible to introduce the limit concept formally and then proceed to develop all of Calculus from it. Logically, there is nothing wrong with this approach, and indeed, this is exactly how most Calculus books present the topic. But the limit concept is very subtle. Unless you understand exactly what issues it is meant to address it is very difficult to understand why it takes the form that it does.

So, we will continue to build on our intuitive approach. However, our focus has changed. In Part I we worked intuitively to build confidence in the tools we were building. Here in Part II, our intention is to highlight how and where our intuition falls short, so that when we finally define the limit concept rigorously in Definition #27 it will be clear why it must have the form

---

[6]For us rigorous means that we can provide an argument that even Bishop Berkeley would accept.

that it does. What this means is that while our intention is to finally provide the rigor we've been lacking we will not actually achieve that until the end of Chapter 16

12.2   Secants and Tangents

"Calculus required continuity, and continuity was supposed to require the infinitely little; but nobody could discover what the infinitely little might be."

– Bertrand Russell, (1872–1970)

In Part I we defined the derivative of $y = y(x)$ to be the differential ratio $\frac{dy}{dx}$, but Berkeley shows in *The Analyst* that there are considerable difficulties with this approach. How else might we define the derivative? This is our next puzzle.

If we want to construct the line tangent at a particular point, $(x_0, y(x_0))$ on a given curve we immediately have this problem: We only have one point, but there are (infinitely) many lines through that point. A few of them are shown at the right. How could we possibly pick the tangent line out of this mess?

The only distinguishing feature that the tangent line has is that it is in fact tangent to our curve. That is not much to go on. But it is not nothing either.

To form a line we desperately need another point. But where to find one? The only other points we have to work with are points on the curve itself.

Choose a new point, say $(x_1, y(x_1))$, on our curve but a little to the right of $(x_0, y(x_0))$ and draw the line between $(x_0, y(x_0))$ and $(x_1, y(x_1))$ as shown in the sketch at the left. Recall from Chapter 5 that the trigonometric secant function is so called because it is the length of a line segment which cuts the circle. The brown line in this sketch cuts the curve so it is called a **secant line**.

Similarly, if we choose a point a little to the left of $(x_0, y(x_0))$ and draw another secant line (shown in purple) it should be clear that the tangent line will be between the two secant lines in the sketch at the right.

We have eliminated a lot of potential tangent lines, but we haven't eliminated all of them. Is there a way we could refine our search to reduce the set of possible tangent lines even further?

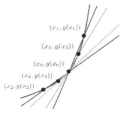

Sure. Choose x_3 between x_0 and x_1 and draw the (blue) secant line from x_0 to x_3, and then choose x_4 between x_0 and x_2 and draw the (green) secant line through them to get the sketch at the left. It is clear that we have eliminated more potential tangent lines, and that by continuing to choose points even closer to x_0 we can eliminate even more of them.

This approach seems to have some potential but there are at least two difficulties:

1. So far we've relied heavily on diagrams to motivate our approach, and we know that diagrams can be misleading. However this is not as serious as it seems to be because we are only using the diagrams to motivate a new definition for the derivative. Once that definition is in place we can disregard the diagrams and work directly with the definition regardless of the shape of the graph.

   You should generate a few graphs of your own, different from ours and from each other, to confirm that our arguments work for them as well.

2. We've been drawing the tangent lines but we need to keep in mind that the line tangent to the graph of our function at a point is not the derivative of the function. The derivative is the slope of the tangent line. And slope is a number. The pictures we've drawn so far are very suggestive but they don't give us numbers.

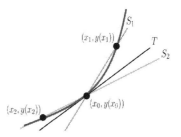

For the time being, we will handle the first difficulty by ignoring it. That is, we will continue to use diagrams to motivate our ideas, but when we are done we will have circle back and ask ourselves if our reliance on those diagrams has caused us to miss any special cases which need to be addressed.

To handle the second difficulty consider the sketch at the right. It is clear that if the tangent line, T, is caught between lines secant lines S_1 and S_2, then the *slope* of T is necessarily caught between the *slope* of S_1 and the *slope* of S_2. Thus we have

$$\text{slope of } S_1 = \frac{y(x_1) - y(x_0)}{x_1 - x_0} > \text{slope of } T > \frac{y(x_2) - y(x_0)}{x_2 - x_0} = \text{slope of } S_2.$$

A specific example will be helpful.

Example #82:

Suppose $y = x^2$. We would like to compute the derivative (slope of the line tangent to the graph) of y at the point $x = 2$ by the the procedure indicated above.

Before we start, observe that from our work with differentials we know what we are expecting to get. It is

$$y'(2) = \left.\frac{dy}{dx}\right|_{x=2} = \left.2x\right|_{x=2} = 2 \cdot 2 = 4.$$

Taking $x_1 = 2.1$ and $x_2 = 1.9$, gives

$$\frac{y(2.1) - y(2)}{2.1 - 2} > y'(2) > \frac{y(1.9) - y(2)}{1.9 - 2}$$
$$\frac{(2.1)^2 - (2)^2}{.1} > y'(2) > \frac{(1.9)^2 - y(2)}{.9}$$
$$4.1 > y'(2) > 3.9.$$

So our proposed procedure seems to be heading us in the right direction. If we take $x_3 = 2.01$ and $x_4 = 1.99$ we get

$$4.01 > y'(2) > 3.99.$$

We say that $y'(2)$ is **bounded**, and that the numbers 4.01 and 3.99 are the **bounds**.

Problem #481:
Compute bounds on the derivatives of each function given at $x = 2$ by using the values of x_1 and x_2 given below.

(i) $y = x^2$,   **(ii)** $y = x^3$,   **(iii)** $y = -\frac{1}{x}$, and   **(iv)** $y = x^{1/2}$

(a) $x_1 = 2.001$, $x_2 = 1.999$ **(c)** $x_1 = 2.00001$, $x_2 = 1.99999$

(b) $x_1 = 2.0001$, $x_2 = 1.9999$ **(d)** $x_1 = 2.000001$, $x_2 = 1.999999$

The results in Problem #481 are looking very promising indeed. Since they are looking so promising we'll take a few minutes to simplify our notation a bit.

It is tedious to have all of these subscripted x variables $(x_0, x_1, x_2, \cdots)$ so we will define an equivalent, but more useful, notation. The basic idea here is that we move to a new point a little bit away from x_0 and form the quotient that gives the slope of the secant line at that point. To construct the first secant line we took x_1 to be a number a little to the right of x_0. However, if we take h to be a positive number near zero then $x_0 + h$ expresses the same idea. Similarly, to construct a secant line a little to the left of x_0 we take h to be a negative number near zero so that $x_0 + h$ expresses the same idea.

We can capture both situations notationally by agreeing that h is a number (either positive or negative) which is close to zero. Thus when h is positive the point $x_0 + h$ is to the right, and when h is negative the point $x_0 + h$ is to the left of x_0 as shown in the diagram at the right.

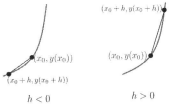

When we express the idea this way we no longer need to generate all of the independent variables, $x_1, x_2, x_3, \ldots$. We can accomplish the same thing by taking $x_h = x_0 + h$, where h is some arbitrary real number, which is close to zero. Each value of h gives us a different secant line through the point $(x_0, y(x_0))$, and its slope will be

$$\frac{y(x_0 + h) - y(x_0)}{(x_0 + h) - x_0} = \frac{y(x_0 + h) - y(x_0)}{h} \tag{12.1}$$

By the Principle of Local Linearity we see that when h is very small the quotient $\frac{y(x_0+h)-y(x_0)}{h}$ will be very close to the the slope of the tangent line.

There is also a small technical matter we need to think about: Do we really need to consider secant lines on either side of x_0 (for both positive and negative values of h)? Would it not be sufficient to consider just the secant lines on the right formed from the sequence $x_1 = 2.1, x_1 = 2.01, x_1 = 2.001, \ldots$? It seems pretty clear that the slopes we get, $4.1, 4.01, 4.001, \ldots$ are getting closer to 4. Isn't that enough?

No, it is not. But not because there is any inherent logical flaw in doing so. This has more to do with the properties we want the derivative to have than any purely logical consideration, so we'll hold off further discussion until Section 14.3.

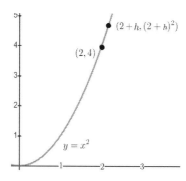

Returning to the example $y = x^2$ at $x = 2$, we let h be any number except zero and find of the secant line through $(2, 4)$ and $(2 + h, (2 + h)^2)$. We can't let h be zero because if it is zero then $(2, 4)$ and $(2 + h, (2 + h)^2)$ are the same point and we can't construct the secant line. We *must* have $h \neq 0$ just to get started. In that case we have

$$\frac{y(2 + h) - y(2)}{h} = \frac{(2 + h)^2 - 2}{h} = \frac{4 + 4h + h^2 - 4}{h}$$
$$= \frac{4h + h^2}{h}$$
$$= 4 + h. \tag{12.2}$$

This is interesting. Do you recognize this computation? It should be familiar to you. This is precisely the same computation you did when you used Fermat's adaptation of the Method of Adequality to find tangent lines in Problem #20 of Chapter 2. The only difference, really, is that at this point Fermat would simply set $h = 0$ and move on. We can't do that because we need two distinct points to specify a (secant) line. If $h = 0$ we only have one. This is frustrating because we can see that setting $h = 0$ will give us $y'(2) = 4$ which we know to be the correct value.

Berkeley pointed out the problem of setting $h = 0$ in *The Analyst* (his Increments are what we've called h):

> " . . . this reasoning is not fair or conclusive. For when it is said, let the Increments vanish, i.e. let the Increments be nothing, or let there be no Increments, the former Supposition that the Increments were something, or that there were Increments is destroyed, and yet as a Consequence of that Supposition, i.e. an Expression got by virtue thereof, is retained. Which . . . is a false way of reasoning. Certainly when we suppose the Increments to vanish, we must suppose their Proportions, their Expressions, and every thing else derived from the Supposition of their Existence to vanish with them."

Requiring h to be non-zero at the beginning of our argument, and zero at the end is tantamount to requiring h to be zero and not zero simultaneously which is not possible. So h can't be zero. But it can be very close to zero. Moreover as it gets closer to zero ($h \to 0$) it is clear that $4 + h \to 4$.

This should also feel very familiar to you. Do you see that we're talking about a limit? From Equation (12.2) we see that as $h \to 0$,

$$\frac{y(2 + h) - y(2)}{h} = 4 + h \to 4.$$

Moreover, by the Principle of Local Linearity as $h \to 0$ the secant and tangent lines become indistinguishable. Thus it appears that the limit

$$\lim_{h \to 0} \frac{y(2 + h) - y(2)}{h} = \lim_{h \to 0} \frac{4 + 4h + h^2 - 4}{h} = \lim_{h \to 0} 4 + h = 4$$

will be the value of the derivative, $y'(2)$, of $y(x)$ at $x = 2$.

<u>End Of Example #82</u>

Our discussion in Example #82 suggests that we can use the limit concept to finally resolve the logical difficulties inherent in a naive[7] use of the differential as a foundation for Calculus, and that is exactly our present goal.

In this second part of this text we will finally build a viable theory to support Calculus which even Bishop Berkeley would have to accept. We begin with the following definition. This is the modern definition of the derivative.

<u>Definition 15</u>: **The Derivative**

Suppose f is a function, and that x is a real number. If $\lim_{h \to 0} \dfrac{f(x + h) - f(x)}{h}$ exists then we say that f is **differentiable at** x and that the derivative of f at x is given by:

$$f'(x) = \frac{\mathrm{d}f}{\mathrm{d}x} = \lim_{h \to 0} \frac{f(x + h) - f(x)}{h} \tag{12.3}$$

if this limit exists. If the limit does not exist then the derivative also does not exist at x.

Definition #15 defines the derivative locally, "at x." This may seem to be a mere formality but it is not. When we write $f(x)$ it is easy to fall into the habit of thinking of x as representing all of the points in the domain of f. But that is fundamentally wrong. The variable x always represents a single point in the domain of f. Always. No exceptions. When its value is unknown we call it[8] x because this is simpler than saying "whatever point we're interested in." This is why the symbol $f(x)$ is pronounced "f of x," or "f at x."

In Example #82 we evaluated the derivative of $f(x) = x^2$ at the single point $x = 2$. It appears that if we want to evaluate the derivative of $f(x) = x^2$ at $x = 3$ and $x = 4$ we need to compute $\lim_{h \to 0} \frac{f(3+h) - f(3)}{h}$, and $\lim_{h \to 0} \frac{f(4+h) - f(4)}{h}$. But it is tedious to compute the derivative of a function one specific point at a time. If we leave x unspecified and compute $f'(x) = \lim_{h \to 0} \dfrac{f(x + h) - f(x)}{h}$ we obtain the value of the derivative of f at the single, but unspecified point x. We can then find the derivative of f at any point by replacing x with whatever point we are interested in.

Problem #482:

Use the techniques we saw in Chapter 11 to compute $f'(x)$ by evaluating a limit. Check your work by differentiating using differentials.

(**Comment:** Do not use L'Hôpital's Rule. L'Hôpital's Rule requires that we be able to differen-

---

[7]We say "naive" because the fact is that the differential concept actually can be made fully rigorous and thus can serve as a foundation for Calculus just as well as the limit theory we are currently pursuing. Such a foundation was built by the mathematician Abraham Robinson is his 1966 book *Non-Standard Analysis*. However Robinson used ideas and techniques from modern mathematical logic which were not available to mathematicians of the seventeenth century. Because they are they are not available to us either, we will justify our methods using the older, slightly simpler, limit theory.

[8]Or y, or z, or Fred, Ethel, Ricky, or Lucy. These are all just names we give to a specific quantity which is unknown.

tiate these functions. Since that is exactly what this problem asks you to do, using L'Hôpital's Rule would be circular reasoning.)

(a) $f(x) = x^2$ **(c)** $f(x) = x^6 - 7x^4$ **(e)** $f(x) = \frac{1}{x^3}$ **(g)** $f(x) = x^{1/2}$

(b) $f(x) = 2x^2 - x$ **(d)** $f(x) = \pi$ **(f)** $f(x) = -\frac{1}{x}$ **(h)** $f(x) = x^{1/3}$

When a function is differentiable at all of the points in its domain it is said to be **differentiable on its domain** or just **differentiable**[9].

Drill #483:

Which of the functions in Problem #482 are **differentiable** and which are not? Identify all points of non-differentiability.

If you look closely at Definition #15 you can see Leibniz' differentials lurking in the background[10]. If we let $\Delta y = f(x + h) - f(x)$ and $\Delta x = h$ then for values of h very close to zero we have.

$$f'(x) \approx \frac{\Delta y}{\Delta x} = \frac{f(x + h) - f(x)}{h}.$$

The approximation gets better as $\Delta x \to 0$ (equivalently, as $h \to 0$) so you can see that Definition #15 avoids the infinitely small by replacing differentials with Δx (equivalently h) which is a small, but finite, number which is only considered in the limit as $\Delta x \to 0$. In particular, Δx is not an infinitesimal. But it is allowed to become as close to zero as needed while remaining finite in size. Needless to say, limits are much harder to work with than differentials. Their saving grace is if they can be made logically unassailable with a proper definition. Bishop Berkeley would approve.

For the rest of this text we pursue two over–arching goals. The first is to rigorously recapture from Definition #15 all of the differentiation rules we are already familiar with. We will address that in the first section of the next chapter. Keep in mind that we are not developing the differentiation rules. We already know them, and by now you should be quite skillful at their use. Our goal now is to show rigorously that by using Definition #15 we can recapture all of the properties that we found so useful before.

To do this we will need several properties of limits which we will state – without proof – in the next section. Then we will prove that our differentiation rules and the First Derivative Test are valid using Definition #15. However all of this will be done under the assumption that the limit properties in the next section are actually true.

Our second goal is to prove, rigorously that the limit properties in the next section are actually true. We will do this in Chapter 16.3.

---

[9]In practice we are often quite loose with the term **differentiable**. Most people would call the functions $f(x) = \sqrt{x}$ and $g(x) = \sqrt[3]{x}$ **differentiable** even though they both fail to be differentiable at $x = 0$.

[10]Newton's fluxions are nowhere to be seen, however.

Chapter 13

The Differentiation Rules via Limits

13.1 The Limit Rules (Theorems)

"In the old days when people invented a new function they had something useful in mind. Now, they invent them deliberately just to invalidate our ancestors' reasoning, and that is all they are ever going to get out of them."

– Henri Poincaré (1854 – 1912)

In this section we will state several theorems about limits which we will need in the sections following. The limit concept is very subtle and our understanding of it is still quite intuitive. We are not yet quite prepared to prove these theorems so we will leave these theorems unproven for now. Our immediate goal is simply to understand what they say and learn how to use them. In the next section we will begin using these theorems to show how the limit in Definition #15 allows us to recapture all of the major results we used in Part I of this text.

In Chapter 16 we will finally discard our intuitive definition of a limit (Definition #12) and formally define both a limit at infinity (Theorem 26) and a limit at a point (Theorem 27). Then we will return to the theorems in this section and (finally) prove rigorously that they are, in fact, true. Until then any result which relies on the theorems in this section should be considered contingent.

In Chapter 11 we stated the following three theorems about limits "at infinity."

1. the limit of a sum is the sum of the limits (Theorem 8),

2. the limit of a product is the product of the limits (Theorem 9) and,

3. the limit of a quotient is the quotient of the limits (Theorem 10).

All three of these theorems remain true if x is approaching some finite number, a, instead of infinity.

Theorem 15: [The Limit of a Sum is the Sum of the Limits]

Let a be some real number. Suppose that the functions $f(x)$ and $g(x)$ are defined on some open interval about a except, possibly, at a itself.

Then if $\lim\limits_{x \to a} f(x) = L$ and $\lim\limits_{x \to a} g(x) = M$, then

$$\lim_{x \to a} [f(x) + g(x)] = L + M = \lim_{x \to a} f(x) + \lim_{x \to a} g(x).$$

Theorem 16: [The Limit of a Product is the Product of the Limits]

Let a be some real number. Suppose that the functions $f(x)$ and $g(x)$ are defined on some open interval about a except, possibly, at a itself.

If $\lim\limits_{x \to a} f(x) = L$ and $\lim\limits_{x \to a} g(x) = M$ then

$$\lim_{x \to a} (f(x) \cdot g(x)) = \left(\lim_{x \to a} f(x) \right) \cdot \left(\lim_{x \to a} g(x) \right) = L \cdot M.$$

Theorem 17: [The Limit of a Quotient is the Quotient of the Limits]

Let a be some real number. Suppose that the functions $f(x)$ and $g(x)$ are defined on some open interval about a except, possibly, at a itself.

Then if $\lim\limits_{x \to a} f(x) = L$ and $\lim\limits_{x \to a} g(x) = M \neq 0$ then

$$\lim_{x \to a} \frac{f(x)}{g(x)} = \frac{\lim\limits_{x \to a} f(x)}{\lim\limits_{x \to a} g(x)} = \frac{L}{M}.$$

Notice that in addition to changing ∞ to some real number, a, we have added two qualifications to the statement of each of these theorems from Chapter 11:

1. "Suppose that the functions $f(x)$ and $g(x)$ are defined on some open interval about a" and,

2. "except, possibly, at a itself"

To see why these are necessary recall that we're going to use limits to define the derivative as in Theorem 15 so we'll need to evaluate the limit $f'(x) = \lim\limits_{h \to 0} \frac{f(x+h)-f(x)}{h}$. Clearly the expression $\frac{f(x+h)-f(x)}{h}$ is not defined at $h = 0$. But we're only interested in its value **in the limit** as $h \to 0$ which means that h must be able to get close to 0. That is, there must be an open interval around 0 where the expression $\frac{f(x+h)-f(x)}{h}$ is defined.

But we don't care if $\frac{f(x+h)-f(x)}{h}$ is defined at $h = 0$ or not. It is irrelevant to our purpose. So we state explicitly that we do not consider whether $h = 0$.

Ok, but why did we insert the word "possibly"? Wouldn't it be enough to simply say "except at a"?

We need to say "possibly" because these theorems, like all theorems, are stated with as much generality as possible. For example, consider the function $f(x) = 2x$. Had we not included "possibly" in the conditions of our theorems the limit: $\lim_{x \to 3} 2x$, which is clearly equal to 6, would have to be considered undefined because $f(x) = 2x$ is defined at $x = 3$. This distinction[1] may seem like a very fussy, and unimportant detail right now, but it will be important when we discuss the meaning of continuity in Section 13.1.

Example #83:

Suppose

$$f(x) = \begin{cases} 2x & \text{if } x \neq 3 \\ 10 & \text{if } x = 3 \end{cases}.$$

Then

$$\lim_{x \to 3} f(x) = 6.$$

In particular the limit is not 10.

Here is how we would evaluate this limit using the tools we currently have at our disposal.

We're interested in the limit as $x \to 3$ so in particular we do not need to consider the case when $x = 3$. But as long as $x \neq 3$ we have $f(x) = 2x$ so

$$\lim_{x \to 3} f(x) = \lim_{x \to 3} 2x.$$

As x gets close to 3 it is clear that $2x$ gets close to 6. Therefore

$$\lim_{x \to 3} f(x) = 6.$$

Notice that our reasoning is a little vague in the last step because we had to resort to the phase "gets close to," and we know from our work in Chapter 11.4 that this is not a precise phrase. This is the best we can do now because we have not yet rigorously defined a limit. We will do that in Chapter 16.

End Of Example #83

Problem #484:

By reasoning in a manner similar to Example #83 show that $\lim_{x \to 3} f(x) = 9$ for each function.

---

[1] In the eighteenth century there was a, public, protracted, and vitriolic argument between Benjamin Robins and James Jurin over exactly this point. Jurin would have claimed that the statement $\lim_{x \to 3} 2x = 6$ is meaningless. Robins would have said it has meaning because it is obviously true. The point here is not that either man was right or wrong, but rather that it depends on how we define limits. By one definition Robins was correct, by another Jurin was. Their controversy was the result of the incomplete understanding of limits that prevailed at the time.

(a) $f(x) = x^2$

(b) $f(x) = \begin{cases} x^2 & \text{if } x \neq 3 \\ \text{undefined} & \text{if } x = 3 \end{cases}$

It will be tedious to write (and to read) the phrase "Suppose that $f(x)$ is defined on some open interval about a except, possibly, at a itself" every time we need it so it is customary to say something more like "Suppose $f(x)$ is defined **near** a" instead. Because we are trying to be as precise, and rigorous as possible we will formalize this by redefining the word **near**.

Definition 16: **Near**

We say that $f(x)$ has some property **near**[2] $x = a$ if $f(x)$ has that property on an open interval about $x = a$, except possibly at a itself.

We have the following theorem.

Theorem 18: [**The Limit of a Constant is the Constant**]

Suppose a and L are real numbers, and $f(x) = L$ near a. Then

$$\lim_{x \to a} f(x) = L.$$

Notice that Theorem 18 would be considerably less useful had we not required that $f(x) = L$ for x near a, rather than $f(x) = L$ on its entire domain. For example, as stated Theorem 18 allows us to conclude that if

$$H(x) = \begin{cases} 1 & \text{if } x \geq 0 \\ -1 & \text{if } x < 0 \end{cases}$$

then

$$\lim_{x \to 5} H(x) = 1$$

and

$$\lim_{x \to -5} H(x) = -1$$

because there are open intervals about $x = 5$ and $x = -5$ where $H(x) = 1$, and $H(x) = -1$, respectively.

Since there is no such interval about $x = 0$, $\lim_{x \to 0} H(x)$ is undefined.

---

[2]Notice that this is not what "near" means in ordinary speech. This is one of the things that makes it difficult to read mathematics. We routinely co-opt words from natural languages (like English) and redefine them to fit our needs. In this case our purpose requires that we change the definition of "near" slightly as you've seen. Because "near" is a common word and you have a lifetime of experience using it, it can be very difficult to cast off your preconceptions. The familiar definition you learned in childhood will intrude and cause confusion. It is hard to overcome this. Refer back to the definition frequently until you have internalized the mathematical definition.

Drill #485:

  (a) Find an open interval about 5 where $H(x) = 1$.

  (b) Find an open interval about -5 where $H(x) = -1$.

(**Comment:** There are many to choose from in both parts. Choose only one for each.)

Drill #486:

Suppose
$$f(x) = \begin{cases} 1; & \text{if } x > 1 \text{ or if } x = -2 \\ -2; & \text{if } x \le 1 \text{ and } x = -2. \end{cases}$$

Determine whether the following statements are true or false.

  (a) $f(x) = 1$ near $x = 4$.

  (b) $f(x) = 1$ near $x = 1$.

  (c) $f(x) = -2$ near $x = 1$.

  (d) $f(x) = 1$ near $x = -2$.

  (e) $f(x) = -2$ near $x = -2$.

  (f) $f(x) = 0$ near $x = 0$.

Problem #487:

Explain, that the following statements are true by citing Theorem 15 through Theorem 18 as needed.

  (a) $\displaystyle\lim_{x \to 0} \left(\frac{5x}{x} + \frac{\pi x}{x} \right) = 5 + \pi$

  (b) $\displaystyle\lim_{x \to 2} \left(\frac{x - 2}{x - 2} + \frac{3x - 6}{x - 2} \right) = 4$

  (c) $\displaystyle\lim_{x \to 5} \left(2x + 3x^2 \right) = 85$

  (d) $\displaystyle\lim_{x \to -1} \left(\frac{x^2 - 1}{x + 1} + \frac{x^2 + 3x + 2}{x + 1} \right) = -1$

Problem #488:

Notice that neither $\displaystyle\lim_{x \to 0} \frac{1}{x}$ nor $\displaystyle\lim_{x \to 0} \left(\frac{-1}{x} \right)$ exists. However their sum,

$$\lim_{x \to 0} \left(\frac{1}{x} + \frac{-1}{x} \right) = \lim_{x \to 0} 0 = 0$$

does exist. Explain why this does not contradict Theorem 15.

Problem #489:

Suppose $g(x) \neq 0$ near $x = a$ and $\lim\limits_{x \to a} \frac{f(x)}{g(x)}$ exists. Use Theorem #16 to show that if $\lim\limits_{x \to a} g(x) = 0$ then $\lim\limits_{x \to a} f(x) = 0$.

(**Hint:** Consider $f(x) = \frac{f(x)}{g(x)} \cdot g(x)$ for x near a.)

(**Comment:** This problem shows that if $\lim\limits_{x \to a} g(x) = 0$ then the only way that $\lim\limits_{x \to a} \frac{f(x)}{g(x)}$ can exist is if we have a L'Hôpital Indeterminate. It can also be used to prove Lemma 20 as you will see when we get to it.)

The following Corollary says that if $f(x)$ is approaching L_f and we multiply $f(x)$ by a number, k, then the product $kf(x)$ approaches kL_f. It follows from Theorem 18 and Theorem 16.

Corollary 19:   If $\lim\limits_{x \to a} f(x) = L_f$ and k is a real number then $\lim\limits_{x \to a} kf(x) = k\lim\limits_{x \to a} f(x) = kL_f$.

Drill #490: Prove Corollary 19.

The Limit of a Composition and Continuity at a Point

The concept of **continuity** is essential to Calculus, but you may have noticed that we have carefully avoided it as much as possible until now. This is because defining continuity is similar to defining the line tagent to a curve (Definition #2). We need to think carefully about what we want the term **continuous** to mean, and then craft our definition to capture that meaning. This would have been very difficult to do without a fairly sophisticated understanding of the limit concept.

So stop and think about this for a moment. What do we mean when we say a curve is **continuous**? A first, intuitive definition usually goes something like this: "A function is continuous if you can draw its graph without lifting your pencil from the paper," but this is unsatisfactory for a number of reasons. In particular, it is impossible to apply in most cases. Think about it. Have often have you seen the entire graph of any function? Usually we just draw the part neat the origin and put arrowheads on both ends of the graph. We need something more precise.

At the end of Example #80 we remarked that it is only when $f(x)$ is continuous at $x = g(a)$ that $\lim\limits_{x \to a} f(g(x))$ is equal to $f\left(\lim\limits_{x \to a} g(x)\right)$, but we did not discuss the matter any further. It is time for that discussion.

First, notice that when you think closely about the statement "$f(x)$ is continuous at $g(a)$" it appears to be nonsense, because $g(a)$ is the value of f at the single value $g(a)$ but . Does it make sense to you that a curve can be continuous at a single value of its domain? In ordinary usage the concept of continuity requires an interval to be continuous on, doesn't it?

Since we need the concept of "continuity at a point," we define it.

Definition 17: **Continuity at a Point**

A function f, whose domain is an interval in $\mathbb{R}$, is continuous at $x = a$ in the interval, if and only if $\lim\limits_{x \to a} f(x) = f(a)$, (alternatively, if $\lim\limits_{h \to 0} f(a + h) = f(a)$).

If f is continuous at every point in its domain we'll just call it a continuous function.

The sketch at the right shows that Definition #17 recovers the intuitive notion that a function is continuous if we can draw its graph without lifting pen from page. Both of the functions, $f(x)$ and $g(x)$ are identical everywhere except at $x = 1$. Clearly, to draw $g(x)$, which is discontinuous at $x = 1$, we must lift our pen from the page. This is not true of the graph of $f(x)$, which is continuous.

The following lemma is true and the proof will be valid once the limit theorems have been proven in Chapter 16.

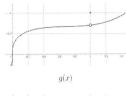

$g(x)$

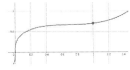

$f(x)$

Lemma 20: [**Differentiability Implies Continuity**]

If $f(x)$ is differentiable at $x = a$ then $f(x)$ is also continuous at $x = a$.

Problem #491: Use the result of Problem #489 to prove Lemma 20.

When we were studying horizontal asymptotes in Section 11.4 we encountered Theorem 11 (the Squeeze Theorem "at" Infinity). But the Squeeze Theorem is also valid if $x \to a$, where a is a real number.

Theorem 21: [**The Squeeze Theorem (The Finite Case)**]

If $\alpha(x) \le f(x) \le \beta(x)$ for x near a and

$$\lim_{x \to a} \beta(x) = \lim_{x \to a} \alpha(x) = L$$

then $\lim\limits_{x \to a} f(x) = L$ also.

Theorem 21 is illustrated below, but a formal proof will not be given until Chapter 16.

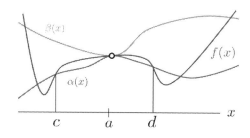

Problem #492:
Consider the two functions defined in the sketch below:

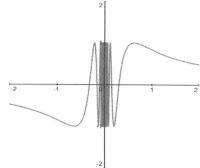

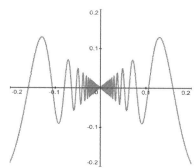

$$T(x) = \begin{cases} \sin\left(\frac{1}{x}\right), & x \neq 0 \\ 0, & x = 0 \end{cases} \qquad U(x) = \begin{cases} x \sin\left(\frac{1}{x}\right), & x \neq 0 \\ 0, & x = 0 \end{cases}$$

(a) Use Theorem 21 to show that $U(x)$ is continuous at $x = 0$.
(**Hint:** What functions is $U(x)$ caught between?)

(b) Use Definition 17 to show that $T(x)$ is not continuous at $x = 0$.
(**Hint:** Try the substitution $z = \frac{1}{x}$ for $x \neq 0$. What would $\lim\limits_{x \to 0} T(x)$ look like in terms of z?)

Theorem 22: [**The Limit of a Composition is the Composition of the Limits**]
Suppose $\lim\limits_{x \to a} g(x) = L_g$ and that $f(x)$ is continuous at L_g. Then

$$\lim_{x \to a} f(g(x)) = f\left(\lim_{x \to a} g(x)\right) = f(L_g).$$

Essentially this says that we can interchange the function f and the "lim" symbols if f is continuous at $g(a)$.

13.2   The General Differentiation Theorems, via Limits

". . . one way in math to take care of destabilizing problems is to legislate them out of existence . . . by loading theorems with stipulations and exclusions designed to head off crazy results."

– David Foster Wallace (1962 - 2008)

Since we will now be proving the the differentiation rules rigorously we will call them what they really are: Theorems. Because limits are much less intuitive than differentials we'll want to be as efficient as possible when using them. The sooner we can build up some tools to make things easier, the better.

Also, in this section we will add a new differentiation rule (theorem): The Chain Rule. Or rather, we will give a name to an already familiar technique and elevate it's status by providing a formal proof. Proving the Chain, Product, and Quotient Differentiation Rules using limits will require a good deal of cleverness. These proofs will also uncover some unexpected subtleties along the way.

Before we begin there is one more point that needs to be clear. Because differentiation is now defined via a limit and limits are defined at a point we can only differentiate a function at a point. We usually say that limit evaluation and differentiability are **local properties**. If we don't specify the "at x" the convention is that the function is differentiable at every point in its domain.

The proofs of the Constant, Sum, and Constant Multiple Differentiation Rules are all completely straightforward so we will leave them as exercises[3] for you.

Theorem 23: [**The Constant Rule for Differentiation**]

If L is some number and $f(x) = L$ for all real values of x near[4] L, then $f'(x) = 0$ at every real number x near[5] L.

Proof: By Definition #12.3

$$f'(x) = \lim_{h \to 0} \frac{f(x+h) - f(x)}{h}.$$

But $f(x+h) = L = f(x)$ so

$$f'(x) = \lim_{h \to 0} \frac{L - L}{h} = \lim_{h \to 0} \frac{0}{h} = 0.$$

∎

---

[3]Frequently students will simply ignore problems that are described as straightforward. Don't make that mistake. Straightforward does not mean easy, and it does not mean unimportant. We are leaving these problems for you so you can gain experience using limits in the simplest cases, not because they are unimportant.

[4]"Near" means on an open interval about L. Recall Definition 16.

[5]On the same open interval.

Theorem 24: [**The Sum Rule for Differentiation**]
   If $\alpha(x)$ and $\beta(x)$ are differentiable at x and $f(x) = \alpha(x) + \beta(x)$, then $f(x)$ is also differentiable at x and

$$f'(x) = \alpha'(x) + \beta'(x).$$

Problem #493: Use Definition 15 to prove the Sum Rule for Differentiation.

   Recall that when we first established the General Differentiation Rules using differentials in Chapter 3 we said that the Constant Multiple, Power and Quotient Rules for differentiation were just conveniences because they depend on the other rules.

   This is still true of course (except for the caveat in the point of rigor below) which means that we don't have to prove any of them using limits. For example, since the Constant Rule and the Product Rule are now established theorems we can use these to prove the Constant Multiple Rule directly, without having to resort to using limits.

Theorem 25: [**The Constant Multiple Rule for Differentiation**]
   If $f(x)$ is differentiable at x and K is a constant then $\alpha(x) = Kf(x)$ is also differentiable and

$$\alpha'(x) = Kf'(x).$$

Problem #494: Use the Definition #15 to prove the Constant Multiple Rule.

13.3   The Chain Rule

To understand the Chain Rule we will need to slightly blur the distinction between function and variable.

Example #84:

   Here's what we mean: The formula $y = (2x^2 - 6x)^3$, is given entirely in terms of the variables x, and y. To differentiate using differentials we would make the (variable) substitution $z = 3x^2 + 6x$ so that $y = z^3$. In that case, $dy = 3z\,dz = 3\left(3x^2 + 6x\right)^2 (6x+6)\,dx$, and dividing through by dx gives us the derivative of y with respect to x,

$$\frac{dy}{dx} = 3z\,dz = 3\left(3x^2 + 6x\right)^2 (6x + 6). \tag{13.1}$$

But Definition #15 requires that we think about functions, not variables so let's translate this problem into the language of functions. If $y = \left(2x^2 - 6x\right)^3$, clearly y is a function of (depends on) x. Naming that function f, we have $y = f(x)$. Replacing y with $f(x)$, we get $f(x) = (2x^2 - 6x)^3$.

Similarly, if $z = 3x^2 + 6x$ then z is also a function of (depends on) x, and naming that function β we have $z = \beta(x)$. Replacing z with $\beta(x)$ we have $f(x) = (\beta(x))^3$. If we suppress the "(x)" part of $\beta(x)$, we see that f can also be thought of as a function of (depends on) β so that

$$f(\beta) = \beta^3$$

is also a valid representation of our function. If we now define $\alpha(\beta) = \beta^3$ we see that

$$f(x) = \alpha(\beta).$$

Looking again at Equation 13.1, and mixing the differential and functional notations a bit we see that

$$f'(x) = \frac{dy}{dx} = 3z\,dz = \underbrace{3\left(3x^2 + 6x\right)^2}_{\frac{d\alpha}{d\beta} = \alpha'(\beta)} \underbrace{(6x + 6)}_{\frac{d\beta}{dx} = \beta'(x)} = \alpha'(\beta) \cdot \beta'(x).$$

Thus if $f(x) = \alpha(\beta(x))$ is the composition of $\alpha(x)$ and $\beta(x)$ then

$$f'(x) = \alpha'(\beta(x))\beta'(x).$$

This is the Chain Rule. We have expressed the Chain Rule in this form so that we can prove it rigorously, not so that we can use it. The substitution process using differentials still works so there is no reason to stop using substitution when you are actually computing derivatives.

End Of Example #84

Theorem 26: [The Chain Rule]

Suppose that $\beta(x)$ is differentiable at x, that $\alpha(x)$ is differentiable at $\beta(x)$ and that $\Delta\beta \neq 0$ near x. Then the composition,

$$f(x) = \alpha(\beta(x))$$

is also differentiable, and

$$f'(x) = \alpha'(\beta(x)) \cdot \beta'(x). \qquad (13.2)$$

Digression #21: The Origins of the Chain Rule

Before the invention of Calculus, arithmetic primers gave the name "The Chain Rule" to the computational technique that is used to, among other things, convert money from one currency to another. For example if we need to convert 30 American dollars ($) to British pounds (£) and we know that[a]

$$1 \text{ dollar} = 0.86 \text{ euros, and that } 1 \text{ euro} = 0.9 \text{ pounds.}$$

Then the conversion is

$$\$30 = 30 \, \cancel{\text{dollars}} \times \frac{0.86 \, \cancel{\text{euros}}}{1 \, \cancel{\text{dollars}}} \times \frac{0.9 \, \text{pounds}}{1 \, \cancel{\text{euros}}} = 30 \times 0.86 \times 0.9 \, \text{pounds} = 23.22\pounds$$

We've actually seen this type of conversion before. We used in in Section 5 when we converted angular velocity to linear velocity via the formula:

$$\left(\frac{3 \, \cancel{\text{revolution}}}{1 \, \cancel{\text{minute}}}\right) \cdot \left(\frac{2\pi \, \cancel{\text{radians}}}{1 \, \cancel{\text{revolution}}}\right) \cdot \left(\frac{10 \, \text{meters}}{1 \, \cancel{\text{radians}}}\right) \cdot \left(\frac{1 \, \cancel{\text{minute}}}{60 \, \text{second}}\right) = \frac{\pi \, \text{meters}}{1 \, \text{second}} \approx 3.14 \frac{\text{meters}}{\text{second}}.$$

A similar chain of cancellations will occur when we differentiate a function composition of the form $\alpha(t) = \alpha(\beta(y(x(t))))$. We think of

α as a function of β (so that $\alpha'(\beta) = \frac{d\alpha}{d\beta}$)

β as a function of y (so that $\beta'(y) = \frac{d\beta}{dy}$),

y as a function of x (so that $y'(x) = \frac{dy}{dx}$),

and x as a function of t (so that $y'(x) = \frac{dx}{dt}$).

Putting this all together we see that

$$\alpha'(t) = \frac{d\alpha}{d\cancel{\beta}} \cdot \frac{d\cancel{\beta}}{d\cancel{y}} \cdot \frac{d\cancel{y}}{d\cancel{x}} \cdot \frac{d\cancel{x}}{dt} = \frac{d\alpha}{dt}.$$

The substitutions we used to make things "easier on your eyes" in Section 1.2 is equivalent this chain of cancellations. With the invention of Calculus the older Chain Rule for unit conversion was extended to the differentiation by substitution technique using differentials. Eventually it became the only Chain Rule. When the limit was used to provide rigor to Calculus the name was also applied to Equation (13.2).

---

[a]These numbers were accurate on the day this passage was written. They are almost certainly wrong on the day you are reading it. Don't use them to convert currency.

==================== End Of Digression #21 ====================

Understanding the Chain Rule in this form requires that we blur the distinction between function and variable a bit. When we compute $\frac{d\alpha}{d\beta} = \alpha'(\beta)$ (the derivative of α with with respect to β) we view β as a variable, but when we compute $\frac{d\beta}{dx} = \beta'(x)$ (the derivative of β with respect to x) we view it as a function.

As far as the Chain Rule is concerned it is both.

Proof: Before we begin take specific notice of the assumption "$\Delta\beta \neq 0$ near x" in the statement of the Chain Rule. We will have a few comments about this in Digression #22 after the proof is completed.

We will first establish that

$$\lim_{h \to 0} \Delta\beta = 0. \tag{13.3}$$

Suppose[6] that

$$\beta(x + h) - \beta(x) = \Delta\beta. \tag{13.4}$$

Then

$$\lim_{h \to 0} \beta(x + h) = \lim_{h \to 0} (\beta(x) + \Delta\beta).$$

By Theorem 15 we have

$$\lim_{h \to 0} \beta(x + h) = \lim_{h \to 0} \beta(x) + \lim_{h \to 0} \Delta\beta,$$

and since $\beta(x)$ is differentiable at x we see from Lemma 20 that

$$\beta(x) = \beta(x) + \lim_{h \to 0} \Delta\beta$$

from which Equation (13.3) follows.

To prove the Chain Rule recall that

$$\begin{aligned}
f'(x) &= \lim_{h \to 0} \frac{f(x + h) - f(x)}{h} \\
&= \lim_{h \to 0} \frac{\alpha(\beta(x + h)) - \alpha(\beta(x))}{h}.
\end{aligned}$$

Multiplying by 1 in the form[7] $\frac{\Delta\beta}{\Delta\beta}$ gives

$$f'(x) = \lim_{h \to 0} \left(\frac{\alpha(\beta(x + h)) - \alpha(\beta(x))}{\Delta\beta} \cdot \frac{\Delta\beta}{h} \right). \tag{13.5}$$

From Equation (13.4) we see that $\Delta\beta = \beta(x + h) - \beta(x)$ so

$$= \lim_{h \to 0} \left(\frac{\alpha(\beta(x + h)) - \alpha(\beta(x))}{\Delta\beta} \cdot \frac{\beta(x + h) - \beta(x)}{h} \right).$$

By Theorem 16 we have:

$$= \lim_{h \to 0} \left(\frac{\alpha(\beta(x + h)) - \alpha(\beta(x))}{\Delta\beta} \right) \cdot \lim_{h \to 0} \left(\frac{\beta(x + h) - \beta(x)}{h} \right).$$

---

[6]Because asserting the equality of non-existing objects would be meaningless we assume, implicitly that all limits in this argument exist.

[7]In the past we have called this "uncancelling" $\Delta\beta$. Also, notice that this is where we use the assumption, "$\Delta\beta \neq 0$ near x."

Equation (13.3) says that $h \to 0$ is equivalent to $\Delta\beta \to 0$ so we have

$$f'(x) = \lim_{\substack{h \to 0 \\ \Delta\beta \to 0}} \left(\frac{\alpha(\beta + \Delta\beta) - \alpha(\beta)}{\Delta\beta} \right) \cdot \lim_{h \to 0} \left(\frac{\beta(x + h) - \beta(x)}{h} \right),$$

$$f'(x) = \underbrace{\lim_{\Delta\beta \to 0} \left(\frac{\alpha(\beta + \Delta\beta) - \alpha(\beta)}{\Delta\beta} \right)}_{=\alpha'(\beta)} \cdot \underbrace{\lim_{h \to 0} \left(\frac{\beta(x + h) - \beta(x)}{h} \right)}_{=\beta'(x)}. \tag{13.6}$$

$$f'(x) = \alpha'(\beta) \cdot \beta'(x). \tag{13.7}$$

In Equation (13.7 β is first used as a variable in $\alpha'(\beta)$, and then as the function $\beta(x)$. While this is correct, it is also poor form because it accentuates the dual use of β. To avoid this we usually express the Chain Rule as

$$f'(x) = \alpha'(\beta(x)) \cdot \beta'(x)$$

to emphasize that x, not β, is the variable.   ∎

Digression #22: Why Assume That $\Delta\beta \neq 0$ Near Zero?

Do you see why we had to assume that $\Delta\beta \neq 0$ near x?

Observe that in Equation (13.6) $\Delta\beta$ plays the same role the h plays in Definition (15). In Definition (15) we were careful to insist that h could never equal zero, so if we are going to interpret $\lim_{\Delta\beta \to 0} \left(\frac{\alpha(\beta + \Delta\beta) - \alpha(\beta)}{\Delta\beta} \right)$ as the derivative of α with respect to β, as we did in Equation (13.6), we need to know that $\Delta\beta \neq 0$ when h is near zero.

Our imposition of that constraint means that Theorem #26 does not apply to any function $f(x) = \alpha(\beta(x))$ where $\Delta\beta$ might be equal to zero no matter how close h is to zero. Fortunately, functions of that sort are generally the kinds of "pathological functions" that Poincaré is complained about in the quote at the beginning of this chapter. A valid proof of the Chain Rule without that constraint is possible, but since it would have very little relevance to anything we'll be doing we have chosen to prove only this weaker form of the Chain Rule[a]

If you are unsatisfied with this proof and want to see a proof of the stronger version of the Chain Rule, consider majoring in mathematics. You'll see that and much, much more. In the meantime try working through the following problem.

Problem #495:

(a) Show that the function $\beta(x) = \sin\left(\frac{1}{x}\right)$ does not satisfy the constraint $\Delta\beta \neq 0$ when x is near zero.
(**Hint:** Recall Definition #16.)

(b) As a result of part (a) Theorem 26 does not apply to any of the following functions at $x = 0$. Nevertheless one of them is differentiable at $x = 0$. Use Definition #15 to find out which one.

(i) $T(x) = \begin{cases} \sin\left(\frac{1}{x}\right) & x \neq 0 \\ 0 & x = 0 \end{cases}$.   **(iii)** $V(x) = \begin{cases} x^2 \sin\left(\frac{1}{x}\right) & x \neq 0 \\ 0 & x = 0 \end{cases}$.

(ii) $U(x) = \begin{cases} x \sin\left(\frac{1}{x}\right) & x \neq 0 \\ 0 & x = 0 \end{cases}$.

---

[a]You may be wondering if our choice to go with a weaker form of the Chain Rule means we've given Bishop Berkeley cause for compliant. The answer is no, we haven't. If we'd left off the condition that $\Delta\beta \neq 0$, then our proof would not have been rigorous because we'd have ended by claiming more than we'd proved. As it is, we've only claimed what we have proved.
Rigorous does not mean perfect, it means logical.

━━━━━━━━━━ End Of Digression #22 ━━━━━━━━━━

Example #85:

Suppose that $f(x) = (\sin(x) + \cos(x))^2$. To use the Chain Rule to compute the derivative of $f(x)$ we need to recognize that $f(x)$ is the composition of $\alpha(x) = x^2$, and $\beta(x) = \sin(x) + \cos(x)$ and then apply Theorem 26 as follows.

$$f'(x) = \alpha'(\beta(x)) \cdot \beta'(x)$$
$$= \alpha'(\beta(x)) \cdot (\cos(x) - \sin(x))$$
$$= \alpha'(\sin(x) + \cos(x)) \cdot (\cos(x) - \sin(x))$$
$$f'(x) = 2(\sin(x) + \cos(x)) \cdot (\cos(x) - \sin(x)).$$

End Of Example #85

In our opinion the Chain Rule leaves a lot to be desired as a computational technique. But we don't have to use it that way since Theorem 26 validates the substitutions we have always used.

Drill #496:

Suppose $y = f(x) = (\sin(x) + \cos(x))^2$. Compute the differential dy and then divide through by dx to find the derivative $\frac{dy}{dx}$. Confirm that it is the same as the derivative we found in Example #85.

Problem #497:

Compute $\frac{dy}{dx}$ for each of the following functions by identifying $\alpha(x)$ and $\beta(x)$ such that $y(x) = \alpha(\beta(x))$ and applying the Chain Rule. You may have to do this more than once for a given problem.

In each case confirm that your computation is correct with an appropriate differential substitution.

(a) $y = (3x + 5)^6$

(d) $y = \left(\frac{x - x^{\frac{1}{2}}}{x^3 - 1}\right)^2$

(b) $y = \sec(\tan(x))$

(e) $y = e^{x - \cos^2(x)} + (2x^2 - 3)^{\frac{1}{5}}$

(c) $y = \sqrt[7]{\frac{1}{x} + x^3}$

(f) $y = \sqrt{x + \sqrt[3]{2 + \sqrt[4]{3 - x^2}}}$

13.4 The Product Rule

A rigorous proof of the Product Rule is also fairly complex, but it does not suffer from the kind of technical problems we encountered in the proof of the Chain Rule.

Theorem 27: [The Product Rule for Differentiation]
If $\alpha(x)$ and $\beta(x)$ are differentiable at x then $f(x) = \alpha(x) \cdot \beta(x)$ is differentiable and

$$f'(x) = \alpha(x) \cdot \beta'(x) + \beta(x) \cdot \alpha'(x). \tag{13.8}$$

Proof: We start with the two observations. The first is that

$$f'(x) = \lim_{h \to 0} \frac{f(x + h) - f(x)}{h} = \lim_{h \to 0} \frac{\alpha(x + h)\beta(x + h) - \alpha(x)\beta(x)}{h} \tag{13.9}$$

and the second is that, in limit form, Equation (13.8) is

$$f'(x) = \alpha(x) \left(\lim_{h \to 0} \frac{\beta(x + h) - \beta(x)}{h}\right) + \beta(x) \left(\lim_{h \to 0} \frac{\alpha(x + h) - \alpha(x)}{h}\right). \tag{13.10}$$

It appears then that our goal is to simply reorganize Equation (13.9) until it looks like Equation (13.10). We say "simply" but it will only appear to be simple after we have succeeded. We will proceed slowly.

Observe that if we subtract $\alpha(x + h)\beta(x)$ from the blue part of the numerator in Equation (13.9) we get

$$\alpha(x)\beta(x) - \alpha(x + h)\beta(x) = -\beta(x)\left(\alpha(x + h) - \alpha(x)\right),$$

whereas if we add $\alpha(x + h)\beta(x)$ to the red part of the numerator in Equation (13.9) we get

$$\alpha(x + h)\beta(x + h) + \alpha(x + h)\beta(x) = \alpha(x + h)\left(\beta(x + h) - \beta(x)\right).$$

This suggests that we should both add and subtract the expression $\alpha(x + h)\beta(x)$ to the numerator of Equation (13.9). Doing this and factoring as we've indicated above we get

$$f'(x) = \lim_{h \to 0} \frac{\alpha(x + h)\left(\beta(x + h) - \beta(x)\right) - \left[-\beta(x)\left(\alpha(x + h) - \alpha(x)\right)\right]}{h},$$

By Theorem 15 we can separate this into the limit of the two fractions as follows:

$$f'(x) = \lim_{h \to 0} \left(\frac{\alpha(x+h)\left(\beta(x+h) - \beta(x)\right)}{h} \right) + \lim_{\substack{h \to 0 \\ h > 0}} \left(\frac{\beta(x)\left(\alpha(x+h) - \alpha(x)\right)}{h} \right),$$

and by Theorem 16 we see that

$$f'(x) = \underbrace{\left[\lim_{h \to 0} \alpha(x+h) \right]}_{= \alpha(x)} \underbrace{\left[\lim_{h \to 0} \left(\frac{\beta(x+h) - \beta(x)}{h} \right) \right]}_{= \beta'(x)} + \underbrace{\left[\lim_{h \to 0} \beta(x) \right]}_{\beta(x)} \underbrace{\left[\lim_{h \to 0} \left(\frac{\alpha(x+h) - \alpha(x)}{h} \right), \right]}_{\alpha'(x)}$$

and therefore

$$f'(x) = \alpha(x)\beta'(x) + \beta(x)\alpha'(x).$$

∎

13.5 The Other General Differentiation Rules

Theorem 28: [The Quotient Rule for Differentiation]

We assume that $\alpha(x)$, $\beta(x)$, and $f(x) = \frac{\alpha(x)}{\beta(x)}$ are all differentiable functions[8]. Assume further that $\beta(x) \neq 0$. Then

$$f'(x) = \frac{\beta(x)\alpha'(x) - \alpha(x)\beta'(x)}{\left[\beta(x)\right]^2}.$$

Proving this directly by using limits would be unpleasant, but as we observed in Chapter 3 the Quotient Rule can be viewed as a rearranged version of the Product Rule.

Problem #498: Use the Product Rule to derive the Quotient Rule.

(**Hint:** First solve $f(x) = \frac{\alpha(x)}{\beta(x)}$ for $\alpha(x)$.)

With the Product Rule for Differentiation in place we now have the tools needed to prove the Power Rule for Positive Integer Exponents. The method of proof we outline in the following problem is called **Mathematical Induction**[9] and it can be used in other contexts as well. In fact, most of the "Find the Pattern" problems in this text require an Induction argument for full rigor.

Problem #499: The Power Rule for Positive Integer Exponents

Assume that $\alpha(x) = x^n$ is differentiable at x for any positive integer n.

Part 1: Assume that $n = 1$. Use the limit definition to show that $\alpha'(x) = nx^{n-1}$.

(**Comment:** This says, "The Power Rule holds for $k = 1$.")

---

[8]Notice that we have explicitly assumed that the quotient

[9]We mentioned **Mathematical Induction** In part (d) of Problem #47 back in Chapter 3.

Part 2: Now assume that the Power Rule for Positive Integer Exponents holds for $n = k$, where k is an arbitrary, fixed positive integer.

Let $\beta(x) = x^{k+1}$ and show that $\beta'(x) = (k+1)x^k$.
(**Comment:** This says, "If the Power Rule holds for k then it must also hold for $k+1$.")

Do you see how this proves that the Power Rule holds for any positive integer, n? Write a short paragraph explaining the logic behind this.

With the **Power Rule for Positive Integer Exponents** in place we can extend it to both negative and rational exponents in the same way we did it in Chapter 3. The following problem is essentially a repeat of problems 56 and 57, using Lagrange's prime notation, and function notation, rather than differentials.

Problem #500: The Power Rule for Rational and Negative Exponents

(**a**) Assume n is a positive integer and that $\alpha(x) = x^{-n}$ is differentiable. Show that

$$\alpha'(x) = -nx^{-(n+1)}.$$

(**Hint:** Rewrite $\alpha(x) = x^{-n}$ as $\frac{1}{x^n}$ and use the Quotient Rule for Differentiation and the Power Rule for positive integers.)

(**b**) Assume that q is a non-zero integer and that $\alpha(x) = x^{1/q}$ is differentiable at x. Show that

$$\alpha'(x) = (1/q)x^{(1/q-1)}.$$

(**Hint:** Rewrite $\alpha(x) = x^{1/q}$ as

$$[\alpha(x)]^q = x$$

and use the Chain Rule and the Power Rule for positive integers.)

(**c**) Assume that p and q are integers, $q \neq 0$, and that $\alpha(x) = x^{p/q}$ is differentiable at x. Show that

$$\alpha'(x) = (p/q)x^{(p/q-1)}.$$

(**Hint:** Rewrite $\alpha(x) = x^{p/q}$ as $\alpha(x) = \left(x^{1/q}\right)^p$ and use the Chain Rule and part (b).)

Together the previous two problems prove the Power Rule for rational exponents:

Theorem 29: [**The Power Rule for Rational Exponents**]
Assume that p and q are integers, $q \neq 0$, and that $\alpha(x) = x^{p/q}$ is differentiable at x. Then

$$\alpha'(x) = (p/q)x^{(p/q-1)}.$$

In the statement of Theorem #28 we explicitly assumed that the quotient, $\frac{\alpha(x)}{\beta(x)}$, is differentiable at x. This has the effect that the theorem does not necessarily apply to all possible quotients, in the same way that when we add $\Delta\beta \neq 0$ to the statement of the Chain Rule, the theorem applies to fewer compositions. And just like the Chain Rule the functions that Theorem #28 does not apply to are mostly pathological, and of no use to us right now.

We added the same assumption to Theorem #29 for similar reasons.

Digression #23: Are You a Mathematician?

If leaving these theorems incomplete in this way is troubling to you then you are almost certainly a mathematician by temperament. If you haven't decided on a major yet, consider mathematics. You obviously like it. Why not learn more?

If you find that you simply don't care about completing all of the details and you are not majoring in mathematics, congratulations! You've made the right choice.

Problem #501 will lead you through the steps necessary to prove the Quotient Rule for Differentiation without the assumption that $\frac{\alpha(x)}{\beta(x)}$ is differentiable. Have fun!

Problem #501:

Assume that $\alpha(x)$ and $\beta(x)$ are differentiable and that $\beta(x) \neq 0$, but we make no assumption about the differentiability of $f(x) = \frac{\alpha(x)}{\beta(x)}$.

(a) First prove the special case of the Quotient Rule where $f(x) = \frac{1}{\beta(x)}$.

    (i) Use the limit definition to show that $\beta'(x) = \lim\limits_{h \to 0} \dfrac{\beta(x) - \beta(x+h)}{h\beta(x)\beta(x+h)}$.

    (ii) Now evaluate the limit in part (i) to show that $f'(x) = \frac{-\beta'(x)}{[\beta(x)]^2}$.

(b) Use the Product Rule for Differentiation and the Chain Rule (along with the result of part a) to show that $f(x) = \frac{\alpha(x)}{\beta(x)}$ is differentiable at x and that
$$f'(x) = \frac{\beta(x)\alpha'(x) - \alpha(x)\beta'(x)}{[\beta(x)]^2}.$$

Problem #503 will lead you through the steps necessary to prove the Product Rule for Rational Exponents without the assumption that $x^{\frac{p}{q}}$ is differentiable. It relies on the result of Problem #502. Have fun!

Problem #502:

To prove Theorem 29 we will first focus on the special case of $\beta(x) = x^{\frac{1}{q}}$, q is a non-negative integer.

The key to proving this special case is a generalization of the difference of squares formula: $(a - b)(a + b) = a^2 - b^2$.

(a) Show that $(a - b)(a^2 + ab + b^2) = a^3 - b^3$.

(b) Show that $(a - b)(a^3 + a^2b + ab^2 + b^3) = a^4 - b^4$.

(c) Use **Mathematical Induction** to show that
$$(a - b)(a^{q-1} + a^{q-2}b + a^{q-3}b^2 + \cdots + ab^{q-2} + b^{q-1}) = a^q - b^q.$$

Problem #503:

Assume that p and q are integers and that $q \neq 0$. If we apply Definition #15 to $f(x) = x^{\frac{1}{q}}$, we get
$$f'(x) = \lim_{h \to 0} \frac{(x+h)^{\frac{1}{q}} - x^{\frac{1}{q}}}{h}.$$

(a) Use the substitutions $a = (x+h)^{\frac{1}{q}}$, $b = x^{\frac{1}{q}}$, and part (c) of the previous problem to show that
$$f'(x) = \lim_{a \to b} \frac{a - b}{a^q - b^q} = \frac{1}{qb^{q-1}}.$$

(b) Substitute $b = x^{\frac{1}{q}}$ into the result of part a to obtain
$$f'(x) = \frac{1}{q} x^{\frac{1}{q} - 1}.$$

(c) Use the Chain Rule to show that for $\alpha(x) = x^{\frac{p}{q}}$
$$\alpha'(x) = \frac{p}{q} x^{\frac{p}{q} - 1}.$$

End Of Digression #23

13.6 Derivatives of the Trigonometric Functions, via Limits

 See also the TRIUMPHS Primary Source Project in Appendix A.7.

Theorem 30: [Derivative of $\sin(x)$]
Suppose $\alpha(\theta) = \sin(\theta)$. Then $\alpha'(\theta) = \cos(\theta)$.

Proof: Showing that the derivative of $\sin(\theta)$ is $\cos(\theta)$ is mostly straightforward but we're going to hit a snag partway through. We'll proceed for a bit to see where the trouble is.

Start with the limit definition:

$$\alpha'(\theta) = \lim_{h \to 0} \frac{\sin(\theta + h) - \sin(\theta)}{h}$$

In the numerator we see the expression $\sin(\theta + h)$. Recall the sum formula for the Sine:

$$\sin(A + B) = \sin(A)\cos(B) + \cos(A)\sin(B).$$

Taking $A = \theta$ and $B = h$ we have:

$$\alpha'(x) = \lim_{h \to 0} \frac{\sin(\theta)\cos(h) + \cos(\theta)\sin(h) - \sin(\theta)}{h}$$

Next, if we factor $\sin(\theta)$ out of the terms where it appears and rearrange the numerator a bit we have:

$$= \lim_{h \to 0} \frac{\sin(\theta)(\cos(h) - 1) + \cos(\theta)\sin(h)}{h}.$$

$$= \lim_{h \to 0} \left(\frac{\sin(\theta)(\cos(h) - 1)}{h} + \frac{\cos(\theta)\sin(h)}{h} \right).$$

By Theorem 15:

$$= \lim_{h \to 0} \frac{\sin(\theta)(\cos(h) - 1)}{h} + \lim_{h \to 0} \frac{\cos(\theta)\sin(h)}{h}$$

and by Corollary 19:

$$= \sin(\theta) \underbrace{\left(\lim_{h \to 0} \frac{(\cos(h) - 1)}{h} \right)}_{=0} + \cos(\theta) \underbrace{\left(\lim_{h \to 0} \frac{\sin(h)}{h} \right)}_{=1}.$$

If the values of the two limits are 0 and 1 respectively as we've indicated we can conclude that $\alpha'(\theta) = \cos(\theta)$.

Unfortunately this proof cannot be considered complete until we have shown that these last two limits are what we claim they are. We will do this via the two lemmas below. ∎

It is tempting to use L'Hôpital's Rule to evaluate these limits, especially since it is so very easy to do.

__Drill #504:__ Use L'Hôpitals Rule to show that $\lim_{h \to 0} \frac{(\cos(h) - 1)}{h} = 0$ and that $\lim_{h \to 0} \frac{\sin(h)}{h} = 1$.

Sadly, using Drill #504 to finish the proof of Theorem #30 is an example of circular reasoning. We can't use the fact that the derivative of $\sin(x)$ is $\cos(x)$ to prove that the derivative of $\sin(x)$ is $\cos(x)$. So we will have to find a way to evaluate these limits without using L'Hôpital's Rule.

Lemma 31: $\displaystyle\lim_{h\to 0}\frac{\sin(h)}{h}=1$

Proof:

There are two cases:

Case 1, $\theta \geq 0$: We will use the Squeeze Theorem. Recall that in Section 5.1 we observed that the lengths of certain line segments associated with the unit circle in the first quadrant are equal to the trigonometric functions. The figure at the right shows the relationship between θ, $\sin(\theta)$, and $\tan(\theta)$. Notice in particular that

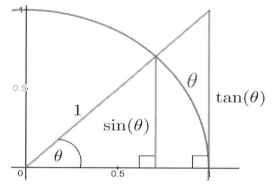

$$\sin(\theta) \leq \theta \leq \tan(\theta).$$

Dividing each expression in the inequality by $\sin(\theta)$ almost does the trick:

$$1 \leq \frac{\theta}{\sin(\theta)} \leq \frac{1}{\cos(\theta)}.$$

In the center we now have the reciprocal of what we need, so we need to invert each expression.

However, keep in mind that these are not equations they are inequalities. When we invert an inequality we must reverse its sense. This gives

$$1 \geq \frac{\sin(\theta)}{\theta} \geq \frac{\cos(\theta)}{1},$$

and this is true on the interval $\left[0, \frac{\pi}{2}\right]$. Since

$$\lim_{\substack{\theta\to 0 \\ \theta>0}} 1 = \lim_{\substack{\theta\to 0 \\ \theta>0}} \cos(\theta) = 1$$

the Squeeze Theorem applies, and we conclude that

$$\lim_{\substack{\theta\to 0 \\ \theta>0}} \frac{\sin(\theta)}{\theta} = 1.$$

Case 2, $\theta < 0$: For this case notice that $\sin(-\theta) = -\sin(\theta)$ so that $\frac{\sin(-\theta)}{-\theta} = \frac{\sin(\theta)}{\theta}$. We make the substitution $\theta = -\phi$ where $\phi > 0$. Therefore when $\theta < 0$ we have

$$\lim_{\substack{\theta\to 0 \\ \theta<0}} \frac{\sin(\theta)}{\theta} = \lim_{\substack{\phi\to 0 \\ \phi>0}} \frac{\sin(-\phi)}{-\phi} = \lim_{\substack{\phi\to 0 \\ \phi>0}} \frac{\sin(\phi)}{\phi} = 1$$

by Case 1.   ■

Problem #505: Show that $\lim\limits_{h \to 0} \frac{(\cos(h)-1)}{h} = 0$.

(**Hint:** It is tempting to model this proof on the proof of Lemma 31. While this can be done, it is delicate. It is simpler to multiply by 1 in the form $\frac{\cos(h)+1}{\cos(h)+1}$. Try that instead.)

Once Problem (505) has been solved the proof that $\frac{\mathrm{d}(\sin(x))}{\mathrm{d}x} = \cos(x)$ is complete.

Problem #506: Prove that $\frac{\mathrm{d}(\cos(\theta))}{\mathrm{d}\theta} = -\sin(\theta)$, using the proof of Theorem 30 as a guide.

Assuming that $\tan(\theta)$, $\cot(\theta)$, $\sec(\theta)$, and $\csc(\theta)$ are differentiable we can now use Theorem 501 to find their derivatives as well. Since this is exactly what we did in Section 5.4 we have the derivatives of all of the trigonometric functions.

13.7   Inverse Functions

Although we have worked with the inverses of some specific functions we have not formally defined what we mean by an inverse. We will remedy that now. We have seen that not all functions can be inverted (see for example, Digression #10) so the first step is to define which functions are invertible.

Informally a function that never takes the same value twice is called a **one-to-one function**[10]. Formally we have the following.

Definition 18: One-To-One Functions

A function, $f(x)$, defined on a domain, D, is said to be one-to-one if, whenever x_1 and x_2 are in D and $x_1 \neq x_2$ then, $f(x_1) \neq f(x_2)$.

Recall that when we tried to invert $\tan(x)$ (which is not one-to-one) in Section (5.6) we got the multifunction $\arctan(x)$. We had to restrict the domain of the tangent function to $\frac{-\pi}{2} \leq x \leq \frac{\pi}{2}$, in order to find an inverse. That restriction gave us a one-to-one function which we could invert because one-to-one functions are the only functions with inverses.

Definition 19: Inverse Functions

Suppose $f(x)$, with domain D and range, R is a one-to-one function. Then the inverse of $f(x)$ is the function $f^{-1}(x)$ with domain R and range[11] D which satisfies the following properties:

1. $f\left(f^{-1}(x)\right) = x$

2. $f^{-1}\left(f(x)\right) = x$

for every value of x in the domain of f (equivalently, in the range of f^{-1}).

Loosely speaking, Definition #19 says that two functions are mutually inverse if they "undo" each other.

---

[10]They are also called **injective**.

[11]Notice that the domain and range have been swapped.

Our next task is to show that the derivatives of the in inverse trigonometric functions are what we expect them to be. Given that we have now obtained the derivatives of all of the trigonometric functions it appears that we could proceed just as we did in Section 5.7 and Section 5.8.

But that would require that we explicitly assume that each of the inverse trigonometric functions is differentiable, similar to the way we found the derivative of a quotient. This is a valid approach of course, but proceeding in that manner would mask some issues that will be of interest to us later. So we will approach the derivatives of inverse functions abstractly by (rigorously) finding a formula for the derivative of the inverse of a generic, invertible function. After that we'll only need to apply the formula to each of the inverse trigonmetric formulas.

Digression #24: Inverse and Derivative Notation

As we saw in Digression 9 there are some difficulties with the notation we use to indicate inverse functions. These problems only get worse when we mix the standard derivative notations with the inverse function notation. Lagrange's prime notation is especially problematic.

For example if $f(x)$ is an invertible function the derivative of $f^{-1}(x)$ could be denoted either as:

$$\frac{\mathrm{d}(f^{-1})}{\mathrm{d}x} \quad \text{or} \quad f^{-1\prime}(x).$$

But both of these are somewhat awkward. Mathematicians also sometimes use the **operator** notation:

$$\mathbf{D}(f(x)) = f'(x) = \frac{\mathrm{d}f}{\mathrm{d}x}$$

and in this situation it minimizes the awkwardness a bit.

As we've seen there can also be some vagueness involving the distinction between functions and variables. For example suppose we want to sketch a graph of this relation between x and y:

$$y - x^3 = 0.$$

The simplest thing to do is to choose a value for either x or y and then figure out what the corresponding y or x is. This is simpler to do that if we rearrange the relation so that we have one variable strictly in terms of ("as a function of") the other. For this particular relation it is easiest to choose a value for x and compute the corresponding y value so we would normally rearrange it as

$$y(x) = x^3. \tag{13.11}$$

Equation 13.11 defines y as a function of x.

But we only solved for y because we could see it was a little easier to do. Otherwise our choice was completely arbitrary. We could also have solved for x giving,

$$x(y) = \sqrt[3]{y}. \tag{13.12}$$

In this case we have x as a function of y.

The two functions, $y(x)$, ("cube") and $x(y)$ ("cube root"), clearly contain the same information as the original relation $y - x^3 = 0$. But they are different, related, functions. They are in fact mutually inverse.

For example suppose we choose $x = 2$ and use Equation (13.11) to find $y = 8$. If we then take $y = 8$ and use Equation (13.12) we find that $x = 2$. That is, $x(y)$ has "undone" $y(x)$ for the single pair $(2, 8)$. Drill #507 asks you to show that it is true for every pair $(x, y(x))$. This "undoing" makes $y(x)$ and $x(y)$ a pair of mutually inverse functions.

But in function notation the variable (frequently x or t) is a placeholder. For example, each of $y(x) = x^3$, $y(t) = t^3$, $f(\alpha) = \alpha^3$, or even $f(\blacksquare) = \blacksquare^3$ defines exactly the same function: The function which cubes its input. It doesn't matter what we call the variable. It just holds a place in the formula that tells us what the input is and what to do with it. Since it doesn't matter what we call the variable we usually call it x unless there is some compelling reason to use something else.

To avoid confusing variable names with function names we usually denote $y(x)$ as $f(x)$. It's inverse, $x(y)$ should probably be denoted as $f^{-1}(y)$. But sadly, recognizing that the variable is just a placeholder in function notation we use the same variable name in both the function and it's inverse. So we denote the inverse of $f(x)$ as $f^{-1}(x)$, even though it would probably make it easier for beginners to use $f^{-1}(y)$, as a reminder that both functions come from the same original relation.

Drill #507:
Prove that $f(x) = x^3$ and $f^{-1}(x) = \sqrt[3]{x}$ are mutually inverse by showing that they satisfy the conditions stated in Definition #19

The notation for inverse functions is not great. It can be very confusing, especially for beginners. Be careful with it.

=========== End Of Digression #24 ===========

Our next task is to show that if $f(x)$ is invertible and differentiable, then f^{-1} is also differentiable[12]. We do this by showing that the limit

$$\mathbf{D}\left(f^{-1}(x)\right) = \lim_{h \to 0} \frac{f^{-1}(x+h) - f^{-1}(x)}{h} \tag{13.13}$$

exists.

In general this is true but there is one exception that has to be addressed. When f is differentiable at a and $f'(a) = 0$ then the limit in Equation (13.13 does not exist. Hence f^{-1} is not differentiable at $f(a)$. More formally, we have the following lemma.

Lemma 32:
If f is an invertible function, $f(a) = b$, f is differentiable at $x = a$, and $f'(a) = 0$, then f^{-1} is not differentiable at $x = b$. That is $\mathbf{D}\left(f^{-1}(b)\right)$ does not exist.

The following proof of this lemma is very challenging to read and understand for several reasons.

First, it is quite abstract. We don't have a particular function to think about so we can't simply write down formulas for the function and its inverse. Instead we have only the generic function, f and its inverse f^{-1}, and we'll need to remember what these symbols represent.

Second, we need to think about the functions f and f^{-1} as well as their derivatives.

Third, instead of using the differential notation, $\frac{df}{dx}$ that we've grown very comfortable with we'll be using the less familiar Lagrange prime notation and the operator notation we just introduced.

----

[12] f^{-1} is obviously invertible

Finally, the nature of the problem forces us to mix these last two notations, using one here and the other there. This can make for difficult reading.

Read slowly. Remember that each symbol has meaning. Take time to understand that meaning and what each formula as a whole is telling you.

We include this proof in its full abstraction for two reasons:

1. To be as precise and as rigorous and we can.

2. We want to give you practice with higher level abstract reasoning in this (fairly) simple case.

The strategy behind the following proof follows the same general scheme as the Sherlock Holmes Maxim that we referred to in Problem #355. We will eliminate the impossible so that "whatever remains, however improbable, must be the truth."

There are two possibilities: Either the derivative of $f^{-1}(b)$ exists or it does not exist. There are two steps:

(1) Assume that the derivative of f^{-1} does exist at $x = b$ and calculate what $\mathbf{D}\left(f^{-1}(b)\right)$ must be.

(2) Show that our computed value is impossible. Then *á la* Holme's Maxim the only possibility left will be that the derivative of f^{-1} does not exist at $x = b$.

Proof of Lemma #32: Assume that f^{-1} is differentiable[13] at $x = b$. Because f and f^{-1} are mutually inverse we know that

$$f\left(f^{-1}(x)\right) = x.$$

Therefore

$$\mathbf{D}\left(f\left(f^{-1}(x)\right)\right) = \mathbf{D}\left(x\right).$$

On the right we have

$$\mathbf{D}(x) = 1.$$

On the left apply the Chain Rule:

$$f'\left(f^{-1}(x)\right) \cdot \mathbf{D}\left(f^{-1}(x)\right) = 1. \tag{13.14}$$

But when $x = b$ we find that $f'\left(f^{-1}(b)\right) = f'(a) = 0$, so that

$$0 = \underbrace{f'\left(f^{-1}(b)\right)}_{=0} \cdot \mathbf{D}\left(f^{-1}(b)\right) = 1$$

or

$$0 = 1$$

which is ridiculous or in Holmes' word, impossible.

---

[13] We don't really believe this assumption. Be sure you are very clear on this point. We make this assumption so that we can use it to derive an absurd result; a contradiction. If there are no errors in our reasoning then the only possible conclusion will be that this assumption is false: f^{-1} is not differentiable at $x = b$.

Therefore our assumption cannot true so f^{-1} is not differentiable at $x = b$. ∎

While valid and correct, this proof is not very enlightening. A well chosen sketch would be much more convincing, if less rigorous.

Problem #508:

Choose a function whose derivative is equal to zero at some point and sketch the graph of your function and its inverse on the same set of axes. Be sure to include the point where the derivative is zero.

Use your graph to explain why the derivative of the inverse of your function does not exist.

We now understand what conditions are necessary for an arbitrary function, $f(x)$, to have a differentiable inverse.

Also, from Equation (13.14) we know what the derivative of the inverse will be if it exists:

$$\mathbf{D}\left(f^{-1}(x)\right) = \frac{1}{f'\left(f^{-1}(x)\right)}.$$

Drill #509:

Let $y = f^{-1}(x)$ and explain how the formula above is equivalent to

$$\frac{\mathrm{d}y}{\mathrm{d}x} = \frac{1}{\frac{\mathrm{d}x}{\mathrm{d}y}} \qquad (13.15)$$

The only thing left is to show that under the conditions on f in Lemma 32 the derivative (that is, the limit which defines the derivative) of the inverse does in fact exist.

Theorem 33: [**The Derivative of Inverse Functions**]

Suppose that

1. f is differentiable at $x = a$,   3. $f'(a) \neq 0$,

2. $f(a) = b$,   4. f^{-1} is continuous at[14] $x = b$.

Then the inverse of f is differentiable at $x = b$ and

$$\mathbf{D}\left(f^{-1}(b)\right) = \frac{1}{f'\left(f^{-1}(b)\right)}.$$

Reading and understanding the notation in Theorem 33 presents the same difficulties we saw in the proof of Lemma 32. Read it carefully. Be patient with yourself and do not rush.

---

[14]In fact, this follows from the continuity of f at $x = a$. We do not have all of the tools necessary to prove this so we must include it in the assumptions of our theorem.

Proof: We want to show that the limit

$$\mathbf{D}\left(f^{-1}(b)\right) = \lim_{h\to 0} \frac{f^{-1}(b+h) - f^{-1}(b)}{h} = \frac{1}{f'\left(f^{-1}(b)\right)}.$$

Since $f(a) = b$ we know that $f^{-1}(b) = a$ so that

$$\lim_{h\to 0} \frac{f^{-1}(b+h) - f^{-1}(b)}{h} = \lim_{h\to 0} \frac{f^{-1}(b+h) - a}{h}$$

Observe that if $b + h$ is in the domain of f^{-1} then it is in the range of f. Thus there is some number in the domain of f (for convenience we'll call it $a + k$) such that $b + h = f(a + k)$. Thus

$$\lim_{h\to 0} \frac{f^{-1}(b+h) - f^{-1}(b)}{h} = \lim_{h\to 0} \frac{f^{-1}(f(a+k)) - a}{h}.$$

Again since f and f^{-1} are mutually inverse they "undo" each other, so $f^{-1}(f(a+k)) = a + k$ so that

$$\lim_{h\to 0} \frac{f^{-1}(b+h) - f^{-1}(b)}{h} = \lim_{h\to 0} \frac{k}{h}.$$

Solving $b + h = f(a + k)$ for h gives $h = f(a + k) - b$ so

$$\lim_{h\to 0} \frac{k}{h} - \lim_{h\to 0} \frac{k}{f(a+k) - b}$$

and since $b = f(a)$ we have

$$= \lim_{h\to 0} \frac{k}{f(a+k) - f(a)}$$

$$= \lim_{h\to 0} \frac{1}{\frac{f(a+k) - f(a)}{k}}.$$

$$= \frac{1}{\lim_{h\to 0} \frac{f(a+k) - f(a)}{k}}.$$

The expression $\lim_{h\to 0} \dfrac{f(a+k) - f(a)}{k}$ would be $f'(a)$ if only we had $k \to 0$ instead of $h \to 0$. What we need to show now is that if $h \to 0$ then $k \to 0$. Then we could write

$$\mathbf{D}\left(f^{-1}(b)\right) = \frac{1}{\lim_{k\to 0} \dfrac{f(a+k) - f(a)}{k}} = \frac{1}{f'(a)} \tag{13.16}$$

and our proof would be complete

Written a little more carefully, what we need to show is that $\lim_{h \to 0} k = 0$. Recall that $a = f^{-1}(b)$, and that $a + k = f^{-1}(b + h)$ so we need to show that

$$\lim_{h \to 0} k = \lim_{h \to 0} [(a + k) - a] = \lim_{h \to 0} \left[f^{-1}(b + h) - f^{-1}(b) \right] = 0$$

or But we assumed that f^{-1} is continuous at $x = b$ which means that

$$\lim_{h \to 0} \left[f^{-1}(b + h) - f^{-1}(b) \right] = 0,$$

and the proof is complete.

One last point: On the left side of formula (13.16) the variable is b and on the right it is a. While this is not strictly wrong it is a more useful theorem if we state it in terms of b alone.

Since $f(a) = b$ we see that $f^{-1}(b) = a$ so

$$\mathbf{D}\left(f^{-1}(b)\right) = \frac{1}{f'(f^{-1}(b))}$$

and the proof is complete. ∎

Using Theorem 33 we can now show that the derivatives of the inverse trigonometric functions and the natural logarithm are exactly what we expect them to be. The difference is that now there is no uncertainty or vagueness in our foundations. No modern Bishop Berkeley can step in and sew doubt.

Example #86: **The Derivative of the Inverse Sine**

Suppose $f(x) = \sin(x)$. Then $f^{-1}(x) = \sin^{-1}(x)$ so

$$\mathbf{D}\left(f^{-1}(x)\right) = \mathbf{D}\left(\sin^{-1}(x)\right) = \frac{1}{f'(f^{-1}(x))}$$

$$= \frac{1}{\cos(\sin^{-1}(x))}$$

$$\mathbf{D}\left(f^{-1}(x)\right) = \frac{1}{\sqrt{1 - x^2}}.$$

End Of Example #86

Problem #510:

Use Theorem 33 to show that each of the following differentiation rules is correct:

(a) $\mathbf{D}\left(\cos^{-1}(x)\right) = \frac{-1}{\sqrt{1-x^2}}$ **(c)** $\mathbf{D}\left(\cot^{-1}(x)\right) = \frac{-1}{1+x^2}$ **(e)** $\mathbf{D}\left(\csc^{-1}(x)\right) = \frac{-1}{|x|\sqrt{x^2-1}}$

(b) $\mathbf{D}\left(\tan^{-1}(x)\right) = \frac{1}{1+x^2}$ **(d)** $\mathbf{D}\left(\sec^{-1}(x)\right) = \frac{1}{|x|\sqrt{x^2-1}}$ **(f)** $\mathbf{D}\left(\ln^{-1}(x)\right) = e^x$

Wait a minute! Did we forget one? What about the natural exponential function? Don't we also have to show that $\mathbf{D}\left(e^x\right) = e^x$?

Drill #511:

Look back at Definition 8 and explain why it is not necessary to use limits to show that $\mathbf{D}\left(e^x\right) = e^x$.

Chapter 14

The First Derivative Test, Redux

"Geometry has always been considered as an exact science, and indeed as the source of the exactness which is widespread among other parts of mathematics. . . But it seems that this feature of exactness does not reign anymore in geometry since the new system of infinitely small quantities has been mixed to it. I do not see that this system has produced anything for the truth and it would seem to me that it often conceals mistakes."

– Michel Rolle (1652-1719)

Assuming that all of the properties of limits we talked about in Section 13.1 can be proved, we have seen that all of the differentiation rules we developed intuitively using differentials in Chapter 3 can be made rigorous using limits.

The question we need to address now is this: Does the need for rigor, which prompted our definition of the derivative (15), get in the way of practical applications such as, say, the First Derivative Test? We will show that such a practical result can still be achieved while maintaining rigor. To do this, we will need a theorem that allows us to relate instantaneous changes to finite changes. The French name for this theorem is "le théorème des accroissements finis" (translated literally as "the Theorem of Finite Increments"). In English it is called the the Mean Value Theorem. We will see how this powerful theorem can be used to transition from theoretical to practical.

14.1 Fermat's Theorem

"It is by logic that we prove, but by intuition that we discover."

– Henri Poincaré (1854-1912)

It is actually a little surprising how much effort it takes to prove the First Derivative Test. We will start by proving some preliminary results that will make it a little easier to follow the logic behind the proof of the First Derivative Test. We'll begin with Fermat's Theorem (Theorem 1) which says that if f attains a maximum (or minimum) at $x = a$ then $f'(a) = 0$. More formally:

Theorem 34: [Fermat's Theorem]

If $f(a)$ is a local extremum (either a maximum or a minimum) of $f(x)$ at $x = a$, and $f(x)$ is differentiable at $x = a$ then $f'(a) = 0$.

Recall that Fermat's Theorem does not say that if $f'(a) = 0$ then $f(a)$ is an extremum. In fact, we know that this is not true. Rather, it states the converse: If we know that $f(a)$ is an extremum and $f'(a)$ exists, then $f'(a) = 0$.

It is very rare that we can develop a proof of a theorem by directly writing down the logical steps in order. Usually the process takes a lot of trying, backtracking, trying again, and so on much as we described in our analogy in Chapter 1 about finding your way out of a forest.

Of course, in a textbook it is not practical to list all of the bad ideas we might have just to see that they are, in fact, bad ideas. So we will use the following **Scrapwork** construct when we are just "thinking about" a problem. The scrapwork is not the proof. The purpose of scrapwork is to engage our intuition and to begin organizing our intuitive understanding so that a rigorous proof will emerge. So, not every statement we make inside a scrapwork construct will necessarily be fully rigorous. If you see a gap in the logic inside a scrapwork construct watch to see how it gets filled in the proof.

Scrapwork

Notice that in Definition 15 the quantity $\frac{f(a+h)-f(a)}{h}$ is the slope of a particular secant line, as in the sketch at the right.

If, as shown in the sketch at the right, $(a, f(a))$ is a (local) maximum then the slope of the secant line in our diagram, $\frac{f(a+h)-f(a)}{h}$, must be negative when $h > 0$. Since the slope is less than zero it follows that

$$f'(a) = \lim_{h \to 0} \frac{f(a+h) - f(a)}{h} \leq 0.$$

Drill #512:

Draw a similar diagram to convince yourself that $f'(a)$ must also be greater than or equal to zero when $h < 0$.

We can now rigorously prove Fermat's Theorem.

End Of Scrapwork

Proof of Fermat's Theorem: We will only prove the case when $f(a)$ is a local maximum. The case of a local minimum is very similar.

Since $f(a)$ is a local maximum there is an interval containing a such that for any h (sufficiently small that $a + h$ is also in the interval), $f(a + h) \leq f(a)$. Thus $f(a + h) - f(a) \leq 0$ as seen in the sketch above. If $h < 0$ then $\frac{f(a+h)-f(a)}{h} \geq 0$ and so

$$f'(a) = \lim_{h \to 0} \frac{f(a + h) - f(a)}{h} \geq 0. \tag{14.1}$$

However if $h > 0$ then

$$f'(a) = \lim_{h \to 0} \frac{f(a + h) - f(a)}{h} \leq 0. \tag{14.2}$$

The only way that inequalities in Formulas (14.1) and (14.2) can be both true is if $f'(a) = 0$.
∎

Problem #513: Use our proof of the maximum case as a guide to constructing a proof of Fermat's Theorem when $f(a)$ is a local minimum.

14.2   Rolle's Lemma and the Mean Value Theorem

Were he alive today Michel Rolle might be horrified to know that his lemma has become a fundamental part of the modern development of Calculus. Like Bishop Berkeley, he was an early critic of Calculus, having once described it as a "collection of ingenious fallacies."

The distinction between a theorem and a lemma is very slight and rather arbitrary. Typically we call a statement[1] a theorem if it is important and requires proof. We call it a lemma if it requires proof itself, and is used to simply the proof of a theorem. This is not a hard-and-fast rule by any means. Sometimes we first prove a lemma as an aid to proving a theorem, only to find that the lemma is actually more important. However, having been originally dubbed a lemma the result is known ever after as a lemma. For example, in the present instance

Michel Rolle
(1659-1719)

we will be using the Extreme Value[2], and Fermat's *Theorems* to prove what often called Rolle's *Lemma*, and then use use Rolle's *Lemma* to prove the Mean Value *Theorem*. Then we will use the Mean Value *Theorem* to prove the First Derivative *Test*. It is all very chaotic.

Lemma 35: [Rolle's Lemma]

Suppose f is continuous on the closed interval $[a, b]$ and differentiable on the open interval (a, b). Suppose further that $f(a) = f(b)$. Then there is at least one number c, in the interval (a, b) such that $f'(c) = 0$.

---

[1] Technically speaking, a statement is not a theorem until it has actually been proved. Until then it is a conjecture.

[2] We will not be proving the Extreme Value Theorem in this text. Although it appears to be obviously true (read it again and see), it is remarkably hard to prove in a fully rigorous fashion. If you feel that you must see the proof you should change your major to mathematics and take a course in Real Analysis.

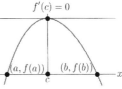

When Rolle's Lemma is visualized, as in the sketch at the right, it is clear what is going on. If $f(a) = f(b)$ then between the points $(a, f(a))$ and $(b, f(b))$ the graph of $f(x)$ will either rise to a maximum or drop to a minimum (not shown) at some point c. In either case, by Fermat's Theorem, the derivative of f at c will be zero. Notice that the slope of the line through $(a, f(a))$ and $(b, f(b))$ is also zero. Thus these two lines are parallel.

Despite the clarity of our sketch, an analytic proof is still required because our sketch does not capture all of the possible ways that Rolle's Lemma can manifest. This is demonstrated in Drill 514 below.

Drill #514:

(a) Sketch the graph of a function (different from the one in our sketch) which satisfies all of the conditions of Rolle's Lemma and convince yourself that the conclusion of Rolle's Lemma must still be true.

(b) Show that the condition that f is continuous on $[a, b]$ is necessary by sketching the graph of a function which violates only that condition and the conclusion of Rolle's Lemma.

(c) Show that the condition that f is differentiable on (a, b) is necessary by sketching the graph of a function which violates only that condition and the conclusion of Rolle's Lemma.

Proof of Rolle's Lemma: By The Extreme Value Theorem (Theorem 5) there is are points α and β in the interval $[a, b]$, such that $f(\alpha)$ is a global maximum, and $f(\beta)$ is a global minimum.

There are two possibilities for α and β:

1. **Both α and β are endpoints of the interval**: In this case since $f(a) = f(b)$ the global maximum and the global minimum are equal. The only way that can happen is if the function is constant on the interval $[a, b]$, and if f is constant then $f'(x) = 0$ for every x in the interval (a, b). So we take c to be any point in (a, b).

2. **At least one of α or β is not an endpoint of the interval**: In this case by Fermat's Theorem, either $f'(\alpha) = 0$, or $f'(\beta) = 0$. So we take $c = \alpha$ or $c = \beta$ as appropriate.

In either case the existence of c in the interval (a, b), with $f'(c) = 0$ is guaranteed. ∎

Theorem 36: [The Mean Value Theorem]
Suppose $f(x)$ is continuous on some closed interval, $[a, b]$, and f is differentiable on (a, b). Then there is at least one number c in the open interval (a, b) such that

$$f'(c) = \frac{f(b) - f(a)}{b - a}.$$ (14.3)

Scrapwork

The Mean Value Theorem (visualized at the left) says that there is a point c, in the interval (a, b) such that the tangent line at c and the line through $(a, f(a)$ and $(b, f(b))$ are parallel. Thus in the special case where $f(a) = f(b)$ the Mean Value Theorem reduces to Rolle's Lemma. In other words the Mean Value Theorem is a generalization of Rolle's Lemma.

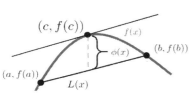

We said we would use Rolle's Lemma to prove the Mean Value Theorem. To do that we'll need to create a function – we'll call it $\phi(x)$ – that satisfies all of the conditions of Rolle's Lemma . From the diagram at the left we have

$$\phi(x) = f(x) - L(x).$$

Do you see that $\phi(x)$ is the function we need?

Drill #515:

Show that $L(x) = \frac{f(b)-f(a)}{b-a}(x - a) + f(a)$.

(**Hint:** $L(x)$ is a straight line and we have the coordinates of two points, $(a, f(a))$ and $(b, f(b))$ on the line.)

Problem #516:

Show that $\phi(x) = f(x) - L(x)$ from the diagram above satisfies all of the conditions of Rolle's Lemma. That is, show that:

(a) $\phi(x)$ is continuous on $[a, b]$.

(b) $\phi(x)$ is differentiable on (a, b).

(c) $\phi(a) = \phi(b) = 0$

End Of Scrapwork

Proof of The Mean Value Theorem:

Observe that

$$\phi(x) = f(x) - \frac{f(b) - f(a)}{b - a}(x - a) + f(a)$$

satisfies all of the conditions of Rolle's Lemma. Therefore, by Rolle's Lemma there is a point c, between a and b such that $\phi'(c) = 0$. Therefore

$$f'(c) - \frac{f(b) - f(a)}{b - a} = 0$$

and so

$$f'(c) = \frac{f(b) - f(a)}{b - a},$$

which completes the proof.   ■

As we mentioned at the beginning of this chapter in French the Mean Value Theorem is known as the *théorème des accroissements finis* or literally the "theorem of the finite increments."

To see why this is an accurate description let $y = f(x)$. Then $f(b) - f(a) = \Delta y$ and $b - a = \Delta x$. So we can re-express Equation (14.3) as $\Delta y = f'(c)\Delta x$. In this form it is clear that the Mean Value Theorem relates the finite increments Δy and Δx to the instantaneous rate of change $f'(c)$.

The English name, "Mean Value Theorem" comes from interpreting the derivative as an instantaneous velocity. If t represents time and $p(t)$ represents position at time t, then $\frac{p(b)-p(a)}{b-a}$ is the average velocity in the time interval $[a, b]$. Since $p'(c)$ is instantaneous velocity at time c, the conclusion of the Mean Value Theorem is that at some point in that interval, instantaneous velocity must match average (mean) velocity. For example, if you travel 50 miles in one hour then your average velocity is $50\frac{\text{miles}}{\text{hour}}$. But it is unlikely that you traveled at exactly $50\frac{\text{miles}}{\text{hour}}$ for the entire hour. However, at one instant (possibly more) you had to have been traveling at exactly $50\frac{\text{miles}}{\text{hour}}$. This is the Mean Value Theorem. It provides the bridge we need to get from infinitesimals to finite intervals.

14.3   The Proof of the First Derivative Test

We stated Theorem 3 in Chapter 8 without stating the conditions that make it true, because at the time our attention was primarily on using it.

Since the focus of our attention here is on what makes the First Derivative Test true we will restate it to reflect our new, and deeper, understanding. Notice that the conclusion is the same, only the conditions have changed.

Theorem 37: [**First Derivative Test**]

Suppose $f(x)$ is continuous on the interval $[\alpha, \beta]$, and differentiable on the interval (α, β). Suppose further that both a and b are in the interval $[\alpha, \beta]$ and $b > a$.

(a) If $f'(x) > 0$ on the interval (α, β) then $f(b) > f(a)$. (That is, the function is increasing on $[\alpha, \beta]$.)

(b) If $f'(x) < 0$ on the interval (α, β) then $f(b) < f(a)$. (That is, the function is decreasing on $[\alpha, \beta]$.)

Proof of Part (a):   We want to use the Mean Value Theorem on the interval $[a, b]$ so we begin by verifying that the conditions of the Mean Value Theorem are satisfied on that interval. Observe that $[a, b]$ is a subinterval of $[\alpha, \beta]$ so $f(x)$ is continuous on $[a, b]$ and differentiable on (a, b).

By the Mean Value Theorem there is a number, c, in the interval (a, b) such that

$$\frac{f(b) - f(a)}{b - a} = f'(c)$$
$$f(b) - f(a) = f'(c)(b - a).$$

Since both $b - a > 0$ and $f'(c) > 0$ are positive, $f(b) - f(a)$ must be positive as well. Therefore

$$f(b) - f(a) > 0 \text{ or } f(b) > f(a).$$

■

Problem #517:
Prove part (b) of the First Derivative Test in two different ways:

(a) By modifying our proof of part (a) of the First Derivative Test as needed.

(b) Let $g(x) = -f(x)$ and apply part (a) of this problem.
(**Comment:** Don't forget to show first that $g(x)$ satisfies the conditions of the Mean Value Theorem.)

While we are in this frame of mind, we'll take a moment to notice that we can use the Mean Value Theorem to prove, rigorously, something that we have alluded to a few times but have never addressed directly. It is clear from our differentiation rules that if two functions differ by a constant, then they have the same derivative. We've mentioned that the converse is true, namely if two functions have the same derivative on an interval then they must differ by a constant. This can be proved in a manner similar to the proof above.

Problem #518:

(a) Suppose $f'(x) = 0$ on the interval (α, β) and that a and b are two points in that interval. Use an argument similar to the proof of the first derivative test to show that $f(a) = f(b)$.

(b) Explain how the result of part (a) says that $f(x)$ must be constant on (α, β).

(c) Show that if $f'(x) = g'(x)$ on the interval (α, β), then

$$f(x) = g(x) + c$$

for some constant c.
(**Hint:** Consider the function $F(x) = f(x) - g(x)$.)

(d) What can be said if $f'(x) = g'(x)$ for all x in some set S which is not an interval?

We did not prove L'Hôpital's Rule (Theorem 14) in Chapter 11 because the general theorem is slightly beyond the scope of this text. But the somewhat simpler first special case, Theorem 12, is a straightforward consequence of the Mean Value Theorem.

Problem #519:

(a) Under the conditions of Theorem 12 explain why

$$\lim_{x \to a} \frac{f(x)}{g(x)} = \lim_{x \to a} \frac{f(x) - f(a)}{g(x) - g(a)}$$

(b) Apply the Mean Value Theorem to the numerator and denominator in part (a) and then prove Theorem 12.
   (**Hint:** Use the fact that in the statement of Theorem 36 c is between a and b.)

Chapter 15

When the Derivative Doesn't Exist

"I turn away with fright and horror from the lamentable evil of functions which do not have derivatives."

– Charles Hermite (1822 - 1901)

"The brilliant Cerebron, . . . discovered three distinct kinds of dragon: the mythical, the chimerical, and the purely hypothetical. They were all, one might say, nonexistent, but each non-existed in an entirely different way."

– Stanislaw Lem (1921 - 2006)

In Section 8.5 we saw that those points where the derivative doesn't exist are possible optimal points but we didn't pursue this any further at the time. However we now need to re-examine the non-existence of derivatives.

We also observed in Section 8.5 that derivatives fail to exist at points where the Principle of Local Linearity does not hold. This is true, but the only way we currently have to determine if the Principle of Local Linearity holds is to look at a graph. While graphs are useful, we have learned that we should not put all of our faith in what we conclude from them.

On the other hand, by Definition #15 the derivative of a function is given by a limit, and from our work in Chapter 11 we know that not all limits exist. For example, if we try to compute the value of $f'(2)$ for some function and we find that $\lim_{h \to 0} \frac{f(2+h)-f(2)}{h}$ is meaningless then f is not differentiable at $x = 2$. In other words, $f'(2)$ does not exist.

So, the limit definition gives us a computational tool we can use to decide the question of differentiability which, as we saw in Chapter 8.5, is crucial to finding possible optimal transition points of a function.

In our comments following Example #53 we listed several functions which are not differentiable at $x = 0$. Of these, the Absolute Value function, $f(x) = |x|$, is probably the simplest to work with, so we will start there.

Example #87: The Absolute Value Function

The Absolute Value function is usually introduced with some vague statement like,

"The absolute value of a number is just the positive version of the number,"

or

"$|x - a|$ gives the length of the line segment between x and a."

These are both true statements and are OK as intuitive definitions, but we will need something more precise from now on. The formal definition of the Absolute Value function is:

Definition 20: The Absolute Value Function

The Absolute Value of x is: $|x| = \begin{cases} x & \text{if } x \geq 0 \\ -x & \text{if } x < 0 \end{cases}$.

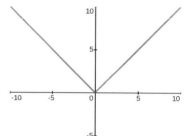

The graph of the Absolute Value function is given at the right. Notice that $f(x) - |x|$ is defined at $x = 0$ since $|0| = 0$, but as we indicated in Section 8.5 the Principle of Local Linearity does not hold at $x = 0$ so we suspect that the Absolute Value function is not differentiable at $x = 0$.

But we now have the ability to confirm our suspicion analytically so let's take a look at this using the limit definition of the derivative. The derivative of $|x|$ at x will be the value of the limit $\lim\limits_{h \to 0} \frac{|x+h|-|x|}{h}$ so the derivative of $|x|$ at $x = 0$ will be:

$$\lim_{h \to 0} \frac{|0 + h| - |0|}{h} = \lim_{h \to 0} \frac{|h|}{h}.$$

OK, but what is this limit? Don't jump to conclusions. Think about this carefully for a few minutes. What do you think $\lim\limits_{h \to 0} \frac{|h|}{h}$ is equal to?

First suppose that h is approaching[1] zero from the positive side. Recall that in Section 11.3 we invented the notation $\lim\limits_{\substack{h \to 0 \\ h > 0}}$ for exactly this situation. In this case h is positive so $|h| = h$ and

$$\lim_{\substack{h \to 0 \\ h > 0}} \frac{|h|}{h} = \lim_{\substack{h \to 0 \\ h > 0}} \frac{h}{h} = \lim_{\substack{h \to 0 \\ h > 0}} 1 = 1$$

which says that the right-hand limit will be one. Now suppose h is very small and negative. In this case h is negative so $|h| = -h$ and

$$\lim_{\substack{h \to 0 \\ h < 0}} \frac{|h|}{h} = \lim_{\substack{h \to 0 \\ h < 0}} \frac{-h}{h} = \lim_{\substack{h \to 0 \\ h < 0}} -1 = -1$$

which says that the left-hand limit will be negative one.

---

[1] To say that h is "approaching" 0 suggests that h is sliding along the horizontal axis toward the origin. We encourage you to think of limits this way. It is a good intuitive approach. However, as we will see in Chapter 16 it isn't quite what is really happening.

But since $\frac{|h|}{h}$ can't be close to 1 and close to -1 simultaneously we can not find a value for $\lim\limits_{h\to 0}\frac{|0+h|-|0|}{h}$ which is correct for both positive and negative values of h. In other words this limit does not exist.

Therefore $\left.\frac{d|x|}{dx}\right|_{x=0}$ does not exist.

Drill #520:

According to Definition 11, since $\left.\frac{d(|x|)}{dx}\right|_{x=0}$ does not exist, the value $x=0$ is a possible transition point for the Absolute Value function. So there might be a local extremum of $f(x)=|x|$ at $x=0$. Is there?

End Of Example #87

Problem #521:

(a) The Absolute Value function is not differentiable at $x=0$ but it is differentiable at every other value of x. Let $f(x)=|x|$ and use Definition 15 to show that:

(i) If $x>0$ then $f'(x)=1$, 　　　　(ii) If $x<0$ then $f'(x)=-1$.

(b) From the discussion in Digression #20 we know that $f(x)=|x|=\sqrt{x^2}$. Use the differentiation rules you learned in Part 1 of this text to show that if $x\neq 0$, then $f'(x)=\frac{x}{|x|}$. How does this compare with your calculations in part (a)?

Example #88:

A slightly less intuitive example is the function $f(x)=\frac{x}{x}$. It is tempting to claim that this is really just $f(x)=1$ since "anything divided by itself is one" but that claim is not true. As we saw in Digression 5 division by zero is undefined, regardless of the numerator. So the expression $\frac{0}{0}$ is undefined, and therefore the function $f(x)=\frac{x}{x}$ is not defined at $x=0$.

It is also tempting to try to invoke L'Hôpital's Rule, since it is true that

$$\lim_{x\to 0}f(x)=\lim_{x\to 0}\frac{x}{x}=\lim_{x\to 0}1=1.$$

But this only says that the limit of $f(x)$ is equal to one, not that $f(x)$ itself is equal to one, at $x=0$. The statement $\lim\limits_{x\to 0}\frac{x}{x}=\lim\limits_{x\to 0}1$ explicitly excludes the point $x=0$ from consideration. This is why when we discussed indeterminate forms in Section 11.4 we were very careful to write $\frac{(\to 0)}{(\to 0)}$ instead of $\frac{0}{0}$. We needed to emphasize that we specifically do not allow the denominator to be equal to zero.

Problem #522:

(a) Use Definition #15 to show that if $f(x) = \frac{x}{x}$ then $f'(0)$ is undefined.
(**Comment:** It is pretty clear that $f'(0)$ is undefined, since $f(0)$ is undefined. We can't have a derivative where we don't have a point. But this is the kind of vague reasoning we are trying to avoid. The purpose of this exercise is to show unequivocally that the limit which defines $f'(0)$ is undefined.)

(b) Use Definition #15 to show that if $f(x) = \begin{cases} \frac{x}{x} & \text{if } x \neq 0 \\ 1 & \text{if } x = 0 \end{cases}$ then $f'(0)$ is defined.

(**Comment:** This time $f(0)$ is defined but this is a silly way to do it. We do this for emphasis.)

End Of Example #88

Example #89:

It is intuitively clear that derivative of the function $f(x) = \sqrt{|x|}$ (at the right) is not defined at $x = 0$. We will confirm our intuition using Definition #15. That is, we'll try to compute the derivative of $f(x)$ at $x = 0$ using Definition #15 and see what goes wrong.

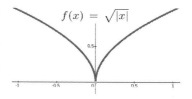

The existence of the derivative of $f(x)$ at $x = 0$ is equivalent to the existence of the limit $\lim\limits_{h \to 0} \frac{f(0+h)-f(0)}{h}$, so we will try to compute this limit and see what happens.

$$f'(0) \stackrel{?}{=} \lim_{h \to 0} \frac{f(0+h) - f(0)}{h} = \lim_{h \to 0} \frac{\sqrt{|h|}}{h}.$$

Problem #523:

(a) Show that $\lim\limits_{\substack{h \to 0 \\ h > 0}} \frac{\sqrt{|h|}}{h} = \infty$.

(b) Show that $\lim\limits_{\substack{h \to 0 \\ h < 0}} \frac{\sqrt{|h|}}{h} = -\infty$.

Problem #523 shows, $\frac{\sqrt{|h|}}{h}$ increases without bound as h approaches zero from the right, and decreases without bound as h approaches zero from the left. Since neither of these limits even exists it follows that $\lim\limits_{h \to 0} \frac{\sqrt{|h|}}{h}$ also does not exist, and therefore $f'(0)$ is not defined[2].

End Of Example #89

---

[2]As a verbal shorthand most people will just say that the right- and left-hand limits are not equal and so $f'(0)$ does not exist. Be sure you understand why this is, strictly speaking, incorrect.

Example #90: **The Heaviside Function**

Problem #521 shows that the derivative of the Absolute Value function (shown at the right) is:

$$H(x) = \begin{cases} 1 & x > 0 \\ -1 & x < 0 \end{cases}.$$

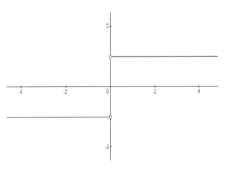

Notice that it is not defined at $x = 0$.

We call $H(x)$ the Heaviside function in honor of Oliver Heaviside (1850-1925). Simple as it is, Heaviside's function is a fundamental tool in signal processing, control theory, and the solution of differential equations.

Problem #524:

(a) Use Definition #15 to show that $H'(x) = 0$ when $x \neq 0$

(b) Explain why the result in part (a) does not contradict Problem #518

End Of Example #90

We first introduced one-sided limits in Section 11.3. At the time our concern was to locate vertical asymptotes so we only looked at limits that were equal to either positive or negative infinity. We see now that these limits can take any value and that they are more fundamental than they first appeared to be. Since we didn't provide a formal definition earlier we will do so now.

Definition 21: **One-sided Limits**

If R is a real number (or ∞ or $-\infty$) and

$$\lim_{\substack{x \to a \\ x > a}} f(x) = R$$

we say that R is the right-hand limit of $f(x)$ at $x = a$.

If L is a real number (or $-\infty$ or $-\infty$) and

$$\lim_{\substack{x \to a \\ x < a}} f(x) = L$$

we say that L is the left-hand limit of $f(x)$ at $x = a$.

Because $f(x)$ can't simultaneously approach two different numbers, if the left and right handed limits both exist but do not agree then $\lim_{x \to a} f(x)$ doesn't exist. This fact will be a useful tool for us later so we state it as a theorem.

Theorem 38:
$\lim\limits_{x \to a} f(x)$ exists if and only if $\lim\limits_{\substack{x \to a \\ x > a}} f(x) = \lim\limits_{\substack{x \to a \\ x < a}} f(x)$. In that case all three limits are equal.

Theorem 38 requires proof but we do not have the tools to prove it here. The appropriate tools will be developed in Chapter 16. Proving this fact is the last problem in this textbook.

15.1   One Sided Derivatives

Since limits may be right-hand or left-hand and the derivative is defined as a limit, it follows that derivatives can be right- or left-hand as well. We will denote the right-hand and left-hand derivatives at $x = a$ with the notation: $f'_R(a)$, and $f'_L(a)$, respectively:

Definition 22: One Sided Derivatives

Given a function, $f(x)$, defined at a point a:

1. f is said to have a right-hand derivative at $x = a$ if the limit

$$f'_R(a) = \lim\limits_{\substack{h \to 0 \\ h > 0}} \frac{f(a+h) - f(a)}{h}$$

exists.

2. f is said to have a left-hand derivative at $x = a$ if the limit

$$f'_L(a) = \lim\limits_{\substack{h \to 0 \\ h < 0}} \frac{f(a+h) - f(a)}{h}$$

exists.

From Theorem #38 and Definition #22 we see that the derivative of a function f, at a point x exists if and only if the right- and left-hand derivatives both exist, and are equal.

Corollary 39:   If $f'_R(x) = f'_L(x)$, then $f(x)$ is differentiable at x and $f'(x) = f'_R(x) = f'_L(x)$.

At zero both the right- and left-hand derivatives of the Absolute Value function $f(x) = |x|$ exist since

$$f'_R(0) = \lim\limits_{\substack{h \to 0 \\ h > 0}} \frac{|0 + h| - |0|}{h} = \lim\limits_{\substack{h \to 0 \\ h > 0}} \frac{h}{h} = 1,$$

and

$$f'_L(0) = \lim\limits_{\substack{h \to 0 \\ h < 0}} \frac{|0 + h| - |0|}{h} = \lim\limits_{\substack{h \to 0 \\ h < 0}} \frac{-h}{h} = -1.$$

but $f'(0)$ does not exist because $-1 \neq 1$.

Problem #525:
Notice that since the Heaviside function at $x = 0$ $H(0)$, is not defined, neither are $H'_R(0)$, $H'_L(0)$, or $H'(0)$.

  (a) Which of these derivatives would be defined if we were to arbitrarily define $H(0) = 1$? Explain.

  (b) Which of these derivatives would be defined if we were to arbitrarily define $H(0) = -1$? Explain.

  (c) Is there a value we could assign to $H(0)$ so that $H'(0)$ is defined. Explain.
      (**Hint:** Review Lemma 20.)

Problem #526:

   Compute the right- and left-hand derivative, and the derivative itself, if they exist, of each of the following functions at the $x = -2, -1, 0, 1$, and 2. If any of these derivatives don't exist explain why not.

  (a) $f(x) = \frac{1}{x}$ **(b)** $f(x) = 3\,|x + 1|$ **(c)** $f(x) = x^{2/3}$ **(d)** $f(x) = \sqrt{|x|}$

Problem #527:
Use the limit definitions to compute the right- and left-hand derivative, of the function, $f(x)$, at $x = -1$, $x = 0$, and $x = 2$. At which of these points is $f(x)$ differentiable?

$$f(x) = \begin{cases} 2 & \text{if } x < -1 \\ -2(x+1)^2 + 2 & \text{if } -1 \le x < 0 \\ x^4 - 4x & \text{if } 0 \le x < 2 \\ -14(x-3)^2 + 22 & \text{if } 2 \le x \end{cases}$$

Problem #528:

  (a) Let $H(x)$ be the Heaviside function and let a be a real number.

    (i) Sketch $H(x - a)$.

    (ii) Use Theorem #38 to show that $H(x - a)$ is not differentiable at $x = a$.

(b) Let b also be a real number, distinct from a, and define

$$f(x) = H(x - a) + H(x - b).$$

(i) Sketch $f(x)$.

(ii) Use Theorem #38 to show that is not differentiable at $x = a$ or $x = b$.

In Section 8.5 we found that the possible transition points come in three "flavors": (1) points where the derivative is zero, (2) points where the derivative is undefined, and, (3) if the function is defined on a closed interval, the endpoints of the interval. We remarked at the time that it seemed odd that the third condition does not involve the derivative while the other two do.

With our new, deeper understanding of differentiation we can show that, in fact, there are really only two kinds of possible transition points, and both can be identified using the derivative. It turns out that the endpoints of an interval are really just points of non-differentiability.

To see this consider any function, $f(x)$ which is continuous on the closed interval $[a, b]$ and differentiable on the open interval (a, b). From Corollary #39 we know that $f'(b)$ only exists if $f'_R(b)$ and $f'_L(b)$ both exist[3].

But the right-hand limit at b doesn't exist. To see this, observe that f is only defined on $[a, b]$. Therefore when $h > 0$ the expression $f(b + h)$ asks us to evaluate f at a point outside its domain, which is meaningless. Thus

$$f'_R(b) = \lim_{\substack{h \to 0 \\ h > 0}} \frac{\overbrace{f(b + h)}^{\text{meaningless}} - f(b)}{h}$$

does not exist. A similar argument shows that $f'_L(a)$ does not exist.

Therefore f' does not exist at the endpoints of a closed interval. As a result the possible transition points of f are only those places where the derivative is zero, or undefined, because the latter category includes the endpoints of closed intervals.

---

[3]They also need to be equal, but that is irrelevant right now.

Chapter 16

Formal Limits

> "... in becoming rigorous, mathematical science takes a character so artificial as to strike everyone; it forgets its historical origins; we see how the questions can be answered, we no longer see how and why they are put."
>
> – Henri Poincaré (1854 – 1912)

We began our treatment of limits in Chapter 11 informally because it can take time to develop a mindset appropriate to a thorough understanding of limits. However, by proving theorems using properties of limits which we have not yet shown to be true we've left a logical hole in the proofs of nearly every theorem, lemma, and corollary we've stated. Bishop Berkeley would be most displeased.

It is time to fill those holes.

Loosely speaking, we know that if, as x gets "closer and closer" to some real number a, the function $f(x)$ gets "closer and closer" to A then $\lim_{x \to a} f(x) = A$. This phrase "closer and closer" is the source of the logical holes we need to fill.

To illustrate what can go wrong with the intuitive approach to limits that we've used so far, consider the limit $\lim_{x \to 1} f(x)$, when

$$f(x) = \frac{1}{\pi} \tan^{-1}(10^8(x - 1)).$$

To get a sense of what this function looks like when we let x get "closer and closer" to 1 we've tabulated a few values of $f(x)$ for x near 1 in the table at the right.

Seems pretty convincing doesn't it? Can we conclude from this table that

x	$f(x)$
1.5	4.999
1.4	4.999
1.3	4.999
1.2	4.999
1.1	4.999
1.01	4.999
1.001	4.999
1.0001	4.999

$$\lim_{x \to 1} \frac{1}{\pi} \tan^{-1}(10^8(x - 1)) = 4.999? \text{ (Or maybe that it is equal to 5?)}$$

Sadly, no. In fact, since $f(x)$ is continuous this limit is equal to zero because

$$f(1) = \frac{1}{\pi} \tan^{-1}(10^8(1 - 1)) = \frac{1}{\pi} \tan^{-1}(0) = 0.$$

Use your favorite computational tool to find a value of x near 1 such that $|f(x)| < 10^{-3}$.

The problem with our example is that none of the x values in the first column is close enough to 1. Sure, the numbers 1 and 1.0001 are very close together. But to evaluate this limit we don't just want to get close, we want to get close enough. For this particular function[1] we'd have to get much closer to 1 before we start to see the values of $f(x)$ getting close to 0.

And that's the problem. The nature of the function we're taking the limit of must be taken into account when we decide what "close enough" means for any particular limit. This isn't as bad as it sounds, but as always precision is crucial. We need a definition of **limit** that doesn't depend on the nature of the function we're investigating. A useful definition will also recover the Differentiation Rules in a manner that even Bishop Berkeley would agree is valid.

We will begin with limits "at infinity" because, paradoxically, these are often the easiest to understand. As we proceed through examples the question you want to keep in the back of your mind is, "For this problem how close is close enough?"

16.1 Getting Around Infinity

It all comes down to understanding infinity, both the infinitely small and the infinitely large. Or rather, it comes down to realizing that we do not understand infinity at all. So, whenever an apparently "infinite quantity" appears we will have to work with and explain it in finite terms. This might sound impossible, but it turns out to be merely difficult.

This approach is within well established mathematical tradition. From the time of the ancient Greeks until the sixteenth century, infinity was carefully excluded from serious mathematical consideration. It was the successful exploitation of the infinitely small (infinitesimals) by Galileo and others that eventually forced mathematicians to study infinity seriously.

Today we tend to conceive of a straight line in infinite terms; as extending infinitely far in two opposite directions. But when Euclid wrote his geometry text *The Elements*, he very carefully avoided allowing the existence of an "infinite line." For Euclid a straight line was what today would be called a line segment: the shortest path between two points.

But this restriction immediately caused problems for Euclid. For some of his constructions he needed to be able to extend his line segment. In modern mathematics this is not a problem since we allow lines to extend infinitely far in either direction. So we'd just move to a new point on the line wherever it needs to be.

But when Euclid specified a line segment $\overline{AB}$ he meant that the points

A and B were the endpoints of the line segment. To avoid infinite lines he extended the line segment $\overline{AB}$ by some definite amount out to a point C, thereby obtaining a new segment $\overline{AC}$, which – and this is the point – is still finite in length. In this way Euclid explicitly allowed line segments to be extendable to any finite length without ever allowing an infinitely long line.

---

[1]It should be clear that we've contrived this function so that we could make this point. It is unlikely that it is useful for any other purpose.

The Infinitely Large

We want to ask, and answer, the question

> *What number does y get close to if $y = \frac{1}{x}$ and we allow x to grow infinitely large?*

as precisely as we can without invoking the notion of the infinitely large. Does this rephrasing work for you?

> *If $y = \frac{1}{x}$, what does y get close to as x grows larger and larger?*

This seems to be better. We have side-stepped the issue of the infinitely large by saying "larger and larger." But unfortunately this rephrasing of the question changes its meaning. To see what we mean, think of x as the radius of a balloon which we want to inflate as much as we possibly can. Suppose we know that when the radius of the balloon is 8 it will pop. To avoid popping our balloon, we blow in enough air during the first second to expand the radius to $x(1) = 4$. In the next second we expand the radius to fill half of the remaining distance to $x(2) = 6$. In the third we repeat the process, expanding it to $x(3) = 7$. And we continue in this fashion. At each second the radius of our balloon expands to half of the remaining distance to 8.

Clearly the balloon's radius grows larger each second, so x grows "larger and larger" as required. But the intent of our original question was for x to become "infinitely large," not for x to remain smaller than 8.

And there is nothing special about 8. If x moves half of the distance to 16 each second, or halfway to 32, or even if it moves halfway to $1,048,576$ at each step we have the same problem. In each case x is growing "larger and larger" but it is not growing in a manner that reflects what we think we mean when we say that x is growing "infinitely large."

Drill #530:

Suppose B is a positive real number, and that $x(0) = 0$. Find a formula for x as a function of time t (in seconds), such that at each integer $t > 0$, the distance from $x(t)$ to B is half of the distance from $x(t-1)$ to B.

In this situation x is said to be **bounded above** because there is an upper bound on how large x can be, despite the fact that x is growing "larger and larger."

Recall that in Section 11.1 we mentioned that the notation $x \to \infty$ should be read aloud as "x increases without bound," so we rephrase our question as

> *If $y = \frac{1}{x}$, what does y get close to as x increases without bound?*

The Infinitely Small

The answer is very clear: y gets closer and closer to zero. But of course, the phrase "closer and closer" is also too vague, and for essentially the same reason that "larger and larger" is too vague to be useful.

Consider our balloon example again. If the radius, x, is constantly increasing but it is bounded above by 8 then x is certainly getting "closer and closer" to 8. But it's also getting "closer and closer" to 9. And 10. And any other number greater than 8.

Again, it is not our conception of the problem that is the difficulty. It is the language we're using. As before, we must choose our words more carefully.

To capture the idea that $y = \frac{1}{x}$ gets "closer and closer" to zero, without ever getting to zero let's think this through, being careful to say exactly what we mean, no more, no less. To begin we ask, "Is there a value of x which forces y to be less than, say $1/2$?"

Keeping in mind that if $a < b$ then $\frac{1}{a} > \frac{1}{b}$, if we need $y < 1/2$ and $y = 1/x$ that means that $1/x < 1/2$. Solving for x we have $x > 2$.

So apparently any value of x strictly greater than 2 will guarantee that y is less than $1/2$.

Stop and think about that last sentence. Do you see that we've actually discovered more than the original question asked for? Our question was, "Is there a value of x which forces y to be less than $1/2$?" But we've actually found all of them. We've found that if x is any number greater than 2 then $y - \frac{1}{x} < \frac{1}{2}$, regardless of which number we use.

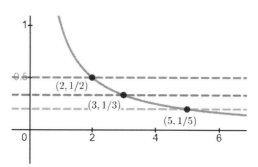

Can we make $y < 1/3$? Sure. Exactly the same analysis will show that if $x > 3$, then $y = \frac{1}{x} < \frac{1}{3}$, or if $x > 4$, then $y < 1/4$, and so on.

Problem #531:

If $y = \frac{1}{x}$ how large must x be in order to guarantee that

(a) $y < 1/5$ **(c)** $y < 1/100$

(b) $y < 1/10$ **(d)** $y < 1/1000000$

It should be clear that we needn't have stopped at one millionth (10^{-6}). The same argument will show that if we want $y = \frac{1}{x} < 10^{-10}$, we need $x > 10^{10}$. And that if we want $y = \frac{1}{x} < 10^{-1000}$, we need $x > 10^{1000}$.

So, by an appropriate choice of x we can make $y = \frac{1}{x}$ as close to 0 as we choose. To be a little more precise we say that we can make y arbitrarily close to zero, even if it never actually is zero. And this is what we really intended when we said that y gets "closer and closer" (or "goes to") zero.

This idea is exactly what the limit notation we introduced in Chapter 11 was intended to capture, so here, at last, are our question and answer precisely stated:

> **Question:** If $y(x) = \frac{1}{x}$, what is $\lim_{x \to \infty} y(x)$?
> **Answer:** $\lim_{x \to \infty} y(x) = 0$?

End Of Example #91

Convincing Berkeley

Is the use of these more precise terms enough to convince Bishop Berkeley?

Clearly not. If we were to show Berkeley that for $y = \frac{1}{x}$ we can guarantee that $y < 1/2$ by taking $x > 2$, his response would simply be, "So what? How do I know you can make y less than $1/3$." Nor will it be sufficient to show that we can make less than $1/3, 1/4, 1/10000$ or any particular number. Berkeley will simply come back to us with a smaller challenge.

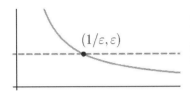

What we have to do is answer all possible challenges at once. This seems like a lot to ask until we think about it a bit. All we really have to do is suppose that we have some small, positive, unspecified number and show that we can find out how large x has to be to make $y = \frac{1}{x}$ less than that number. For the sake of being definite we'll give our number a name. It is traditional to call it[2] ε.

Suppose that $\varepsilon > 0$ and we want to figure out how large to make x to guarantee that $y = \frac{1}{x} < \varepsilon$. If we want $y < \varepsilon$, first substitute $\frac{1}{x}$ for y giving $\frac{1}{x} < \varepsilon$. Solve this for x (remember that if $a < b$ then $\frac{1}{a} > \frac{1}{b}$) so that $x > \frac{1}{\varepsilon}$.

Do you see the significance of this? Because we left ε unspecified (other than requiring it to be positive), we've met all possible challenges. If the challenge is to make y less than $10^{-1000000000}$ our response is, "We've already done that. Just take $\varepsilon = 10^{-1000000000}$. Repeating the computation above gives $x > 10^{1000000000}$.

Now for some function $f(x)$, the statement $\lim_{x \to \infty} f(x) = 0$ has the following precise meaning:

> If for each $\varepsilon > 0$ we can make $f(x) < \varepsilon$ by taking x sufficiently large, then we say that "the limit as x approaches infinity is zero."

To be sure, when we allow $\varepsilon > 0$ to be arbitrary, but unspecified we skirt the edge of the infinitely small. But this is the point. If ε is arbitrary then it can be as small as we need for it to be without ever being infinitely small. This is akin to Euclid allowing lines to be extended to any, unspecified[3], length without allowing them to be infinite in length. This is the idea underlying limits and limit notation.

Be aware that the meaning of the limit notation and the way we tend to speak about limits are inconsistent. This can present a lot of problems for the beginner. If we are speaking loosely, among friends, we would read this statement, $\lim_{x \to \infty} \frac{1}{x} = 0$, as follows:

> "The limit of one over x as x goes to infinity is equal to zero."

This is a very poor way to express the idea we are trying to capture. To say that x "approaches" infinity completely undercuts everything we've said about infinity so far because it treats infinity as if it is an actual number.

We now understand that $\lim_{x \to \infty} \frac{1}{x} = 0$ really means that as x increases without bound, $1/x$ is getting arbitrarily close to zero but what we say is not what the notation means. That incongruity can be very confusing at first. In this text we will be very careful not to speak so casually. At least not until we have more experience with limits.

We have only begun, but this is enough for us to offer a first definition of the limit concept. We generalize slightly.

---

[2]Presumably for "error" since ε is the Greek version of the letter "e."

[3]Be careful. "Unspecified" does not mean "variable." ε is a particular, fixed number. We just don't know which one it is.

Definition 23: Positive Function With Limit Zero at Infinity

Suppose $f(x) > 0$ for all $x > 0$. Then we say that $\lim\limits_{x \to \infty} f(x) = 0$ if and only if for every $\varepsilon > 0$ we can find a real number B with the property that if $x > B$, then $f(x) < \varepsilon$.

$$\overbrace{\phantom{x \text{ is unbounded}}}^{x \text{ is unbounded}} \qquad \overbrace{\phantom{f(x) \text{ is arbitrarily close to zero}}}^{f(x) \text{ is arbitrarily close to zero}}$$

The parameter B is the lower bound that x has to exceed for $f(x)$ to be less than ε. In our first example we had $B = 2$, in our last we had $B = 1/\varepsilon$. Naming the lower bound like this gives us a concrete way to specify how large x has to be. To great extent finding B is the whole problem. This is easier to see in an example.

Example #92:

Show that if $f(x) = \frac{1}{x^2}$, then $\lim\limits_{x \to \infty} f(x) = 0$.

As before take $\varepsilon > 0$. Once epsilon is given[4] your job is to find out how large x has to be to guarantee that $f(x) - \frac{1}{x^2} < \varepsilon$. So we work the problem backwards. That is, we start with $f(x) = \frac{1}{x^2} < \varepsilon$ and solve for ε to find that $x > \frac{1}{\sqrt{\varepsilon}}$.

So if we take $B = \frac{1}{\sqrt{\varepsilon}}$ when $x > B = \frac{1}{\sqrt{\varepsilon}}$ then

$$f(x) = \frac{1}{x^2} < \varepsilon.$$

End Of Example #92

Problem #532:

Use Definition 23 to prove that for each of the functions below $\lim\limits_{x \to \infty} f(x) = 0$. That is, assume $\varepsilon > 0$ is given and find a lower bound B such that if $x > B$ then $f(x) < \varepsilon$.

(a) $f(x) = \frac{1}{x^3}$ (c) $f(x) = \frac{1}{x^5}$ (e) $f(x) = \frac{1}{2x+1}$

(b) $f(x) = \frac{1}{x^4}$ (d) $f(x) = \frac{1}{x+1}$ (f) $f(x) = \frac{1}{5x+7}$

Refining the Definition

Definition 23 works as long as $f(x) > 0$, but without this restriction it fails utterly, as our next example shows:

Example #93:

Suppose $f(x) = -2 - \frac{1}{x}$. Can you guess the value of $\lim\limits_{x \to \infty} f(x)$?

---

[4] Think of epsilon as being handed to you by Bishop Berkeley. You don't get to control it, he does. Moreover all he will tell you about it is that it is a positive number.

Let $\varepsilon > 0$ be given. Then when B has any positive value, if $x > B$ we have

$$f(x) = -2 - \frac{1}{x} < 0 < \varepsilon,$$

and by Definition 23 we conclude that $\lim_{x \to \infty} f(x) = 0$ since all of the requirements of our definition have been met (except, of course, $f(x) > 0$).

Of course, this is nonsense. As we have noted as x increases without bound $\frac{1}{x}$ gets arbitrarily close to zero. So clearly $\lim_{x \to \infty} f(x) = -2$. That we are able to "prove" that $f(x)$ goes to zero simply means that Definition 23 doesn't capture everything we need.

We need a more encompassing definition of a limit.

End Of Example #93

Based on our experience in Example #93 with $f(x) = -2 - \frac{1}{x}$, what would you say needs to be changed in Definition#23 to allow $f(x) \le 0$ as well?

The problem of course, is that if $\varepsilon > 0$ is given the statement $f(x) < \varepsilon$ doesn't really capture the idea that $f(x)$ is near the number zero, only that it is less than the number ε. For example, -1000 is less than ε but it is nowhere near zero. What we need is a way to measure how far $f(x)$ is from zero, regardless of whether in the positive or the negative direction.

That is exactly what the absolute value function measures. For example, both 3 and -3 are the same distance from zero, the first one in the positive and the second one in the negative direction. That is $|3| = |-3| = 3$.

We need to modify our definition so that the distance from y to zero is less than ε. We want $|y| < \varepsilon$, not just $y < \varepsilon$.

Definition 24: Zero Limit at Infinity

Suppose $f(x)$ is defined for all $x > 0$. Then we say that $\lim_{x \to \infty} f(x) = 0$ if and only if for every $\varepsilon > 0$ we can find a real number B with the property that whenever $x > B$, $|f(x)| < \varepsilon$.

Example #94:

Suppose $f(x) = -\frac{1}{x}$. We want to prove rigorously that $\lim_{x \to \infty} f(x) = 0$.

Scrapwork

Let $\varepsilon > 0$ be given.

As we did in Example #92 we find the bound B by working the problem backwards. We want to end with $|f(x)| < \varepsilon$, so that's where we start.

$$|f(x)| < \varepsilon$$
$$|-1/x| < \varepsilon.$$

Since we are only interested in what happens to $f(x)$ as $x \to \infty$, we can safely assume that $x > 0$. Therefore $\left| \frac{-1}{x} \right| = \frac{1}{x}$, so

$$\frac{1}{x} < \varepsilon$$

$$x > \frac{1}{\varepsilon}.$$

Apparently to make $|f(x)| < \varepsilon$ we need $x > \frac{1}{\varepsilon}$, so we take $B = \frac{1}{\varepsilon}$.

End Of Scrapwork

Proof: Let $\varepsilon > 0$ be given. Take $B > \frac{1}{\varepsilon}$.

If $x > B$ then

$$x > \frac{1}{\varepsilon}.$$

Therefore

$$\frac{1}{x} < \varepsilon$$

and

$$\left| -\frac{1}{x} \right| < \varepsilon.$$

So

$$|f(x)| < \varepsilon.$$

Therefore, by Definition #24 $\lim_{x \to \infty} f(x) = 0$. ■

This example displays the format of a limit proof that you need to adhere to. Below is an outline of the format. This is not a course in creative writing. Do not depart from this format.

First: State the challenge, $\varepsilon > 0$.

Second: Specify the bound B (usually in terms of ε).

Third: Show that if $x > B$ then $|f(x)| < \varepsilon$.

Fourth: State your conclusion.

End Of Example #94

Drill #533:
Identify which statements in the proof in Example#94 correspond to the first, second, third, and fourth parts of the format presented above.

Example #95:

Our previous examples and problems in this section were fairly simple as formal limit problems go. This one is more complex.

Use Definition #24 to show that $\lim\limits_{x \to \infty} \frac{1}{5x - x^2} = 0$.

Scrapwork

For a given $\varepsilon > 0$, we want to end up with

$$\left| \frac{1}{5x - x^2} \right| < \varepsilon.$$

Part of what makes this limit more complex is that the part inside the absolute value $\frac{1}{5x - x^2}$, is not always positive. We need to deal with that somehow.

First, since we are only concerned about what happens as $x \to \infty$ it is safe to assume that $x > 0$. In that case, $x = |x|$. Next, observe that if $x > 5$ also, then $x^2 > 5x$. Thus $5x - x^2 < 0$, so that $\left| \frac{1}{5x - x^2} \right| = \frac{1}{x^2 - 5x}$. We could now work backwards like before, and solve for $\frac{1}{x^2 - 5x} < \varepsilon$. This will work fine, but the Algebra gets very messy. Try it and see.

There is a sneaky way to do this that avoids some of the Algebra. Notice that $\frac{1}{x^2 - 5x} = \left(\frac{1}{x - 5} \right) \cdot \left(\frac{1}{x} \right)$. Notice further that if $x > 6$, then $x - 5 > 1$ so that $\frac{1}{x - 5} < 1$. Putting all of this together we we that for $x > 6$,

$$\left| \frac{1}{5x - x^2} \right| = \left| \frac{1}{5 - x} \right| \cdot \left| \frac{1}{x} \right|$$

$$= \left(\frac{1}{x - 5} \right) \cdot \left(\frac{1}{x} \right)$$

$$< 1 \cdot \left(\frac{1}{x} \right) = \frac{1}{x}.$$

Thus to guarantee that $\left| \frac{1}{5x - x^2} \right| < \varepsilon$ we need $\frac{1}{x} < \varepsilon$, or $x > \frac{1}{\varepsilon}$.

End Of Scrapwork

Proof: Let $\varepsilon > 0$ be given. Let B be the larger of 6 and $\frac{1}{\varepsilon}$. If $x > B$ then $x > 6$ so $x - 5 > 1$. Therefore

$$\left| \frac{1}{5 - x} \right| = \frac{1}{x - 5} < 1. \tag{16.1}$$

Since $x > \frac{1}{\varepsilon} > 0$, we see that $\left|\frac{1}{x}\right| = \frac{1}{|x|} = \frac{1}{x} < \varepsilon$. Thus

$$\left|\frac{1}{5x - x^2}\right| = \left|\frac{1}{5 - x}\right| \cdot \left|\frac{1}{x}\right| < 1 \cdot \frac{1}{x} < \varepsilon. \tag{16.2}$$

Therefore by Definition #24,

$$\lim_{x \to \infty} \frac{1}{5x - x^2} = 0.$$

∎

Problem #534:
Explain carefully, and in detail, the reasoning that supports the claims made in Equations 16.1 and 16.2.

End Of Example #95

Notice that in Examples #94 and #95 the scrapwork was an essential part of the solution, but in the formal proof the results of the scrapwork were so abbreviated as to almost not be present. This is part of the formalism of mathematical writing. We try to make sure that everything that needs to be said is said — and absolutely nothing more. In this instance in particular, we are not obligated to explain where the bound B came from, only that it works. It can take time to become comfortable with this presentation style.

Even with practice very few people can read a formal proof without doing the computations necessary to show that all of the claims made are actually true. Keep paper and pencil handy at all times to help you follow the argument.

Problem #535:
For each of the following show that $\lim_{x \to \infty} f(x) = 0$.

(a) $f(x) = \frac{1}{x+2}$

(b) $f(x) = \frac{1}{x^2}$

(c) $f(x) = \frac{1}{x^3}$

(d) $f(x) = \frac{1}{x^3+2}$

(e) $f(x) = -\frac{2}{x}$

(f) $f(x) = \frac{2}{x^2}$

(g) $f(x) = \frac{1}{5x-7}$

(h) $f(x) = \frac{\sin(x)}{x}$
(**Hint:** $|\sin(x)| \leq 1$.)

Definition #24 only tells us what it means when the limit of some function as $x \to \infty$ is zero. But as we observed in Example #93 as x increases without bound $f(x) = -2 - \frac{1}{x}$ approaches -2, not 0. We'll need something more general, but all of the important ideas have been introduced. We generalize Definition #24 as follows.

Definition 25: A Limit at $+\infty$

Suppose that L is a real number and that $f(x)$ is defined for all $x > 0$. Then we say that

$$\lim_{x \to \infty} f(x) = L$$

if and only if for every $\varepsilon > 0$ there is a real number B with the property that whenever[5] $x > B$, $|f(x) - L| < \varepsilon$.

Example #96:

Suppose $f(x) = 1 - \frac{1}{x}$. Intuitively, it is clear that $\lim_{x \to \infty} f(x) = 1$ but we need to prove that this is so.

Scrapwork

Suppose $\varepsilon > 0$ is given. We need to specify a number B (probably in terms of ε), with the property that if $x > B$ then $|f(x) - 1| < \varepsilon$. So we will work backwards from this inequality.

$$|f(x) - 1| < \varepsilon$$
$$\left|\left(1 - \tfrac{1}{x}\right) - 1\right| < \varepsilon$$
$$\left|-\tfrac{1}{x}\right| < \varepsilon$$
$$|x| > \tfrac{1}{\varepsilon}.$$

Thus $x > \frac{1}{\varepsilon}$, and it appears that $|f(x) - 1| < \varepsilon$ as long as x is greater than $\frac{1}{\varepsilon}$.

End Of Scrapwork

Proof: Let $\varepsilon > 0$ be given. Take $x > B = 1/\varepsilon$. Then

$$\left|\tfrac{1}{x}\right| < \varepsilon$$
$$\left|\tfrac{-1}{x}\right| < \varepsilon$$
$$\left|\left(1 - \tfrac{1}{x}\right) - 1\right| < \varepsilon$$
$$|f(x) - 1| < \varepsilon.$$

Therefore by Definition #25,

$$\lim_{x \to \infty} f(x) = 1.$$

■

End Of Example #96

---

[5]Notice that if $L = 0$ this reduces to Definition #24.

Example #97:

In Section 11.1 we approached the problem of finding a horizontal asymptote of $f(x) = \frac{5x}{x+1}$ in the following highly intuitive manner, using the "$(\to \infty)$" notation.

$$\lim_{x\to\infty} \frac{5x}{x+1} = \lim_{x\to\infty} \frac{5x}{x\left(1 + \frac{1}{x}\right)} = \lim_{x\to\infty} \frac{5}{1 + \frac{1}{x}} = \frac{5}{1 + \frac{1}{(\to\infty)}} = \frac{5}{1+0} = 5.$$

So we see that this limit must be equal to five. To prove this rigorously, without referring to infinity, we use Definition 25

Scrapwork

Let $\varepsilon > 0$ be given. As before we work backwards from our goal, $\left|\frac{5x}{x+1} - 5\right| < \varepsilon$.

$$\left|\frac{5x}{x+1} - 5\right| < \varepsilon$$

$$\left|\frac{5x - 5(x+1)}{x+1}\right| < \varepsilon$$

$$\left|\frac{-5}{x+1}\right| < \varepsilon$$

$$\frac{|-5|}{|x+1|} < \varepsilon.$$

As long as $x > -1$ this is the same as

$$\frac{5}{x+1} < \varepsilon. \tag{16.3}$$

so we will stipulate that B (and therefore x) must be at least greater than -1. Solving inequality 16.3 for x we see that $x > \frac{5}{\varepsilon} - 1$ also. So we take B to be the greater of -1 and $\frac{5}{\varepsilon} - 1$. We capture this idea with the notation, $B = \max\left(-1, \frac{5}{\varepsilon} - 1\right)$.

End Of Scrapwork

Problem #536:

(a) Show that we only need the condition $B > \frac{5}{\varepsilon} - 1$ by showing that $B > \frac{5}{\varepsilon} - 1$ implies that $B > -1$.

(b) Suppose that $\varepsilon > 0$ and $B = \frac{5}{\varepsilon} - 1$. Prove that if $x > B$ then $\left|\frac{5x}{x+1} - 5\right| < \varepsilon$.

End Of Example #97

Problem #537:

We want to give a rigorous proof that $\lim\limits_{x \to \infty} \frac{x^2+100}{4x^2} = \frac{1}{4}$.

Let $\varepsilon > 0$ be given.

(a) Do the scrapwork that shows that we must take $x > B = \frac{5}{\sqrt{\varepsilon}}$.

(b) Show that if $x > B = \frac{5}{\sqrt{\varepsilon}}$ then $\left| \frac{x^2+100}{4x^2} - \frac{1}{4} \right| < \varepsilon$.

Problem #538:

Do the scrapwork, and provide a rigorous proof of each of the limits below.

(a) $\lim\limits_{x \to \infty} \frac{1}{x^{1/3}} = 0$ **(b)** $\lim\limits_{x \to \infty} \left(\frac{2}{x^3} - 1 \right) = -1$ **(c)** $\lim\limits_{x \to \infty} \left(\frac{2+x^3}{x^3} \right) = 1$

It should be clear how to define a limit at $-\infty$. All of the same issues of clarity and precision that we encountered before come up here as well. The only difference is that we have to change the sense of our inequalities to reflect that x is decreasing without bound.

Definition 26: A Limit at $-\infty$

Suppose $f(x)$ is defined for all $x < 0$. Then we say that

$$\lim_{x \to -\infty} f(x) = L$$

if and only if for every $\varepsilon > 0$ we can find a real number B with the property that whenever $x < B$, $|f(x) - L| < \varepsilon$.

Problem #539:

Do the scrapwork, and provide a rigorous proof of each of the limits below.

(a) $\lim\limits_{x \to -\infty} \frac{1}{x^{1/3}} = 0$ **(b)** $\lim\limits_{x \to -\infty} \left(\frac{2}{x^3} - 1 \right) = -1$ **(c)** $\lim\limits_{x \to -\infty} \left(\frac{2+7x^3}{x^3} \right) = 7$

16.2   Limits at a Real Number

In the previous section we were focused on the relatively simple limits associated with horizontal asymptotes. But our goal is to use the limit in Definition #15 to prove that the Differentiation Rules we've been using are valid. To do that we will use the following precise, rigorous definition of a limit as $x \to a$ where a is some real number.

Definition 27: The Limit at a Point

Suppose $f(x)$ is a function, and that a is a real number. We say that

$$\lim_{x \to a} f(x) = L$$

if and only if for every $\varepsilon > 0$ there is a $\delta > 0$ with the property that whenever $0 < |x - a| < \delta$, $|f(x) - L| < \varepsilon$.

Take particular notice of the fact that none of the limit definitions (Definitions #25, #26, and #27) do not tell us how to compute the limit. They serve only to rigorously verify what our intuition says the limit should be.

Digression #25: The Absolute Value, again

It can be difficult to work with the absolute value inside of inequalities. To avoid these kinds of problems it is useful to remember that

$$|A| \leq B \text{ if and only if } -B \leq A \leq B. \tag{16.4}$$

Although the latter looks slightly more complicated, it has the advantage that there are no absolute value symbols to trip us up.

End Of Digression #25

Notice the similarities and the differences between Definitions #25, #26, and #27.

We use Definition #27 the same way we used Definition 25: We take $\varepsilon > 0$ as a challenge and find conditions which guarantee that $|f(x) - L| < \varepsilon$. Previously we were interested in the behavior of $f(x)$ "close to infinity" so the condition was that $x > B$ (that x was large enough, loosely speaking). Now we are interested in the behavior of $f(x)$ "close to a" so we need to indicate how close x has to be to a. The $\delta > 0$ in Definition #27 plays the same role that the upper bound B played in Definitions #25 and #26. It locates where x must be in order to guarantee that $|f(x) - L| < \varepsilon$.

The sketch at the right depicts the situation when $\lim_{x \to a} f(x) = L$ visually. (The graph of $f(x)$ appears to be a straight line because we are zoomed in very close to the point (a, L) and the Principle of Local Linearity is in play.) We have indicated that $f(x)$ is not defined at a, but it could be. Limits don't care what happens at a, only what happens near a. To emphasize this point we will usually say that $0 < |x - a| < \delta$, rather than $|x - a| < \delta$. Because the inequality on the left is strict, we do not consider what happens when $x = a$.

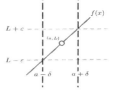

As before ε is the challenge. To show that the limit exists and is equal to L as claimed

$$\overbrace{}^{x \text{ is within } \delta \text{ of } a, x \neq a}$$

our task is to: Find a value of δ such that, as long[6] as x is between $a - \delta$ and $a + \delta$ the

---

[6]More succinctly: $0 < |x - a| < \delta$.

$$\overbrace{f(x) \text{ is within } \varepsilon \text{ of } L}$$

corresponding[7] $f(x)$ will be between $L - \varepsilon$ and $L + \varepsilon$. Visually, this means that the graph of $f(x)$ will be between the dashed horizontal lines as long as x is between the dotted vertical lines.

Definition #27 is the culmination of approximately 200 years of attempts by some very brilliant people to provide a rigorous foundation for Calculus. Don't expect to absorb this easily. It will take time and effort to fully understand and be able to use it. We will start simply.

Drill #540:

Use Definitions #24, #25, #26, and #27 to explain that the following are "obviously" true.

$$\lim_{x \to \infty} f(x) = L \text{ if and only if } \lim_{x \to \infty} (f(x) - L) = 0.$$

$$\lim_{x \to -\infty} f(x) = L \text{ if and only if } \lim_{x \to -\infty} (f(x) - L) = 0.$$

$$\lim_{x \to a} f(x) = L \text{ if and only if } \lim_{x \to a} (f(x) - L) = 0.$$

(**Comment:** We are not looking for a formal proof, just a reasonable explanation.)

Example #98:

Observe that it is intuitively clear that if $f(x) = -x^2 + 2$ then $\lim_{x \to 0} f(x) = 2$. We wish to prove this rigorously.

Scrapwork

Suppose $\varepsilon > 0$ is given. Our goal is to find a $\delta > 0$ such that if $0 < |x - 0| < \delta$ (or just $0 < |x| < \delta$) then $|f(x) - 2| < \varepsilon$.

Solving this for x we have

$$\left| -x^2 + 2 - 2 \right| < \varepsilon$$
$$\left| -x^2 \right| < \varepsilon$$
$$\left| x^2 \right| < \varepsilon.$$

Recall from Digression #20 that $\sqrt{x^2} = |x|$, so we see that $|x| < \sqrt{\varepsilon}$ or, equivalently

$$-\sqrt{\varepsilon} < x < \sqrt{\varepsilon}.$$

It appears that $|f(x) - 2| < \varepsilon$ as long as $|x| < \sqrt{\varepsilon}$, so we take $\delta = \sqrt{\varepsilon}$.

End Of Scrapwork

This was the scrapwork. The proof consists of showing that the condition we found, $|x| < \delta(= \sqrt{\varepsilon})$, actually works.

---

[7]More succinctly: $|f(x) - L| < \varepsilon$.

Proof: Let $\varepsilon > 0$ be given. Take $\delta = \sqrt{\varepsilon} > 0$.

Assume that $0 < |x| < \delta$. Then

$$|x| < \delta$$
$$\sqrt{x^2} < \sqrt{\varepsilon}$$
$$x^2 < \varepsilon$$
$$\left|-x^2\right| < \varepsilon$$
$$\left|-x^2 + 2 - 2\right| < \varepsilon$$
$$|f(x) - 2| < \varepsilon.$$

Therefore $\lim\limits_{x \to 0} f(x) = 2$.   ■

Notice that our proof does not give us any new information since it is intuitively clear that $\lim\limits_{x \to 0}(-x^2 + 2) = 2$. The formalism of a limit merely confirms, in a manner even Bishop Berkeley would accept, what we already know to be true.

Incidentally, since $f(0) = -0^2 + 2 = 2$ we have also just proved that $f(x)$ is continuous at $x = 0$. See Definition #17.

For simple problems like this one the proof consisted of writing the algebraic steps from our scrapwork backwards, as you see. This worked because every algebraic step in the scrapwork was reversible. But don't jump to conclusions. This will not always be the case.

Clearly the scrapwork is the most important part of the solution process for this problem. In a very real sense it actually is the solution. We call it scrapwork because it is the part of the work that you don't show anyone else because it is messy and not well organized[8]. The scrapwork is like the scaffolding used to construct a building. The proof is the building.

It is absolutely necessary to have the scaffolding while construction is ongoing but you tear it down and clean everything up before you move in. In the same way your proof should be a cleaned up version of your scrapwork. If this example were a homework problem, your solution would be the part that appears between **Proof:** and the little black[9] square, ■, at the end.

End Of Example #98

Example #99:

Returning to Example #83 from Section 13.1 recall that we had

$$f(x) = \begin{cases} 3x & \text{if } x \neq 2 \\ 10 & \text{if } x = 2. \end{cases}$$

We had shown by an intuitive argument that $\lim\limits_{x \to 2} f(x) = 6$. Our previous proof lacked rigor, especially in the last step. We will provide a fully rigorous proof now.

---

[8]We kept it clean and orderly here so you could see the reasoning.

[9]When Latin was the language of scholarship a mathematical proof ended with the letters $Q.E.D.$, which are the initials of the phrase *quod erat demonstrandum*, meaning "which was to be demonstrated." Contrary to a popular myth it does not mean "Quite Easily Done." In the late twentieth century this traditional ending began to be replaced by the black square we're using (or some variation of it). It is called a "Halmos" in honor of Paul Halmos, a preeminent mathematician of the 20th century, who popularized it.

Proof: Let $\varepsilon > 0$ be given and take $0 < \delta < \frac{\varepsilon}{3}$. Then if $0 < |x - 2| < \delta$ we have

$$-\delta < x - 2 < \delta$$
$$-\frac{\varepsilon}{3} < x - 2 < \frac{\varepsilon}{3}$$
$$-\varepsilon < 3x - 6 < \varepsilon.$$

Observe that $f(x) = 3x$ since $x \neq 2$. Therefore

$$-\varepsilon < f(x) - 6 < \varepsilon$$

and so

$$|f(x) - 6| < \varepsilon.$$

Therefore $\lim\limits_{x \to 2} f(x) = 6.$ ■

Notice that it is again irrelevant that $f(2) = 10$.

Problem #541:
Use the proof above to recreate the scrapwork that we did before we wrote the proof.

End Of Example #99

Example #100:

   We would like to find the value of $\lim\limits_{x \to \frac{1}{2}} \dfrac{4x^2 - 1}{2x - 1}$, and prove that the value we find is correct.

   Remember that none of our limit definitions tell us how to find the value of a limit, only how to prove that it has a particular value after we've found it. In our examples so far the value of the limits have been intuitively clear so we haven't concerned ourselves with this part of the problem. But before we can prove that a limit has a particular value we obviously need to decide what we believe the limit value is.

   We have several options for doing this. The simplest is guessing, but guessing works best if we have some intuition about the problem. Guessing blindly is usually a waste of time. Nevertheless, guessing is always an option. Can you guess the value of this limit?

   Another simple option is to use a calculator and plug the value of the limit point, in this case $x = \frac{1}{2}$, and see what the calculator comes up with. This will work if the function is continuous at the limit point. But $\frac{4x^2 - 1}{2x - 1}$ is not continuous at $x = \frac{1}{2}$ so that won't help with this problem. Try it and see.

A third, and much more useful option is to sketch the graph of $f(x)$ to see what $f(x)$ is close to near the limit point. The graph of $f(x) = \frac{4x^2-1}{2x-1}$ is given at the right. It is not defined at $x = 1/2$ because when $x = 1/2$ we get zero in the denominator. Nevertheless the limit at $x = 1/2$ seems to exist. As you can see as x approaches $1/2$, $f(x)$ appears to approach 2. Based on this graph it seems likely that the value of the limit is 2.

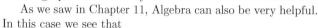

As we saw in Chapter 11, Algebra can also be very helpful. In this case we see that

$$\frac{4x^2-1}{2x-1} = \frac{(2x+1)(2x-1)}{2x-1} = (2x+1) \cdot \frac{2x-1}{2x-1} = (2x+1)$$

where the cancellation in red is only valid when $x \neq \frac{1}{2}$, our limit point is $x = \frac{1}{2}$ so it is not under consideration.

In fact, once we have rigorously proved[10] Theorem #15, Theorem #16, and Theorem #18 from Section 13.1 the following will be a valid proof:

$$\lim_{x \to \frac{1}{2}} \frac{4x^2-1}{2x-1} = \lim_{x \to \frac{1}{2}} \frac{(2x+1)(2x-1)}{2x-1}$$

$$= \left[\lim_{x \to \frac{1}{2}} (2x+1) \right] \left[\lim_{x \to \frac{1}{2}} \frac{2x-1}{2x-1} \right]$$

$$= \lim_{x \to \frac{1}{2}} (2x+1)$$

$$= 2.$$

Problem #542:

Identify where we used Theorem #15, Theorem #16, and Theorem # 18 in the development above.

Because we haven't yet rigorously proved Theorems #15, #16 or #18 we can't use them to construct a rigorous proof. Until they are proved they are not known, they are just believed. Belief is not knowledge.

But there is no problem with using them to gather evidence. So far we have strong evidence that this limit is 2.

Having gathered our evidence, we now believe that $\lim\limits_{x \to \frac{1}{2}} \dfrac{4x^2-1}{2x-1} = 2$. Next we need to do the scrapwork for our proof.

Scrapwork

As always we work backwards from our goal. We need to show that $|f(x) - 2| < \varepsilon$ so

$$\left| \frac{4x^2-1}{2x-1} - 2 \right| < \varepsilon.$$

---
[10]We will do this in Section 16.3.

Since we're not interested in the value of anything at $x = \frac{1}{2}$ (where the denominator is zero) we can factor and cancel, giving

$$\left| \frac{(2x + 1)\cancel{(2x - 1)}}{\cancel{2x - 1}} - 2 \right| < \varepsilon$$

$$|2x + 1 - 2| < \varepsilon$$

$$|2x - 1| < \varepsilon.$$

We see that if $|2x - 1| < \varepsilon$ then

$$-\varepsilon < 2x - 1 < \varepsilon$$

or

$$\frac{1}{2} - \frac{\varepsilon}{2} < x < \frac{1}{2} + \frac{\varepsilon}{2}.$$

So taking $\delta = \frac{\varepsilon}{2}$ will work for this problem.

End Of Scrapwork

Proof: Let $\varepsilon > 0$ be given. Take $\delta = \frac{\varepsilon}{2} > 0$. Then if $0 < \left| x - \frac{1}{2} \right| < \delta$ we have

$$\left| x - \frac{1}{2} \right| < \frac{\varepsilon}{2}$$

$$-\frac{\varepsilon}{2} < x - \frac{1}{2} < \frac{\varepsilon}{2}$$

$$-\varepsilon < 2x - 1 < \varepsilon$$

$$-\varepsilon < 2x + 1 - 2 < \varepsilon.$$

Since $x \neq \frac{1}{2}$ we see that

$$-\varepsilon < \frac{(2x + 1)(2x - 1)}{2x - 1} - 2 < \varepsilon$$

$$-\varepsilon < \frac{4x^2 - 1}{2x + 1} - 2 < \varepsilon$$

$$-\varepsilon < f(x) - 2 < \varepsilon,$$

and so

$$|f(x) - 2| < \varepsilon.$$

Therefore

$$\lim_{x \to \frac{1}{2}} \frac{4x^2 - 1}{2x + 1} = 2$$

$\blacksquare$

A long list of inequalities like those above can be a little intimidating. Don't let that stop you. Verify each transition from one inequality to the other. If you don't see why a particular transition is valid refer back to the scrapwork.

End Of Example #100

Digression #26: Why We Prove Theorems

The proof of any theorem will follow logically from the relevant definitions. However, as we've seen proving that $\lim\limits_{x \to \frac{1}{2}} \dfrac{4x^2 - 1}{2x + 1} = 2$ from Definition #27 was very delicate and troublesome. We'd really like to avoid this if we can.

We prove general theorems so that we can use them as tools. Do we have any tools (theorems) that would have made the proof of

$$\lim\limits_{x \to \frac{1}{2}} \dfrac{4x^2 - 1}{2x + 1} = 2$$

simpler?

Problem #543:

(a) Show that $\lim\limits_{x \to \frac{1}{2}} \frac{4x^2 - 1}{2x + 1}$ satisfies all of the conditions of Theorem 14.

(b) Use Theorem 14 to prove that $\lim\limits_{x \to \frac{1}{2}} \frac{4x^2 - 1}{2x + 1} = 2$.

(c) Explain your proof in part (b) is rigorous.

L'Hôpital's Rule is a very powerful tool which simultaneously evaluates a limit and provides a rigorous proof of the result. And it is much easier to use than Definition #27.

But sadly, it will be of no use to us for the remainder of this chapter. L'Hôpital's Rule relies on knowing that our differentiation rules are valid, and we don't know that yet. That the differentiation rules are valid is exactly what we are trying to show. To use L'Hôpital's Rule would be to engage in circular reasoning, which is invalid.

=========== End Of Digression #26 ===========

Example #101:

In this example we will show rigorously that the derivative of $f(x) = x^2$ is $f'(x) = 2x$. To do that we need to show that

$$\lim\limits_{h \to 0} \dfrac{f(x + h) - f(x)}{h} = 2x.$$

Recall that differentiation is a local property so we are thinking of x as a fixed, but unspecified real number. The variable in this example is h.

Scrapwork

For $\varepsilon > 0$ we need to find $\delta > 0$ such that if $0 < |h| < \delta$, then $\left| \dfrac{f(x+h) - f(x)}{h} - 2x \right| < \varepsilon$.

Working backwards from this we have

$$\left| \frac{(x+h)^2 - x^2}{h} - 2x \right| < \varepsilon$$

$$\left| \frac{x^2 + 2xh + h^2 - x^2}{h} - 2x \right| < \varepsilon$$

$$\left| \frac{2xh + h^2}{h} - 2x \right| < \varepsilon$$

$$|2x + h - 2x| < \varepsilon$$

$$|h| < \varepsilon$$

$$-\varepsilon < h < \varepsilon,$$

so we choose $\delta = \varepsilon$.

End Of Scrapwork

Problem #544:

Use the scrapwork above to write down a rigorous proof that if $f(x) = x^2$ then $f'(x) = 2x$.

End Of Example #101

16.3   Limit Laws (Theorems)

If we can prove each of the limit laws in Chapter 13 rigorously (i.e, using Definition #27) we will have provided a rigorous foundation for Differential Calculus. We will address these now.

To prove the limit laws we will need to make extensive use of what is called the **Triangle Inequality**. We state and prove the Triangle Inequality here so that we can cite it as needed.

Theorem 40: [**The Triangle Inequality**]

For any real numbers x, and y, $|x + y| \leq |x| + |y|$.

The proof of the Triangle Inequality relies on Statement (16.4) from Digression #25.

Proof of The Triangle Inequality: Clearly $-|x| \leq x \leq |x|$ and $-|y| \leq y \leq |y|$. Adding these together we have

$$-|x| - |y| \leq x + y \leq |x| + |y|$$

$$\underbrace{-(|x| + |y|)}_{-B} \leq \underbrace{x + y}_{A} \leq \underbrace{|x| + |y|}_{B}.$$

so by Statement (16.4) we have $|x + y| \leq |x| + |y|$.   ∎

The Limit Laws we need to prove are:

Theorem 18: The Limit of a Constant is the Constant.

Theorem 15: The Limit of a Sum is the Sum of the Limits

Theorem 16: The Limit of a Product is the Product of the Limits

Theorem 22: The Limit of a Composition is the Composition of the Limits, and

Theorem 21: The Squeeze Theorem

We will provide a proof of the "limit at infinity" version of each of these Theorems using Definition #25. We will leave the proof of the "limit at a real number" version using the Definition #27 as an exercise for you. In every case you can model your scrapwork and proof on the ones we provide.

Theorem 41: [**The Limit at Infinity of a Constant Function is the Constant**]
Suppose L and K are real numbers. If $f(x) = K$ for all $x > L$ then $\lim\limits_{x \to \infty} f(x) = K$.

Proof: Let $\varepsilon > 0$ be given. Take $B = L$. Then if $x > B$ we see that

$$|f(x) - K| = |K - K| = 0 < \varepsilon.$$

Therefore

$$\lim_{x \to \infty} f(x) = K.$$

∎

The formalism we're using requires that we specify some value for B. It was convenient to specify $B = L$, but in this proof any value for $B \geq L$ would have worked as well.

Theorem 42: [**The Limit at Negative Infinity of a Constant Function is the Constant**]
Suppose U and K are real numbers. If $f(x) = K$ for all $x < U$ then $\lim\limits_{x \to -\infty} f(x) = K$.

Problem #545:
Use the proof of Theorem 41 as a model to construct a proof of Theorem #42.

Theorem 43: [**The Limit at a Point of a Constant Function is the Constant**]
Suppose K is a real number and a is a point in the domain of $f(x)$. If $f(x) = K$ near a then $\lim\limits_{x \to a} f(x) = K$.

Problem #546:

Use the proof of Theorem 41 as a model to construct a proof of Theorem #43.

(**Hint:** Despite the apparent simplicity of this problem there is a lot going on here. Recall that "near" means that $f(x) = K$ on some open interval, say (c, d), containing a except possibly at a (see Definition 16). You need to find a $\delta > 0$ such that if $-\delta < x - a < \delta$ then $f(x) = K$. That is, you need an interval of length 2δ with a as the midpoint where $f(x) = K$. But there is no guarantee that a is the midpoint of the interval (c, d). This would be an excellent time to engage your visual intuition by drawing a sketch so you can "see" the problem.)

The Limit of a Sum

Theorem 44: [The Limit of a Sum at Infinity]

If $\lim\limits_{x \to \infty} f(x) = L_f$ and $\lim\limits_{x \to \infty} g(x) = L_g$ then $\lim\limits_{x \to \infty} (f(x) + g(x)) = L_f + L_g$.

Scrapwork

As always we begin by assuming that $\varepsilon > 0$ has been given.

We want to show that if x is large enough (larger than some specified B) then

$$|(f(x) + g(x)) - (L_f + L_g)| < \varepsilon. \tag{16.5}$$

The only information we have to work with is the knowledge that

$$\lim_{x \to \infty} f(x) = L_f \text{ and } \lim_{x \to \infty} g(x) = L_g,$$

which means that we can make $|f(x) - L_f|$ and $|g(x) - L_g|$ as close to zero as we wish, provided we make x large enough. Rewriting the left-hand side of Equation 16.5 and invoking the Triangle Inequality we see that

$$|(f(x) + g(x)) - (L_f + L_g)| = |(f(x) - L_f) + (g(x) - L_g)|$$
$$\leq |f(x) - L_f| + |g(x) - L_g|.$$

But as we've observed we can make $|f(x) - L_f|$ and $|g(x) - L_g|$ as close to zero as we wish, provided we take x large enough. To be precise, there is a number B_f such that if $x > B_f$ then $|f(x) - L_f| < \frac{\varepsilon}{2}$. Similarly there is a number B_g such that if $x > B_g$ then $|g(x) - L_f| < \frac{\varepsilon}{2}$.

Since we need for both of these things to happen a sufficiently large value of x is one where $x > B_f$ and $x > B_g$.

End Of Scrapwork

Proof: Let $\varepsilon > 0$ be given.

Since $\lim\limits_{x \to \infty} f(x) = L_f$ there is a bound, B_f such that if $x > B_f$ then $|f(x) - L_f| < \frac{\varepsilon}{2}$.

Since $\lim\limits_{x\to\infty} g(x) = L_g$ there is a bound, B_g such that if $x > B_g$ then $|g(x) - L_g| < \frac{\varepsilon}{2}$.

Take $B = \max(B_f, B_g)$. Then if $x > B$ then $x > B_f$ and $x > B_g$. Thus by the Triangle Inequality (Theorem #40)

$$\begin{aligned}
|(f(x) + g(x)) - (L_f + L_g)| &= |(f(x) - L_f) + (g(x) - L_g)| \\
&\leq |f(x) - L_f| + |g(x) - L_g| \\
&< \frac{\varepsilon}{2} + \frac{\varepsilon}{2} \\
&= \varepsilon.
\end{aligned}$$

Therefore $\lim\limits_{x\to\infty} (f(x) + g(x)) = L_f + L_g$. ∎

Problem #547:

Use the proof of Theorem 44 as a model to construct a proof of Theorem #45 below.

Theorem 45: [The Limit of a Sum at Negative Infinity]

If $\lim\limits_{x\to-\infty} f(x) = L_f$ and $\lim\limits_{x\to-\infty} g(x) = L_g$ then $\lim\limits_{x\to-\infty} (f(x) + g(x)) = L_f + L_g$.

Problem #548:

Use the proof of Theorem 44 as a model to construct a proof of Theorem #46 below.

Theorem 46: [Limit of a Sum at a Point]

Suppose that a is some real number, $\lim\limits_{x\to a} f(x) = L_f$ and $\lim\limits_{x\to a} g(x) = L_g$. Then

$$\lim\limits_{x\to a} (f(x) + g(x)) = L_f + L_g.$$

The Squeeze Theorem

Theorem 47: [The Squeeze Theorem at Infinity]

If $\alpha(x) \leq f(x) \leq \beta(x)$ on some interval, (c, ∞) and

$$\lim\limits_{x\to\infty} \alpha(x) = \lim\limits_{x\to\infty} \beta(x) = L$$

then $\lim\limits_{x\to\infty} f(x) = L$ also.

Proof: Let $\varepsilon > 0$ be given.

Since $\lim_{x \to \infty} \alpha(x) = L$ there is some a real number B_α, such that if $x > B_\alpha$ then $|\alpha(x) - L| < \varepsilon$. From Equation (16.4) we see that for $x > B_\alpha$:

$$-\varepsilon < \alpha(x) - L < \varepsilon.$$

Similarly there is a real number B_β, such that if $x > B_\beta$ then $|\beta(x) - L| < \varepsilon$. So for $x > B_\beta$:

$$-\varepsilon < \beta(x) - L < \varepsilon.$$

Take $B = \max(c, B_\alpha, B_\beta)$. Then if $x > B$

$$-\varepsilon < \alpha(x) - L < f(x) - L < \beta(x) - L < \varepsilon.$$

In particular, $-\varepsilon < f(x) - L < \varepsilon$ so from Equation (16.4) we see that $|f(x) - L| < \varepsilon$.

Therefore $\lim_{x \to \infty} f(x) = L$. ∎

Problem #549: Use the proof of Theorem 47 as a model to prove Theorem 48 below.

Theorem 48: [The Squeeze Theorem at Negative Infinity]

If $\alpha(x) \leq f(x) \leq \beta(x)$ on some interval, $(-\infty, c)$ and

$$\lim_{x \to -\infty} \alpha(x) = \lim_{x \to -\infty} \beta(x) = L$$

then $\lim_{x \to -\infty} f(x) = L$ also.

Problem #550: Use the proof of Theorem 47 as a model to prove Theorem!49 below.

Theorem 49: [The Squeeze Theorem, at a Point]

If $\alpha(x) \leq f(x) \leq \beta(x)$ near a and $\lim_{x \to a} \alpha(x) = \lim_{x \to a} \beta(x) = L$ then $\lim_{x \to a} f(x) = L$ also.

The Limit of a Composition

Recall that at the end of Example #80 in Section 11.4 we commented that it is only true that $\lim_{x \to a} f(g(x))$ is equal to $f\left(\lim_{x \to a} g(x)\right)$ when f is continuous at $g(a)$.

The following example demonstrates why we need for f to be continuous at $g(a)$.

Example #102:

Let $f(x) = \begin{cases} 5 & \text{if } x \geq 1 \\ 0 & \text{if } x < 1 \end{cases}$ and $g(x) = \frac{x}{x+1}$. Observe that $g(x) < 1$ when $x > 0$, that $\lim_{x \to \infty} g(x) = 1$, and that f is not continuous at $x = 1$.

We have $f\left(\underbrace{\lim_{x\to\infty} g(x)}_{=1}\right) = f(1) = 5$ and $\lim_{x\to\infty} f(g(x)) = \lim_{x\to\infty} f\left(\underbrace{\frac{x}{x+1}}_{<1}\right) = 0$. Therefore

$$f\left(\lim_{x\to\infty} g(x)\right) \neq \lim_{x\to\infty} f(g(x)).$$

End Of Example #102

Theorem 50: [The Limit of a Composition at Infinity]

Suppose $\lim_{x\to\infty} g(x) = L_g$ and $f(y)$ is continuous at $y = L_g$. Then

$$\lim_{x\to\infty} f(g(x)) = f(L_g) = f\left(\lim_{x\to\infty} g(x)\right).$$

Scrapwork

It will be helpful to have a visual guide for this proof so we will rely on diagrams here in the scrapwork. Our finalized proof below will not.

Let $\varepsilon > 0$ be given. We need to show that we can find a $B > 0$ such that if $x > B$ then $|f(g(x)) - f(L_g)| < \varepsilon$.

Since f is continuous at $y = L_g$ Definition #17 tells us that $\lim_{y\to L_g} f(y) = f(L_g)$

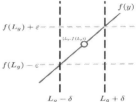

Thus Definition #27 tells us that there there is a real number $\delta > 0$ such that if $|y - L_g| < \delta$ then $|f(y) - f(L_g)| < \varepsilon$, as visualized in the sketch at the right.

Next, consider what it means to say that $\lim_{x\to\infty} g(x) = L_g$. It means that if we take x large enough we can make $g(x)$ as close to L_g as we would like. In particular, we would like for $|g(x) - L_g| < \delta$ as in the sketch below.

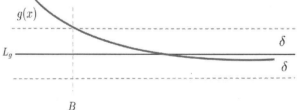

Therefore, we can find a number B such that for every $x > B$, $|g(x) - L_g| < \delta$. If we take $y = g(x)$, then we have $|y - L_g| < \delta$.

From the continuity of f at L_g we know that $|g(x) - L_g| = |y - L_g| < \delta$ means that

$$|f(g(x)) - f(L_g)| = |f(y) - f(L_g)| < \varepsilon.$$

End Of Scrapwork

Proof: Let $\varepsilon > 0$ be given.

Since $f(y)$ is continuous at L_g there is a real number $\delta > 0$ such that

$$\text{if } |y - L_g| < \delta \text{ then } |f(y) - f(L_g)| < \varepsilon.$$

Since $\lim_{x \to \infty} g(x) = L_g$ there is a real number B such that

$$\text{if } x > B \text{ then } |g(x) - L_g| < \delta.$$

Take B be the lower bound needed to guarantee that $|g(x) - L_g| < \delta$. If $x > B$ then since $y = g(x)$

$$|y - L_g| = |g(x) - L_g| < \delta,$$

and since $|y - L_g| < \delta$ we see, from the continuity of f at L_g that $|f(y) - f(L_g)| < \varepsilon$.

Therefore $\lim_{x \to \infty} f(g(x)) = f(L_g) = f\left(\lim_{x \to \infty} g(x)\right).$

∎

Problem #551:

Use the proof of Theorem 50 as a model to construct a proof of Theorem 51 below.

Theorem 51: [**The Limit of a Composition at Negative Infinity**]

Suppose $\lim_{x \to -\infty} g(x) = L_g$ and $f(y)$ is continuous at $y = L_g$. Then

$$\lim_{x \to -\infty} f(g(x)) = f(L_g) = f\left(\lim_{x \to -\infty} g(x)\right).$$

Problem #552:

Use the proof of Theorem 50 as a model to construct a proof of Theorem 52 below.

Theorem 52: [**The Limit of a Composition at a Point**]

Suppose $\lim_{x \to a} g(x) = L_g$, and that $f(y)$ is continuous at $y = L_g$. Then

$$\lim_{x \to a} f(g(x) = f(L_g) = f\left(\lim_{x \to a} g(x)\right).$$

The Limit of a Product

Theorem 53: [The Limit of a Product at Infinity]
If $\lim\limits_{x \to \infty} f(x) = L_f$ and $\lim\limits_{x \to \infty} g(x) = L_g$ then $\lim\limits_{x \to \infty} (f(x) \cdot g(x)) = L_f \cdot L_g$.

The proof of Theorem 53 is very straightforward once the following two lemmas have been proved. We state these lemmas here so that we can refer to them in the proof of Theorem 53 but the proof of Theorem (53) is not complete until these lemmas have been proved.

Lemma 54:
If $\lim\limits_{x \to \infty} f(x) = L_f$ and $\lim\limits_{x \to \infty} g(x) = L_g$ then $\lim\limits_{x \to \infty} (f(x) \cdot g(x) - f(x) \cdot L_g) = 0$.

Lemma 55:
If $\lim\limits_{x \to \infty} f(x) = L_f$ and $\lim\limits_{x \to \infty} g(x) = L_g$ then $\lim\limits_{x \to \infty} (f(x) \cdot L_g - L_f \cdot L_g) = 0$

Proof of Theorem 53: Let $\varepsilon > 0$ be given.

Observe that

$$|f(x) \cdot g(x) - L_g \cdot L_f| = \left| f(x) \cdot g(x) \underbrace{-f(x) \cdot L_g + f(x) \cdot L_g}_{=0} - L_f \cdot L_g \right|.$$

Adding and subtracting the same term like this is a highly non-intuitive, but common "trick." Most mathematicians call it "adding zero" since middle terms add to zero. We (the authors) call this "uncanceling" because the middle terms cancel. It is hard to tell *a priori* when this trick will work. Sometimes you just have to try something and see what happens.

In this case our uncanceling allows us to use the Triangle Inequality effectively. From the Triangle Inequality We see that

$$\begin{aligned}
|f(x) \cdot g(x) - L_g \cdot L_f| &= |f(x) \cdot g(x) - f(x) \cdot L_g + f(x) \cdot L_g - L_f \cdot L_g| \\
&\leq |f(x) \cdot g(x) - f(x) \cdot L_g| + |f(x) \cdot L_g - L_f \cdot L_g|
\end{aligned}$$

By Lemma #54 there is a real number B_1 such that if $x > B_1$ then

$$|f(x) \cdot g(x) - f(x) \cdot L_g| < \frac{\varepsilon}{2}.$$

By Lemma #55 there is a real number B_2 such that if $x > B_2$ then

$$|f(x) \cdot L_g - L_f \cdot L_g| < \frac{\varepsilon}{2}.$$

Take $B = \max(B_1, B_2)$. If $x > B$ then

$$|f(x) \cdot g(x) - L_g \cdot L_f| \leq \underbrace{|f(x) \cdot g(x) - f(x) \cdot L_g|}_{< \frac{\varepsilon}{2}} + \underbrace{|f(x) \cdot L_g - L_f \cdot L_g|}_{< \frac{\varepsilon}{2}} \qquad (16.6)$$

Therefore $\lim\limits_{x \to \infty} f(x) \cdot g(x) = \lim\limits_{x \to \infty} f(x) \cdot \lim\limits_{x \to \infty} g(x)$. ∎

Proving Lemma #54

To prove Lemma #54 we need to guarantee that if x is large enough then

$$|f(x) \cdot g(x) - f(x) \cdot L_g| = |f(x)| \, |g(x) - L_g| < \varepsilon,$$

where ε is an arbitrary, positive, real number. An "obvious" strategy is to observe that since we know that $\lim\limits_{x \to \infty} g(x) = L_g$ it must be that if x is large enough then $|g(x) - L_g| < \frac{\varepsilon}{|f(x)|}$.

But that strategy will fail. Here's why. Definition #25 says that if $\lim\limits_{x \to \infty} g(x) = L_g$ then for any single real number ε we can find a B such that if $x > B$ then $|g(x) - L_g| < \varepsilon$. But $\frac{\varepsilon}{|f(x)|}$ is not a single real number. For each distinct value of $x > B$ we'll have a (possibly) different value of $f(x)$. We have no definition, and no theorem that says we can do this. So we can't. That strategy won't work. At least it won't work in its most obvious form.

But it will work if we can replace $|f(x)|$ by some fixed value. The following lemma states that since $f(x)$ has a finite limit, it must be bounded. This will allow us to replace $|f(x)|$ with that bound, which is a fixed parameter, in our proof of Lemma #54.

Lemma 56:

If $\lim\limits_{x \to \infty} f(x) = L_f$ then there are positive real numbers N and β, such that if $x > \beta$, then $|f(x)| < N$.

Proof: Since $\lim\limits_{x \to \infty} f(x) = L_f$ there is a positive number β such that if $x > \beta$ then $|f(x) - L_f| < 1$. So for $x > \beta$,

$$-1 < f(x) - L_f < 1$$
$$L_f - 1 < f(x) < L_f + 1.$$

Now choose any positive number N with

$$-N < L_f - 1 < f(x) < L_f + 1 < N,$$

and it follows that if $x > \beta$ then $|f(x)| < N$. ■

Drill #553: Draw a convincing diagram of Lemma #56 and its proof.

Proof of Lemma #54: From Lemma #56) we see that there are positive real numbers N and β, such that for all $x > \beta$

$$|f(x)(g(x) - L_g)| = |f(x)| \, |g(x) - L_g| < N \, |g(x) - L_g|.$$

Let $\varepsilon > 0$ be given.

Since $\lim\limits_{x \to \infty} g(x) = L_g$ there is a real number B_g such that for all $x > B_g$

$$|g(x) - L_g| < \frac{\varepsilon}{N}.$$

Take $B = \max(\beta, B_g)$. Then for all $x > B$ we have

$$
\begin{aligned}
|f(x)(g(x) - L_g)| &= |f(x)|\,|g(x) - L_g| \\
&< N\,|g(x) - L_g| \\
&< N\frac{\varepsilon}{N} \\
&= \varepsilon.
\end{aligned}
$$

Therefore $\lim_{x \to \infty} (f(x) \cdot g(x) - f(x) \cdot L_g) = 0$. ∎

Proving Lemma #55

To prove Lemma #55 we need to guarantee that if x is large enough then

$$
|f(x) \cdot L_g - L_f L_g| = |L_g|\,|f(x) - L_f| < \varepsilon,
$$

where ε is an arbitrary real number. This is very similar to our goal in proving Lemma #54. But this time the "obvious" strategy will work. Almost.

That is, as long as $L_g \neq 0$ we can guarantee that $|L_g|\,|f(x) - L_f| < \varepsilon$ by taking x large enough to guarantee that $|f(x) - L_f| < \frac{\varepsilon}{|L_g|}$.

We will need to handle the case $L_g = 0$ separately.

Proof of Lemma #55: Let $\varepsilon > 0$ be given.

There are two cases.

Case 1, $L_g \neq 0$: Because $\lim_{x \to \infty} f(x) = L_f$ there is a real number B such that if $x > B$ then $|f(x) - L_f| < \frac{\varepsilon}{|L_g|}$

So if $x > B$ then $|L_g|\,|f(x) - L_f| < |L_g| \cdot \frac{\varepsilon}{|L_g|} = \varepsilon$.

Therefore $\lim_{x \to \infty} (L_g f(x) - L_g L_f) = 0$ when $L_g \neq 0$.

Case 2, $L_g = 0$: In this case $|L_g|\,|f(x) - L_f| = 0 \cdot |f(x) - L_f| = 0 < \varepsilon$.

Therefore $\lim_{x \to \infty} (L_g f(x) - L_g L_f) = 0$ when $L_g = 0$.

Since the limit is zero in both cases we see that $\lim_{x \to \infty} (L_g f(x) - L_g L_f) = 0$. ∎

Having completed the proofs of Lemma #54 and Lemma #54 our proof of Theorem #53 is now also complete.

The proofs of these two lemmas was not for the faint of heart. None of the individual pieces was difficult to follow, but putting them all together in the right order was delicate.

On the other hand, once Lemmas #54 and #55 are known the proof of Theorem #53 becomes even simpler as the next drill shows.

Problem #554:

As you've seen using the limit definition (using ε and δ) to prove theorems is hard. But, as we said in Digression #26, the whole point of proving theorems is to give ourselves more refined tools that we can use instead of resorting to definitions.

(a) Now that we have Lemma #54 and Lemma #55 there is actually a simpler way to prove Theorem #53. Observe that

$$\underbrace{f(x) \cdot g(x) - L_g \cdot L_f}_{\Gamma(x)} = \underbrace{[f(x) \cdot g(x) - f(x) \cdot L_g]}_{\alpha(x)} + \underbrace{[f(x) \cdot L_g - L_f \cdot L_g]}_{\beta(x)} \qquad (16.7)$$

and complete the proof by citing Lemma #54 and Lemma #55 and the appropriate, previously proven, limit theorem.
(**Hint:** The right side of Equation (16.7) is a sum.)

(b) Lemma #55 can also be proved without resorting to the limit definition (using ε and δ). Prove it by citing Lemma 54 and the appropriate, previously proved, limit theorems.

If you find yourself becoming completely absorbed in, and possibly even enjoying the details of these arguments you are surely a mathematician by inclination, if not by training (yet). There are more, and more interesting, results where these came from. Change your major and come join us. Sometimes we bring cookies.

Problem #555: Use our proof of Theorem 53 as a model to prove Theorem 57 below.

Theorem 57: [The Limit of a Product at Negative Infinity]
If $\lim\limits_{x \to -\infty} f(x) = L_f$ and $\lim\limits_{x \to -\infty} g(x) = L_g$ then $\lim\limits_{x \to -\infty} (f(x) \cdot g(x)) = L_f \cdot L_g$.

Problem #556: Use our proof of Theorem 53 as a model to prove Theorem 58 below.

Theorem 58: [Limit of a Product at a Point]
Suppose that $\lim\limits_{x \to a} f(x) = L_f$ and $\lim\limits_{x \to a} g(x) = L_g$ for some real number a. Then

$$\lim\limits_{x \to a} (f(x) \cdot g(x)) = L_f \cdot L_g.$$

Finally, we come to the limit of a quotient. Given how much trouble the limit of a product gave us, it is a little scary to think about proving that the limit of a quotient is the quotient of limits from the definition.

This trepidation is justified. It is very tricky to prove — from the definition — that the limit of a quotient is what we expect it to be. Fortunately we won't have to. We now have enough theorems (tools) available that we no longer have to work directly from the limit definition.

However we will need to dispose of the following small detail.

The Function $f(x) = \frac{1}{x}$ is Continuous Wherever It Is Defined

---

Lemma 59:

The function $f(x) = \frac{1}{x}$ is continuous at $a \neq 0$.

You will need Lemma 59 to solve Problem 558 below. We will provide the scrapwork and leave the formal proof as a problem for you.

Scrapwork

To keep things simple (this is scrapwork, after all) we will first assume that $a > 0$. If we have an $\varepsilon > 0$ then by Theorem 17 we need to find a $\delta > 0$ such that if $|x - a| < \delta$ then $\left| \frac{1}{x} - \frac{1}{a} \right| < \varepsilon$. As usual we work backwards.

Combining the fractions we see that

$$\left| \frac{1}{x} - \frac{1}{a} \right| = \frac{|a - x|}{a\,|x|} = \frac{|x - a|}{a\,|x|},$$

so we need to find a $\delta > 0$ such that $|x - a| < \delta$ ensures that $\frac{|x-a|}{a|x|} < \varepsilon$.

At first it appears that all we need to do choose $\delta < \varepsilon \cdot a \cdot |x|$. If we could do that we'd have $|x - a| < \delta = \varepsilon \cdot a \cdot |x|$ in which case

$$\left| \frac{1}{x} - \frac{1}{a} \right| = \frac{|x - a|}{a\,|x|} = \frac{|x - a|}{a} \cdot \frac{1}{|x|} < \varepsilon.$$

But of course we've seen this before. Just as in the proof of Lemma 54, δ must be a constant; it cannot depend on x. So we need to replace $\frac{1}{x}$ with a constant somehow. The Algebra here gets a bit delicate. We strongly recommend that you visualize each step of the following argument with a sketch like the one we used in the scrapwork for Theorem 50

Suppose we choose $\delta > 0$ such that

$$|x - a| < \frac{a}{2}.$$

Then we see that

$$-\frac{a}{2} < x - a < \frac{a}{2}$$

or

$$\frac{a}{2} = a - \frac{a}{2} < x < a + \frac{a}{2} = \frac{3a}{2}. \tag{16.8}$$

Thus if we make $|x - a| < \frac{a}{2}$, we see that $0 < \frac{a}{2} < x$ and so[11]

$$\frac{1}{|x|} = \frac{1}{x} < \frac{2}{a}$$

for all $x > 0$.

---

[11]Notice that we are using the left side of Formula (16.8), not the right side.

Therefore $\left|\frac{1}{x} - \frac{1}{a}\right| = \frac{|x-a|}{a} \cdot \frac{1}{|x|} < \frac{2}{a^2}|x-a|$. Thus if we choose δ to be the lesser of $\frac{a}{2}$ and $\frac{\varepsilon a^2}{2}$ we have everything we need to conclude that $\lim_{x \to a} \frac{1}{x} = \frac{1}{a}$ for $a > 0$.

End Of Scrapwork

Problem #557:

(a) Use the scrapwork above to show that if $a > 0$ then $\lim_{x \to a} \frac{1}{x} = \frac{1}{a}$.

(b) If $a < 0$ we could replicate the proof in part (a), but keeping track of all of the sign changes will be burdensome. Otherwise it is really the same proof. Instead, notice that if $a < 0$ then $-a > 0$ and so by part (a)

$$\lim_{y \to -a} \frac{1}{y} = \frac{1}{-a}.$$

Use this observation to prove that if $a < 0$ then $\lim_{x \to a} \frac{1}{x} = \frac{1}{a}$.
(**Hint:** Let $y = -x$.)

Armed with this and our Limit Theorems, we can tackle the proof of the next theorem without resorting back to definitions.

Theorem 60: [The Limit of a Quotient is the Quotient of the Limits]
Suppose a is positive infinity, negative infinity, or some real number, that $\lim_{x \to a} f(x) = L_f$, and that $\lim_{x \to a} g(x) = L_g \neq 0$. Then

$$\lim_{x \to a} \frac{f(x)}{g(x)} = \frac{L_f}{L_g}.$$

Problem #558:

(a) Prove that if $\lim_{x \to \infty} f(x) = L_f$ and $\lim_{x \to \infty} g(x) = L_g \neq 0$ then

$$\lim_{x \to \infty} \frac{f(x)}{g(x)} = \frac{L_f}{L_g}.$$

(**Hint:** Rewrite $\frac{f(x)}{g(x)}$ as $f(x) \cdot (g(x))^{-1}$. Which of our theorems can you apply?)

(b) Prove that if $\lim_{x \to -\infty} f(x) = L_f$ and $\lim_{x \to -\infty} g(x) = L_g \neq 0$ then

$$\lim_{x \to -\infty} \frac{f(x)}{g(x)} = \frac{L_f}{L_g}.$$

(c) Prove that if a is some real number, and $\lim_{x \to a} f(x) = L_f$, and $\lim_{x \to a} g(x) = L_g \neq 0$. Then

$$\lim_{x \to a} \frac{f(x)}{g(x)} = \frac{L_f}{L_g}.$$

We have one last loose end to tie up. Recall that Theorem #38 in Chapter 15 says that a limit exists if and only if the right- and left-hand limits both exist and are equal. One-sided limits are informally defined in Definition #21. But an informal definition is not sufficiently precise to support constructing a proof, so here is the formal Definition of a right-hand limit.

Definition 28: Right-Hand Limit

Suppose $f(x)$ is defined on some interval (a, b). Let L be a real number. We say that

$$\lim_{\substack{x \to a \\ x > a}} f(x) = L$$

provided that for each $\varepsilon > 0$, there is a δ with $0 < \delta < b - a$ such that if $a > x > a + \delta$, then $|f(x) - L| < \varepsilon$.

Problem #559:

(a) Use Definition 28 as a model to state a similar definition for $\lim_{\substack{x \to a \\ x < a}} f(x) = L$

(b) Prove Theorem #38 from Chapter 15.

As you can see, rigorous demonstrations, as necessary as they are, can become complicated and tedious. Perhaps this explains why the practice of Calculus predated its theory.

We have defined the derivative by Definition 15; derived all of our differentiation rules via this definition, and shown – rigorously – that founding Calculus on the theory of limits gives us all of the properties we found useful in Part 1 of this textbook. At long last, this places a solid, logical, and rigorous foundation underneath the Differential Calculus of Newton and Leibniz.

And Bishop Berkeley has nothing left to criticize.

Appendix A

TRIUMPHS: Primary Source Projects (PSPs)

Reading the original words of the mathematicians of the past who actually created and shaped mathematics is an especially powerful tool for learning not only the important ideas of the subject, but also the motivations behind those ideas and the process of discovery itself. The Primary Source Projects (PSPs) created by the National Science Foundation funded *TRans-foming Instruction in Undergraduate Mathematics Instruction via Primary Historical Sources* (TRIUMPHS) offer precisely this kind of learning experience.

A collection of over 80 PSPs on a wide range of topics from courses across the undergraduate mathematics curriculum and all are freely available for download at the TRIUMPHS website: https://blogs.ursinus.edu/triumphs/. A number of these projects have also been published in *Convergence!*, the Mathematical Association of America's online journal for the history of mathematics and its use in teaching, which is itself a wonderful resource.

The TRIUMPHS Project's PSPs cover a wide range of topics in all areas of mathematics. We have included here a few which are specific to Calculus.

Each of the PSPs in this Appendix was developed with a specific core topic from today's calculus curriculum in mind. As you work through these projects, you will encounter those core topics through excerpts from the actual writings of Fermat, l'Hôpital, d'Alembert, Euler, Fourier and others. Don't worry if you don't understand everything in these excerpts when you first read them! To help you explore and interpret what they mean, PSPs also include a series of tasks for readers that will help you to unpack the mathematical ideas they contain and build your own understanding of those ideas. To get the most out of these tasks, some will be best worked out on your own before an in-class discussion, many will work well for discussion in small groups during class, others could be the focus of a whole-class discussion, and a few might be assigned for completion as follow-up to work done in class. However your course instructor assigns them for completion, you will want to carefully work through each and every task in a PSP. Each project also contains a discussion of the mathematical significance of the primary source, along with some biographical information about its author and the historical context in which he worked, that will help you further develop an understanding of the topic it covers.

Acknowledgements The development of all TRIUMPHS's student projects has been partially supported by funding from the National Science Foundation's Improving Undergraduate STEM Education Program under Grant Nos. 1523494, 1523561, 1523747, 1523753, 1523898, 1524065, and 1524098. Any opinions, findings, and conclusions or recommendations expressed in this project are those of the author and do not necessarily represent the views of the National Science Foundation.

For more information about the NSF-funded project TRansforming Instruction in Undergraduate Mathematics via Primary Historical Sources (TRIUMPHS), visit `http://blogs.ursinus.edu/triumphs/`.

A.1   Fermat's Method for Finding Maxima and Minima

Kenneth M. Monks
Department of Mathematics
Front Range Community College – Boulder County Campus,
Longmont, CO 80501
kenneth.monks@frontrange.edu

A central theme of most introductory calculus courses is that of *optimization*. Given a real-valued function $f(x)$, one wishes to find its maxima and minima on some specified interval of real numbers. Typically the backbone of this method is a theorem called *Fermat's Theorem* or *Fermat's Stationary Point Theorem* which is stated and illustrated below.

Fermat's Theorem

If a real-valued function $f(x)$ is differentiable on an interval (a, b) and $f(x)$ has a maximum or minimum at $c \in (a, b)$, then $f'(c) = 0$.

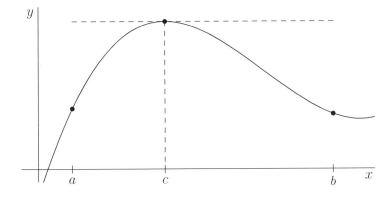

Most modern calculus courses use this theorem as the rationale behind locating the maximum and minimum values of a continuous function $f(x)$ on an interval $[a, b]$, whose existence is guaranteed by the Extreme Value Theorem. The standard algorithm is to make a list of the following x-values:

- the endpoints $x = a$ and $x = b$,

- any points $x \in (a, b)$ such that $f(x)$ is not differentiable,

- and any points $x \in (a, b)$ such that $f'(x) = 0$ (often called *stationary points* or *critical points*).

Then, one calculates $f(x)$ for each x-value, which produces a list of y-values. Among this list, the biggest value of $f(x)$ is the absolute maximum and the smallest is the absolute minimum.

Task 1 Briefly explain how Fermat's Theorem serves as the basis for the optimization algorithm described above.

For the rest of this project, the method above will be referred to as the *modern method*, in contrast to *Fermat's method*, which we will now explore!

A.1.0.1 Fermat's Method... and Descartes' Doubts!

Fermat's Theorem is so-called because it is traceable back to the ideas of Pierre de Fermat[1] (1601–1665). Nonetheless, it is fascinating to consider how different his method looks from the modern method![2] His original writing, displayed below, is found in his 1636 treatise *Method for the Study of Maxima and Minima* [Fermat 1636]. It should be noted the original was in Latin. Fermat's work in this document was translated into English by Jason Ross, working from the French translation by Tannery and Henry [Fermat 1891] (who modified some of Fermat's original notation).

Let a be an arbitrarily chosen unknown of the question (whether it has one, two, or three dimensions, as follows from the statement). We will express the maximum or minimum quantity in terms of a, by means of terms of any degree. We will then substitute $a + e$ for the primitive unknown a, and express the maximum or minimum quantity in terms containing a and e to any degree. We will *ad-equate*, to speak like Diophantus,[3] the two expressions of the maximum and minimum quantity, and we will remove from them the terms common to both sides. Having done this, it will be found that on both sides, all the terms will involve e or a power of e. We will divide all the terms by e, or by a higher power of e, such that on at least one of the sides, e will disappear entirely. We will then eliminate all the terms where e (or one of its powers) still exists, and we will consider the others equal, or if nothing remains on one of the sides, we will equate the added terms with the subtracted terms, which comes to be the same. Solving this last equation will give the value of a, which will lead to the maximum or the minimum, in the original expression.

---

[1] Born in Beaumont-de-Lomagne in the south of France, Pierre de Fermat spent most of his life in Toulouse and Orléans, where he was educated as, and then worked as, a lawyer/jurist. He found respite from his demanding career by pursuing his true love: mathematics! Fermat championed the idea of *pure* mathematics; he was rarely motivated by problems pertaining to the physical world but rather loved mathematics for its own inherent beauty and challenge.

[2] Part of this difference, of course, has to do with the passage of time and the evolution of how we are expected to write mathematics. However, part of it is also due to Fermat's unique personal style; he had a reputation for coming up with results in secret and then sending the result out into the mathematical community with no indication of how one might have come upon that, almost as a puzzle for the world to solve! Mathematics historian Victor Katz writes "In many cases it is not known what, if any, proofs Fermat constructed nor is there always a systematic account of certain parts of his work. Fermat often tantalized his correspondents with hints of his new methods for solving certain problems. He would sometimes provide outlines of these methods, but his promises to fill in gaps 'when leisure permits' frequently remained unfulfilled." [V. J. Katz 1998, page 433]

[3] Diophantus (c. 200CE–c. 284CE) was a mathematician in the city of Alexandria who wrote in Greek. His word $\pi\alpha\rho\iota\sigma\acute{o}\tau\eta\varsigma$ (parisotes), meaning *approximately equal*, was translated into Latin as *adaequo* by the French mathematician Claude Gaspard Bachet de Méziriac (1581–1638). Fermat read Bachet's version of Diophantus' work [M. G. Katz, Schaps, and Shnider 2013].

∝∝

| Task 2 | Compare and contrast the modern method with Fermat's method. Can you find three similarities between them? Can you find three differences between them?

Fermat himself was very pleased with this method, as he later made the following claim.

∝∝

It is impossible to give a more general method.

∝∝

Before we begin to analyze the algorithm described above to see exactly what is happening, read it a second time. Are you filled with a bit of doubt as to whether or not this method is valid? Are you filled with a bit of curiosity as to where on earth this method might have come from? If so, you are in the best of company. Rene Descartes[4] (1596–1650) read Fermat's treatise in 1638 after it was passed on to him by Mersenne.[5] Descartes' response to Mersenne was somewhat dismissive; as quoted in [Mahoney 1994, p. 177], it included the remark "...if ...he speaks of wanting to send you still more papers, I beg of you to ask him to think them out more carefully than those preceding."

In this project, we aim to determine if Descartes was right, that Fermat's method was not so carefully thought out. Or, on the other hand, was it a perfectly well-thought out method, but Fermat simply chose to withhold the details of how he arrived at this method?

A.1.1 Examples of Fermat's Method

As one should begin any mathematical investigation, we first work out a few examples. In this section, we work through three problems that Fermat himself used to demonstrate his method, to see if our modern method reproduces the same results.

A.1.1.1 First Example

∝∝

Let us take an example:

Divide the line AC at E, such that $AE \times EC$ be a maximum.

---

[4]Rene Descartes was born near Tours, France. He is perhaps most famous today for his philosophical works, specifically as the writer of the phrase "je pense, donc je suis" (in English, "I think, therefore I am") from his *Discourse on the Method* [Descartes 1637]. However, he also left mathematics with incredibly important and lasting advances. He showed the power of symbolic algebra with regards to solving difficult geometric problems: he marked points in the plane using distances x and y measured along lines, much as we do today [Grabiner 1995].

[5]Marin Mersenne (1588–1648) was the central communications clearinghouse of a group of mathematicians and physicists. He would receive, copy, record, and distribute materials as they worked. Fermat and Mersenne began a correspondence in 1636.

Let us take $AC = b$; let a be one of the segments, and let the other be $b - a$, and the product whose maximum we have to find is: $ba - a^2$. Now let $a + e$ be the first segment of b, the second $b - a - e$, and the product of the two segments will be: $ba - a^2 + be - 2ae - e^2$.

It must be *co-equal to the preceding*: $ba - a^2$;
Removing the common terms: $be \sim 2ae + e^2$;
Dividing all the terms: $b \sim 2a + e$;
Remove e: $b = 2a$.
To solve the problem, therefore, the half of b must be taken.

⚬⚬

Task 3 First, we solve the same problem using the modern method. Denote by b the fixed total length of AC (just as Fermat did). Then denote by x the length of AE, which implies $b - x$ is the length of EC.

(a) With the above notation, what is the function $f(x)$ that we are trying to maximize? What interval of x values are we considering?

(b) Apply the modern method to find the absolute maximum of this function $f(x)$. Does it confirm the result Fermat presents?

In practice, we tend to calculate the derivative of a function using all of the standard slick and convenient formulas with which we have become familiar: power rule, product rule, quotient rule, and chain rule. However, sometimes the limit definition of the derivative lends a bit more insight into a problem than those other formulas lend. Here our "problem" is trying to make sense of Fermat's method!

Specifically, for the next task we apply the limit definition of the derivative, written as

$$f'(x) = \lim_{\Delta x \to 0} \frac{f(x + \Delta x) - f(x)}{\Delta x}.$$

Task 4 (a) Take your function $f(x)$ from the previous task, and again find the zeros of the derivative. However, this time, don't worry about taking that limit so early in the process. Instead, just write down the equation

$$\frac{f(x + \Delta x) - f(x)}{\Delta x} = 0.$$

Simplify it as much as possible, and then, right at the very end, take the limit as Δx goes to zero.

(b) Explain why the manipulation you performed above is equivalent to starting with

$$f(x + \Delta x) = f(x),$$

simplifying, dividing both sides by Δx, and then setting all the remaining occurrences of Δx to zero.

(c) Now revisit Fermat's method. When you compare your work to Fermat's, can you find similar steps? Which symbol in the modern method corresponds to Fermat's a? Which symbol in the modern method corresponds to Fermat's e?

A.1.1.2   Second Example

The result of the previous example is a slight rephrasing of what is today known as the *vertex formula*: the fact that a quadratic polynomial in x will achieve its absolute maximum or minimum when x is the negative of the linear coefficient divided by twice the leading coefficient. Fermat's method worked out perfectly reasonably in this case. But perhaps it was only because the example was so clean! Let us examine a more complicated application of Fermat's method. This example was a followup note that Fermat wrote to his original treatise, titled *On the Same Method* [Fermat 1891, page 126].

By the means of my method, I would like *divide a given line AC at a point B, such that $AB^2 \times BC$ be the maximum* of all solids which could be formed in the same fashion by dividing the line AC.

Let us suppose, in algebraic notation, that $AC = b$, the unknown $AB = a$; we will have $BC = b - a$, and the solid $a^2 b - a^3$ must satisfy the proposed condition.

Now taking $a + e$ in place of a, we have for the solid

$$(a + e)^2 (b - e - a) = ba^2 + be^2 + 2bae - a^3 - 3ae^2 - 3a^2 e - e^3.$$

I compare this to the first solid: $a^2 b - a^3$, as if they were equal, when in fact they are not.

. . .

Then, I subtract the common terms from both sides,

. . .

this done, one side of the equation has nothing, while the other is

$$be^2 + 2bae - 3ae^2 - 3a^2 e - e^3.$$

. . .

Dividing all terms by e, the *adequality* will hold between $be + 2ba$ and $3ae + 3a^2 + e^2$. After this division, if all terms may again be divided by e, the division must be repeated, until there is a term that can no longer be divided by e, or, to employ the terminology of Viète[6], a term which is no longer affected by e. But, in the proposed example, we find that the division cannot be repeated; so, we have to stop there.

---

[6]François Viète (1540–1603) was a mathematician who worked as a codebreaker for several of the kings of France. He introduced a system of symbolic algebra, which Fermat used and referenced here. Viète used vowels for unknowns and consonants for knowns. To our modern eyes, using a as an unknown instead of x might look a bit odd; this is because eventually Descartes' convention (using the letters x, y, z to represent unknowns) caught on rather than Viète's!

Now, I remove all the terms affected by e; on one side there remains $2ba$, while the other has $3a^2$, terms between which it is necessary to establish not a feigned comparison or an *adequality*, but rather a true equation. I divide both sides by a; giving me $2b = 3a$, or $b/a = 3/2$.

Let us return to our original question, and divide AC at B such that $AC/AB = 3/2$. I say that the solid $AB^2 \times BC$ is the maximum of all those which can be formed by dividing the line AC.

ᗱᗴ

Task 5

(a) Check Fermat's work in the example above, filling in the details of the algebra that he glossed over. Can you confirm each of his steps?

(b) Verify that Fermat's result matches what is produced by the modern method. Specifically, maximize the function

$$f(x) = (b - x)x^2$$

on the interval $[0, b]$.

(c) To see the equivalence of the two methods, let us once again compare with the limit definition of the derivative. Take the function $f(x) = (b - x)x^2$, and instead of first calculating $f'(x)$ and then setting that equal to zero, recall that

$$f'(x) = \lim_{\Delta x \to 0} \frac{f(x + \Delta x) - f(x)}{\Delta x},$$

so we should get the same result as if we had set

$$f(x + \Delta x) = f(x),$$

divided both sides by Δx, and then set all remaining Δx to zero. Work this out to see if it matches what is produced by Fermat's method.

Task 6

Let us observe Fermat's results regarding "**all solids**" by actually looking at a few solids!

(a) First, notice that when he said "**all solids**", he was not talking about solids like balls, tetrahedra, etc. What kinds of solids was he restricting his attention to? How can you tell?

(b) Fermat claimed that to produce the biggest possible volume, one should "**divide AC at B such that $AC/AB = 3/2$**." Let us test this claim by working out some specific examples. In particular, choose the length AC to be equal to 12. Then, try dividing the line AC four different ways, such that AC/AB has ratio 3/1, 2/1, 3/2, and 1/1. Each time, draw a sketch of the resulting solid whose volume is $AB^2 \times BC$. Label the edges and calculate the volumes. Which of those four solids has the biggest volume, and does that outcome agree with Fermat's claim?

A.1.1.3   Third Example

It appears that Fermat's method works fine, but both of the examples we considered so far involved polynomial functions. Maybe if we try a function that is not a simple polynomial, then the method will fail! Fermat wrote this example, titled *Appendix to the Method of Maxima and Minima*, in 1644 [Fermat 1891, page 136].

∽∾∽

Radicals are often encountered in the course of working problems.

> ... *Given a semicircle of diameter AB, with perpendicular DC drawn upon its diameter, find the maximum of the sum AC + CD.*

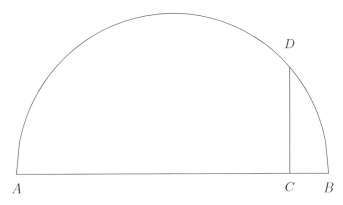

Let the diameter be taken as b, and let $AC = a$. We will thus have $CD = \sqrt{ba - a^2}$. The question becomes the maximization of the quantity $a + \sqrt{ba - a^2}$.

∽∾∽

Task 7 In trying to maximize the sum $AC + CD$, Fermat simply set $AC = a$. His formula for CD, however, takes some work to verify.

(a) Label the center of the circle as E. Explain why the measure of DE is $b/2$.

(b) Explain why the measure of CE is $a - b/2$.

(c) Use the Pythagorean Theorem on $\triangle CDE$ to calculate the length of CD in terms of b and a. Verify Fermat's formula for CD.

Pretty clearly, answering this question for a circle of a specific size answers it for all circles, since the maximum length path would scale with the radius of the circle. Thus, for simplicity, we choose to solve the problem in the case $b = 1$.

Task 8 (a) Use Fermat's method to find the maximum of the quantity $a + \sqrt{a - a^2}$. That is, set up the adequality between $a + \sqrt{a - a^2}$ and the same expression with $a + e$ substituted for a. Then continue to follow the steps in Fermat's method!

(b) Use the modern method to confirm the answer that Fermat's method gives. That is, use the chain rule to find the derivative of $f(x) = x + \sqrt{x - x^2}$. Then find the maximum by solving for the zeros of the derivative. Also, identify the domain of x-values that are being considered.

Let us call attention to one particularly nice aspect of Fermat's method; it requires far less knowledge of derivatives than the modern method. For example, in the previous problem involving the expression with the square root, we were able to eliminate the root by performing the basic algebraic step of squaring both sides rather than needing to evaluate the derivative of a square root function!

A.1.2 Resolution

The preceding examples have illustrated that Fermat's method is actually very similar to the modern method, just written in different notation.

(a) Explain why Fermat's method and the modern method are essentially equivalent. Where do they differ?

(b) Why does it make sense that Fermat's method would have had to rely more on algebra and less on analysis than the modern method? (For a hint, consider the year in which he was working! Do a bit of research and see if you can find who came up with our modern definitions of limits and derivatives, and when that happened!)

Thus, Fermat's method was not laid out hastily, but rather was a lovely and valid mathematical method. Descartes himself eventually agreed! Descartes later said "...seeing the last method that you use for finding tangents to curved lines, I can reply to it in no other way than to say that it is very good and that, if you had explained it in this manner at the outset, I would have not contradicted it at all." [Mahoney 1994, page 192]

References

Katz, Victor J (1998). *A History of Mathematics: An Introduction, Second Edition*. Addison-Wesley.

Fermat, Pierre de (1636). "Methodus ad disquirendam maximam et minimam (Method for the Study of Maxima and Minima)". In: Translated from the *Oeuvres de Fermat* by Jason Ross, available at `science.larouchepac.com/fermat/fermat-maxmin.pdf`.

— (1891). *Oeuvres de Fermat*. Translated into French by Charles Henry and Paul Tannery. Paris: Gauthier-Villars et fils.

Katz, Mikhail G., David M. Schaps, and Steven Shnider (2013). "Almost Equal: The Method of Adequality from Diophantus to Fermat and Beyond". In: *Perspectives on Science* 21.3.

Descartes, René (1637). *Discourse on Method; and, Meditations on First Philosophy*. This edition was published in 1998, translated by Donald A. Cress. Indianapolis: Hacket Publishing Company.

Grabiner, Judith (1995). "Descartes and Problem Solving". In: *Mathematics Magazine* 68, pp. 83–97.

Mahoney, Michael Sean (1994). *The Mathematical Career of Pierre de Fermat, 1601-1665: Second Edition*. Princeton University Press.

A.1.3   Recommendations for Further Reading

A fun and enriching comparison with Descartes' *method of normals* for optimization would be a great follow-up to this project. (Some suspect that Descartes' initial distaste for Fermat's method was because it aimed to solve the same problem as his method of normals, and was created at about the same time [V. J. Katz 1998, pages 472 and 473].) However, proper attention to Descartes' method is likely to move well beyond the standard topics of a first-semester calculus classroom. To do this in detail might be better suited for a multivariable calculus class, where one can appropriately discuss the ideas of the normal vector and the radius of curvature. To this end, the author recommends Jerry Lodder's PSP *The Radius of Curvature According to Christiaan Hyugens* (available at `https://digitalcommons.ursinus.edu/triumphs_calculus/4`) in addition to the description of Descartes' method given in *A History of Mathematics: An Introduction* [V. J. Katz 1998] cited above.

For students that are pursuing a degree in mathematics, this topic is a perfect warmup to the eventual study of Abraham Robinson's theory of nonstandard analysis (laid out beautifully in his 1966 work *Non-standard Analysis* from Princeton University Press (1996), ISBN 978-0-691-04490-3). It could be worth mentioning that it is possible to more formally prove the correctness of Fermat's method using the hyperreal numbers, where Fermat's e represents an infinitesimal. However, to formally construct the aforementioned number system requires a substantial amount of set theory and logic, and it is probably an appropriate journey for junior or senior level undergraduate studies at the earliest.

Acknowledgments

The author would like to thank the TRIUMPHS PIs and Advisory Board for the very helpful feedback throughout the writing of this project, in particular David Pengelley for bringing the author's attention to the bonus question suggested under Suggestions for Classroom Implementation.

A.2 Fourier's Proof of the Irrationality of e

Kenneth M. Monks

Department of Mathematics

Front Range Community College – Boulder County Campus,

Longmont, CO 80501

kenneth.monks@frontrange.edu

We begin with a short passage from Aristotle's[7] *Prior Analytics*[8]. This translation was completed by Oxford scholars in 1931 and compiled by Richard McKeon into *The Basic Works of Aristotle* [McKeon 1941].

∞∞∞

§I.23. For all who effect an argument *per impossibile* infer syllogistically what is false, and prove the original conclusion hypothetically when something impossible results from the assumption of its contradictory; e.g. that the diagonal of a square is incommensurate with the side, because odd numbers are equal to evens if it is supposed to be commensurate.

∞∞∞

The goal of this project is to work through a proof of the irrationality of the number e due to Joseph Fourier. This number would not have even been *defined* in any publication for another two millennia[9] (plus a few years) after the writing of *Prior Analytics*! So, the reader may wonder why we are rewinding our clocks so far back. Well, it turns out that the key ideas required to understand Fourier's proof of the irrationality of e can be traced right back to that passage from Aristotle.

In Section A.2.1, we extract the key pattern of Aristotelian logic needed to understand Fourier's proof, and give it a bit more of a modern formulation. In Section A.2.2, we embark on a detailed exploration of the idea of two numbers being "incommensurate", and then in Section A.2.3 we recast that idea in terms of important sets of numbers which have come to characterize so much of modern mathematics. In Section A.2.4, we examine Fourier's proof (as written by de Stainville) of the irrationality of e. For a lovely epilogue (epi-natural-log?), we witness in Section A.2.5 how Liouville extended Fourier's argument to learn a bit more about just how interesting a number e is.

---

[7] Aristotle (384 BCE–322 BCE) was born in northern Greece. His father, a doctor, wanted him to go into medicine. However, both of Aristotle's parents passed when he was quite young, so he ended up enrolling at Plato's Academy in Athens at the age of seventeen. There he received an education from Eudoxus (among others), whose work was incorporated into Euclid's *Elements*, who was running the academy in Plato's absence. Aristotle eventually became a teacher at the academy, a position he held for twenty years [O'Connor and Robertson 1999a].

[8] Written or dictated by Aristotle in roughly 350 BCE, *Prior Analytics* was most likely a collection of lecture notes. It is today considered the first writing on pure logic, dealing largely with syllogisms and how statements about particulars can relate to statements about universals [McKeon 1941]. It contains the now famous argument that goes as follows: every Greek is a person and every person is mortal, therefore every Greek is mortal.

[9] It was first formulated by Jakob Bernoulli in the context of compound interest in 1683 [Hoffman 1980].

A.2.1   Proof by Contradiction

Let us revisit the Aristotle passage in slightly more bite-size pieces.

ᗕᗕᗕᗕᗕᗕᗕᗕᗕᗕᗕᗕᗕᗕᗕᗕᗕᗕᗕᗕᗕᗕᗕᗕᗕᗕᗕᗕᗕᗕᗕᗕᗕᗕᗕᗕᗕ

> For all who effect an argument *per impossibile* infer syllogistically what is false, and prove the original conclusion hypothetically when something impossible results from the assumption of its contradictory. . .

ᗕᗕᗕᗕᗕᗕᗕᗕᗕᗕᗕᗕᗕᗕᗕᗕᗕᗕᗕᗕᗕᗕᗕᗕᗕᗕᗕᗕᗕᗕᗕᗕᗕᗕᗕᗕᗕ

For our purposes here, the phrase "infer syllogistically" can be simply taken to mean that one concludes a statement from two or more prior statements. We can then analyze what the other items refer to. We have the following:

- "original conclusion," meaning what is desired to be proven,

- "its contradictory," meaning the negation of what is desired to be proven, and

- "what is false," meaning some statement previously known to be false.

This process, by which one proves a statement by assuming its negation and then deducing a known falsehood, is today most commonly called "proof by contradition"[10], and remains one of the most powerful tools in the mathematician's toolbox. Let us digest this with an example. Sometimes before using a pattern of logic in a mathematical argument, it helps to see it applied in a nonmathematical setting. Here we show an argument that is considered the birth of modern climate science, taken from none other than our guest of honor, Joseph Fourier, in his 1827 paper *On the Temperatures of the Terrestrial Sphere and Interplanetary Space* (translated in [Pierrehumbert 2004]).

ᗕᗕᗕᗕᗕᗕᗕᗕᗕᗕᗕᗕᗕᗕᗕᗕᗕᗕᗕᗕᗕᗕᗕᗕᗕᗕᗕᗕᗕᗕᗕᗕᗕᗕᗕᗕᗕ

> The Earth is heated by solar radiation. . . Our solar system is located in a region of the universe of which all points have a common and constant temperature, determined by the light rays and the heat sent by all the surrounding stars. This cold temperature of the interplanetary sky is slightly below that of the Earth's polar regions. The Earth would have none other than this same temperature of the Sky, were it not for . . . causes which act . . . to further heat it.

ᗕᗕᗕᗕᗕᗕᗕᗕᗕᗕᗕᗕᗕᗕᗕᗕᗕᗕᗕᗕᗕᗕᗕᗕᗕᗕᗕᗕᗕᗕᗕᗕᗕᗕᗕᗕᗕ

This very consequential passage is often cited today as the first proof of the existence of the greenhouse effect. We claim this is an Aristotelian argument *per impossibile*! Or in modern terms, a proof by contradiction.

---

[10]Note that the translator's choice of words here, *reductio per impossibile*, is one way to describe contradiction (having reduced one's hypothesis to an impossible conclusion). However, it is common today to instead call proof by contradiction by another of Aristotle's argument forms, namely *reductio ad absurdum* (reducing one's hypothesis to an absurd conclusion). The difference is subtle but sometimes incredibly important!

Task 1 In Fourier's argument above, which words play the roles of which parts in Aristotle's argument? Specifically, find in Fourier's words the following components of an argument *per impossibile*, as identified by Aristotle:

    — "original conclusion",

    — "its contradictory",

    — "[syllogistic inference]", and

    — "what is false".

A.2.2   Incommensurate Numbers

As we have seen, Aristotle's choice of example for a proof by contradiction involved the idea of "incommensurate numbers". In this section, we wish to elaborate upon what exactly that phrase means.

To the ancient Greeks, two quantities would be considered *commensurate* if they could both be expressed as a whole number of multiples of the same length. For example, the circumference of a circle of radius 2 and the circumference of a circle of radius 3 would be commensurate. One could take the circumference of a circle of radius 1; the former would be twice that measurement and the latter would be three times that measurement. Thus, the two quantities are commensurate (they can be measured together).

Let us look at another example of commensurate lengths in a figure, to hopefully get a bit more of a feel for what that relation means.

Task 2 Let $\triangle ABC$ be a triangle, let D be the intersection of its three medians[11], and let E be the midpoint of side BC. Explain why the lengths of AE and AD are commensurate. (**Hint:** There is a famous theorem from Euclidean geometry regarding the above configuration. However, if you do not recall it, or you did not encounter it on your mathematical path, perhaps begin by measuring AE and AD in some special cases, like the case where $\triangle ABC$ is an equilateral triangle or a right triangle. Then see if you can recall or look up the general theorem.)

We now revisit the final line in the Aristotle passage.

><small>∞∞</small>
>
>... the diagonal of a square is incommensurate with the side, because odd numbers are equal to evens if it is supposed to be commensurate.
>
><small>∞∞</small>

Aristotle does not give the details or intermediate steps of this argument; it is not obvious at all how the assumption of commensurability of the diagonal of the square with the side of the square results in an odd number equalling an even number. However, his casual mention of it indicates that it was likely a well-known argument in his time, even though we have no written record of exactly what that argument was. Here, we present one such possible

---

[11] Recall that a *median* of a triangle is a segment that connects a vertex to the midpoint of the opposite side.

argument, admittedly using more symbolic algebra than the Greeks had available to them at the time, but it will use the same essential ideas[12].

Task 3   (a) The *common measure* of two lengths can be defined as the largest possible length that the two lengths are both integer multiples of. For example, the common measure of a segment of length 9 and a segment of length 12 would be a segment of length 3, since the first is three times longer ($3 \cdot 3 = 9$) and the second is four times longer ($4 \cdot 3 = 12$). Explain why, given two quantities a and b having common measure c, at least one of the numbers a/c and b/c must be odd.

(b) Let the points A, B, C, D be the vertices of a square, labelled in clockwise order. Let d be the common measure of AB (a side) and AC (a diagonal). Thus, $|AB| = d \cdot m$ for some whole number m and $|AC| = d \cdot n$ for some whole number n. Explain why one of m or n must be odd.

(c) Apply the Pythagorean Theorem to $\triangle ABC$ to deduce that $2m^2 = n^2$.

(d) Explain why if n is odd, then "odd numbers are equal to evens", as Aristotle says.

(e) Explain why if n is even and m is odd, then again "odd numbers are equal to evens", as Aristotle says.

(f) Explain why we do not need to consider the case were n and m are both even.

(g) To place the argument into proper form, clearly identify what the three key components are in this case: "original conclusion", "its contradictory", and "what is false". In the end, what have we successfully demonstrated?

A.2.3   Some Fundamental Sets of Numbers

Though by no means an exhaustive list, we now present a few fundamental sets of numbers[13]. Mathematicians use these particular number systems so frequently that there is a standard notation that has been adopted to refer to them, which we show below.

- **Natural Numbers.** The set $\mathbb{N}$ of natural numbers is the set of all positive whole numbers, along with zero[14]. That is,

$$\mathbb{N} = \{0, 1, 2, 3, 4, 5, \ldots\}$$

- **Integers.** The set of integers $\mathbb{Z}$ is the set of all whole numbers, whether they are positive, negative, or zero. That is,

$$\mathbb{Z} = \{\ldots, -4, -3, -2, -1, 0, 1, 2, 3, 4, \ldots\}$$

- **Rational Numbers.** The set of rational numbers $\mathbb{Q}$ is the set of all numbers expressible as a fraction whose numerator and denominator are both integers.

---

[12]For a slightly more complicated but purely geometric argument, see [Katz 1998, p. 51].

[13]There are a great many more number systems mathematicians work with, for example quaternions and integers mod n. However, they do not come up in the primary sources we include in this project.

[14]Some mathematicians do not include zero in the set of natural numbers. Here, we do.

- **Real Numbers.** The set of real numbers $\mathbb{R}$ is the set of all numbers expressible as a decimal expansion (finite or infinite).

- **Complex Numbers.** The set $\mathbb{C}$ of complex numbers is the set of all numbers expressible as $a + bi$, where a and b are real numbers, and i is a symbol such that $i^2 = -1$.

The figure below illustrates the relationships among these number systems, each labelled with the corresponding blackboard bold letter[15], along with a few examples from each set of numbers. Note the inclusion of each number system in the next: every natural number is also an integer, every integer is rational, and so on. For example, the number 2 is in the set of complex numbers because the set of complex numbers contains all of the other sets shown here.

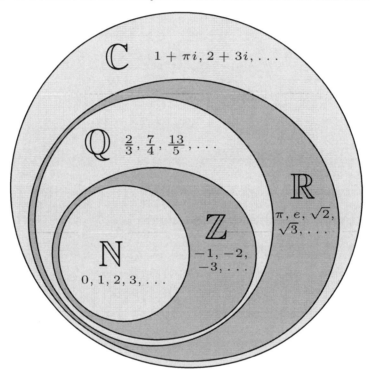

We define one last term before proceeding.

- A number is called *irrational* if it is real but not rational. That is, r is irrational if and only if $r \in \mathbb{R}$ but $r \notin \mathbb{Q}$.

More visually, we are trying to identify what numbers lie outside the region marked with $\mathbb{Q}$ but inside the region marked with $\mathbb{R}$ in the diagram above. Such numbers are called *irrational*, and the diagram shows a few famous ones: $\pi, e, \sqrt{2}$, and $\sqrt{3}$.

---

[15] If one wants an easy way to remember this notation: we have simply $\mathbb{N}$ for <u>N</u>atural, $\mathbb{R}$ for <u>R</u>eal, and $\mathbb{C}$ for <u>C</u>omplex. The two that don't seem to match their leading letter also have good reasons for their naming: $\mathbb{Z}$ for <u>Z</u>ahl, which is German for "number", and $\mathbb{Q}$ for <u>Q</u>uotient.

Task 4 (a) What does the discussion above have to do with numbers being incommensurate? Explain why a number is *rational* if and only if it is commensurate with an integer[16].

(b) Set $|AB| = 1$ in Task 3. What does that imply the length $|AC|$ equals?

(c) Use the results of Task 3 along with your work in this task to explain why $\sqrt{2}$ is irrational.

Thus, using a *per impossibile* argument, we have verified that $\sqrt{2}$ really does belong in the part of the diagram in which it was placed!

More generally, in order to use proof by contradiction to show that a real number r is irrational, one can perform the following steps:

1. Assume r is rational.

2. Thus, there must exist some integers m and n with $r = \frac{m}{n}$.

3. Use the equation $r = \frac{m}{n}$ and known properties of the number r to deduce a statement we know is false.

4. Conclude that our assumption of r being rational must have been false, so r is in fact irrational.

Task 5 (a) Take the argument for the irrationality of $\sqrt{2}$ and adapt it to write a proof of the irrationality of $\sqrt{3}$.

(b) Suppose you try to adapt it to prove the irrationality of $\sqrt{4}$. Where does the argument break down?

A.2.4   Fourier's Proof of the Irrationality of e

Joseph Fourier (1768–1830) was born into a working-class family in Auxerre, France. He quickly entered unfortunate circumstances: at the age of eight he became an orphan. Luckily, he obtained admission to a local military school, where he received an education from the Benedictine monks of Saint-Maur. In 1790, they gave him a mathematics teaching appointment at their school in Auxerre, where he also taught rhetoric, history, and philosophy. He later became a founding faculty member at the École Polytechnique in Paris, where Napoleon sometimes attended lectures. This led to Napoleon's request for Fourier's help in the administration of Egypt after its occupation by France in 1798. Upon his return to France, Fourier served as the prefect of the Department of Isère, where he led extensive infrastructure projects to quell chronic infections that were emanating from marshes in the area. In 1817, he was elected to the Académie des Sciences, and five years later he became their perpetual secretary. (For more on Fourier's life, see [Hutchins 1952].)

Thus, Fourier was quite the busy person, not only as an academic but also as a civil servant. Perhaps then, it is not terribly surprising that Fourier himself never wrote out and published

---

[16]If you have had a course in discrete mathematics, you may have seen the notion of *equivalence relation* and *equivalence class*. In that case, you may reinterpret this task as the following slightly stronger statement: prove that "commensurate" is an equivalence relation, and that the set of rational numbers is the equivalence class of 1. If you have not yet had a course in discrete mathematics, revisit this footnote once you do!

his proof that e is irrational! Rather, it appears in the book *Mélanges d'analyse algébrique et de géométrie* [Stainville 1815, p. 339] (*Mixtures of algebraic analysis and geometry*) by Janot de Stainville[17] (1783–1828), who explained how the proof was communicated to him.

⣿⣿⣿⣿⣿⣿⣿⣿⣿⣿⣿⣿⣿⣿⣿⣿⣿⣿⣿⣿⣿⣿⣿⣿⣿⣿⣿⣿⣿⣿⣿⣿⣿⣿⣿⣿⣿⣿⣿

> Note: this demonstration has been shared with me by Mr. Poinsot, who had it from Mr. Fourier.

⣿⣿⣿⣿⣿⣿⣿⣿⣿⣿⣿⣿⣿⣿⣿⣿⣿⣿⣿⣿⣿⣿⣿⣿⣿⣿⣿⣿⣿⣿⣿⣿⣿⣿⣿⣿⣿⣿⣿

The "Mr. Poinsot" he refers to is Louis Poinsot[18] (1777–1859). Poinsot and Fourier share a particular honor: they are both included among the seventy-two names of prominent mathematicians and scientists engraved into the Eiffel Tower! Let us now walk through this proof together.[19]

⣿⣿⣿⣿⣿⣿⣿⣿⣿⣿⣿⣿⣿⣿⣿⣿⣿⣿⣿⣿⣿⣿⣿⣿⣿⣿⣿⣿⣿⣿⣿⣿⣿⣿⣿⣿⣿⣿⣿

> After having found an approximate value for the number e, it is good to consider it in itself, and to demonstrate that not only is it comprised between 2 and 3, but that no rational fraction comprised between these two numbers can represent it; first it is greater than 2, because the two first terms of the series
>
> $$1 + 1 + \frac{1}{2} + \frac{1}{2.3} + \frac{1}{2.3.4} + \text{etc.},$$
>
> are both equal to one, and the sum of the other terms is positive, but this sum is less than the sum of the terms of the equation
>
> $$\frac{1}{2} + \frac{1}{2^2} + \frac{1}{2^3} + \text{etc.},$$
>
> which is equal to one, because it derives from the division of 1 by $2 - 1$, it follows that the sum of the fractions
>
> $$\frac{1}{2} + \frac{1}{2.3} + \frac{1}{2.3.4} + \text{etc.},$$
>
> is necessarily less than one, and thus, that the number e is lesser than 3.

⣿⣿⣿⣿⣿⣿⣿⣿⣿⣿⣿⣿⣿⣿⣿⣿⣿⣿⣿⣿⣿⣿⣿⣿⣿⣿⣿⣿⣿⣿⣿⣿⣿⣿⣿⣿⣿⣿⣿

Task 6 Although this is a very nicely written argument, a few steps could benefit from more detail. To this end, explain carefully why each of the following claims is true:

---

[17] Nicolas Dominique Marie Janot de Stainville was a member of the École Polytechnique class of 1802. He was then hired back by his alma mater to work as a tutor in 1810 [Verdier 2008].

[18] Louis Poinsot was a student and then later a professor at École Polytechnique in Paris. He is perhaps best remembered for having written *Eléments de statique*, which is today considered to be the founding work on geometric mechanics.

[19] Note that we are reproducing the original notation symbol for symbol. The lower dots are used to indicate multiplication. For example, de Stainville uses 1.2 to represent "1 times 2" rather than a decimal form of six-fifths. Furthermore, note that de Stainville's order of operations had the lower dot evaluated *after* addition, which is the opposite of what we typically do with multiplication vs addition.

(a) "this sum is less than the sum of the terms of the equation"

(b) "because it derives from the division of 1 by $2 - 1$." (In particular, be sure to identify which famous formula is being applied on that step!)

(c) "the number is less than 3."

Having established that e is in fact some real number between 2 and 3, de Stainville moved on to present Fourier's proof of irrationality[20].

∞∞∞

I also affirm that no rational fraction can represent it, because if an irreducible fraction m/n was equal to it, we would have

$$\frac{m}{n} = 2 + \frac{1}{2} + \frac{1}{2.3} + \cdots + \frac{1}{2..n} + \frac{1}{2..n.n+1} + \text{etc.};$$

but if we multiply the two sections of this equation by the multiplication $1.2..n$ of the set of natural numbers, until the one that indicates the denominator of the fraction that lies in the first section, we will have

$$\{1.2\ldots n-1\}m = \text{ an integer } + \frac{1}{n+1} + \frac{1}{n+1.n+2} + \frac{1}{n+1.n+2.n+3} + \text{etc.,}$$

or

$$\frac{1}{n+1} + \frac{1}{n+1.n+2} + \frac{1}{n+1.n+2.n+3} + \text{etc.}$$

is smaller than

$$\frac{1}{n+1} + \frac{1}{(n+1)^2} + \frac{1}{(n+1)^3} + \text{etc.,}$$

and since this last quantity is equal to

$$\frac{1}{(n+1)-1},$$

and that the first member is a whole number, it follows that to a whole number one would add a fraction lesser than $1/n$, the result would be a whole number, which is absurd; and thus it is equally absurd to suppose that the number e would be rational, and thus it is irrational.

∞∞∞

---

[20]Notice that de Stainville's argument that $2 < e < 3$ and Fourier's proof of the irrationality of e have something in common: they both depend on the formula $e = \sum_{n=0}^{\infty} \frac{1}{n!}$. This formula was due to the exceptionally talented and indescribably influential Swiss mathematician Leonhard Euler (1707–1783). Be aware that there are plenty of other ways to define e, however. Jakob Bernoulli (1655–1705) gave the first construction of the number as $e = \lim_{n\to\infty} \left(1 + \frac{1}{n}\right)^n$ in the context of studying compounded interest. Euler initially defined e to be the number that satisfied the special limit $\lim_{h\to 0} \frac{e^h - 1}{h} = 1$ as he was looking for a nice base for calculating logarithms (see [Ruch 2017] for a PSP that guides the reader through Euler's paper which demonstrated the equivalence of the three definitions stated above). Euler gave other characterizations of e, including continued fraction expansions relating to solutions of Ricatti differential equations, which he used to prove the irrationality of e (see the article *Who proved e is irrational?* [Sandifer 2006] for a guided tour of Euler's work on this).

Let us process this proof by rewriting it in a more modern form, updating our language and notation a bit.

Task 7 Fill in the missing parts of the proof that e is irrational. The blanks are labelled (a),(b),..., (m).

Proof. First let's write e as an infinite series. To do this, recall the power series for the exponential function:

$$e^x = \underline{\quad (a) \quad}$$

Set $x = 1$ to get an infinite series expression for the number e:

$$e = e^1 = \underline{\quad (b) \quad}$$

We proceed by using the classic proof technique called $\underline{\quad (c) \quad}$. Accordingly, we assume e is rational and then show that it leads to an impossible statement.

Proceeding, we assume e is rational. Then, there exist some $m, n \in \mathbb{N}$, with $n > 1$, such that

$$e = \underline{\quad (d) \quad}$$

We now identify the statement that will produce our contradiction. We will prove both of the following:

1. The quantity $\frac{1}{n+1} + \frac{1}{(n+1)(n+2)} + \frac{1}{(n+1)(n+2)(n+3)} + \cdots$ **is** an integer.
2. The quantity $\frac{1}{n+1} + \frac{1}{(n+1)(n+2)} + \frac{1}{(n+1)(n+2)(n+3)} + \cdots$ **is not** an integer.

The first statement is demonstrated as follows. We multiply both sides of the above equation by $\underline{\quad (e) \quad}$ to obtain

$$n!e = (n-1)!m.$$

Notice that the right-hand side is an integer because $\underline{\quad (f) \quad}$. Thus, the left-hand side, $n!e$, must also be an integer. Notice however, the left-hand-side can be decomposed as follows by substituting the infinite series for e and applying the distributive law:

$$\begin{aligned}
n!e &= n!\left(1 + \frac{1}{1!} + \frac{1}{2!} + \cdots + \frac{1}{n!} + \frac{1}{(n+1)!} + \cdots\right) \\
&= n!\left(1 + \frac{1}{1!} + \frac{1}{2!} + \cdots + \frac{1}{n!}\right) + n!\left(\frac{1}{(n+1)!} + \frac{1}{(n+2)!} + \frac{1}{(n+3)!} + \cdots\right).
\end{aligned}$$

The first term, $n!\left(1 + \frac{1}{1!} + \frac{1}{2!} + \cdots + \frac{1}{n!}\right)$, is an integer because $\underline{\quad (g) \quad}$. Subtracting that term from both sides, we can rewrite the above equation as

$$\frac{1}{n+1} + \frac{1}{(n+1)(n+2)} + \frac{1}{(n+1)(n+2)(n+3)} + \cdots = n!e - n!\left(1 + \frac{1}{1!} + \frac{1}{2!} + \cdots + \frac{1}{n!}\right).$$

We now proceed to show the second statement: that the quantity of interest is not an integer. In particular, we will show that $\left(\frac{1}{n+1} + \frac{1}{(n+1)(n+2)} + \frac{1}{(n+1)(n+2)(n+3)} + \cdots \right)$ lies between $\frac{1}{n+1}$ and $\frac{1}{n}$. However, there are no integers between $\frac{1}{n+1}$ and $\frac{1}{n}$, since they are both between 0 and 1. Proceeding, we have

$$\frac{1}{n+1} < \frac{1}{n+1} + \frac{1}{(n+1)(n+2)} + \frac{1}{(n+1)(n+2)(n+3)} + \cdots \tag{A.1}$$

$$< \frac{1}{n+1} + \frac{1}{(n+1)(n+1)} + \frac{1}{(n+1)(n+1)(n+1)} + \cdots \tag{A.2}$$

$$= \frac{1}{n+1} + \frac{1}{(n+1)^2} + \frac{1}{(n+1)^3} + \cdots \tag{A.3}$$

$$= \frac{\frac{1}{n+1}}{1 - \frac{1}{n+1}} \tag{A.4}$$

$$= \frac{1}{n}. \tag{A.5}$$

The above steps are justified as follows. The inequality on line (1) is true because ___(h)___. To get from line (1) to line (2), we use the fact that ___(i)___. The link between line (2) and line (3) is simply algebra. To get from line (3) to line (4), we sum an infinite geometric series with common ratio ___(j)___ and initial term ___(k)___. The transition from line (4) to line (5) again follows from ordinary algebraic simplification.

Thus, we have demonstrated that

$$\frac{1}{n+1} < \left(\frac{1}{n+1} + \frac{1}{(n+1)(n+2)} + \frac{1}{(n+1)(n+2)(n+3)} + \cdots \right) < \frac{1}{n},$$

as desired. Since $\frac{1}{n+1}$ and $\frac{1}{n}$ are strictly between 0 and 1, the quantity

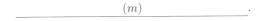

___(l)___

must lie strictly between 0 and 1 as well. However, there are no integers between 0 and 1, so that quantity cannot be an integer.

Thus, if our assumption that e is rational were true, we would be able to prove the existence of a quantity that both is and is not an integer at the same time. This is a contradiction. Therefore, we conclude that

___(m)___.

$\square$

After reading a long and complicated argument, some small "sanity check" kind of questions are often helpful with regards to moving the argument from a place of "I didn't disagree with that at any particular step" to the much better place of "ok, that argument feels intuitive to me". The following tasks hopefully help with that!

Task 8 First, let's make sure we understand the logic of the above argument.

(a) Identify Aristotle's key components in this argument. Specifically, identify each of the "original conclusion", "its contradictory", and "what is false"? At the end of all of this work, what have we successfully demonstrated?

(b) The contradiction was established by using the assumption of the rationality of e to prove two statements (labelled "1." and "2." in the proof) that were in direct opposition to each other. Which one was actually true?

Task 9 To help visualize what exactly happened in the argument above, plot the following five quantities in order on a number line: $0, 1, \frac{1}{n}, \frac{1}{n+1}$, and $\frac{1}{n+1} + \frac{1}{(n+1)(n+2)} + \frac{1}{(n+1)(n+2)(n+3)} + \cdots$.

Task 10 Why can we assume that $n > 1$? (**Hint:** Revisit the first primary source passage from de Stainville!) Furthermore, why was that important? Where was that fact used in the proof?

A.2.5 What about e^2?

In his paper *Sur l'irrationaliteé du nombre e = 2,718...*, Joseph Liouville[21] (1809–1882) adapted Fourier's methods to prove that e^2 is also irrational. We trace through his argument here.

∞∞

We will prove that the number e, the base of Napierian[22] logarithms, isn't a rational value. One should add, it seems to me, that the same method also proves that e can't be the root of a second degree equation with rational coefficients, which means that one could not have

$$ae + b/e = c,$$

a being a whole positive number and b, c whole numbers, positive or negative.

Indeed, if we replace in this equation e and $1/e$ or e^{-1} by their expansions deduced from the expansion of e^x, since we multiply the two numbers by $1.2.3 \ldots n$, we will easily find

$$\frac{a}{n+1}\left(1 + \frac{1}{n+2} + \cdots\right) \pm \frac{b}{n+1}\left(1 - \frac{1}{n+2} + \cdots\right) = \mu,$$

---

[21] Liouville's father, like Fourier, had worked with Napoleon during wartime. Liouville began study at the École Polytechnique in Paris in 1825. Upon graduating, he went on to become an enormously consequential mathematician with regards to the study of transcendental numbers. Liouville considered the number $0.1100010000000000000000001000\ldots$ that has a 1 in any position given by $n!$ for some natural number n, and 0 otherwise. He proved this number was transcendental in the landmark paper *Sur les classes très étendues de quantités dont la valeur n'est ni algébrique ni mĉme réductible à des irrationelles algébriques* [Liouville 1851].

[22] This refers to what is today usually called "natural log". This adjective is being applied in honor of its inventor, John Napier (1550–1617), a Scottish mathematician and physicist.

μ being a whole number. One can always make it so that the factor

$$\pm \frac{b}{n+1}$$

is positive; it will suffice to assume n is even if b is < 0 and n is odd if b is > 0; by taking n as very large, the equation that we just wrote is absurd; because its first section is essentially positive and very small, will be comprised between 0 and 1, and can't be equal to a whole μ. Thus, etc.

⋙⋘

Task 11 In Liouville's proof above, he never wrote out any representation of the number e^2 itself. Why does his argument truly prove that quantity is irrational as claimed? (**Hint:** Take the equation $ae + b/e = c$ from the above passage and multiply both sides by e.)

Task 12 Quite a bit of work is hidden in the early parts of this argument, as well as in Liouville's claim that the "first section is essentially positive and very small" and thus "will be comprised between 0 and 1". Let us fill in some details in that claim.

(a) Start with the infinite series expansions for both e and e^{-1}. Substitute them into the equation $ae + b/e = c$, and show the algebra needed to reach the statement

$$\frac{a}{n+1}\left(1 + \frac{1}{n+2} + \cdots\right) \pm \frac{b}{n+1}\left(1 - \frac{1}{n+2} + \cdots\right) = \mu.$$

What terms had to be pushed to the right-hand side to be part of the integer μ?

(b) Write out the equation for $n = 3$ and $n = 4$. In these examples, can you verify the claim that "n is even if b is < 0 and n is odd if b is > 0" in these two specific cases? Does it make sense that this would generalize to any n? Explain why or why not.

(c) We now focus on the expressions

$$\left(1 + \frac{1}{n+2} + \cdots\right)$$

and

$$\left(1 - \frac{1}{n+2} + \cdots\right).$$

Liouville was perhaps a bit terse in only include two terms in each! Write out these series again but show four terms in each instead of just two, just to make sure we see the general pattern.

(d) In de Stainville's writeup of Fourier's proof of the irrationality of e, he uses a comparison with a geometric series to show that

$$\frac{1}{n+1} + \frac{1}{(n+1)(n+2)} + \frac{1}{(n+1)(n+2)(n+3)} + \cdots < 1/n.$$

Use a similar argument to show that

$$\left(1 + \frac{1}{n+2} + \cdots\right) < 2$$

for all $n > 1$.

(e) Conclude that the same upper bound holds for the magnitude of the corresponding alternating series. That is,

$$\left|\left(1 - \frac{1}{n+2} + \cdots\right)\right| < 2$$

as well.

(f) Explain why Liouville's claim that the expression

$$\frac{a}{n+1}\left(1 + \frac{1}{n+2} + \cdots\right) \pm \frac{b}{n+1}\left(1 - \frac{1}{n+2} + \cdots\right)$$

"will be comprised between 0 and 1" is true as long as n is chosen to be at least $2a + 2|b|$.

Task 13 Once again, to be certain we understand the logic of the argument given above, identify Aristotle's key components. Specifically, what are the "original conclusion", "its contradictory", and "what is false" in this argument? In the end, what has Liouville successfully demonstrated?

We now compare two numbers whose irrationality we demonstrated in this project: e and $\sqrt{2}$.

Task 14 In a sense, e is somehow *more* irrational than $\sqrt{2}$. In particular,...

(a) ...if you square $\sqrt{2}$, do you get a rational number? Why or why not?

(b) ...if you square e, do you get a rational number? Why or why not?

The above observation starts to hint at the idea of a *transcendental number*: a number that cannot be obtained as a root of a polynomial with integer coefficients. While the square root of 2 is certainly irrational, it is a root of a polynomial with integer coefficients, namely $x^2 - 2$. However, it turns out that e is in fact transcendental as well as irrational. This fact is much more difficult to prove than the irrationality of e. Liouville in fact attempted this but never succeeded! It was proven almost thirty years after e's irrationality was published, by Charles Hermite[23] (1822–1901) [Hermite 1873]. Though the argument proved more difficult, it had something in common with all the arguments in this PSP: Hermite's proof still proceeded *per impossibile*!

---

[23]Charles Hermite was born in Dieuze, Lorraine, France. He became known not only for his contributions to number theory, analysis, linear algebra, and differential equations, but also for his spectacular teaching! [O'Connor and Robertson 1999b]

References

O'Connor, J J and E F Robertson (1999a). "Aristotle Biography". In: `mathshistory.st-andrews.ac.uk/Biographies/Aristotle/`.

McKeon, Richard (1941). *The Basic Works of Aristotle*. Ed. by Richard McKeon. From the front matter: "The numbers set within the text of this edition refer to the corresponding lines of the Greek text in the great modern edition of Aristotle's work published between 1830 and 1870 by the Berlin Academy." Translated by A J Jenkinson. New York: Random House.

Hoffman, Joseph E (1980). *Dictionary of Scientific Biography*. ISBN 978-0-684-10114-9. New York: Charles Scribner's Sons, pp. 46–51.

Pierrehumbert, Raymond (2004). "Warming the world." In: *Nature*. Translation of *Mémoire sur les Températures du Globe Terrestre et des Espaces Planétaires*, originally published in *Annales de Chimie et de Physique, Tome* XXVII (pp.136-167). Available at `https://users.physics.ox.ac.uk/~pierrehumbert/papers/Fourier1827Trans.pdf`, p. 677.

Katz, Victor J (1998). *A History of Mathematics: An Introduction, Second Edition*. Addison-Wesley.

Hutchins, Robert Maynard, ed. (1952). *Britannica Great Books of the Western World*. William Benton.

Stainville, Janot de (1815). *Mélanges d'analyse algébrique et de géométrie*. Courcier.

Verdier, Norbert (Sept. 2008). "L'irrationalité de *e* by Janot de Stainville, Liouville and some others." In: Bibnum Mathematics: Available at `journals.openedition.org/bibnum/670`.

Ruch, David (2017). "Euler's Rediscovery of *e*." In: `https://digitalcommons.ursinus.edu/triumphs/_analysis/3/`.

Sandifer, Ed (Feb. 2006). "How Euler Did It: Who Proved *e* is Irrational?" In: `eulerarchive.maa.org/hedi/HEDI-2006-02.pdf`.

Liouville, Joseph (1851). "Sur les classes très étendues de quantités dont la valeur n'est ni algébrique ni mme réductible à des irrationelles algébriques". In: *Journal Math. Pures et Appl.*, pp. 133–142.

O'Connor, J J and E F Robertson (1999b). "Hermite Biography". In: `mathshistory.st-andrews.ac.uk/Biographies/Hermite/`.

Hermite, Charles (1873). "Sur la fonction exponentielle." In: *Comptes rendus de l'Académie des Sciences (Paris)* 77 (5), pp. 18–24.

Acknowledgments

The author would especially like to thank two of his incredible former students: Diane Van Tiggelen, who provided translations for the French primary sources used in this PSP, and Jenna Allen, who created the number system diagram in Section A.2.3 in the context of creating a calculus OER together.

A.3   L'Hôpital's Rule

Daniel E. Otero
Department of Mathematics,
Xavier University,
Cincinnati, OH, 45207-4441
otero@xavier.edu

Students of the differential calculus learn that the fundamental notion of the derivative of a function depends on evaluating this limit:

$$f'(a) = \lim_{x \to a} \frac{f(x) - f(a)}{x - a}.$$

One's success in obtaining the limit is not at all obvious, since in the quotient that appears here, both the numerator and denominator approach 0, leaving us to puzzle over what to make of the indeterminate value $\frac{0}{0}$. However, this is a momentary setback; we are soon shown clever algebraic techniques for surmounting this $\frac{0}{0}$ problem. These algebraic manipulations allow us to develop the familiar differentiation rules for many of the functions that turn up in standard applications of calculus in the natural and social sciences.

What may be more surprising to learn is that one of the early successes of the calculus was the discovery of a result that allowed the evaluation of limits of precisely this $\frac{0}{0}$ indeterminate form, and which depended for its success on the calculation of derivatives! This result was announced in the very first comprehensive book-length treatment of the differential calculus in 1696. It is named L'Hôpital's Rule, after the author of this same book, so its historical pedigree is deep, and is further reflected in that nearly every first-semester calculus student still learns L'Hôpital's Rule today, more than 300 years later, as the chief method for evaluating limits of indeterminate type.

In this project, we will first examine limits of indeterminate type $\frac{0}{0}$ as they might appear in a natural setting. Then, we will read from L'Hôpital's early calculus book about how differential calculus was understood then as a literal calculus of differentials, well before the notion of a function's derivative was formulated. We will then see how differentials were employed to justify this eponymous Rule. Finally, we will see how to apply the Rule to evaluate some limits of indeterminate type.

A.3.1   Limits of Indeterminate Type

Let's set the stage with an exploration of the behavior of certain kinds of rational functions[24]:

Task 1   (a) Use a graphing utility to produce a graph of the rational function

$$r(x) = \frac{x^3 + 3x - 4}{x - 1}$$

---

[24]Recall that, by analogy with rational numbers, a rational function $r(x)$ is one that is defined as a quotient $\frac{p(x)}{q(x)}$ of two polynomials $p(x)$ and $q(x)$.

over the interval $-2 \leq x \leq 2$. What sort of curve is this?

(b) Now graph the function $s(x) = x^2 + x + 4$ over the same interval $-2 \leq x \leq 2$, and compare it with part (a). Describe the relationship between the functions $r(x)$ and $s(x)$ that is borne out in their graphs.

(c) Build a five-column table of values like the one below, in which the first column lists the inputs $x = -2, -1, 0, 1, 2$, while the second, third and fourth columns list the corresponding outputs for the numerator polynomial $p(x) = x^3 + 3x - 4$, the denominator polynomial $q(x) = x - 1$, and their quotient, the rational function $r(x)$. In the fifth column, supply the outputs for the function $s(x)$.

x	$p(x)$	$q(x)$	$r(x)$	$s(x)$
-2				
-1				
$\vdots$				

How does this information shed light on the relationship between $r(x)$ and $s(x)$?

(d) Now try factoring the polynomial $p(x)$. How does this help explain the relationship between $r(x)$ and $s(x)$?

(e) More generally (that is, for every possible value of x), how do the values of the functions $r(x)$ and $s(x)$ differ?

(f) Use a graphing utility to produce a graph of the rational function

$$t(x) = \frac{x^3 + 3x^2 - 4}{x - 1}$$

over the interval $-4 \leq x \leq 4$. (*Note the slight difference between the formulas for $t(x)$ and $r(x)$.*) Describe as best you can the differences between the graphs of $t(x)$ and $r(x)$.

Task 2 (a) As in Task 1, use a graphing utility to produce a graph of the rational function

$$R(x) = \frac{x^4 - 6x^2 + 1}{x^2 - 2x - 1}$$

over the interval $-4 \leq x \leq 4$. What sort of curve is this? How can you tell?

(b) It's far more difficult to factor the numerator polynomial $P(x) = x^4 - 6x^2 + 1$ (and the denominator polynomial $Q(x) = x^2 - 2x - 1$ for that matter) than in the example in Task 1. Nonetheless, can you still find a quadratic function $S(x)$ that agrees with $R(x)$ at every point where $R(x)$ is defined? Describe your thinking about this problem.

(c) Now produce a graph of the rational function

$$T(x) = \frac{x^4 - 6x^2 - 1}{x^2 - 2x - 1}$$

over the interval $-4 \leq x \leq 4$. (Again, note the slight difference between the formulas for $T(x)$ and $R(x)$.) Describe as best you can the differences between the graphs of $T(x)$ and $R(x)$.

Task 3   (a) Use a graphing utility to produce a graph of the two functions

$$w(x) = \frac{2^x - 1}{2x} \quad \text{and} \quad W(x) = \frac{2^x + 1}{2x}$$

over the interval $-4 \leq x \leq 4$. What can you say about the y-intercepts of these two functions?

(b) The numerator functions $u(x) = 2^x - 1$ and $U(x) = 2^x + 1$ are not polynomials (even though the common denominator function $v(x) = V(x) = 2x$ is). So $w(x)$ and $W(x)$ are *not* rational functions. Describe how this difference prevents us from analyzing the behavior of the functions $w(x)$ and $W(x)$ in the same way that we dealt with $r(x)$ and $R(x)$ in the previous two tasks.

(c) You may have recognized that $w(0)$ and $W(0)$ are undefined, but your graphs of these functions may make it hard to tell. Indeed, the graph indicates that $w(x)$ is perfectly well defined at every other value of x besides $x = 0$, and that

$$\lim_{x \to 0} w(x)$$

is also well defined! Numerically determine the value of this limit to four decimal place accuracy by computing values of $w(x)$ for at least five increasingly smaller positive values of $w(x)$ and at least five increasingly larger negative values of $w(x)$.

Task 4   (a) Is the function $r(x)$ from Task 1 continuous everywhere? Is the function $R(x)$ from Task 2 continuous everywhere? How about $w(x)$ from Task 3? In each case, explain how you know that the particular function is continuous at every real number, or how it fails to meet the criteria for being continuous at certain points.

(b) Given your results in Tasks 1, 2 and 3, what common properties can you identify about the behavior of the three functions $r(x)$, $R(x)$ and $w(x)$ at the given input values?

If you successfully completed the tasks above, you probably noticed that they illustrate a particular phenomenon in which a given function is undefined at a particular input value $x = a$, despite appearing to be otherwise well-behaved, in the sense that at every other input value the function is both continuous and smooth[25]! Moreover, the function is "as close as possible"

---

[25]This term "smooth" is not often included in the standard terminology of a calculus student, so here's a definition: a function is *smooth* at a particular input value if it and its derivatives, to arbitrarily high order, are well defined there. In particular, all polynomial, exponential and trigonometric functions are smooth at every point where the functions are defined.

to being continuous at the relevant point since the *limiting value* of the function exists there even though the *function value* does not.

Recall that a function f of a real variable x is *continuous at a point* $x = a$ provided three conditions hold:

1. the function is defined there, that is, $f(a)$ exists;
2. the limiting value of the function is defined there, that is, $\lim_{x \to a} f(x)$ exists;
3. and the two values agree: $\lim_{x \to a} f(x) = f(a)$.

Most functions that are studied in calculus courses are continuous at all points where they are defined. Indeed, we often depend on this to help us evaluate the limit computations we encounter: often, our first inclination on needing to determine a limit $\lim_{x \to a} f(x)$ is to rely on the continuity of the function f by simply evaluating $f(a)$.

But in the situations described in the Tasks above, the functions $r(x)$ and $R(x)$ turn out to be discontinuous at $x = 1$, and $w(x)$ is discontinuous at $x = 0$, all because the given functions are *undefined* at the relevant point, making it impossible to use this method to determine the limiting values. Moreover, the three functions were discontinuous *in the same way*: each is the quotient of a numerator and denominator function that vanishes at the particular input value, meaning that an attempt to evaluate the function at this input leads to the value $\frac{0}{0}$, a meaningless and undefined quantity.

If $u(x)$ and $v(x)$ are a pair of functions that satisfy $\lim_{x \to a} u(x) = 0$ and $\lim_{x \to a} v(x) = 0$, then we call

$$\lim_{x \to a} \frac{u(x)}{v(x)} \tag{A.6}$$

a **limit of indeterminate type** $\frac{0}{0}$.

Now in the case of $r(x)$ and $R(x)$ in the Tasks above, even though we were presented with a limit of indeterminate type, we found a way to determine it because the numerator and denominator functions were polynomials with a common factor, a factor which was entirely responsible for the vanishing of the numerator and denominator. We were able to divide out the offending factor and thereby resolve the limit.

But this was not the case in Task 3; the best we could do there was to approximate the desired limit. Ah, never fear! This is a job for … calculus! Indeed, as we shall discover below, resolving the problem of limits of indeterminate type was among the first of many successful applications of the new calculus techniques that were developed in the late seventeenth century.

A.3.2 L'Hôpital's *Analyse* and the Calculus of Differentials

What we call calculus today was first formulated as a body of related mathematical techniques by two men working independently in the late 1600s: Isaac Newton (1642–1727) in Britain, and Gottfried Leibniz (1646–1716) on the European Continent. Leibniz discovered simple symbolic computational techniques, a "calculus"[26] as he called it, that led to the development of a

---

[26]The word *calculus* is Latin for "pebble", describing the token that was used on ancient counting boards as an aid for doing arithmetic in the times before modern mechanical or electronic computers. Leibniz used the word to refer to the new calculation methods he had discovered.

systematic mathematical theory for the motion of physical objects. Newton's success in using these ideas to explain the celestial motions of the planets in their elliptical orbits, and at the same time, how falling bodies behaved here on earth[27], turned the heads of mathematicians and scientists across Europe at the dawn of the eighteenth century. Scientists would spend the next 400 years extending the reach of application of the ideas first formulated by these two men, building the mathematical tools fundamental to the development of astronomy, physics, chemistry, biology, engineering sciences, and eventually computer science, thereby ushering in the modern age of technology, a movement still playing out in our times.

Among the first scientists to contribute to this development were three contemporaries of Newton and Leibniz: a pair of Swiss-born mathematicians, Jakob Bernoulli (1655–1705) and his younger brother Johann Bernoulli (1667–1748), and a French nobleman, Guillaume François Antoine, Marquis de l'Hôpital (1661–1704). Jakob, the older brother, successfully deflected his father's desire for him to study theology at the University of Basel, taking up mathematics instead. His younger brother Johann was another disappointment to his father, as he was expected him to take up the profitable family business but was drawn into the exciting new world of mathematics to which Jakob introduced him. In the 1680s, the two brothers became experts in the new calculus espoused by Leibniz, with whom they communicated through letters and in the pages of new academic journals that were being published. Eventually, both would hold the chair of Mathematics at the University of Basel, Johann succeeding Jakob there in 1705 after the death of his elder brother.

As a young aristocrat in his twenties, the Marquis de L'Hôpital had to abandon a career in the military due to severe nearsightedness. But he was passionate about mathematics, so he attached himself to a circle of mathematicians in Paris, where the new analytic theories of Newton and Leibniz were being discussed and studied. There, in 1691, L'Hôpital made the acquaintance of Jophann Bernoulli, discovering that the younger man had a much stronger command of these ideas than did he. Soon after they met, L'Hôpital, anxious to learn what he could of the new mathematical theories, engaged Johann to give him private lectures on the calculus, both in Paris and at the nobleman's estate in Oucqes just outside the city, and he provided Johann with handsome compensation for his pains. This arrangement ultimately led to the publication by L'Hôpital of the first comprehensive treatment of the subject of the differential calculus, *Analyse des infiniment petits pour l'intelligence des lignes courbes* [*Analysis of the infinitely small, for the understanding of curved lines*] in 1696 (and then in a posthumous second edition in 1715) [L'Hôpital 1715].[28] It is in L'Hôpital's *Analyse* that we find the very first application of the subject to the resolution of limits of indeterminate type!

Leibniz' version of the calculus began as a theory not about derivatives, in the way that we learn the subject today, but about *differentials*. We see this in the way that L'Hôpital sets out his (that is, Bernoulli's) understanding of calculus in the opening chapter of the *Analyse*.

ⲟⲭⲟ

Chapter 1. In Which We Give the Rules of This Calculus

---

[27]Newton published his wildly popular *Philosophiae Naturalis Principia Mathematica* (*Mathematical Principles of Natural Philosophy*) in 1687, but did so without acknowledging the new concepts of his calculus due to his extreme reluctance to divulge any methods. His calculus would later be published posthumously, in *The Method of Fluxions* (1736).

[28]The book has recently been released in a modern English translation [Bradley, Petrilli, and Sandifer 2015], from which the excerpts found in these pages have been drawn.

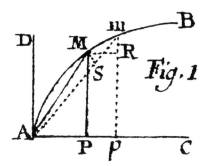

Definition. The infinitely small portion by which a variable quantity continually increases or decreases is called the *Differential*. For example, let AMB be an arbitrary curved line (Fig. 1) which has the line AC as its axis or diameter, and has PM as one of its ordinates.[29] Let pm be another ordinate, infinitely close to the first one. Given this, if we also draw MR parallel to AC, and the chords AM Am, and describe the little circular arc MS of the circle with center A and radius AM, then Pp is the differential of the AP, Rm the differential of PM, Sm the differential of AM, and Mm the differential of the arc AM. Furthermore, the little triangle MAm, which has the arc Mm as its base is the differential of the segment AM, and the little region $MPpm$ is the differential of the region contained by the straight lines AP and PM, and by the arc AM. [...]

Note. In what follows, we will make use of the symbol d to denote the differential of a variable quantity that is expressed by a single letter and, in order to avoid confusion, the letter d will not be used in any other way in the following calculations. If, for example, we denote AP by x, PM by y, AM by z, the arc AM by u, the curvilinear region APM by s, and the segment AM by t, then dx denotes the value of Pp, dy that of Rm, dz that of Sm, du that of the little arc Mm, ds that of the little region $MPpm$, and dt that of the little curvilinear triangle MAm.

Task 5 (a) What do you think L'Hôpital meant by "infinitely small"? Is it the same as having no size? For instance, in Fig. 1, even though pm is meant to be drawn "infinitely close" to PM, there is clearly a measurable gap between them. How big is the corresponding differential Pp (later called dx) supposed to be? Are P and p different points? Share your thoughts about these questions.

(b) Sketch for yourself a larger version of L'Hôpital's Figure 1 complete with the labeled points $A, B, C, D, M, m, P, p, R, S$. (You can omit the notation for "Fig. 1".) Then attach labels for the various differentials dx, du, ds and dt to the proper element for each in the diagram.

(c) In what ways are these differential quantities geometrically similar?

[29] In L'Hôpital's day, mathematicians preferred the classical terms *abscissa* and *ordinate* for what we today call respectively the x- and y-coordinates of a point.

⦿⦿⦿⦿⦿⦿⦿⦿⦿⦿⦿⦿⦿⦿⦿⦿⦿⦿⦿⦿⦿⦿⦿⦿⦿⦿⦿⦿⦿⦿⦿⦿⦿⦿⦿⦿⦿⦿⦿

Postulate. We suppose that a curved line may be considered as an assemblage of infinitely many straight lines, each one being infinitely small, or (what amounts to the same thing) as a polygon with an infinite number of sides, each being infinitely small, which determine the curvature of the line by the angles formed amongst themselves. We suppose, for example, that the portion Mm of the curve …may be considered to be straight lines on account of their infinite smallness. …

Chapter 2. Use of the Differential Calculus for Finding the Tangents of All Kinds of Curved Lines

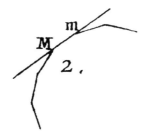

Definition. If we prolong one of the little sides Mm (Fig. 2) of the polygon that makes up a curved line, this little side, thus prolonged is called the Tangent to the curve at the point M or m.

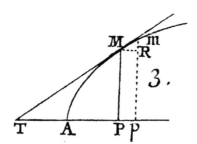

⦿⦿⦿⦿⦿⦿⦿⦿⦿⦿⦿⦿⦿⦿⦿⦿⦿⦿⦿⦿⦿⦿⦿⦿⦿⦿⦿⦿⦿⦿⦿⦿⦿⦿⦿⦿⦿⦿⦿

Task 6 The curve AM in Figure 3 at the end of the last excerpt[30] could be a sketch of the graph of the function $y = \sqrt{x}$, where A is the origin of the coordinate system and M and m are other points on this parabolic curve. (We know that the curve is a parabola since it is a portion of the graph of the equation $x = y^2$.)

(a) Let's take $M = (\frac{1}{4}, \frac{1}{2})$ on this portion the curve. Use your knowledge of calculus to determine the equation of the tangent line MT to this curve at M.

---

[30]This figure is reproduced again at the bottom of this page.

(b) If M and m are the same two points displayed in the "close-up" of Figure 2, how close together are these points meant to be?

(c) In Figure 2, the "little side" Mm lies to the right of M; let m' denote the other endpoint of the "little side" to the left of M so that $m'M$ is the adjacent side to Mm of the "polygon with an infinite number of sides" that makes up the curve. How close together are M and $'m$?

(d) If the "prolongation" of Mm produces the tangent line to the curve at M containing the point T, does the "prolongation" of $m'M$ also produce a tangent line to the curve at M? How many tangent lines are there to the curve at M? On a related note, what is the measure of the angle $m'Mm$? Can you bring some clarity to an understanding of these diagrams?

Perhaps Task 6 has seeded doubt in your mind that L'Hôpital and Bernoulli (and Leibniz, who they were following) had any idea what they were doing, basing their understanding of calculus on such problematic notions as the "infinitely small". If we read on, however, it will become clear that they really did have the basic ideas right.

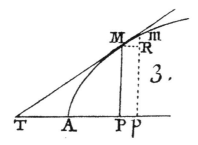

Proposition I.

Problem. (§9) Let AM be a curved line (Fig. 3) where the relationship between the abscissa AP and the ordinate PM is expressed by any equation. At a given point M on this curve, we wish to draw the tangent MT.[31]

We draw the ordinate MP and suppose that the straight line MR that meets the diameter at the point T is the tangent we wish to find. We imagine another ordinate mp infinitely close to the first one, with a little straight line MR parallel to AP. Now denoting the given quantities AP by x and PM by y (so that Pp or $MR = dx$ and $Rm = dy$), the similar triangles mRM and MPT give* $mR(dy) : RM(dx) :: MP(y) :$

---

[31] It is worth noting that L'Hôpital wrote this before the notion of the slope of a line was developed. He and his contemporaries were genuinely interested in the geometric problem of *drawing* the tangent to the curve at the point, and his goal here is to find a method for doing this.

*Translator's Footnote: In [L'Hôpital 1715] the notation $a \,.\, b :: c \,.\, d$ was used to express equal proportion; we write this instead as $a : b :: c : d$. We note further that in [L'Hôpital 1715] the right parenthesis following dx was omitted.

$PT = \frac{y\,dx}{dy}$. Now, by means of the differential of the given equation, we find a value for dx in terms that are multiplied by dy. This (being multiplied by y and divided by dy) will give the value of the subtangent PT in terms that are entirely known and free of differentials, which can be used to draw the tangent that we wish to find.

$\infty\!\infty$

Task 7   (a) Explain why the triangles mRM and MPT are similar, to justify the proportion $mR : RM :: MP : PT$.

(b) Substitute differentials for the first three of the four magnitudes in the proportion above, expressing the proportion as an equation of fractions, to conclude, as indicated by L'Hôpital, that $PT = \frac{y\,dx}{dy}$.

(c) Rewrite the last equation in the form $PT = \frac{y}{(dy/dx)}$, then use the calculus you're familiar with to find the derivative of $y = \sqrt{x}$, and substitute it into this formula. As a result, determine a formula for PT in terms of x.

(d) Finally, use the fact that we chose $M = (\frac{1}{4}, \frac{1}{2})$ to determine the coordinates of T from your result in part (c). Do you get the same answer as the x-intercept of the tangent line you found in Task 6(a)?

From the time of the ancient Greeks, geometers knew how to draw the tangent to a parabola at any point on the curve, so this problem outlined in L'Hôpital's *Analyse* was not a discovery made possible by the invention of calculus but rather a confirmation of the power of the newer techniques. Further proof of the power of calculus came from its ability to extend geometers' ability to deal with other kinds of curves besides the traditional parabola.

$\infty\!\infty$

Let the general equation be $y^m = x$, which expresses the nature of all parabolas to infinity, when the exponent m denotes a whole or fractional positive number, and of all hyperbolas when it denotes a negative number. Taking differentials, we have $my^{m-1}\,dy = dx$ and thus $PT\left([\text{or}]\frac{y\,dx}{dy}\right) = my^m = mx$, substituting the value x for y^m.

$\infty\!\infty$

Task 8   Verify that setting $m = 2$ in the paragraph above leads to the case of the traditional parabola, which L'Hôpital worked out in his Proposition I.

In the previous source excerpt, L'Hôpital calls the procedure that takes the equation of the "general parabola" $y^m = x$ and produces from it the equation $my^{m-1}dy = dx$ "taking differentials". It is important to note that in the early years of calculus, the fundamental idea was not the derivative, but the differential. It was only about 100 years later, after they grew comfortable using the ideas of Leibniz's calculus, that mathematicians realized that the most powerful manifestation of differentials was in determining their ratios, and that a more convenient way to organize calculus was not in terms of relations between differentials, as in the equation $my^{m-1}dy = dx$, but rather to focus on the properties of their ratios, as in the equivalent equation

$$\frac{dy}{dx} = \frac{1}{m}x^{(1-m)/m}.$$ (A.7)

When Joseph-Louis Lagrange (1736–1813) wrote up lecture notes for his calculus students at the École Polytechnique in Paris in the 1790s [Lagrange 1806], his reformulation of the theory introduced the *derivative* of a function $y = f(x)$, which he denoted $y' = f'(x)$, as the ratio of the differentials $\frac{dy}{dx}$. This began a shift in the standard treatment of the subject in which derivatives of functions superseded the differentials of quantities as the main focus of attention in calculus.

Task 9 Solve $y^m = x$ for y, then compute the derivative to verify equation (A.7).

Task 10 Suppose that Figure 3 now displays (the upper part of) the graph of a *cubical parabola* $y^3 = x$. If M is the point with coordinates $(8, 2)$, use L'Hôpital's result in the last excerpt above to determine the coordinates of the point T. Use a graphing utility to produce a graph of this curve and the tangent line at the point M.

A.3.3 L'Hôpital's Rule: Determining Limits of Indeterminate Type

Chapter 2 of L'Hôpital's *Analyse* is a presentation of Leibniz's theory of differentials as told by Bernoulli and organized by L'Hôpital. The next chapters of the book apply these ideas to the study of the properties of a variety of curves. Then in Chapter 9, attention is turned to the problem of limits of indeterminate type.

∞∞

Chapter 9. The Solution of Several Problems That Depend upon the Previous Methods

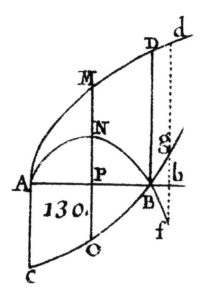

Proposition I.

Problem. (§163) *Let AMD (Fig. 130) be a curved line ($AP = x, PM = y$, and $AB = a$) such that the value of the ordinate y is expressed by a fraction, in which the numerator and the denominator each becomes zero when $x = a$, that is to say, when the point P falls on the given point B. We ask what the value of the ordinate BD ought to be.*

Let it be understood that there are two curved lines ANB and COB that have the line AB as a common axis, and which are such that the ordinate PN expresses the numerator, and the ordinate PO the denominator of the general fraction that corresponds to all of the ordinates PM, so that $PM = \frac{AB \times PN}{PO}$. It is clear that these two curves meet at the point B because, by the assumption, PN and PO each becomes zero when the point P falls on B.

To assist us in discussing L'Hôpital's Proposition I, let's introduce some other symbols for reference purposes: let u represent the ordinate PN in Fig. 130 in the source above, and let v denote the ordinate PO. For simplicity, we further assume that AB has a certain length, i.e., $AB = a$.

Task 11 | Given this additional notation, explain the connection between the Problem that L'Hôpital presents here and the concept of a limit of indeterminate type $\frac{0}{0}$ which was defined in equation (A.6) back in Section 1 of this project.

L'Hôpital and Bernoulli use differentials to solve the problem of limits of indeterminate type $\frac{0}{0}$. The following excerpt immediately follows the previous one in L'Hôpital's *Analyse*.

∞∞∞

Given this, if we imagine an ordinate bd infinitely close to BD, which meets the curved lines ANB and COB at f and g [respectively], then we will have $bd = \frac{AB \times bf}{bg}$, which (see §2) does not differ from BD. It is therefore only a question of finding the ratio of bg to bf. Now, it is clear that as the abscissa AP becomes AB, the ordinates PN and PO become null, and that as AP becomes Ab, they become bf and bg. From this, it follows that these ordinate themselves, bf and bg, are the differentials of the ordinates at B and b with respect to the curves ANB and COB. Consequently, if we take the differential of the numerator and we divide it by the differential of the denominator, after having let $x = a = Ab$ or AB, we will have the value that we wish to find for the ordinate bd or BD. This is what we were required to find.

∞∞∞

Task 12 | Since we have set $u = PN$ and $v = PO$ in Fig. 130, which quantities in the excerpt above correspond to the differentials du and dv?

Task 13 | According to L'Hôpital, what exactly is the thing he refers to that "we were required to find"? Fill in the missing blanks below to express it in terms of x, y, u and v.

> **Theorem (Proposition I, Updated using Limits).** *Let u and v be ordinates of curves measured against an axis whose abscissa is called x; further, suppose that u and v both approach _____ when x approaches _____. Then (despite the fact that $y = $ _____/_____ is undefined when $x = $ _____), the limiting value of y as x approaches _____ (a limit of indeterminate type $\frac{0}{0}$) satisfies*
> $$\lim_{x \to a} \frac{u}{v} = \lim_{x \to a} \text{_____} . \tag{A.8}$$

A natural question to ask might be, "Why didn't L'Hôpital make use of the language of limits to state his proposition, as we did above?" This question has an easy answer: the concept of a limit hadn't yet been formulated in L'Hôpital's day! Nor would it happen for more than 100 years after L'Hôpital and Bernoulli worked on these problems. Limits were introduced as a way to clarify these central ideas by Augustin-Louis Cauchy (1789–1857) in lecture notes for the course he taught to young engineers at the École Polytechnique in Paris in the 1820s.

Task 14 | Reread the statement of L'Hôpital's Problem at the beginning of his Chapter 9. When he asks "what the value of the ordinate BD ought to be," how might we formulate this question in modern mathematical language?

When we learn about differentials in a presentation of calculus today, they are usually introduced in terms of functions, since today's calculus is founded on the analysis of functions. If $y = f(x)$ is a (differentiable) function of x, we interpret the differential dx of the independent variable essentially as Leibniz, Bernoulli and L'Hôpital did, as an infinitely small change in x, and then define the differential of y in terms of dx as

$$dy = f'(x)\, dx, \qquad (A.9)$$

reflecting precisely how y must change *with respect to* x.

This reformulation of the differential in terms of derivatives allows us to replace the differentials du and dv in equation (A.8) with expressions involving derivatives instead. In particular, since

$$\frac{du}{dv} = \frac{u'(x)\, dx}{v'(x)\, dx} = \frac{u'(x)}{v'(x)},$$

we can restate L'Hôpital's Proposition I in the following more modern form, now known as ...

Theorem (L'Hôpital's Rule). *Let $u(x)$ and $v(x)$ be (differentiable) functions of x which satisfy $u(a) = v(a) = 0$. Then $y = \dfrac{u(x)}{v(x)}$ is undefined at $x = a$, but the limiting value of y at $x = a$, a limit of indeterminate type $\dfrac{0}{0}$, satisfies*

$$\lim_{x \to a} \frac{u(x)}{v(x)} = \lim_{x \to a} \frac{u'(x)}{v'(x)}. \qquad (A.10)$$

⬛ **Task 15** ⬛ Apply L'Hôpital's Rule (A.10) to evaluate these limits of indeterminate type $\dfrac{0}{0}$:

(a) $\displaystyle\lim_{x \to 1} r(x)$, from Task 1.

(b) $\displaystyle\lim_{x \to 1} R(x)$, from Task 2.

(b) $\displaystyle\lim_{x \to 0} w(x)$, from Task 3.

Apparently, soon after Bernoulli discovered this Rule for evaluating limits of indeterminate type $\frac{0}{0}$, he crafted an imposing challenge problem that required this Rule for its solution. He then sent the challenge problem to his circle of mathematician colleagues in Paris. Eventually, the problem made its way to L'Hôpital, who wrestled with it without success for many months, and repeatedly entreated Bernoulli in letters to tell him how to solve the problem. Naturally, this same problem became the first example to illustrate the technique in L'Hôpital's *Analyse*.

∞∞∞

Example I. (§164) Let

$$y = \frac{\sqrt{2a^3x - x^4} - a\sqrt[3]{aax}}{a - \sqrt[4]{ax^3}}.$$

It is clear that when $x = a$, then the numerator and denominator of the fraction both become equal to zero. This is why we take the differential of the numerator

$$\frac{a^3 dx - 2x^3 dx}{\sqrt{2a^3 x - x^4}} - \frac{aa\, dx}{3\sqrt[3]{axx}}$$

and we divide it by the differential of the denominator

$$-\frac{3a\, dx}{4\sqrt[4]{a^3 x}},$$

after having let $x = a$. That is to say, we divide $-\frac{4}{3}a\, dx$ by $-\frac{3}{4}dx$, which gives $\frac{16}{9}a$ as the value of BD that we wish to find.

◯◯

Task 16   (a) Why is

$$\lim_{x \to a} \frac{\sqrt{2a^3 x - x^4} - a\sqrt[3]{a^2 x}}{a - \sqrt[4]{ax^3}}$$

a limit of indeterminate type $\frac{0}{0}$?

(b) Set $a = 2$ everywhere in the expression that L'Hôpital calls y. Then set $u(x)$ equal to the numerator expression of y and $v(x)$ equal to the denominator expression. Compute their differentials $du = u'(x)\, dx$ and $dv = v'(x)\, dx$, following equation (A.9). Do your answers agree with what L'Hôpital obtains above (after setting $a = 2$ in each result, of course)?

(c) Return to the limit in (a) above, where we once more treat a as an unspecified but fixed value. Now use (A.10), the modern formulation of L'Hôpital's Rule, to evaluate the limit. Do you obtain the same answer that L'Hôpital obtains at the end of the excerpt above?

The next example presented was much simpler than the first. But its inclusion here by L'Hôpital was rather to show off to his contemporaries how much easier his new method of solution was than an older method developed by René Descartes (1596–1650) to deal with similar problems, a method that required first transforming the expression of the formula for the curve to remove any square roots.

◯◯

Example II. (§165) Let

$$y = \frac{aa - ax}{a - \sqrt{ax}},$$

We find that $y = 2a$ when $x = a$.

We might have solved this example without the need of the calculus of differentials

. . .

∞◎◎◎∞

Task 17 Rewrite the problem in L'Hôpital's **Example II** of finding y "when $x = a$" by using limit notation, then determine that limit using his Rule (A.10).

A.3.4   Conclusion

L'Hôpital's Rule – or rather, Bernoulli's form of the Rule, the form that L'Hôpital stated in his *Analyse* – has been extended to apply to other limits of indeterminate type. Consider the following variations, which are just a sampling of the many extensions [Spivak 1980, p. 198]:

> **Theorem (L'Hôpital's Rule for One-Sided Limits).** *Let $u(x)$ and $v(x)$ be functions of x which have one-sided limits $\lim\limits_{x \to a^+} u(a) = \lim\limits_{x \to a^+} v(a) = 0$. Then*
>
> $$\lim_{x \to a^+} \frac{u(x)}{v(x)} = \lim_{x \to a^+} \frac{u'(x)}{v'(x)} \, .$$
>
> *The similar statement for one-sided limits from below at a also holds.*

> **Theorem (L'Hôpital's Rule for Limits at ∞).** *Let $u(x)$ and $v(x)$ be differentiable functions of x which satisfy $\lim\limits_{x \to \infty} u(a) = \lim\limits_{x \to \infty} v(a) = 0$. Then*
>
> $$\lim_{x \to \infty} \frac{u(x)}{v(x)} = \lim_{x \to \infty} \frac{u'(x)}{v'(x)} \, .$$
>
> *The similar statement holds if ∞ is replaced with $-\infty$ everywhere.*

> **Theorem (L'Hôpital's Rule for Limits of Indeterminate Type $\frac{\infty}{\infty}$).** *Let $u(x)$ and $v(x)$ be differentiable functions of x which satisfy $\lim\limits_{x \to \infty} u(a) = \lim\limits_{x \to \infty} v(a) = \infty$. Then*
>
> $$\lim_{x \to \infty} \frac{u(x)}{v(x)} = \lim_{x \to \infty} \frac{u'(x)}{v'(x)} \, .$$
>
> *The similar statement holds if ∞ is replaced with $-\infty$ everywhere, and even if ∞ is replaced with a^+ or a^-.*

References

L'Hôpital, Guillaume François Antoine de (1715). *Analyse des infiniment petits, pour l'intelligence des lignes courbes*. 2nd. Paris: Montalant.

Bradley, Robert E., Salvatore J. Petrilli, and C. Edward Sandifer (2015). *L'Hôpital's Analyse des Infinitements Petits: an annotated translation with source material by Johann Bernoulli*. Science Networks Historical Studies 50. Birkhäuser.

Lagrange, Joseph-Louis (1806). *Leçons sur le calcul des fonctions*. 2nd. Paris: Courcier.

Spivak, Michael (1980). *Calculus*. 2nd. Publish or Perish, Inc.

Rickey, V. Frederick (1996). "L'Hospital's Rule". In: May 29, 1996. URL: `http://fredrickey.` `info/hm/CalcNotes/L'Hospital.pdf`.

Acknowledgments

The author acknowledges the inspiration to prepare this lesson after rereading [Rickey 1996] a second time in the summer of 2018, the first time being more than twenty years earlier, when this brief article was issued as part of the packet of readings given to all participants at the NSF-funded Institute for the History of Mathematics and Its Use in Teaching, run by Victor Katz, Fred Rickey and Steven Schott in the mid-1990s at American University in Washington, DC.

A.4 Investigations Into d'Alembert's Definition of Limit

David Ruch

Department of Mathematics,

Department of Mathematical and Computer Sciences,

Metropolitan State University of Denver,

ruch@msudenver.edu

A.4.1 Introduction

The modern definition of a limit evolved over many decades. One of the earliest attempts at a precise definition is credited to Jean-Baptiste le Rond d'Alembert (1717–1783), a French mathematician, philosopher and physicist.[32] Among his many accomplishments, d'Alembert was a co-editor of the *Encyclopédie*, an important general encyclopedia published in France between 1751 and 1772. This work is regarded as a significant achievement of the Enlightenment movement in Europe.

D'Alembert argued in two 1754 articles of the *Encyclopédie* that the theory of limits should be put on a firm foundation.[33] As a philosopher, d'Alembert was disturbed by critics who pointed out logical problems with limits and the foundations of calculus. He recognized the significant challenges of these criticisms, writing in [d'Alembert 1754a] that

> This metaphysics [of calculus], of which so much has been written, is even more important, and perhaps as difficult to develop as these same rules of the calculus.

In this project we will investigate d'Alembert's limit definition and study the similarities and differences with our modern definition.

A.4.2 D'Alembert's Limit Definition

By 1754 mathematical techniques using calculus were quite advanced. D'Alembert won a 1747 prize for his work in partial differential equations, but became embroiled in arguments with Leonhard Euler (1707–1783) and others over methodology and foundational issues. These squabbles contributed to his interest in clearing up the foundations of limits and convergence.

---

[32] Early chapters of d'Alembert's biography read like something out of *Masterpiece Theater*. He was born out of wedlock and left as an infant at the church Saint Jean le Rond in Paris. His mother, Claudine Guérin de Tencin, was a runaway nun who established a well-known Paris *salon*, a carefully orchestrated social gathering that brought together important writers, philosophers, scientists, artists and aristocrats for the purpose of intellectual and political discussions. Tencin never acknowledged d'Alembert as her son, and his father, Louis-Camus Destouches, found another woman to raise young Jean. Destouches died in 1726, but left funds for Jean's education. D'Alembert did well in school and became active as an adult in the philosophy, literature, science and mathematics of his day, standing "at the very heart of the Enlightenment with interests and activities that touched on every one of its aspects" [Hankins 1990].

[33] The first of these articles was entitled "Limite (Mathématiques)," and the second "Calcul différentiel."

Here is d'Alembert's limit definition from the *Encyclopédie* [d'Alembert 1754b]:

∞∞

Limit. (Mathematics) One says that a magnitude is the *limit* of another magnitude, when the second may approach the first more closely than by a given quantity, as small as one wishes, moreover without the magnitude approaching, being allowed ever to surpass the magnitude that it approaches; so that the difference between a quantity and its *limit* is absolutely unassignable.

For example, suppose we have two polygons, one inscribed and the other circumscribed about a circle; it is clear that one may increase the sides as much as one wishes, and in that case each polygon will approach ever more closely the circumference of the circle; the perimeter of the inscribed polygon will increase, and that of the circumscribed polygon will decrease; but the perimeter or edge of the first will never surpass the length of the circumference, and that of the second will never be smaller than that same circumference; the circumference of the circle is therefore the limit of the increase of the first polygon and the decrease of the second.

∞∞

Let's examine some examples.

Task 1 Draw a diagram for a circle of radius 1 and an inscribed regular polygon with $n = 8$ sides. Use some basic trigonometry to find the exact length of the polygon's perimeter. How close is it to the circle's circumference?

Task 2 Consider d'Alembert's "inscribed polygon $\to$ circle" limit example and his definition.

Assume for simplicity that the inscribed polygons are regular with n sides centered at the circle's center. These polygons have perimeter formula

$$perimeter = 2n \cdot radius \cdot \sin\left(\pi/n\right)$$

(a) For 'given quantity' 0.1 and a circle of radius 1, how many sides for the regular inscribed polygon are needed to guarantee the 'second may approach the first more closely than' given quantity 0.1? Technology will be helpful!

(b) How many sides are needed for a circle of radius 1 and 'given quantity' 0.01?

(c) *(Optional)* As a bonus, derive the given perimeter formula.

Note that d'Alembert's definition is lacking in precise, modern mathematical notation. Also observe that the polygon/circle example is for the limit of a *sequence*. Here is a standard first-year calculus book definition of limit for a sequence:

First-Year Calculus Definition. A sequence $\{a_n\}$ has the **limit** L and we write

$$\lim_{n \to \infty} a_n = L \quad \text{or} \quad a_n \to L \text{ as } n \to \infty$$

if we can make the terms a_n as close to L as we like by taking n sufficiently large.

Rewriting the example in Task 2 in modern limit notation, we thus have

$$\lim_{n\to\infty} 2n \cdot r \cdot \sin(\pi/n) = 2\pi \cdot r,$$

where r represents the radius of the circle. Today's notation for sequences also uses modern subscript notation. For instance, setting $p_n = 2n \cdot r \cdot \sin(\pi/n)$ gives us the sequence $\{p_n\}$. Since $\lim_{n\to\infty} p_n = 2\pi r$, we can also write $p_n \to 2\pi r$ as $n \to \infty$.

Task 3 Use calculus to verify that $p_n \to 2\pi r$ as $n \to \infty$, where $p_n = 2n \cdot r \cdot \sin(\pi/n)$.

Task 4 Consider the sequence $\{a_n\}$ with $a_n = \dfrac{n}{2n+1}$.

  (a) Find the limit of this sequence by any means.

  (b) For 'given quantity' 0.01, suppose we want a_n and its limit to 'differ by as little as' 0.01. What is "sufficiently large" for n to guarantee that a_n and its limit differ by 0.01 or less?

  (c) Repeat part (b) for 'given quantity' 0.001.

Later in his *Encyclopédie* article on limits [d'Alembert 1754b], d'Alembert wrote the following:

⬡⬡⬡

Strictly speaking, the *limit* never coincides, or is never equal to the quantity of which it is the *limit*; but the latter approaches it ever more closely, and may differ from it by as little as one wishes. The circle, for example, is the *limit* of the inscribed and circumscribed polygons; for strictly it never coincides with them, though they may approach it indefinitely.

⬡⬡⬡

Task 5 Look closely at d'Alembert's phrase 'Strictly speaking, the *limit* never coincides, or is never equal to the quantity of which it is the limit' and notice that it does not appear in the First-Year Calculus definition. Find a simple convergent sequence that violates this requirement of d'Alembert's limit definition.

Task 6 Consider d'Alembert's phrase 'without the magnitude approaching, being allowed ever to surpass the magnitude that it approaches' and notice that it does not appear in the First-Year Calculus definition. Find a simple convergent sequence that violates this requirement of d'Alembert's limit definition.

A.4.3   A More Precise Definition of Limit

As we have seen, d'Alembert's 1754 limit definition doesn't fully apply to some types of sequences studied by today's mathematicians. It is interesting to note that during d'Alembert's era there was some debate regarding whether or not a quantity could ever reach or surpass its limit.[34] Based on your work with d'Alembert's definition of limit, what do you think was d'Alembert's opinion on these questions?

During the 1800s mathematicians reached a consensus that limits could be attained, and a convergent sequence could indeed oscillate about its limit. We see the First-Year Calculus definition allows for these possibilities; however, it is too vague for actually constructing complex proofs. We can remedy this problem by clarifying the logic and converting some verbal descriptions into algebraic inequalities.

Task 7   Use inequalities and the quantifier expressions "for all" and "there exists" to help rewrite d'Alembert's limit definition for sequences in a less verbal form. The First-Year Calculus Definition and a graph of the sequence $\{a_n\}$ should be helpful in getting started. You should introduce a variable ϵ to represent the allowable difference or tolerance between a sequence term a_n and the limit itself, and another variable M to measure n being "sufficiently large." Be sure to include d'Alembert's requirements that sequence terms can neither surpass nor coincide with the limit in your answer.

Task 8   Now use inequalities and the quantifier expressions "for all" and "there exists" to rewrite the First-Year Calculus limit definition for sequences, without the extra requirements that d'Alembert imposed in his definition. Then comment on the differences between this definition and your definition from Task 7.

Task 9   Use your definition from Task 8 to prove that sequence $\left\{\dfrac{n}{2n+1}\right\}$ converges.

Task 10   Suppose that a sequence $\{c_n\}$ converges to limit 1. Use your definition from Task 8 to prove that there exists a natural number M for which $0.9 < c_n < 1.1$ whenever $n \geq M$.

A.4.4   Conclusion

Historians have noted that definitions of limit were given verbally by mathematicians of the 1600s and 1700s. However, to make these ideas useful in rigorous proofs, it is important to translate the verbal limit definition into one with clear logic and algebraic language, as you accomplished in Task 8. The mathematician Augustin-Louis Cauchy (1789–1867) is usually credited with being the first to do this, using ϵ and precise inequalities in some of his proofs. Even so, his definition of limit was verbal and similar to d'Alembert's, except that for Cauchy limits could be attained and surpassed, as in the modern definition. The modern limit definition we see today finally matured in the work of Karl Weierstrass (1789–1867) and his students.

How influential was d'Alembert's limit definition? This is hard to say, since d'Alembert only used his definition to carry out one proof. Certainly his advocacy for a precise limit definition may have influenced mathematicians such as Cauchy, and can thus be considered a worthy contribution to the evolution of the rigorous limit definition we use today.

---

[34]For more on these issues in the evolution of the limit concept, see J. Grabiner's fascinating book [Grabiner 2010].

References

Hankins, Thomas L. (1990). *Jean d'Alembert: Science and the Enlightenment*. New York: Gordon and Breach.

d'Alembert, Jean le Rond (1754a). "Calcul différentiel (Differential Calculus)". In: *Encyclopédie ou Dictionnaire raisonné des sciences, des arts et des métiers*. Vol. 9. English translation by G. Bringman (2003) in *The Encyclopedia of Diderot & d'Alembert Collaborative Translation Project*, Ann Arbor: Michigan Publishing, University of Michigan Library. `http://hdl.handle.net/2027/spo.did2222.0001.091`. Paris: Chez Braisson, David, Le Breton and Durand, pp. 985–988.

— (1754b). "Limite (Mathématiques) [Limit (Mathematics)]". In: *Encyclopédie ou Dictionnaire raisonné des sciences, des arts et des métiers*. Vol. 9. English translation by J. Stedall in [Stedall, 2008, pp. 297–298]. Paris: Chez Braisson, David, Le Breton and Durand, p. 542.

Grabiner, Judith (2010). "The Calculus as Algebra". In: *A Historian Looks Back*. Washington DC: Mathematical Assocation of America, pp. 1–124.

Acknowledgments

The author gratefully acknowledges this support, with special thanks to TRIUMPHS PI Janet Heine Barnett, who helped with suggestions for producing the Calculus 2 version of the original project.

A.5 The Radius of Curvature According to Christiaan Huygens

Jerry Lodder

Mathematical Sciences; Dept. 3MB, Box 30001;

New Mexico State University; Las Cruces, NM 88003;

`jlodder@nmsu.edu`

A.5.1 The Longitude Problem

An outstanding problem of navigation during the sixteenth, seventeenth and eighteenth centuries was determining longitude at sea. Countless lives were lost and ships were wrecked simply because the ship's captain did not know how far east or west the ship was with respect to an imaginary line (semi-circle) called the Prime Meridian, or with respect to any given meridian for that matter. This problem is chillingly described in *The Illustrated Longitude* [Sobel and Andrewes 1995], from which we relate one incident. In September, 1740, Captain George Anson (1697–1762) of the British Royal Navy set sail for the South Pacific aboard the *Centurion*, under orders to disrupt the Spanish trading monopoly in the Pacific. On March 7, 1741, the *Centurion* entered the Pacific Ocean from the Atlantic by passing through the Straits Le Maire at the southern end of South America. Then a violent storm blew in from the west, lasting some 58 days, unduly delaying the voyage and disorienting the *Centurion*. Many of the captain's men began to die of scurvy. Having rounded Cape Horn and now off the western coast of South America, the captain set sail for Juan Fernández Island for fresh food and water. Sailing north, Anson reached the proper latitude of the island (about 35°S) on May 24, 1741, but he could only guess whether the island lay east or west of his current position. The captain guessed west and sailed in that direction for four days only to find nothing. Changing course by 180°, he then sailed east for about two days only to sight the steep cliffs of Spanish controlled Chile. Anson turned around again, sailed west and reached Juan Fernández Island on June 9, 1741, with only about half of his men remaining [Sobel and Andrewes 1995, pp. 21–25]. What was the root cause of Captain Anson not being able to find the island? Anson knew his latitude, but he was unable to determine his longitude, namely how far east or west he was.

The determination of latitude can be reduced to a simple trigonometrical calculation given the length of a shadow of an object (of known height) at high noon, when the sun is at its highest elevation for the day.

Task 1 Suppose that on the day of Spring Equinox (or Autumn Equinox), a 1' pole casts a shadow of 0.4' at high noon. Determine the latitude of the observer at this location (in the Northern Hemisphere). Be sure to explain your answer. (For days other than an equinox, the tilt of the Earth could be looked up in a table and would be used to adjust the above calculation.)

Hint: Since the sun is at such a great distance from the Earth, the rays of sun light are essentially parallel to each other when they reach the Earth. At high noon during an equinox, these rays are directly over head at the Equator. See Figure A.1.

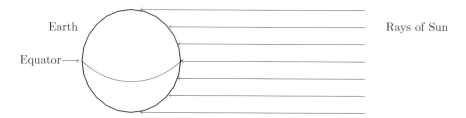

Figure A.1: High Noon During an Equinox.

Consider now the 1' pole perpendicular to the Earth, and imagine a line connecting the pole to the center of the Earth, O. The length of the pole is exaggerated in Figure A.2, where angle α denotes the latitude of the observer in the Northern Hemisphere. Now draw a separate right triangle with legs being the pole and its shadow, and the hypotenuse formed by a ray of sun light. Finish Exercise (A.5.1).

Figure A.2: Determining Latitude.

Could the determination of longitude be reduced to a simple calculation as in Exercise (A.5.1)? Certainly the sun (in its apparent motion) travels from east to west across the sky. Could the position of the sun be used to determine longitude? How? When the sun reaches its highest elevation on a given day, shadows are at their shortest, marking high noon. If a sailor knew when high noon occurred (or will occur) at the port of embarkment, then the difference between when noon occurs aboard ship and at the port of embarkment could be converted into a longitude reading, indicating how far west (or east) the ship is from its port.

Task 2 Suppose that a ship sets sail from England with a clock set to give time in Greenwich, England, through which the Prime Meridian passes. After sailing for several days on the open sea, suppose further that noon occurs on ship when the clock giving time in Greenwich reads 1:00 P.M.

(a) Is the ship sailing west or east of Greenwich? Justify your answer.

(b) How many degrees is the ship west of Greenwich? Explain your answer. Hint: There are 360° in a circle and the sun circles the Earth once every 24 hours (in its apparent motion).

The reader should now verify that one minute discrepancy between the time aboard ship and the time at the port of embarkment (or any given, fixed location) corresponds to $0.25°$ of longitude. Using $R = 3960$ miles as the radius of the Earth, then $0.25°$ of longitude at the Equator (a great circle on the Earth) corresponds to $(0.25)(\pi/180)R \approx 17$ miles, a non-trivial distance. However, a clock that is one minute off, even during a lengthy voyage, could result in a navigational error as large as 17 miles.

One solution to the longitude problem would be to construct a very accurate clock, set the clock to give time at Greenwich, England, and then send the clock to sea aboard ship. This project discusses Christiaan Huygens's (1629–1695) work on constructing a pendulum clock that theoretically keeps perfect time. Huygens described the path of the pendulum bob as one "whose curvature is marvelously and quite rationally suited to give the required equality to the pendulum" [Huygens 1986, p.11]. With these words, Huygens has identified a key concept, *curvature*, used to this day in physics and calculus to describe motion along a curved path. Alas, a pendulum clock behaved erratically on the high seas, and did not solve the longitude problem for naval navigation, although it remained the standard for terrestrial time keeping until the development of spring balance timepieces. So acute was the need to determine longitude that the British government had already issued the Longitude Act in 1714 that offered a first prize of £20,000 for a method to determine longitude to an accuracy of half a degree of a great circle [Sobel and Andrewes 1995, p.66]. There were also second and third prizes. Using the idea of a spring balance, John Harrison (1693–1776) perfected a sea clock that did solve the longitude problem. Due to prejudice against a clock method and in favor of a lunar method to solve the longitude problem, Harrison received marginal credit for his work during his lifetime, much of it spent perfecting his various timekeepers [Sobel and Andrewes 1995].

In the next section we turn to a detailed study of Huygens's work on the isochronous pendulum, a pendulum clock that theoretically keeps perfect time. To describe the path of a pendulum bob in terms of its curvature, Huygens first offers a geometric construction for what is known as the *radius of curvature* (see below). Since his work predates the development of calculus by Issac Newton (1642–1727) and Gottfried Wilhelm Leibniz (1646–1716), Huygens relies on known techniques from Euclidean geometry, such as similar triangles, to capture the ratios of certain side lengths that play the role of certain derivatives. The geometric idea of a tangent line had been known well before Huygens, which he uses adroitly. The goal of this project is to follow Huygens's clever geometric arguments and then, through guided exercises, rewrite the expression for the radius of curvature in terms of derivatives, and finally to reconcile this with the modern equation for curvature found in many calculus textbooks. For further details on the construction of an isochronous pendulum, see Huygens's *Horologium oscillatorium* (The Pendulum Clock) [Huygens 1967, pp. 86–365] originally published in 1673, translated into English [Huygens 1986], and presented as part of a book chapter on curvature [Knoebel et al. 2007, pp. 174–178].

A.5.2 Huygens and The Radius of Curvature

Holland during the seventeenth century was a center of culture, art, trade and religious tolerance, nurturing the likes of Harmenszoon van Rijn Rembrandt (1606–1669), Johannes Vermeer (1632–1675), Benedict de Spinoza (1632–1677) and René Descartes (1596–1650). Moreover, the country was the premier center of book publishing in Europe during this time with printing presses in Amsterdam, Rotterdam, Leiden, The Hague and Utrecht, all publishing in various languages, classical and contemporary [Hazard 1963, p. 88]. Into this environment was born Christiaan Huygens, son of a prominent statesman and diplomat.

The young Huygens showed an interest in astronomy, developed improved methods of grinding and polishing lenses for telescopes, and made notable discoveries about the rings of Saturn and the length of the Martian day [Simmons 1985, p. 801]. During a visit to Paris in 1655, the Dutchman began to study probability, and authored the book *De Ratiociniis in Aleae Ludo* (On the Calculations in Games of Chance), published in 1657 [Katz 1998, p. 456]. At the invitation of Jean-Baptiste Colbert (1619–1683), minister of King Louis XIV (1638–1715), Huygens moved to Paris in 1666 as a member of the newly established *Académie des Sciences*, where he resided for the next 15 years. Aside from his work on pendulum clocks, he formulated a principle for the conservation of energy for an elastic collision of two bodies, and correctly identified the centripetal force of an object moving in circular motion, closely related to the radius of curvature. Newton held the work of Huygens in high regard, and used the Dutch scholar's results in some of his own investigations [Simmons 1985, p. 802]. Unfortunately, growing religious intolerance for Protestants in Paris prompted Huygens to return to The Hague in 1681. Later in life, he launched a study of microscopy in loose connection with Anton van Leeuwenhoek (1632–1723), and developed highly original ideas in protozoology. In 1690 Huygens published his *Traité de la Lumière* (Treatise on Light), in which he proposed a wave theory of light. His final publication, *Cosmotheoros*, appeared posthumously, and contains a summary of what was known about the universe at the time. We turn now to the master's work on horology (the study of clocks and clock making).

In a burst of creativity during 1659 Christiaan Huygens developed a pendulum clock that theoretically keeps perfect time [Huygens 1986; Yoder 1988]. In the years prior to his landmark discovery, Huygens had studied the simple pendulum, which consisted of a bob attached by a thread to a fixed point. The bob then oscillated in a circular arc. As a timekeeper, the simple pendulum is not entirely accurate, since the time required to complete one oscillation depends on the amplitude of the swing. The greater the swing, the more time is needed for an oscillation. Huygens's genius was to discover a curve for which the time of an oscillation is independent of the swing amplitude, an idea which at first glance seems a virtual impossibility.

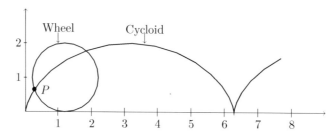

Figure A.3: A Cycloid.

Such a curve is described either as isochronous or as tautochronous, both terms referring to the "same-time" property at which the bob reaches its lowest point, regardless of the amplitude. Astonishingly Huygens showed that the shape of the isochrone is given by a curve that had been studied intensely and independently during the seventeenth century, namely a cycloid.

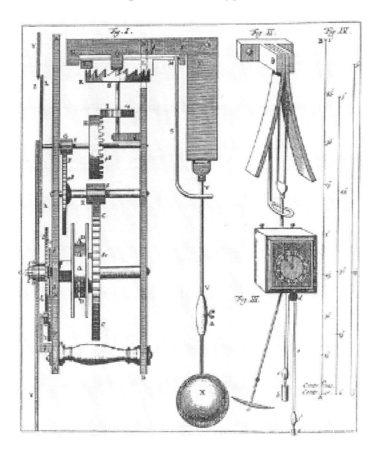

Figure A.4: Huygens's Pendulum.

Consider a point P on the circumference of a wheel and suppose that the wheel begins to roll along a flat surface. The curve traced by the point P is called a cycloid (Figure A.3). For use in the pendulum, this curve could simply be turned upside down (inverted), which would then serve as the path of the bob. The cycloid had already occupied the minds of influential scholars such as Galileo, Torricelli, Mersenne, Roberval, Fermat, Descartes, Pascal, and others [Boyer and Merzbach 1989], yet none of them discovered its isochronous property.

   Of course, once the shape of the isochrone had been determined, the problem of forcing a pendulum bob to oscillate along such a curve remained. This the Dutch scholar solved by placing two curved metal or wooden plates at the fulcrum of the pendulum (Figure A.4, II). As the bob swings upward, the thread winds along the plates, forcing the bob away from the path of a perfect circle, and as the bob swings downward, the thread unwinds. This leads then to another problem in what today would be called mathematical physics—what should be the shape of the metal plates? Huygens called the curve for the plates an evolute of the cycloid or

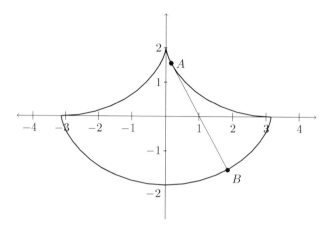

Figure A.5: The Isochronous Pendulum.

evolutus (unrolled) in the original Latin, and went on to discuss the mathematical theory of evolutes for general curves, not just cycloids. The key idea for the construction of the evolute is this. Suppose (Figure A.5) that the thread leaves the plate at point A, the bob is at B, and segment AB is taut. Although B is no longer traversing a circle, the bob is instantaneously being forced around a circle whose center is A and radius is AB. To find A and AB, simply determine the circle which best matches the (lower) cycloid at point B. The length of AB became known as the radius of curvature of the cycloid at point B, while A became known as the center of curvature. Surprisingly, the evolute of a cycloid is another congruent cycloid, shifted in position.

Huygens made ready avail of the geometric idea of a tangent line, which was part of the mathematical culture at the time. Specifically Huygens wishes to study the curvature of arc ABF (see Figure A.6) at the point B. To do so, he considers the circle, say C_1, that best matches the curve at the point B. Suppose this circle has center D and radius BD. Huygens then considers another point F very close to B. Let C_2 be the circle that best matches the curve at point F with its own radius of curvature given by FE. Extend lines BD and FE to meet at point G, assuming that arc ABF is concave down. Then BG plays the role of the radius of curvature at either points B or F, and as F approaches B, BG approaches the exact value of the radius of curvature at B (or F). Since the tangent to a circle is perpendicular to its radius, and the circle C_1 approximates the curve very well at the point B, the tangent to the curve, BH, is perpendicular to BG, ($BH \perp BG$), a fact that Huygens uses liberally.

Task 3 Given a circle of radius 1 and a circle of radius 10, which would you describe as more sharply curved? Today, a circle of radius r is said to have a value of curvature given by $k = 1/r$ at all of its points. What is the curvature of the circle C_1?

Huygens wishes to find an expression for BG, except he does so entirely in terms of geometric quantities. Let's read and verify a few of Huygens's original statements as translated from his 1673 treatise *Horologium oscillatorium* (The Pendulum Clock) [Huygens 1986; Huygens 1967].

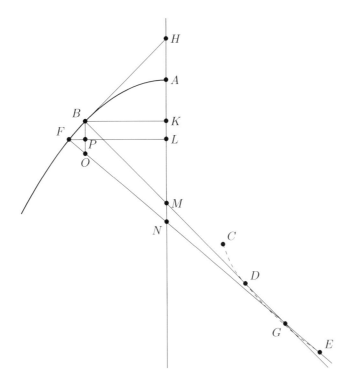

Figure A.6: The Radius of Curvature.

In proposition XI from this treatise Huygens demonstrates how an evolute of a given curve (curve ABF in Figure A.6) can be constructed from its radii of curvature.

∞∞∞

Huygens, from

The Pendulum Clock

PROPOSITION XI

Given a curved line, find another curve whose evolution describes it. ...

Let ABF (see Figure A.6) be any curved line, or part thereof, which is curved in one direction. And let KL be a straight line to which all points are referred. We are required to find another curve, for example DE, whose evolution will describe ABF. ...

Next select the points B and F, which are close to each other. ... BD and FE must intersect since they are perpendicular to the curve BF on its concave side. ...

Task 4 Why are BD and FE perpendicular to the curve BF?

And if the interval BF is taken to be infinitely small, these three points $[D, G, E]$ can be treated as one. As a result the line BH, after having been drawn, is tangent to the curve at B and also can be thought of as tangent at F. Let BO be parallel to KL, and let BK and FL be perpendiculars to KL. FL cuts the line BO at P, and let M and N be the points where the lines BD and FE meet KL. Since the ratio of BG to GM is the same as that of BO to MN, then when the latter is given, so is the former.

Task 5 Verify that $BG/GM = BO/MN$. Hint: Use similar triangles.

And when the line BM is given in length and in position, so is the point G on the extension of BM, and also D on the curve CDE, since we have taken G and D to be one. ...

Now since the ratio of BO to MN is composed of the ratio of BO to BP ... and the ratio of BP to MN ....

Task 6 Write an equation for the above statement about ratios. How is Huygens using the word "and" (translated from the Latin)? What would be the modern phrasing of the above statement? Be sure that you have the correct answer to this before proceeding.

... the ratio of BO to BP or of NH to LH ...

Task 7 Verify that $BO/BP = NH/LH$. Carefully justify your answer and identify all similar triangles used. Consider using two pairs of similar triangles for a total of four triangles.

... the ratio of BP or KL to MN ...

Task 8 Verify that $BP/MN = KL/MN$. Briefly justify your answer.

Task 9 Finally, verify that $BO/MN = (NH/LH)(KL/MN)$, and state why

$$\frac{BG}{GM} = \frac{HN}{HL} \frac{KL}{MN}.$$

Huygens ends his derivation of BG with what amounts to a verbal description of the above equality about ratios. In a specific example knowledge of the point M and the ratios HN/HL, KL/MN would determine the position of G and the distance BG, which is the radius of curvature.

A.5.3   The Modern Equation for Curvature

We wish to compare the modern equation for curvature with Huygens's expression of ratios. Since his work occurs just before the dawn of calculus, infinitesimals will be used in the sequel. Notice how the vertical line KL in Figure A.6 serves as a reference line for forming the ratios needed for BG. Today, such a vertical line would be called the y-axis. Treating this as the axis for the independent variable, we could write curve ABF as $x = f(y)$, i.e., x is a function of y. Suppose that $B(x_1, y_1)$ and $F(x_2, y_2)$ are two points on the graph of $f(y)$ which are infinitesimally close. With this interpretation, increasing values of y point downward and increasing values of x point to the left, so that point B is reached before point F, when traversing arc ABF, starting at A and moving toward F. Let

$$dy = y_2 - y_1, \quad dx = x_2 - x_1.$$

Then the derivative of $f(y)$ at (x_1, y_1) or at (x_2, y_2) (with respect to y) is given by $\frac{dx}{dy}$. Moreover, the length of the line segment joining (x_1, y_1) and (x_2, y_2) is

$$ds = \sqrt{(dx)^2 + (dy)^2},$$

and this segment may be considered tangent to $x = f(y)$ at either of the two points. Line FL can be considered as the x-axis and point L taken as the origin, although any horizontal line could be considered as the x-axis.

Task 10 From the equation

$$\frac{HN}{HL} = \frac{HN}{FH}\frac{FH}{HL},$$

conclude that

$$\frac{HN}{HL} = \left(\frac{ds}{dy}\right)^2$$

by arguing that

$$\frac{FH}{HL} = \frac{ds}{dy} \quad \text{and} \quad \frac{HN}{FH} = \frac{ds}{dy}.$$

Hint: Try similar triangles.

Task 11 Next show that

$$\frac{MN}{KL} = 1 + \left(\frac{LN - KM}{KL}\right).$$

Task 12 Use geometry to conclude that $LN = x_2 \frac{dx}{dy}$. Explain conceptually why

$$\frac{LN - KM}{KL} = \frac{d}{dy}\left(x\frac{dx}{dy}\right).$$

Hint: Interpret $LN - KM$ as the first difference of a certain function and interpret KL as a small change along the y-axis, i.e., dy. Here x denotes the first coordinate of a generic point (x, y) on the curve ABF, i.e., on the graph $x = f(y)$.

Task 13 Use the product rule to compute
$$\frac{d}{dy}\left(x\,\frac{dx}{dy}\right).$$

Task 14 Using the geometry of $\triangle BKM$ and $\triangle BPF$, show that $BM = x\frac{ds}{dy}$ and substitute this into the equation
$$MG = BG - BM\,.$$

Task 15 From Exercise (A.5.2) compute BG in terms of infinitesimals. Note that $\dfrac{d^2x}{dy^2}$ may be treated as $\dfrac{d(dx)}{(dy)(dy)}$, where $d(dx)$ is the second difference of the quantity x.

Task 16 Find an expression for $k = 1/BG$, the curvature of curve ABF at the point B in terms of infinitesimals, and compare this with the derivative equation for the curvature of a plane curve given in a calculus text. Why might you now wish to switch dx and dy? Does a minus sign occur in front of your equation for $1/BG$? Do you know why?

Task 17 Graph $y = 4 - x^2$ in the xy-plane (x is the independent variable, as usual). Using the derivative equation for curvature, compute the curvature of this function at the values:

(a) $x = -1$,

(b) $x = 0$,

(c) $x = 1$.

Extra Credit A. Build an actual isochronous pendulum with a bob attached to a thread that is constrained by a cycloid. The fulcrum of the pendulum should be at the cusp of the cycloid. One method to do this would be to print a graph of a cycloid on paper, transfer the paper to a cork board and use push pins to outline the cycloid. Another method would be to use a 3-D printer. Build a second (identical) isochronous pendulum. Release the two pendulum bobs at different points and see whether they reach the vertical position at the same time.

Extra Credit B. Report on the brachistochrone problem, to which the cycloid is also a solution. Given two points A and B in the xy-plane, not on the same vertical line (but A with a larger y-component than B) construct a physical brachistochrone from A to B along which a marble could be rolled. Physically demonstrate that a marble released from point A reaches B along the brachistochrone sooner than it would if rolled along a flat line segment from A to B.

References

Sobel, D. and J.H. Andrewes (1995). *The Illustrated Longitude: The True Story of a Lone Genius Who Solved the Greatest Scientific Problem of His Time.* New York: Walker and Company.

Huygens, C. (1986). *The Pendulum Clock or Geometrical Demonstrations Concerning the Motion of Pendula as Applied to Clocks.* Trans. by R.J. Blackwell. Ames Iowa: The Iowa State University Press.

— (1967). *Oeuvres complètes de Christiaan Huygens, tome 18.* Amsterdam: Société Hollandaise des Sciences.

Knoebel, A. et al. (2007). *Mathematical Masterpieces: Further Chronicles by the Explorers.* New York: Springer Verlag.

Hazard, P. (1963). *The European Mind, 1680–1715.* Trans. by J.L. May. Cleveland Ohio: World Publishing Co.

Simmons, G.F. (1985). *Calculus with Analytic Geometry.* New York: McGraw Hill, Inc.

Katz, V.J. (1998). *A History of Mathematics: An Introduction.* second. New York: Addison-Wesley.

Yoder, J.G. (1988). *Unrolling Time: Christiaan Huygens and the Mathematization of Nature.* Cambridge: Cambridge University Press.

Boyer, C.B. and U.C. Merzbach (1989). *A History of Mathematics, second edition.* New York: John Wiley & Sons.

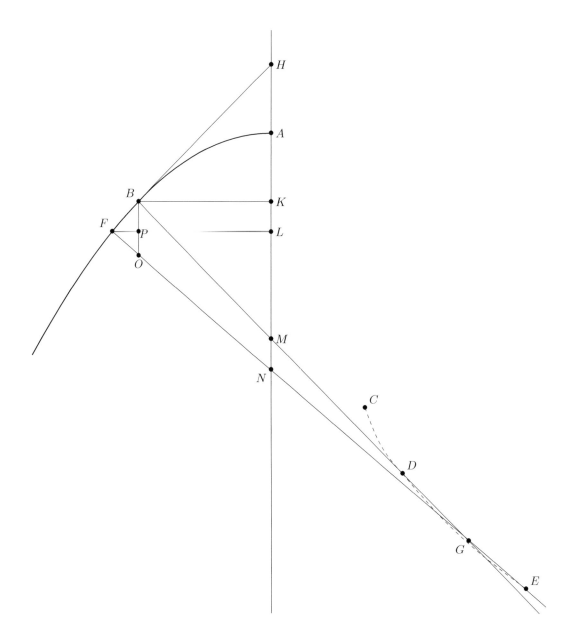

The Radius of Curvature.

A.6 How to Calculate π: Machin's Inverse Tangents

Dominic Klyve

Department of Mathematics

Central Washington University, Ellensburg, WA 98926

`dominic.klyve@cwu.edu`

A.6.1 Introduction

The[35] challenge of estimating the value of π is one which has engaged mathematicians for thousands of years. Calculating its value to more than a few digits, however, is a difficult challenge which can't be easily overcome simply by working harder on the problem. Instead, progress in digit calculation almost always requires a new idea. In this project, we shall explore an idea of John Machin (1686–1751), an eighteenth-century English astronomer.

While Machin's primary job was as a professor of astronomy, he was also interested in mathematics. His astronomical work, in fact, wasn't particularly successful – he was best known for an attempt to use Newton's law of gravity to precisely explain the motion of the moon. His attempt failed, though we should perhaps not be too harsh on him, as it would be twenty more years before anyone found a solution. Machin was more successful in other areas; he served as the secretary of England's Royal Society for 30 years, was one of the people asked to serve on a committee to investigate who should receive credit for developing calculus,[36] and once broke a world record.

It is the last of these that interests us in this project, as Machin became in 1706 the first person to compute π to 100 digits. Not only did he compute the most precise value then known, but the methods he used were the basis of several π calculation records set in the succeeding centuries. Interestingly, none of Machin's ideas required mathematics beyond a first-year Calculus class. In this project, you will work through his methods, and will have a chance to recreate some of his calculations yourself.

A.6.2 Part 1: It all started with arctangent

The first big idea that Machin needed was that the arctangent function (also called the inverse tangent function, and either denoted as arctan or $\tan^{-1}$) could be written as an infinite series. Today we learn this as one example of a "Taylor series", a subject that is usually taught in a second calculus class. In fact, the series predated calculus. Gottfried Leibniz (1646–1716) had discovered the series in 1673, and his formula was only one case of a more general formula discovered by Indian mathematicians several hundred years earlier Roy 1990. Following longstanding tradition, we will refer to the following as *Leibniz's formula*:

$$\arctan(x) = x - \frac{x^3}{3} + \frac{x^5}{5} - \frac{x^7}{7} + \frac{x^9}{9} - \frac{x^{11}}{11} \pm \cdots = \sum_{n=0}^{\infty} \frac{(-1)^n x^{2n+1}}{2n+1},$$

---

[35]The author is grateful to Frederick Rickey, whose article "Machin's Formula for Computing Pi" Rickey 2010 formed the basis for much of this project. Rickey's paper, "Machin's Formula for Computing Pi" has not been published, but can be found via a web search for its title, or by contacting this PSP's author directly.

[36]At the time, most English mathematicians thought that Isaac Newton should get credit for inventing/discovering calculus, while most mathematicians from continental Europe thought that credit should go to Gottfried Leibniz. Although this may seem unimportant now, it was a big enough deal at the time to merit an official committee investigation by the Royal Society of London.

where $|x| \leq 1$.

Leibniz wanted to consider how he could use this series to calculate π. The easiest method, of course, might be simply to find a value of x for which $\arctan(x) = \pi$.

Task 1
a. Explain why there is no value of x for which $\arctan(x) = \pi$.

b. Is there a value of x for which $\arctan(x) = \frac{\pi}{2}$? If yes, what is it? If not, why not?

c. Is there a value of x for which $\arctan(x) = \frac{\pi}{3}$? If yes, how could you use that value of x and the series above to estimate π?

If $\arctan(x)$ is a convenient fraction of π, then equivalently we could look for a convenient fraction of π the tangent of which is an easy-to-use value. The next task asks you to explore this possibility.

Task 2 Consider the values $\frac{\pi}{3}$, $\frac{\pi}{4}$, $\frac{\pi}{5}$, and $\frac{\pi}{6}$. Find the tangent of each. Which gives the value which is simplest and easiest to compute with?

You may have found, as Leibniz did, the rather lovely fact that $\tan(\frac{\pi}{4}) = 1$, and thus $\arctan(1) = \frac{\pi}{4}$.

Task 3 Substitute 1 for x in Leibniz's formula. Does it allow you to calculate the value of π? Why or why not?

Task 4 Using a calculator, compute the value of the sum after the first 10 terms. How closely does the value approximate $\pi/4$?

Task 5 If you can program a computer or calculator (or if you are feeling particularly patient), compute the value of the sum after the first 100 terms. How closely does the sum approximate $\pi/4$ now? What can you say about how useful Leibniz's formula is for calculating π?

Leibniz's series, using 1 for x, is a marvelous example of a formula that is beautiful but not useful. It looks quite elegant on the page even to someone not trained in mathematics:

$$\frac{\pi}{4} = 1 - \frac{1}{3} + \frac{1}{5} - \frac{1}{7} + \frac{1}{9} - \frac{1}{11} \pm \cdots,$$

and it represents the surprising fact the digits of π, which seem to be random in almost every sense, can be calculated by something that is not random at all. Although this could work in theory, it would take a heroic amount of calculation to use this equality to get an accurate value for π.

Leibniz himself would have known this, as did his contemporary Isaac Newton. In fact, in a letter Isaac Newton wrote to Leibniz about a similar series (this one to represent the value of $\frac{\pi}{2\sqrt{2}}$), he mentioned this fact:

⚬⚬

... to find the length of the quadrant[al arc of which the chord is unity] to twenty decimal places, it would require about 5 000 000 000 terms of the series, for the calculation of which 1000 years would be required.[37]

⚬⚬

(Note that the series Newton referred to here is $\frac{\pi}{2\sqrt{2}} = 1 + \frac{1}{3} - \frac{1}{5} + \frac{1}{7} - \frac{1}{9} + \frac{1}{11}$. Can you see the difference between this and the Leibniz series?)

Task 6 How reasonable is Newton's time estimate for how long this would take to calculate by hand? Let's explore it a bit:

    a. How many terms would you need to calculate each year to calculate 5 000 000 000 terms in 1000 years?

    b. Assuming you never take a vacation, how many terms is this each day?

    c. If we further assume that you work on this 12 hours each day, how many terms is this each hour? Each minute?

    d. Do you think 1000 years is reasonable estimate?

However long it would take to get a value of π accurate to 20 decimal places, it's clear that in the computer era, the formula of Leibniz was not the best way to go. Clearly a new idea would be needed. In the following, we will follow Machin's idea to begin with arctan(1) and look for ways to rewrite it to make it easier to compute.

A.6.3 Part 2: Addition and Subtraction formulas for tangent

In a previous class, you may have seen the addition and subtraction formulas for tangent. In case you don't remember them, these are:

$$\tan(\alpha + \beta) = \frac{\tan\alpha + \tan\beta}{1 - \tan\alpha\tan\beta}$$

and

$$\tan(\alpha - \beta) = \frac{\tan\alpha - \tan\beta}{1 + \tan\alpha\tan\beta}.$$

Task 7 Use one or both of these formulas to derive a *double-angle formula* for tangent. That is, find the value of $\tan(2\theta)$ in terms of $\tan\theta$.

Task 8 Now go one step farther, and derive a quadruple-angle formula for tangent. This time you will find the value of $\tan(4\theta)$ in terms of $\tan\theta$.

An English lawyer named Francis Maseres (who we will meet below) would call these formulas Lemma 1 and Lemma 2.

---

[37] Newton wrote this letter on 24 October 1676. This the first letter in the Newton-Leibniz correspondence, is known to historians as the *epistola posterior*. Text from *The Correspondence of Isaac Newton, vol. 2 (1960)*, edited by H. W. Turnbull, p. 138–139 Newton and Turnbull 1961. For more on this, see Nick Mackinnon's article Newton's Teaser." Mackinnon 1992

A.6.4 Part 3: Choosing a better angle

The inspired work of Machin takes the double-angle formula as the starting point for his calculation of π. The following text comes from *Scriptores logarithmici; or a Collection of Several Curious Tracts on the Nature and Construction of Logarithms ...* Maseres 1791, compiled by Francis Maseres[38] (1731–1824) over a sixteen-year period starting in 1791. Maseres' description seems to be the earliest surviving account of Machin's method, and we will explore it in the next section of this project.

Machin's first task was to find an angle with two important properties:

1. The tangent of the angle is a simple, easy-to-use small fraction; and

2. Using the double-angle formula, one can use this angle to find the tangent of an angle very close to π/4.

(As a bonus, it would be nice if plugging the fraction into Leibniz's series led to an easy-to-calculate value.)

Before we see what Machin chose, let's try to find such an angle ourselves.

Task 9 The most obvious starting point is to take half of the angle in which we are interested. Half of π/4 is, of course, π/8. Is the tangent of π/8 close to any simple fraction?

Task 10 Try finding (with a calculator) $\tan(\pi/16), \tan(\pi/32)$, and $\tan(\pi/64)$. Which of these (if any) are close to simple fractions?

Let's now see how Machin began:

∽⊗⊗⊗∽

As the famous quadrature of the late Mr. John Machin, Professor of Astronomy in Gresham College, is extremely expeditious, and but little known, I shall take this opportunity of explaining it as follows.

Since the chief advantage consists in taking small arcs whose tangents shall be numbers easy to manage, Mr. Machin very properly considered that, since the tangent of 45° is 1, and that, the tangent of any arc being given, the tangent of double that arc can easily be had; if there be assumed some small simple number as the tangent of an arc, and then the tangent of the double arc be continually taken, until a tangent be found nearly equal to 1, which is the tangent of 45°; by taking the tangent answering to the small difference of 45° and this multiple, there would be had two very small tangents, viz. the tangent first assumed, and the tangent of the difference between 45° and the multiple arc; and that, therefore, the lengths of the arcs corresponding to these two tangents being calculated, and the arc belonging to the tangent first assumed being so often doubled as the multiple directs, the result, increased or decreased by that other arc, according as the multiple should be below or above it, would be the arc of 45°.

---

[38]Maseres was a wealthy English lawyer and judge, and a Fellow of the Royal Society. He had a deep passion for mathematics and both wrote mathematical texts and used some of his fortune to help publish the mathematical works of others. It is also notable that he lived for more than 93 years.

Having thus thought of his method, by a few trials he was lucky enough to find a number (and perhaps the only one) proper for this purpose; viz. knowing that the tangent of 1/4 of 45° is nearly $= 1/5$, he assumed 1/5 as the tangent of an arc.

⊙⊙⊙

Task 11 In order to understand this, we will first make sure that we know how to find the tangent of an angle by looking at a unit circle diagram:

1. Draw a unit circle
2. Draw a line from the origin at 45° to the x-axis.
3. Add a line tangent to the circle at the point $(0, 1)$.
4. Find the length of that tangent line between the x-axis and the 45° line you drew.
5. Try the same steps, but with an arbitrary angle θ. What is the length of the tangent line to $(0, 1)$ and the line you drew at angle θ now?

Task 12 We should now be able to draw a diagram showing Machin's setup.

1. Draw a unit circle
2. Draw a line from the origin at 45° to the x-axis.
3. Add a line tangent to the circle at the point $(0, 1)$.
4. Draw a line from the origin at angle θ whose tangent is 1/5.
5. Draw similar lines for angles 2θ and 4θ. If your diagram is accurate, you should see that the lines for 4θ and 45° are quite close. How does this relate to Task 11?

Task 13 Explain why it was not just a matter of luck that Machin found this value.

Task 14 Do you think $\frac{1}{5}$ is indeed the only such tangent value that would work? Why or why not?

Task 15 Use your work in Task 12 to write an expression using arctangent to find an approximation to $\frac{\pi}{4}$.

Let us follow Machin's work further. Let θ be the inverse tangent of 1/5 (so $\theta = \tan^{-1}\frac{1}{5}$). Based on our picture, it seems our next task is to find the tangent of 4θ. We expect it will be close to 1; we now need to discover just how close.

Maseres continued his description of Machin's work as follows:

⊙⊙⊙

These things being premised, the method itself may be explained as follows.

3. Let AE be an arc whose tangent AB is 1/5 of the radius MA [see Figure 1 below]; and let AF be double, and AG quadruple, of AE, and AK an arc of 45°; and

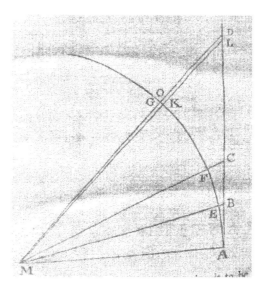

Figure A.7: Machin's setup to estimate $\tan^{-1}(1/5)$

let AC, AD, AL, be the tangents of the arcs AF, AG, and AK, respectively. Put $AM = 1$, $AB = b$, $AC = c$, and $AD = d$. Then by the first of the foregoing Lemmas, we shall have $c = \frac{2b}{1-bb} = \frac{\frac{2}{5}}{1-\frac{1}{25}} = \frac{\frac{2}{5}}{\frac{24}{25}} = \frac{2}{5} \times \frac{25}{24} = \frac{5}{12}$; and $d = \frac{2c}{1-cc} = \frac{\frac{10}{12}}{1-\frac{25}{144}} = \frac{\frac{10}{12}}{\frac{119}{144}} = \frac{10}{12} \times \frac{144}{119} = \frac{10 \times 12}{119} = \frac{120}{119}$.

Task 16 Redraw the picture, and label the lengths of all the line segments with the labels given by Maseres ($AB = b$, etc.).

Task 17 Recalling that $\theta = \tan^{-1}\left(\frac{1}{5}\right)$, use the double-angle formula for tangent you calculated above to calculate $\tan(2\theta)$. Does your answer match the one given by Maseres?

Task 18 Now use your quadruple-angle formula to calculate $\tan(4\theta)$. Does your answer match that of Maseres this time?

Task 19 We conjectured above that $\tan(4\theta)$ would be close to 1. Is it?

At this point, Machin was very close to deducing his famous formula that allowed him to calculate π. He simply needed to calculate the difference bewteen the angles $\frac{\pi}{4}$ and $4\arctan(\frac{1}{5})$.

⊂◯⊃◯⊂◯⊃◯⊂◯⊃◯⊂◯⊃◯⊂◯⊃◯⊂◯⊃◯⊂◯⊃◯⊂◯⊃◯⊂◯⊃◯⊂◯⊃◯⊂◯⊃◯⊂◯⊃◯⊂◯⊃◯⊂◯⊃◯⊂◯⊃◯⊂◯⊃◯⊂◯⊃◯

Therefore d or AD, is greater than 1, or AM, and consequently than AL; and consequently AG is greater than AK, or $45°$. Draw KO [tangent to GK at K], and tangent GK, the difference of the arcs AG, AK, (or rather, because it is so extremely small, conceive it to be drawn) and call it e; then (by Lemma 2) we shall have $e = \frac{d-1}{1+d} = \frac{\frac{120}{119}-1}{1+\frac{120}{119}} = \frac{\frac{1}{119}}{\frac{239}{119}} = \frac{1}{239}$. Find now the lengths of the arcs AE, and GK, from their tangents b and e, or $\frac{1}{5}$ and $\frac{1}{239}$, by the last of the foregoing lemmas; and from quadruple the former arc subtract the latter arc, and the remainder will be the length of an arc of $45°$, which multiplied by 4 gives the length of the circumference. [p. 290–291]

⊂◯⊃◯⊂◯⊃◯⊂◯⊃◯⊂◯⊃◯⊂◯⊃◯⊂◯⊃◯⊂◯⊃◯⊂◯⊃◯⊂◯⊃◯⊂◯⊃◯⊂◯⊃◯⊂◯⊃◯⊂◯⊃◯⊂◯⊃◯⊂◯⊃◯⊂◯⊃◯⊂◯⊃◯

Task 20 In the equation $e = \frac{d-1}{1+d}$, the values e, d, and 1 are each the tangent of something. Rewrite this equation using tangent(*some angle*) in place of each of them.

Task 21 Convert the last sentence of the text above to an equation for $\frac{\pi}{4}$ using arctangents. Then explain how your equation relates to the geometry in the picture.

Now that we've recovered Machin's formula, it's time to see whether it will allow us to efficiently calculate a value for π. Using the formula (hopefully you've just found this)

$$\frac{\pi}{4} = 4\arctan\left(\frac{1}{5}\right) - \arctan\left(\frac{1}{239}\right),$$

let's use the infinite series for arctangent again, and see whether we can get a better value than we did before.

Task 22 Use the first ten terms of the infinite series for arctangent to estimate $\arctan(\frac{1}{5})$.

   a. How large is the last term you found?

   b. Using a calculator, determine how closely the sum of the first ten terms approximates the true value.

Task 23 Use the first ten terms infinite series for arctangent to estimate $\arctan(\frac{1}{239})$.

   a. How large is the last term you found?

   b. Using a calculator, determine how closely the sum of the first ten terms approximates the true value.

Task 24 Combine the values you have found in your formula to estimate $\frac{\pi}{4}$, and therefore to estimate π. How accurate is your approximation? How does this compare to the first ten terms of the series you used in Task 4 with $\arctan(1)$?

Conclusion

In the end, John Machin used his formula, and a lot of hard work, to calculate π to 100 decimal places, a record for his time. More importantly, every more precise calculation of π over the next century was based on his methods (with some clever modifications from Leonhard Euler). It turns out that the tools of calculus can go a long way toward solving some of the longest-standing mathematics challenges of the world.

References

Rickey, V. Frederick (2010). "Machin's Formula for Computing Pi (unpublished)". In.

Roy, Ranjan (1990). "The discovery of the series formula for π by Leibniz, Gregory and Nilakantha". In: *Mathematics Magazine* 63.5, pp. 291–306.

Newton, Isaac and Herbert Westren Turnbull (1961). "The Correspondence of Isaac Newton". In.

Mackinnon, Nick (1992). "Newton's teaser". In: *The Mathematical Gazette* 76.475, pp. 2–27.

Maseres, Francis (1791). *Scriptores logarithmici; or a Collection of Several Curious Tracts on the Nature and Construction of Logarithms...* London.

A.7 The Derivatives of the Sine and Cosine Functions

Dominic Klyve
Department of Mathematics
Central Washington University
Ellensburg, WA 98926
dominic.klyve@cwu.edu

A.7.1 Introduction

All students of calculus learn the "definition of the derivative." It's possible you have even been asked to memorize it for a test or quiz. Most calculus books published today use the "limit" definition, which states that for a given function $f(x)$, the value of the derivative $f'(x)$ is equal to

$$\lim_{h \to 0} \frac{f(x+h) - f(x)}{h},$$

provided the limit exists.

With this definition, it's not too hard to calculate some simple derivatives, such as the derivative of $f(x) = x^2$. For other functions this is quite a bit harder. For example, the calculation of the derivative of $f(x) = \sin(x)$ is quite complicated, and involves knowing the value of other limits.

However, the limit definition is not the only way derivatives have been described or defined historically. In fact, this definition didn't appear in the mathematical literature until the 1800's – more than 150 years after the discovery of calculus. Before the limit definition became standard, several others were used. There are good reasons that these have been dropped from common use (later mathematicians came to view them as less rigorous, and were concerned about potential errors), but in some cases other definitions can make understanding derivatives quite a bit easier.

This project concerns one of these other definitions, and uses it to calculate the derivative of some trigonometric functions in a way which you may find quite a bit more straightforward than what appears in your calculus book. All of the text below comes from Leonhard Euler's *Institutiones Calculi Differentialis* (Foundations of Differential Calculus) Euler 1755. Written almost 100 years after calculus was invented by Isaac Newton and Gottfried Leibniz, the book represents Euler's attempt to take all of the ideas from differential calculus which had been developed up to that time (including multivariable calculus and differential equations) and put them together in one self-contained book.

In the preface to his book, Euler started by explaining what functions are. This may seem odd, but the idea of a function was quite new at the time – we can think of functions as high-tech tools which were developed to make calculus easier. In fact, some historians give Euler credit for inventing the function Edwards 2007. In part 1, you will read Euler's explanation and answer some questions. In part 2 (to be done in class the next day), you will dive into more details of Euler's work.

A.7.2 Part 1: Introducing the derivative

Let's start by reading some of Euler's writing:

∞∞

Those quantities that depend on others in this way, namely, those that undergo a change when others change, are called *functions* of these quantities. This definition applies rather widely and includes all ways in which one quantity can be determined by others. Hence, if x designates the variable quantity, all other quantities that in any way depend on x or are determined by it are called its functions. Examples are x^2, the square of x, or any other powers of x, and indeed, even quantities that are composed with these powers in any way, even transcendentals, in general, whatever depends on x in such a way that when x increases or decreases, the function changes.

∞∞

Task 1   (a) Locate the definition of a function in your calculus book. How is Euler's explanation similar to (or different than) yours?

(b) What do you think Euler meant by "transcendentals"? Give a few examples of functions that we would consider to be transcendental functions today.

As soon as he explained functions, Euler immediately moved on to the core idea of his entire book – an understanding of derivatives. Read through what he wrote about this in the following excerpt, and then answer Task 2. Following that task, we will consider this excerpt one paragraph at a time in order to examine it in more detail.

∞∞

From this fact there arises a question; namely, if the quantity x is increased or decreased, by how much is the function changed, whether it increases or decreases? For the more simple cases, this question is easily answered. If the quantity x is increased by the quantity ω, its square x^2 receives an increase of $2x\omega + \omega^2$.

Hence, the increase in x is to the increase of x^2 as ω is to $2x\omega + \omega^2$, that is, as 1 is to $2x + \omega$. In a similar way, we consider the ratio of the increase of x to the increase or decrease that any function of x receives.

Indeed, the investigation of this kind of ratio of increments is not only very important, but it is in fact the foundation of the whole of analysis of the infinite. In order that this may become even clearer, let us take up again the example of the square x^2 with its increment of $2x\omega + \omega^2$, which it receives when x itself is increased by ω. We have seen that the ratio here is $2x + \omega$ to 1. From this it should be perfectly clear that the smaller the increment is taken to be, the closer this ratio comes to the ratio of $2x$ to 1.

However, it does not arrive at this ratio before the increment itself, ω, completely vanishes. From this we understand that if the increment of the variable x goes to zero, then the increment of x^2 also vanishes. However, the ratio holds as $2x$ to 1. What we have said here about the square is to be understood of all other functions of x; that is, when their increments vanish as the increment of x vanishes, they have a certain and determinable ratio. In this way, we are led to a definition of differential calculus: It is *a method for determining the ratio of the vanishing increments that any functions take on when the variable, of which they are functions, is given a vanishing increment.*

∞∞

Task 2 (a) What do you think Euler's goal was in this excerpt?

(b) Write at least one comment and one question that you have about what Euler was doing here.

A.7.3 Part 2: Exploring the derivative

Let's go back and look more closely at Euler's work.

> From this fact there arises a question; namely, if the quantity x is increased or decreased, by how much is the function changed, whether it increases or decreases? For the more simple cases, this question is easily answered. If the quantity x is increased by the quantity ω, its square x^2 receives an increase of $2x\omega + \omega^2$.

Euler here meant that given a function (we would write it as $f(x) = x^2$), changing the argument from x to $x + \omega$ increases the value of the function by $2x\omega + \omega^2$.

Task 3 Try this for yourself. Given $f(x) = x^2$, calculate the difference between $f(x + \omega)$ and $f(x)$.

However, Euler was quick to point out that he was not primarily interested in the amount that $f(x)$ changes, but in the ratio of the change in $f(x)$ to the change in x:

> Hence, the increase in x is to the increase of x^2 as ω is to $2x\omega + \omega^2$, that is, as 1 is to $2x + \omega$. In a similar way, we consider the ratio of the increase of x to the increase or decrease that any function of x receives.

Task 4 Compare Euler's claim about ratios to the definition of the derivative given at the beginning of this project. How are they similar? How are they different?

Euler only needed to introduce one more important idea, namely that he will often think of ω as a very (very!) small value, and will still be interested in the ratio he described above.

> Indeed, the investigation of this kind of ratio of increments is not only very important, but it is in fact the foundation of the whole of analysis of the infinite. In order that this may become even clearer, let us take up again the example of the square x^2 with its increment of $2x\omega + \omega^2$, which it receives when x itself is increased by ω. We have seen that the ratio here is $2x + \omega$ to 1. From this it should be perfectly clear that the smaller the increment is taken to be, the closer this ratio comes to the ratio of $2x$ to 1.

(a) Look at your calculations in Task 3. Is it true that the ratio of $f(x+\omega) - f(x)$ to ω gets closer to $2x$ when ω gets smaller?

(b) Again, how does this idea compare with the definition of the derivative at the beginning of this project?

Historically, there had been a lot of arguments about what it means to have a number (like ω) be almost equal to 0, but not be 0. Euler was very familiar with these arguments, and he was eager to convince the reader that there were no philosophical problems with his method for differential calculus. He concluded his argument, and explained the nature of calculus itself, in the next section.

However, it does not arrive at this ratio before the increment itself, ω, completely vanishes. From this we understand that if the increment of the variable x goes to zero, then the increment of x^2 also vanishes. However, the ratio holds as $2x$ to 1. What we have said here about the square is to be understood of all other functions of x; that is, when their increments vanish as the increment of x vanishes, they have a certain and determinable ratio. In this way, we are led to a definition of differential calculus: It is *a method for determining the ratio of the vanishing increments that any functions take on when the variable, of which they are functions, is given a vanishing increment.*

Task 6 (a) What do you think of Euler's claim that "...if the increment of the variable x goes to zero, then the increment of x^2 also vanishes. However, the ratio holds as $2x$ to 1."? Are you convinced?

(b) How does this claim compare with the limit definition of the derivative?

(c) Which of these methods of finding the derivative of x^2 do you prefer, and why?

Although Euler initially used the symbol ω to represent an increment, he soon changed notation – since the increment he was considering represented a very small change in x, he would call it dx for the remainder of his book (the "d", for him, suggested "difference").

A.7.4   Part 3: Trigonometric functions

Euler used some parts of his *Foundations of Differential Calculus* to give an explanation for why calculus works, and devoted much of the rest to solving lots of derivative problems. By the 201st paragraph (all paragraphs are numbered), Euler was ready to tackle $\sin(x)$. Read through this paragraph at least once in its entirety to get an overall view of how he did this. In the tasks that follow this excerpt, we will break his argument down piece by piece in order to examine it in detail.

∞∞∞

201. There remain some quantities ... namely the sines and tangents of given arcs, and we ought to show how these are differentiated. Let x be a circular arc and let $\sin x$ denote its sine, whose differential we are to investigate. We let $y = \sin x$ and replace x by $x + dx$ so that y becomes $y + dy$. Then $y + dy = \sin(x + dx)$ and

$$dy = \sin(x + dx) - \sin x.$$

But
$$\sin(x + dx) = \sin x \cdot \cos dx + \cos x \cdot \sin dx,$$

and since, as we have shown in the *Introductio*,

$$\sin x = \frac{x}{1} - \frac{x^3}{1 \cdot 2 \cdot 3} + \frac{x^5}{1 \cdot 2 \cdot 3 \cdot 4 \cdot 5} - \cdots,$$

$$\cos x = 1 - \frac{x^2}{1 \cdot 2} + \frac{x^4}{1 \cdot 2 \cdot 3 \cdot 4} - \cdots,$$

when we exclude the vanishing terms, we have $\cos dx = 1$ and $\sin dx = dx$, so that

$$\sin(x + dx) = \sin x + dx \cos x.$$

Hence, when we let $y = \sin x$, we have

$$dy = dx \cos x.$$

Therefore, the differential of the sine of any arc is equal to the product of the differential of the arc and the cosine of the arc.

∞∞∞

Task 7   (a) What do you think Euler's goal was in this excerpt?

      (b) Write at least one comment and one question that you have about what Euler was doing here.

There was a lot to understand in the passage above. Let's break it down to look at it more closely.

∞∞∞

201. There remain some quantities ... namely the sines and tangents of given arcs, and we ought to show how these are differentiated. Let x be a circular arc and let $\sin x$ denote its sine, whose differential we are to investigate. We let $y = \sin x$ and replace x by $x + dx$ so that y becomes $y + dy$. Then $y + dy = \sin(x + dx)$ and

$$dy = \sin(x + dx) - \sin x.$$

∞∞∞

Task 8   Note here that Euler is thinking of dy as the amount that the sine function changes between x and $x + dx$. Sketch and label a graph in a way that demonstrates his claim that $dy = \sin(x + dx) - \sin x$.

In the next part of his work, Euler needed two new ideas. One, the addition formula for $\sin(x)$, you probably learned in precalculus. It says that

$$\sin(a + b) = \sin(a) \cdot \cos(b) + \cos(a) \cdot \sin(b).$$

Task 9 Let's make sure we believe this addition formula.

(a) Let $a = \pi/6$ and $b = \pi/3$, and check to see whether the equation above holds. (You should be able to do this without a calculator.)

(b) Test this again with $a = \pi/6$ and $b = \pi/6000$ (or some other very small angle). What do you notice about the two terms on the right side of the equation for the addition formula?

The second idea that Euler needed in order to find the derivative of sine involves representing transcendental functions (like sine) as the sum of infinitely many powers of x. To Euler, this was also part of precalculus, and he included details in his precalculus book called the *Introductio in Analysin Infinitorum* (or *Introduction to the Analysis of the Infinite* for short), but these days we usually teach this idea (called "Taylor Series") in our calculus classes. Look ahead in your book's Table of Contents, and you may find that you will study Taylor Series in a few weeks.

Happily, we don't need to know much about these fascinating function representations to follow what Euler did next. All we need to know is that $x - \frac{x^3}{6} + \frac{x^5}{120}$ is really close to $\sin x$ — especially for small values of x! Similarly, $\cos x$ is very close to the value of $1 - \frac{x^2}{2} + \frac{x^4}{24}$.

Task 10 (a) Try this for yourself. Pick a smallish value of x (anything less than 0.25 in absolute value, say), and use your calculator to find $\sin x$ and $x - \frac{x^3}{6} + \frac{x^5}{120}$. How close are the two values? Try the same thing for the approximation to $\cos x$ given above.

(b) If you have a graphing calculator, try graphing both $\sin x$ and $x - \frac{x^3}{6} + \frac{x^5}{120}$. Do they seem to be equal near 0? Where do they seem to start to diverge?

We are now ready to read Euler's calculation of the derivative of $\sin x$.

⚬⚬⚬

But

$$\sin(x + dx) = \sin x \cdot \cos dx + \cos x \cdot \sin dx,$$

and since, as we have shown in the *Introductio*,

$$\sin x = \frac{x}{1} - \frac{x^3}{1 \cdot 2 \cdot 3} + \frac{x^5}{1 \cdot 2 \cdot 3 \cdot 4 \cdot 5} - \cdots,$$

$$\cos x = 1 - \frac{x^2}{1 \cdot 2} + \frac{x^4}{1 \cdot 2 \cdot 3 \cdot 4} - \cdots,$$

when we exclude the vanishing terms, we have $\cos dx = 1$ and $\sin dx = dx$, so that

$$\sin(x + dx) = \sin x + dx \cos x.$$

Hence, when we let $y = \sin x$, we have

$$dy = dx \cos x.$$

Therefore, the differential of the sine of any arc is equal to the product of the differential of the arc and the cosine of the arc.

Task 11   (a) What did Euler mean by the "vanishing terms"? (Consider what happens to the representations of $\sin x$ and $\cos x$ when x is very close to 0.)

       (b) Check Euler's algebra to see if you agree with his conclusions.

Euler next calculated the derivative of $\cos x$ in a similar way. You may recall (do you?) the addition formula for cosine, namely that $\cos(a + b) = \cos(a) \cdot \cos(b) - \sin(a) \cdot \sin(b)$.

Task 12   Use this law and the method Euler followed for sine to work out the derivative of $\cos(x)$. Does this match what is given in your book?

References

Euler, Leonhard (1755). *Institutiones calculi differentialis.* Teubner.

Edwards, Harold (2007). "Euler's definition of the derivative". In: *Bulletin of the American Mathematical Society* 44.4, pp. 575–580.

Appendix B

TRIUMPHS: Notes to the Instructor

B.1   Fermat's Method for Finding Maxima and Minima

PSP Content: Topics and Goals

This Primary Source Project (PSP) is intended to enrich an introductory Calculus student's grasp on the definition of the derivative and how it relates to finding maxima and minima of functions. The key competencies that come up in this project are as follows:

- Definition of the derivative

- Rules for calculating derivatives

- Tangents

- Optimization

Student Prerequisites

In this project, we assume the student has already been exposed to the limit definition of the derivative as well as the usual rules for calculating derivatives (in particular, chain rule and power rule). We also assume the student has been exposed to the Extreme Value Theorem.

PSP Design, and Task Commentary

This PSP will expose the student to the original, more algebraic framework for finding extrema of functions. Hopefully, seeing some of the standard textbook exercises on maxima and minima (like Fermat's example in Section A.1.1.1) approached with a different method and with different notation will break students out of recipe-thinking with regards to optimization.

Fermat provided many more examples of his method of adequality throughout his life, but many of these use rather sophisticated constructions from geometry. While beautiful in and of themselves, the author feared that these would be too much of a departure from the standard calculus curriculum. The three examples chosen for this PSP were purposefully selected because of their similarity to the types of textbook optimization problems that are typically assigned in a first-semester calculus course.

Section A.1.1.3 is the one section where Fermat's original solution via adequality is intentionally not shown. The hope is that by that point, the student can not only confirm Fermat's results using the modern method, but can carry out Fermat's method as well!

Note that the final task does not ask for a rigorous proof of the equivalence of the modern method to Fermat's method, but rather an intuitive justification. See the section below on Recommendations for Further Reading for what such a proof would entail!

Suggestions for Classroom Implementation

The author strongly suggests the instructor work through the entire project before using it in class. In particular, it is easy to make a simple error in the mess of Section A.1.1.3.

The reading and tasks of Section A.1.0.1 make an ideal class preparation assignment, while completion of the remainder of the PSP might be more well-suited for a mix of in-class work and homework.

If the instructor desires an interesting wrap-up discussion for this project, a peculiar phrase in the first primary source passage provokes an interesting question. While laying out his method, Fermat said "We will divide all the terms by e, **or by a higher power of** e, **such that on at least one of the sides**, e **will disappear entirely.**" This prompts a question: can it ever happen that we divide by a higher power of e rather than just e itself? Fermat's three examples included here only required division by a single power of e, and even after further reading of Fermat's work, the author was unable to find an example where Fermat divided by any higher power of e.

The absence of such an example in Fermat's work is perhaps with good reason! Under mild assumptions (like the function in question having a convergent power series on an interval containing the max/min one seeks) one can show that only a constant function $f(a)$ could result in the quantity $f(a + e) - f(a)$ being divisible by e^2. For if it were possible to write $f(a + e) - f(a) = e^2 \cdot g(a, e)$ for some polynomial $g(a, e)$ (possibly of infinite degree), then dividing both sides by e would produce

$$\frac{f(a + e) - f(a)}{e} = e \cdot g(a, e).$$

Taking the limit of both sides as e approaches zero implies

$$f'(a) = 0$$

since $\lim_{e \to 0} g(a, e)$ converges to $g(a, 0)$. Since the derivative of f is identically zero, f must be a constant function.

That analysis raises a further interesting question: why did Fermat include that phrase regarding dividing by a higher power of e? Was Fermat simply unsure that it couldn't happen, and mentioned it in passing just in case it ever did? This seems plausible. Though our proof above is not particularly difficult, it uses a heavy tool from a toolbox that was unavailable to Fermat, namely the idea of a power series expansion of a function.

Though it is unlikely we will be able to definitively resolve the question of what Fermat's intents were with that phrase, having a discussion like the one above could be a nice way to wrap up the project with a class. If nothing else, it can show the students the fascinating thought exercises prompted by looking at primary sources! It is hard to imagine such a question coming up in the context of reading a polished modern textbook.

Copies of these PSPs are available at the TRIUMPHS website (see URL in Acknowledgements). The author is happy to provide LaTeX code for this project. It was created using Overleaf which makes it convenient to copy and share projects and can allow instructors to adapt this project in whole or in part as they like for their course.

Sample Implementation Schedule (based on a 50 minute class period)

This miniPSP can easily be implemented in one class period. The author has used this in the following manner, with good results:

- Assign students to read and complete tasks through the end of Section A.1.0.1 as a class preparation assignment.

- Begin class with 10 minutes to have students share a few of the observations they came up with when comparing/contrasting the methods. and hold a discussion based on those questions, ideally with the primary source on the projector in front of you.

- Allow them to work through the PSP for the next 35 minutes in small groups as you and/or learning assistants walk through the classroom and help.

- In the last 5 minutes, it is sometimes nice to call the students together to regroup for a brief discussion. See if anyone has thoughts on why Fermat's method and the modern method are equivalent! It may be helpful to call their attention to the idea that $f(x+\Delta x)$ and $f(x)$ are very close to being equal for very small Δx if $f(x)$ has a maximum or minimum at x (and perhaps draw a picture to this effect on the board). It can also be a nice followup to mention that the method does not seem to have a way to distinguish saddle points!

- The students can complete all remaining unfinished tasks for homework. Note that it is likely they will still have most of Sections A.1.1.2 and A.1.1.3 to complete, but this should be doable for homework if they successfully made it through Section A.1.1.1.

B.2 Fourier's Proof of the Irrationality of e

PSP Content: Topics and Goals

This Primary Source Project (PSP) is intended to show students how the methods of series and their analysis are not only useful for Computation, but also for proving theoretical results. The key competencies that come up in this project are as follows:

- Power series for e^x

- Infinite geometric series formula

- Comparison test arguments

Student Prerequisites

In this project, we assume the student has already seen the standard treatments of the three topics listed above.

PSP Design, and Task Commentary

This PSP will expose the student to arguments that extensively use the power series for e^x and geometric series, but in the context of proofs of the irrationality of certain numbers. This serves as a fabulous warm-up for a student who later takes an introduction to proof course; all arguments in this PSP use proof by contradiction.

Suggestions for Classroom Implementation

Instructors are strongly encouraged to work the entire PSP before using it in class: although only simple techniques are employed, the proofs are a bit subtle!

If one wishes to shorten the PSP, one could delete Section A.2.5 entirely (though it is very fun). Finishing with Section A.2.4 still tells a perfectly complete story in and of itself! Section A.2.5 is also a bit more challenging; one reasonable implementation would be to require the completion of the PSP through Section A.2.4 for the whole class, but then use Section A.2.5 as an option for extra credit.

Copies of these PSPs are available at the TRIUMPHS website (see URL in Acknowledgements). The author is happy to provide LaTeX code for this project. It was created using Overleaf which makes it convenient to copy and share projects and can allow instructors to adapt this project in whole or in part as they like for their course.

Sample Implementation Schedule (based on a 50-minute class period)

The author recommends two full 50-minute class periods for implementation of this PSP.

- The readings and tasks of the PSP up to and including Section A.2.3 can be assigned as preparation for class.

- Start class with 20 minutes of followup discussion on the first two sections. In particular, make sure the students are clear on all vocabulary involved.

- The next 30 minutes could consist of students working in small groups, working to understand the argument in Section 4.

- During the first 20 minutes of the following class, the instructor could have students present solutions to the Section 4 argument and make sure everyone really understands it.

- The remainder of the second class can be devoted to Section 5, with its completion assigned for homework.

Connections to other Primary Source Projects

The following additional projects based on primary sources are also freely available for use in teaching standard topics in the calculus sequence. The PSP author name of each is given (together with the general content focus, if this is not explicitly given in the project title). With the exception of the final project in the list (which requires up to 2 full weeks for implementation), each of these is a mini-PSP that can be completed in 1–2 class days. Classroom-ready versions of these projects can be downloaded from `https://digitalcommons.ursinus.edu/triumphs_calculus`.

- The Derivatives of the Sine and Cosine Functions, Dominic Klyve

- Fermat's Method for Finding Maxima and Minima, Kenneth M Monks

- Beyond Riemann Sums: Fermat's Method of Integration, Dominic Klyve

- How to Calculate π: Buffon's Needle (calculus version), Dominic Klyve (integration by parts)

- Gaussian Guesswork: Elliptic Integrals and Integration by Substitution, Janet Barnett

- Gaussian Guesswork: Polar Coordinates, Arc Length and the Lemniscate Curve, Janet Barnett

- Gaussian Guesswork: Infinite Sequences and the Arithmetic-Geometric Mean, Janet Barnett

- Investigations Into d'Alembert's Definition of Limit (calculus version), Dave Ruch (sequence convergence)

- How to Calculate π: Machin's Inverse Tangents, Dominic Klyve (infinite series)

- Euler's Calculation of the Sum of the Reciprocals of Squares, Kenneth M Monks (infinite series)

- The Radius of Curvature According to Christiaan Huygens, Jerry Lodder

Another PSP that connects very nicely to this one is *Euler's Rediscovery of e* by David Ruch [Ruch 2017], which shows the origin of the infinite series for e that Fourier's proof depends on. Although that PSP is intended for use in an introductory course in analysis, it is quite appropriate for a second-semester calculus classroom if one simply stops at Task 5.

Recommendations for Further Reading

Charles Hermite's paper [Hermite 1873], in which e is proven to be transcendental, would be a fabulous (though challenging) follow-up for the advanced student.

B.3   L'Hôpital's Rule

PSP Content: Topics and Goals

This project is designed to present L'Hôpital's Rule to first semester calculus students as something more than just a computational trick, or the topic that comes up in the next section of the textbook. Students will learn the story of the development of this standard tool from the calculus toolkit, while at the same time gaining a deeper appreciation of the fundamental idea that the derivative can be understood as a ratio of infinitesimally small differentials. They should leave this experience understanding L'Hôpital's Rule, and a few of its main variants as well.

The project may also be used as an enrichment experience for students in a history of mathematics course who have already taken a calculus course.

Student Prerequisites

Students should have learned what a derivative is, and become familiar with the standard differentiation rules, including the rule for differentiating exponential functions (like $y = 2^x$, which appears in Task 3). It would be helpful to have been introduced to the definition of continuity at a point as well.

PSP Design, and Task Commentary

The project is laid out in four sections. In the first, we introduce the student to limits of indeterminate type $\frac{0}{0}$ in the form of rational functions with a linear polynomial denominator that divides into the numerator polynomial, producing a function that appears to be well behaved at the zero of the denominator except that it is undefined there. The student is led through Tasks 1 and 2 to discover the source of the misbehavior. In Task 3, the student is presented with a function that is not rational, but still offers a limit of indeterminate type $\frac{0}{0}$ to illustrate that the algebraic approach possible in the case of rational functions will not resolve the problem of evaluating the limit here. Instead, we guide the student to approximate the limit instead.

In section 2, the student learns the story of the Marquis de L'Hôpital and his association with Johann Bernoulli that led to the writing of L'Hôpital's *Analyse* [L'Hôpital 1715]. Excerpts from the first two chapters of the *Analyse* lay out the differential calculus as understood by them and by Leibniz, its first proponent and Bernoulli's mentor. The student is challenged in Task 5(a), and again in Task 6(d), to make sense of their powerful but ill-defined notion of "infinitely small" that rested at the foundation of their theory of differentials. Still, these ideas work, and in Tasks 7-10, the student will recognize how differentials lead to the same answers that derivatives (with which they are already somewhat familiar) can produce.

In section 3, L'Hôpital (and Bernoulli) present the eponymous Rule. Task 13 is of importance, to assist the student to make sense of what the Rule says and how one might interpret it in more modern language. Task 15 is the first example of putting L'Hôpital's Rule to work, and it is with the functions that student encountered in Tasks 1-3. Tasks 16 and 17 guide the student through the two examples that L'Hôpital presented 300 years ago.

Suggestions for Classroom Implementation

It would be ideal for calculus students to encounter this project in lieu of the textbook presentation (or instructor's lecture) on L'Hôpital's Rule. Students doing the project well after they have learned calculus needn't be concerned about such timing. Of course, there is also a world of difference between implementing the project with first year college students versus third- or fourth-year students; the former will require much more coaching to do advance preparation and will need more attention with regard to communicating their ideas, both orally and in written work. So plan for additional time when using the PSP with a less experienced crowd.

LATEX code of this entire PSP is available from the author by request to facilitate preparation of advanced preparation / reading guides or 'in-class worksheets' based on tasks included in the project. The PSP itself can also be modified by instructors as desired to better suit the goals they have for the course they are teaching.

Sample Implementation Schedule (based on a 50 minute class period)

This suggestion implementation schedule is meant to accommodate two ambitious 50-minute periods (or two more relaxed 75-minute periods). Regardless of the duration of the classroom periods, instructors are advised to impress upon their students the importance of advance reading and problem-solving homework as preparation for the classroom experience when implementing this PSP. Unprepared students will retard the experience for others, costing valuable class time.

The actual number of class periods spent on the project naturally depends on the instructor's goals and on how the PSP is actually implemented with students. Higher estimates on the number of days for implementation assume that most work is completed by students working in small groups during class time.

Day One (preparation, class period, and homework). One week before the first day of implementation, the instructor should assign reading the PSP from the opening page through the first excerpt from Chapter 1 of L'Hôpital's *Analyse* (p. 539). In addition, students should be challenged to write up complete solutions to Tasks 1-4 in preparation for the first period. (This will include obtaining printouts of graphs from Tasks 1-3.) The first minutes of that period can be given over to students comparing their solutions to these Tasks with each other in small groups and airing any matters of concern across the entire class, especially with regard to Task 4(b), where answers are likely to vary and could be tentative and vague. This discussion should end with a clear enunciation of what it means for a limit to be of indeterminate type $\frac{0}{0}$.

The rest of the period can be devoted to helping the students make sense of the excerpts from Chapters 1 and 2 of the *Analyse*. The PSP author has enjoyed some success by having a student read aloud source texts in the classroom while the other students follow along; this focuses the entire class on the same topics. After the reading, they can be sent into small groups to work together, on Task 5 after reading the first excerpt, on Task 6 after the second, and on Task 7 after the third. Formal write-ups of their work on these three Tasks, together with preparation for Day Two, will be the homework for the next period. (Task 8 is optional.)

Day Two (preparation, class period, and homework). Students should be asked to read through the rest of the PSP, from p. 542 to the end. This is likely to be very challenging for them to understand, but the point is that they be introduced to the text to pave the way for the work of the classroom.

Set them to work in their small groups for 10-15 minutes to perform the verification in Task 9; this should help them to tie together somewhat the familiar notion of a derivative with the less familiar notion of differentials. Assign Task 10 for homework later as a further exercise along these lines.

The next 20-30 minutes will be required to carefully read through the first two source texts from Chapter 9 of the *Analyse* and process this information by working through Tasks 11, 12 and 13. Ideally, the goal is to be able to formulate L'Hôpital's Rule in its modern form and confirm an understanding of how it resolves limits of indeterminate form by completing Task 15. With what time is left in the period, students can work in groups to verify L'Hôpital's examples in Tasks 16 and 17. Formal write-ups of the Tasks identifed here (together with some other exercises that practice the application of L'Hôpital's Rule for calculus students) should be assigned for the final homework.

Connections to other Primary Source Projects

The PSP *An Introduction to a Rigorous Definition of Derivative*, by Dave Ruch, investigates early attempts to identify the right idea on which to found the differential calculus. The project exposes students to Newton's fluxions, Leibniz's differentials (again as presented by L'Hôpital in the *Analyse*), and Cauchy's limit of the difference quotient. It also presents some of the struggles by nineteenth century mathematicians like G. J. Houël to clarify what it meant for a function to be differentiable.

B.4   Investigations Into d'Alembert's Definition of Limit

PSP Content: Topics and Goals

This mini-Primary Source Project (mini-PSP) is designed to investigate the definition of limit for sequences, beginning with d'Alembert's definition and a modern Introductory Calculus text definition. Similarities and differences are explored.

Two versions of this project are available, for very different audiences.

- One version is aimed at Calculus 2 students studying sequences for the first time. **This is the version you are currently reading.** D'Alembert's definition is completely verbal, and Section 2 tasks lead students through some examples based on that definition. Other tasks in that section ask students to find examples illustrating the difference between the modern conception of limit and that of d'Alembert. Section 3 examines these differences in a more technical fashion by having students write definitions for each using inequalities and quantifiers; this section is more appropriate for use in honors courses or as extra credit, and could be omitted by instructors who wished to pursue a more informal approach to sequences. Some historical remarks are given in a concluding section.

- A longer version is aimed at Real Analysis students. It includes several tasks based on D'Alembert's verbal definition that are more technical than those that appear in the Calculus 2 version, as well as an additional section that investigates two limit properties stated by d'Alembert (in an excerpt that is not included in the Calculus 2 version). That additional section includes tasks that prompt students to write modern proofs of those properties.

The specific content goals of this version of the project are as follows.

1. Develop familiarity with sequence convergence through examples based on d'Alembert's verbal definition.

2. Analyze subtleties of the limit definition: whether sequence terms can 'surpass' or coincide with the limit.

3. Develop a modern limit definition with quantifiers for sequences based on d'Alembert's definition and an Introductory Calculus text definition.

Student Prerequisites

This version of the project is written for a course in Calculus 2 with the assumption that students have limited familiarity with either sequences or with quantifiers.

PSP Design, and Task Commentary

This mini-PSP is designed to take up to two days of classroom time where students work through tasks in small groups. Some reading and tasks are done before and after class. If time does not permit a full implementation with this methodology, instructors can use more class time for guided discussion and less group work for difficult parts of the project.

The PSP is designed to be used largely in place of a textbook section introducing the definition of limit for sequences. The differences between the d'Alembert and modern definition can help students realize subtleties and the precision of the modern definition.

Task 7 in Section 3 may be difficult for students, even those enrolled in honors courses or those completing it as extra credit. Encouraging students to draw a plot and labels for ϵ and M should help. Leading questions to help them realize that the definition needs to start with "for all $\epsilon > 0$" may also be helpful. Including d'Alembert's requirements that sequence terms can't "surpass" or coincide with the limit is challenging but pedagogically useful.

Suggestions for Classroom Implementation

Advanced reading of the project and some task work before each class is ideal but not necessary. See the sample schedule below for ideas.

LaTeX code of this entire mini-PSP is available from the author by request to facilitate preparation of advanced preparation / reading guides or 'in-class worksheets' based on tasks included in the project. The mini-PSP itself can also be modified by instructors as desired to better suit their goals for the course.

Sample Implementation Schedule (based on a 50-minute class period)

This PSP is designed to take 1–2 class days.

Students read through the first d'Alembert excerpt and do preparatory work on Task 1 before the first class. After a class discussion of this task, students work through Tasks 2–6 in groups. (Although Task 3 could instead be assigned as an individual homework task.) As needed, the remainder of these tasks could be assigned as homework for Day 2.

For instructors who choose to complete the optional Section 3, students spend the majority of time during the second class day in group work on Task 7; this task is critical for the remainder of the section, so a class discussion is advisable to make sure everyone understands it before continuing. Tasks 8–10 could be assigned for homework.

Connections to other Primary Source Projects

The following additional projects based on primary sources are also freely available for use in teaching standard topics in the calculus sequence. The PSP author name of each is given (together with the general content focus, if this is not explicitly given in the project title). With the exception of the final two projects in the list (which require 4 and 6 days respectively for full implementation), each of these can be completed in 1–2 class days. Classroom-ready versions of these projects can be downloaded from `https://digitalcommons.ursinus.edu/triumphs_calculus`.

- Investigations Into d'Alembert's Definition of Limit (calculus version), Dave Ruch
- L'Hôpital's Rule, Danny Otero
- The Derivatives of the Sine and Cosine Functions,16 Dominic Klyve
- Fermat's Method for Finding Maxima and Minima, Kenneth M Monks
- Beyond Riemann Sums: Fermat's Method of Integration, Dominic Klyve
- How to Calculate π: Buffon's Needle (calculus version), Dominic Klyve (integration by parts)
- Gaussian Guesswork: Elliptic Integrals and Integration by Substitution, Janet Heine Barnett
- Gaussian Guesswork: Polar Coordinates, Arc Length and the Lemniscate Curve, Janet Heine Barnett
- Gaussian Guesswork: Infinite Sequences and the Arithmetic-Geometric Mean, Janet Heine Barnett
- How to Calculate π: Machin's Inverse Tangents, Dominic Klyve (infinite series)
- Euler's Calculation of the Sum of the Reciprocals of Squares, Kenneth M Monks (infinite series)
- Fourier's Proof of the Irrationality of e, Kenneth M Monks (infinite series)
- Braess' Paradox in City Planning: An Application of Multivariable Optimization, Kenneth M Monks
- Stained Glass, Windmills and the Edge of the Universe: An Exploration of Green's Theorem, Abe Edwards
- The Radius of Curvature According to Christiaan Huygens, Jerry Lodder

B.5   The Radius of Curvature According to Christiaan Huygens

This Primary Source Project is written for a calculus course covering the curvature of plane curves, usually taught in conjunction with understanding motion (velocity and acceleration) of vector-valued functions. Many calculus textbooks define curvature as the magnitude of the rate of change of the unit tangent vector with respect to arc length, although such an opaque definition offers little insight into what curvature was designed to capture Lodder 2003, not to mention its rich historical origins. The project offers Christiaan Huygens's (1629–1695) geometric construction of the radius of curvature and discusses its use in Huygens's design of an isochronous pendulum clock. A perfect timekeeper, if one could be constructed to operate at sea, would solve the longitude problem for naval navigation during The Age of Exploration

Sobel and Andrewes 1995. John Harrison (1693–1776) did construct a sea clock that solved the longitude problem, although he used springs instead of a pendulum. He received only marginal credit for his work during his lifetime Sobel and Andrewes 1995.

The project is divided into three sections. The first is an introduction describing the longitude problem and a potential solution with an accurate clock. The first two exercises, (A.5.1) and (A.5.1) are elementary and could be assigned as warm-up homework for in-class discussion. Depending on the students' background, the instructor should probably review the meaning of latitude, longitude, the Prime Meridian, a great circle, and arc length along a great circle of the Earth. The second section contains excerpts from Huygens's original work *Horologium oscillatorium* (The Pendulum Clock) Huygens 1986; Huygens 1967. Understanding Huygens's geometric construction requires a careful study of Figure A.6, particularly curve ABF and points H, K, L, M, and N, all lying on the same vertical line. The exercises involve verifying Huygens's statements about the various segments in this figure, which comprise the radius of curvature. Huygens relies on similar triangles, substitution and the geometric idea of a tangent line. The solution to some exercises simply involves writing Huygens's verbal description of ratios as algebraic equations, such as Exercise (A.5.2), where $BO/MN = (BO/BP)(BP/MN)$. Other exercises require the identification of several pairs of similar triangles, particularly Exercise (A.5.2). For ease of reference, Figure A.6 is reproduced on a separate page following these notes, which could be photocopied and distributed to the class.

Allow about one week to cover sections one and two. From Huygens's final description of the radius of curvature, segment BG in Figure A.6, a numerical calculation for its value, in a specific example, could be covered in class. For the curve $y = 4 - x^2$, given point B as $(-1, 3)$ and F as $(-1.1, 2.79)$, segment lengths HN, HL, KL, MN and BM could be computed numerically by placing the y-axis along line HL. This appears as an exercise in *Mathematical Masterpieces* Knoebel et al. 2007, p. 176, reproduced below for the reader's convenience.

Exercise B.5.1. *[Optional] In this exercise the radius of curvature of $y = 4 - x^2$ is estimated at the point $B(-1, 3)$ using the geometric ideas of Huygens. In modern terminology, let the y-axis be placed along the line HL (Figure A.6), and suppose that the x-axis is parallel to the line FL so that B has coordinates $(-1, 3)$. What is the y-coordinate of the point K? Using a modern equation for the slope of the tangent line to $y = 4 - x^2$ at B, find the y-coordinate of H. Find the y-coordinate of M from the equation of the line perpendicular to $y = 4 - x^2$ at B. Let $F(-1.1, 2.79)$ be another point on the parabola $y = 4 - x^2$, close to B. From F, determine the y-coordinates of L and N. From the equations*

$$BG = BM + MG, \qquad \frac{BG}{MG} = \frac{HN}{HL}\frac{KL}{MN}$$

estimate BG, the radius of curvature of the parabola at B. Repeat the construction using the same point B, now considering F as $(-1.01, 2.9799)$. □

Section three contains a construction for the modern equation of curvature by assigning infinitesimals (dx, dy, ds) to Huygens's work. This culminates in Exercise (A.5.3), which requires the use of nearly all the previous exercises for this section. Allow one week also to cover this section in its entirety. Once the derivative formula for curvature has been completed, this could be used to compute the curvature of $y = 4 - x^2$ at $x = -1$ and compared to the geometric (numerical) example above. For further details about curvature and in particular Newton's derivation for the radius of curvature in terms of his fluxion notation (not given in this project), see the text *Mathematical Masterpieces* Knoebel et al. 2007. In fact, the chapter "Curvature and the Notion of Space" from this text Knoebel et al. 2007 could serve as a semester-long undergraduate course in differential geometry or the history of mathematics.

The following is a sample timeline for covering the project over a two-week implementation, three 50-minute class sessions per week.

Day 1. As advance reading, ask students to study pp. 1–3 of the project before class, and prepare questions. During class the instructor may wish to review the meaning of latitude and longitude, and explain the longitude problem for navigation at sea (during the sixteenth, seventeenth, and eighteenth centuries). Field questions about determining latitude and longitude. Assign Exercises (A.5.1), (A.5.1).

Day 2. As advance reading, ask students to study pp. 4–7 of the project before class, and prepare questions. During class, the instructor may wish to review the construction of a cycloid, and develop a parametric equation for a cycloid, particularly if such an equation is present in the calculus text being used for the course. As an enrichment activity, the instructor could use graphic software to plot the parametric equation of a cycloid and project this on screen. Field questions about the reading. Review similar triangles, and the equality of ratios of corresponding sides in similar triangles. Discuss Exercises (A.5.2), (A.5.2) in class, and perhaps assign Exerciese (A.5.2), (A.5.2).

Day 3. As advance reading, ask students to study p. 8 of the project before class, and prepare questions. This is the heart of Huygens's geometric construction for capturing the radius of curvature as a limiting process via certain ratios. As in-class activities, group work, group presentations, or assigned homework, cover Exercises (A.5.2) through (A.5.2). After Exercise (A.5.2) is complete, the instructor may wish to demonstrate how Huygens's work determines the radius of curvature by covering optional Exercise (B.5.1) above. Time permitting, an extra day could be devoted to a discussion of Exercise (B.5.1).

Day 4. As advance reading, ask students to study p. 9, particularly Exercises (A.5.3), (A.5.3) before class, and prepare questions. Begin a discussion of differentials, and how a ratio of sides in a triangle can be used to capture the quotient of two differentials. Field questions about the Exercises (A.5.3), (A.5.3), and assign these as homework. If time permits, begin a discuss of Exercise (A.5.3), which requires a conceptual understanding of what a derivative is as well as an identification of what function is being differentiated.

Day 5. As advance reading, ask students to study Exercises (A.5.3) through (A.5.3) before class, and prepare questions about these exercises. Also, ask students what type of information segment MN may contain in terms of derivatives. Discuss the conceptual underpinnings of Exercise (A.5.3) during class. Notice that segment MN measures how quickly the radial lines BG and FG are approaching each other. Since a radial line is perpendicular to the tangent line, a radial line contains first derivative information about the original function (or graph). How two radial lines differ would then contain second derivative information about the function. Exactly what expression in terms of second derivatives MN/KL represents follows from Exercises (A.5.3) through (A.5.3). Cover Exercises (A.5.3) through (A.5.3) as in-class activities, group activities, group presentations, or assigned homework.

Day 6. As advance reading, ask students to study Exercises (A.5.3), (A.5.3), and prepare questions about these exercises before class. Begin a discussion about the needed steps to complete Exercise (A.5.3), which is rather lengthy. Note that the final derivative formula for BG, the radius of curvature, is preceded by a negative sign, since BG represents a length, and curve ABF is concave down with $\overrightarrow{HL}$ being the axis of the independent variable and $\overrightarrow{LF}$ the axis of the dependent variable. An engaging in-class activity is to ask students to determine the concavity of curve ABF with respect to the axes of the independent and dependent variables. As a final step for Exercise (A.5.3), the roles of x and y may be switched to reconcile Huygens's construction with the modern convention of letting x denote the independent variable when differentiating functions $y = f(x)$ today. Assign Exercises (A.5.3), (A.5.3). If time permits, begin Exercise (A.5.3), and compare this to Exercise (B.5.1) above, or discuss a comparison of these exercises during the next class session.

The above syllabus for the project is ambitious, and exercises can be assigned at the instructor's discretion.

B.6   How to Calculate π: Machin's inverse tangents

This is one of a proposed series of Primary Source Projects which explore ways that mathematicians have used material now in the undergraduate curriculum to estimate the value π. Other projects[1] examine the methods of Archimedes and Georges LeClerc, Compte de Buffon.

PSP Content: Topics and Goals

This Primary Source Project (PSP) has two primary goals: to give students an interesting and concrete example of the use of Taylor series, and to use systematic deduction to motivate the seemingly "out-of-nowhere" formula of Machin that $\frac{\pi}{4} = 4\arctan\frac{1}{5} = \arctan\frac{1}{239}$. The PSP is designed to be used in a Calculus II course, but might also profitably used in a course in Applied Analysis or the History of Mathematics. If the instructor is comfortable with their students not understanding the motivation for Taylor series, it could even be used in a trigonometry class as a chance to practice and use double-angle formulas.

Student Prerequisites

While the project expects that students have seen Taylor series and will not be intimidated by Leibniz's formula, this is not a prerequisite – most students could use the formula simply by plugging in values. It is also expected, though not required, that students know the tangent double-angle formula. Since the project presents the formula, an ability to see a new identity and to possess the algebraic skills to put it to use suffices.

Suggestions for PSP Implementation

The following suggestions assume use in a Calculus 2 class with class lengths of approximately 50 minutes. The outline below uses a few minutes at the end of Day 0, all of Day 1, and the

---

[1] Not all of these projects are completed at the time of this writing

first day of Day 2 for the mini-PSP.

- **Day 0.** The instructor spends about 10 minutes at the end of class discussing the fact that some mathematicians have wanted to calculate π with increasing accuracy for over 2000 years – and that in fact some people still pursue this problem today. The instructor then mentions that one of the best methods involves a topic from calculus: Taylor Series (if used in a trigonometry course, one might instead point out that the method involves tangent formulas).

  Day 0 Homework: Parts 1 and 2 can reasonably be assigned as homework before the first day of class work.

- **Day 1.** After a brief (less than 10-minute) discussion of questions on the homework, students should work in groups on Part 3. Many groups will complete most of Tasks 10–18 together.

  Day 1 Homework: Assign Tasks 19–21 (together with unfinished work from Day 1).

- **Day 2.** Students should be able to compare their answers from the homework in groups, and to complete Tasks 22–25 in half of a 50-minute class period. The instructor can then choose either to have a class discussion on the project (the author would make this choice) or to move on to new material.

  Day 2 homework: Students should write up their solutions to all tasks to be turned in and evaluated. It's best to give them a few days to do this.

LaTeXcode of the entire PSP is available from the author by request to facilitate preparation of reading guides or other assignments related to the project. The PSP itself can also be modified by instructors as desired to better suit their goals for the course.

Commentary on Selected Student Tasks

Task 5 is needlessly laborious for someone who cannot program, and I would never assign it as a computational exercise to students who can't.

In Task 14, especially strong students could be asked to find a better angle than 1/5, or at least a different angle, and to construct a Machin-like formula using it.

Recommendations for Further Reading

Those interested in a more careful discussion of the calculation above, together with thoughts on alternate ways to teach it and on the symbol π itself, are encouraged to read V. Frederick Rickey's "Machin's Formula for Computing Pi", a work to which this PSP is indebted. Rickey's paper has not been published, but can be found via a web search for its title, or by contacting this PSP's author directly.

B.7   The Derivatives of the Sine and Cosine Functions

Goals

This Primary Source Project (PSP) has two primary goals: to help students develop a deeper and more intuitive understanding of the limit definition of the derivative, and to understand why the derivative of sine is cosine, using a proof which may seem more straightforward than the version which usually appears in modern Calculus books. A secondary goal is to calculate derivatives using nothing more than trigonometric identities and algebra – possibly rendering some of calculus less mysterious.

Background

The PSP has only one primary source: Leonhard Euler's *Foundations of Differential Calculus*, published in 1755. It was the first calculus book to use functions; indeed, Euler himself had been the first mathematician to regularly use an approach which looks like functions to us today about seven years earlier, in his great "pre-calculus" book, the *Introductio in analysin infinitorum* (*Introduction to the Analysis of the Infinite*). While the use of functions makes the material more accessible to our students today, Euler's approach is different enough from that of modern calculus books to force students to think carefully about the material.

The major difference in Euler's approach is the lack of limits in his work. The limit concept would not be formally defined and made a part of mathematics for almost a century; Euler based his calculus (following Leibniz) on the differential dx, which was an infinitely small increment of the variable x. While the logical issues in this approach would force 19th-century mathematicians to abandon the approach (in favor of limits), Euler saw no such issues. (I have found that my students, likewise, are unbothered by the notion of an infinitely small increment in x, or by considering the corresponding increment $f(x+dx) - f(x)$.)

Perhaps the most surprising aspect of Euler's approach is his use of Taylor series. In fact, he introduced these in the *Introductio*, and thought of them as a pre-calculus idea. This project may be the first time that students see these series, but they do not need any of the theory of Taylor series in the project. The approximations of sine and cosine via a three-term Taylor series are presented as a *fait accompli*, and students are given an opportunity to convince themselves that the approximations seem valid, even if they can't explain why. It is hoped that this exposure will make Taylor series slightly more approachable when they encounter them in the future, but this is not a major goal of the project.

Prerequisite knowledge

Students need very little prerequisite knowledge to complete this PSP. It will help if they have seen the trigonometric identities used in the project, but the identities are re-introduced here in case they have not. It would be useful for students to have been introduced to the limit definition of the derivative, as this project would then provide them with a second lens through which to view the concept, though this is not strictly necessary either. No other background outside of algebra is required.

Preparing to teach this PSP

This PSP is designed with a certain implementation in mind (although many other approaches are, of course, possible). Part 1 is intended to be assigned as pre-reading homework. Students should read the primary source material and answer Tasks 1 and 2 before coming to class. Time in class can be spent with a combination of students working in small groups or with guided lecture. (I prefer the former, but if students are not used to working in groups in class, more instructor guidance will likely be needed.)

Note that Part 2 contains two distinct kinds of questions – mathematical questions, in which students do calculations, and more abstract questions, in which students are asked to reflect on Euler's approach to derivatives, and to compare it to the one they have been taught. Students will often be able to complete this entire section in a 50-minute class period, and will begin working on Part 3. If Part 3 is not completed during class, one good option is to ask students to complete Task 7 as homework, with the plan of finishing the rest of the task during class the second day.

When groups have finished their work, I suggest wrapping up the project with a guided discussion in which students (and the instructor) reflect on the two ways they have now seen to find derivatives. Students may at this point ask if they can try using Euler's differentials to find derivatives of other functions, as well. One fun example to demonstrate or give them to try as an optional and/or bonus problem (and a hard one to Google!) is $\ln(x)$. I would give students the hint that $\ln(1 + x)$ can be approximated via Taylor Series as $\ln(x + 1) \approx x - \frac{x^2}{2} + \frac{x^3}{3}$, and turn them loose!

The LaTeX source file for this mini-PSP is available from the author by request at `dominic.klyve@cwu.edu`.

Made in the USA
Monee, IL
29 May 2024

59054736R00330